Design of Machine Elements

THIRD EDITION

M. F. SPOTTS

Professor of Mechanical Engineering
The Technological Institute
Northwestern University

Design of
Machine Elements

THIRD EDITION

PRENTICE-HALL, INC.
Englewood Cliffs, N. J.

Library of Congress Card Catalog Number: 61-14847.

Current printing (last digit):

15   14   13   12   11   10   9

PRINTED IN THE UNITED STATES OF AMERICA

20053-C

*Throughout the wide fields of engineering, the most
fundamental requirement is a sound knowledge of the first
principles of mechanics coupled with an intimate understanding of the properties of materials. More problems
arise from weaknesses in mechanical design than from
any other cause, impressing upon us the necessity of being
well versed in the basic principles of mechanical engineering.*

SIR GEORGE H. NELSON, *President,
Institute of Electrical Engineers*

Preface to Third Edition

"ENGINEERING DESIGN is the process of applying the various techniques and scientific principles for the purpose of defining a device, a process, or a system in sufficient detail to permit its physical realization."[1]

In its broadest sense, the word design embraces a considerable portion of the essence and theme of engineering. It is essentially a decision-making process. Direct involvement in actual design work is probably the best form of training to enhance the student's capabilities in this direction.

The ability of a designer to make worthwhile decisions depends upon his working knowledge of the "various techniques and scientific principles" which assist him in synthesizing a device or system which will have the desired performance characteristics. It is only when such techniques and principles have become sufficiently familiar to constitute working tools that the designer is free to give his main attention to the larger aspects of the problem as a whole.

After the principal features of a design have been decided upon, the necessity arises for the proper proportioning of the individual members. It is obvious that this phase of the work is important since the failure of a single element will frequently invalidate the whole. At this time the designer is faced with the necessity of making proper provision for such qualities as material selection, heat treatment, strength, fatigue resistance, lubrication, wear, and tolerances. Such properties can be determined by well-established techniques and practices. The object of the third edition of this book is to provide a collection of the most widely used of such methods and to simplify and streamline them to the point where their application may become as systematic as possible.

M. F. Spotts

EVANSTON, ILLINOIS

[1] From "Interim Report of the Committee on Engineering Design," Massachusetts Institute of Technology, November 3, 1959, p. 5.

Preface to Second Edition

THE GRATIFYING RECEPTION of the first edition of this book has inspired the author to seek methods for extending its usefulness. The present edition is somewhat larger in size because of a more detailed presentation of certain topics and the inclusion of many more problems and worked-out examples.

The attempt is made at all times to instill a professional viewpoint in the student and prepare him to meet the actual conditions he will find upon leaving the university. It was therefore deemed wise to retain the academic level of the book, and at the same time aid the student by the addition of a large number of easy problems by which he can readily acquire a working knowledge of the theories of the text. As before, answers are given to the problems.

Among the many changes, mention may be made of the following. The second chapter, Working Stresses, has been expanded to include methods for both static and fluctuating loads when acting on ductile or brittle materials.

Several new topics important to the design of shafting have been included in Chapter 3. Data on standard-size spring wire are given in Chapter 4, as well as equations for the design of rubber springs. The Unified Thread is given in Chapter 5.

Chapter 8 now includes data for the design of partial journal bearings of various size bearing arcs. Methods for determining the gears of a train of specified ratio are given in Chapter 10, but material previously given on the extended center distance method has been deleted.

Chapter 11 on bevel, worm, and helical gears has been rewritten and enlarged. The section on cams in Chapter 12 has also been rewritten.

The author has been in close touch with teachers throughout the country and has made an effort to ascertain their viewpoints and methods of presenting machine design courses. He wishes to take this opportunity to express appreciation for many helpful suggestions.

M. F. Spotts

EVANSTON, ILLINOIS

Preface to First Edition

THIS BOOK is the outgrowth of over twenty years' experience in industry and in the classroom. The author has taught the contents many times to third- and fourth-year college students. When used as a two-semester text, there is ample material from which a teacher may select those portions best fitted to the needs of his students. Since most teachers of machine design prefer their own order for the presentation of the various topics, it was deemed advisable to have the chapters independent of each other; therefore they can be studied in any order. If a complete machine is to be designed, the text will serve as a reference work or source book for information on the various elements. It is believed that engineers and designers in industry will find this book useful in their professional work.

Before a new idea or process in any branch of engineering or natural science can be utilized, it must be embodied in a suitable physical form. For this reason, a knowledge of the principles of mechanical design is a necessary part of an engineer's training, even though the student may not expect to become a professional designer. Increases in sizes, speeds, and working stresses during recent years demand, as never before, that the calculations of the designer should predict the maximum degree of reliability and economy in construction and in operation. Although conclusions obtained by computation must always be tempered with judgment and experience, the analytical equations do show the manner in which results will be affected should changes take place in the values of any of the variables. To be able to create a logical and successful device, an engineer must possess common sense, analytical ability, and sound judgment. There is no doubt that the student will be aided in developing these qualities by acquiring a working knowledge of the principles explained in this book.

It has been the author's experience that a brief review of strength of materials is beneficial to most students before the study of machine elements is encountered. Moreover, certain fundamental rules must be emphasized again and again before the student becomes aware of their importance. The first chapter, therefore, gives a survey of the theory which is prerequisite for a sound course in machine design.

Methods based on rational analysis have been utilized throughout the book. The well-known basic theories of design are clearly presented, as well as some of the newer methods now being employed. Mathematical derivations are given in full, but have been simplified wherever possible. Tables are included giving the properties of engineering materials as determined by laboratory tests; however, design data usually obtained from catalogs and handbooks have been omitted. The text contains many illustrative examples and solutions, as well as a large number of problems to be worked by the student. Each chapter is concluded with a brief bibliography for the assistance of those who may wish to pursue the study of the various machine elements more extensively.

The author wishes to extend thanks to Dean O. W. Eshbach of the Technological Institute, Northwestern University, and to Professor S. P. Timoshenko, Stanford University, for interest and encouragement during the writing of this book. The author also acknowledges with sincere appreciation the generous assistance given him by colleagues at the University and in industry. Gratitude is especially due to Professor E. F. Obert, who read the entire manuscript and made many valuable suggestions.

M. F. Spotts

EVANSTON, ILLINOIS

Introduction

1. Machine design. Machine design is the art of planning or devising new or improved machines to accomplish specific purposes. In general, a machine will consist of a combination of several different mechanical elements properly designed and arranged to work together, as a whole. During the initial planning of a machine, fundamental decisions must be made concerning loading, type of kinematic elements to be used, and correct utilization of the properties of engineering materials. Economic considerations are usually of prime importance when the design of new machinery is undertaken. In general, the lowest over-all cost is desired. Consideration should be given not only to the cost of design, manufacture, sale, and installation, but also to the cost of servicing. The machine should of course incorporate the necessary safety features and be of pleasing external appearance. The objective is to produce a machine which is not only sufficiently rugged to function properly for a reasonable life, but is at the same time cheap enough to be economically feasible.

The engineer in charge of the design of a machine should not only have adequate technical training, but must be a man of sound judgment and wide experience, qualities which are usually acquired only after considerable time has been spent in actual professional work. A start in this direction can be made with a good teacher while the student is yet at the university. However, the would-be designer must expect to get a substantial portion of his training after leaving school through further reading and study, and especially by being associated in his work with competent engineers.

2. Design of machine elements. This book, as the title indicates, will not deal with the broader aspects of the design of complete machines, but will attempt to explain the fundamental principles required for the correct design of the separate elements which compose the machine.

The principles of design are of course universal. The same theory or equations may be applied to a very small part, as in an instrument, or to a larger but similar part used in a piece of heavy equipment. In no case, however, should mathematical calculations be looked upon as absolute and final. They are all subject to the accuracy of the various assumptions which must necessarily be made in engineering work. Sometimes only a portion of the total number of parts in a machine are designed on the basis of analytic calculations. The form and size of the remaining parts are then usually determined by practical considerations. On the other hand, if the machine is very expensive, or if weight is a factor, as in airplanes, design computations may then be made for almost all the parts.

The purpose of the design calculations is of course to attempt to predict the stress or deformation in the part in order that it may safely carry the loads which will be imposed upon it, and that it may last for the expected life of the machine. All calculations are, of course, dependent on the physical properties of the construction materials as determined by laboratory tests. A rational method of design attempts to take the results of relatively simple and fundamental tests such as tension, compression, torsion, and fatigue and apply them to all the complicated and involved situations encountered in present-day machinery.

In addition, it has been amply proved that such details as surface condition, fillets, notches, manufacturing tolerances, and heat treatment have a marked effect on the strength and useful life of a machine part. The design and drafting departments must specify completely all such particulars, and thus exercise the necessary close control over the finished product.

Training in rapid and accurate numerical work is invaluable to the designer. The designer should keep an accurate notebook, as it is frequently necessary for him to refer to work which he has done in the past. A sketch, carefully drawn to scale, is also a necessity, and provides a convenient place for putting down a portion of the data used in connection with the problem. It goes without saying that all data, assumptions, equations, and calculations should be written down in full in order to be intelligible when referred to at a later date. The student should start forming such habits, and it is recommended that the problems in this book be worked out and preserved as reference material.

Contents

Bending loads in two planes. 11. Shaft on three supports. 12. Crankshafts. 13. Critical speed of rotating shaft. 14. Deflection of shaft of nonuniform diameter. 15. Slope of shaft by elastic energy. 16. Torsion of noncircular shaft. 17. Torsion of wide rectangular bar. 18. Torsion of rectangular bars, general case. 19. Composite sections. 20. Materials used for shafting.

1. Helical springs. 2. Effect of end turns for compression springs. 3. Properties of spring materials. 4. Design for fluctuating loads. 5. Vibration or surging of helical springs. 6. Commercial tolerances. 7. Helical extension springs. 8. Helical springs of rectangular wire. 9. Helical springs with torsional loading. 10. Leaf springs. 11. Energy storage by springs. 12. Rubber springs.

1. Kinds of threads. 2. Standardized threads. 3. Unified threads. 4. American National threads. 5. Identification symbols. 6. Effect of initial stress. 7. Effect of spring washers and gaskets. 8. Power screws. 9. Stress due to impact load. 10. Friction of screws. 11. Stress concentration. 12. Locknuts. 13. Materials and methods of manufacture.

1. Forces in flat belts. 2. Action of belt on pulley. 3. Coefficient of friction and working stresses. 4. Design of belts by tables. 5. Pivoted motor drive. 6. Length of belt. 7. V-belts. 8. Designing when pulleys are of unequal diameters. 9. Disk clutch. 10. Cone clutch. 11. Band brakes. 12. Block brake with short shoe. 13. Pivoted block brake with long shoe. 14. Brake with pivoted symmetrical shoe. 15. Lining pressures. 16. Heating of brakes.

1. Fabrication by welding. 2. Fusion welding. 3. Strength of fusion welds. 4. Design equations for fillet weld. 5. Stress concentration in welds. 6. Eccentrically loaded welds. 7. Resistance welding. 8. Soldering and brazing. 9. Furnace brazing. 10. Riveted joint with central load. 11. Stresses in rivets. 12. Stresses in cylindrical shell. 13. Riveted joint with eccentric load.

Design of Machine Elements

THIRD EDITION

1

Fundamental Principles

DESIGN methods for the various machine elements are founded on the theories of mechanics and strength of materials. The scope of such theories is very extensive, and the purpose of this chapter is to present, for review and ready reference, those topics which are generally used by designers, and which will be referred to throughout the book. These theories are more or less simplified approximations, and attention should be directed to the limitations imposed by the assumptions which had to be made in arriving at working formulas.

A thorough grounding in these fundamentals will prove of great value in attacking new and unfamiliar problems. In fact, only after such theories have become working tools is it possible to achieve the broad perspective and balanced judgment which must be expressed by the really competent machine designer.

A, area

b, width of cross section parallel to neutral axis

c, maximum distance, neutral axis to edge of cross section

d, distance, diameter of circle

E, modulus of elasticity

FS, factor of safety

G, modulus of elasticity in shear

h, height of cross section perpendicular to neutral axis

i, radius of gyration

I, moment of inertia

l, length

M, bending moment

P, load

r, radius of circle, radius to center of curvature of deflected beam

s, s_n, normal stress

s_s, shear stress

s_x, normal stress, x-direction

s_y, normal stress, y-direction

s_{xy}, shear stress, x- and y-directions

s_1, maximum normal stress

s_2, minimum normal stress

s_{smax}, maximum shear stress

s_{yp}, yield point stress

v, distance on cross section of beam perpendicular to neutral axis

V, total shear force on cross section

w, distributed load, lb per unit length

y, deflection of beam

γ, (gamma), shearing deformation, wt per cu in. of a material

δ, (delta), axial deformation

ϵ, (epsilon), strain or elongation

μ, (mu), Poisson's ratio

1. Statical Equilibrium

When a body is at rest, or in motion with constant velocity, the external forces acting upon it are in equilibrium. This statement applies to the body as a whole or to any portion of it. When a force analysis is to be made, it is sometimes advantageous to consider only a portion of the body which can be obtained by assuming that cutting planes are passed through the body at the desired locations. The internal forces which were acting at the locations of the cuts must then be represented as a system of external forces properly distributed to maintain equilibrium of the separate parts and to preserve the original state of stress in the material. When a problem is analyzed in this manner the loading will consist entirely of external forces and moments. It is not necessary to consider the internal stresses.

Statical equilibrium means that both forces and moments are in balance. When a body is in equilibrium, the sum of the components of the forces in any given direction must be equal to zero. Likewise the moments about any given line as an axis must be equal to zero. If the body is undergoing acceleration, the effects of inertia must be included in the equilibrium equations.

2. Engineering Materials

The mathematical equations used in designing are derived for an idealized material which is assumed to have the following properties.

(a) *Perfect Elasticity.* Loads or forces acting on a body cause changes in its shape and dimensions. A perfectly elastic material is one that returns to its original form immediately upon removal of the loads. The equations used in designing are nearly always derived on the assumption of perfect elasticity. If the material is such that this assumption cannot be made, the mathematical complications, in many cases, become too great for practical calculations. It should never be forgotten, however, that in some cases there may be a considerable variation between the actual stresses in the body and the stresses obtained from the equations for an idealized substance. A material may exhibit a high degree of elasticity for small loads, but may retain a permanent deformation when the loads become sufficiently great.

(b) *Homogeneity.* A homogeneous body is one that has the same properties throughout its entire extent.

(c) *Isotropy.* An isotropic material is one whose elastic properties are the same in all directions.

Actually, a metal is not a homogeneous substance. It consists of an aggregate of very small crystals whose strength depends upon their orientation with respect to the applied force. When the minute crystals have a random orientation, the location in the body, or the inclination at which a test specimen is taken, has no effect on the results of the test. The assumption that the material is homogeneous and isotropic, for all practical purposes, is fulfilled. This is true for cast, hot rolled, or annealed metals. In contrast, materials that have been cold rolled or drawn may have a preferred orientation of crystals, and may exhibit a definite grain effect with a variation in strength depending on the direction of the applied load. The assumption cannot be made that such materials are homogeneous and isotropic.

3. Tension and Compression Stress

The eyebar, in Fig. 1-1(a), which supports the load P, is said to be in *tension*, or to have an internal force of tension. Such a force causes an increase in the length of the bar. A solution for the stress can be effected by means of cutting planes as described in Section 1.

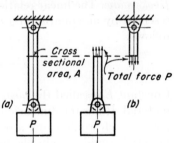

If the bar, shown in Fig. 1-1(a), is cut normal to its axis, as shown in Fig. 1-1(b), equal and opposite tension forces, uniformly distributed, must be applied to the cut surfaces. In magnitude, each must be equivalent to the load P. The average stress s, or force per unit of cross-sectional area A, is then equal to P divided by A. Hence

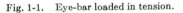

Fig. 1-1.   Eye-bar loaded in tension.

$$s = \frac{P}{A} \tag{1}$$

Thus the magnitude of the external forces on the cross sections in Fig. 1-1(b) constitutes the measure of the internal force in the bar shown in

Fig. 1-1(a). Forces are usually expressed in pounds and areas in square inches.

It is, of course, obvious that this solution is correct only if the assumption regarding the distribution of stress on the cut surfaces is correct. Had the bar been cut near one end where the shape is no longer a prism, it is apparent that the situation would be more complicated, and the stress system would no longer be simple tension uniformly distributed over the cross section.

Since the assumption relative to homogeneity of the material is never exactly fulfilled, the stresses on the cross section will not be entirely uniform but will be subject to small local variations. Equation (1) does, however, give the average value of the tensile stress.

A *compressive stress* is one which causes a decrease in the length of the body in the direction of the force.

The total change of length in a uniform body caused by an axial load is called the *deformation*, δ. If the deformation is divided by the original length, l, of the body, the result is the deformation per unit length, and is called *elongation* or *strain*, ϵ. It can be represented mathematically by the equation

$$\epsilon = \frac{\delta}{l} \tag{2}$$

Although elongation ϵ is a dimensionless number, it is customary to speak of it in terms of inches per inch.

For most materials used in engineering, stress and strain are directly proportional; when this condition exists, the material is said to follow *Hooke's law*. The linear relationship between stress and strain can be represented by an equation if a constant of proportionality is introduced as follows:

$$s = \epsilon E \qquad \text{or} \qquad \epsilon = \frac{s}{E} \tag{3}$$

Constant E is called the *modulus of elasticity*, or *Young's modulus*, for the material. It has the dimension of stress and can be visualized as the tensile stress which would cause a body to double in length, $\epsilon = 1$, provided the material would remain elastic with such excessive loading. Values of E for common materials used in engineering are given in Table 2-1 of the following chapter.

Substitution of Eqs. (1) and (3) into Eq. (2) gives the important relationship

$$\delta = \frac{Pl}{AE} \tag{4}$$

Equations (3) and (4) are valid either for tension or compression. Tension stress and increase of length are considered positive, whereas compressive stress and decrease in length are considered negative.

Example 1. In Fig. 1-1, let load P be equal to 5,000 lb, and let the bar be 3 in. wide and 0.5 in. thick. The uniform portion of the bar is 60 in. long. The material is steel.

(a) Find the stress in the uniform portion of the bar.
(b) Find the deformation of the uniform portion of the bar.

Solution.

Cross-sectional area: $\qquad A = 3 \times 0.5 = 1.5$ in.^{2}

Stress, by Eq. (1): $\qquad s = \dfrac{5,000}{1.5} = 3,333$ psi

Deformation, by Eq. (4): $\quad \delta = \dfrac{5,000 \times 60}{1.5 \times 30,000,000} = 0.00667$ in.

For statical equilibrium, the summation of the forces in any direction must equal zero, and the summation of the moments about any axis also must equal zero. The following equations must therefore be fulfilled.

$$\Sigma F = 0, \qquad \Sigma M = 0$$

4. Statically Indeterminate Problems in Tension and Compression

Machine parts are sometimes arranged in a manner whereby the axial forces cannot be determined by the equations of statics alone. Such force systems are said to be statically indeterminate. They are characterized by the presence of more supports or members than the minimum required for the equilibrium of the structure. For such situations, the deformations of the parts must be taken into consideration. The following example will illustrate a typical method for solving such problems.

Example 2. Find the force in each of the vertical bars in Fig. 1-2. The weight can be assumed to be rigid and to maintain the connections for the three vertical bars in a straight line. Assume the support at the top to be rigid also.

Solution. Because both geometry and loading are symmetrical, the forces will be equal in the two outer bars. From statical equilibrium, the following equation can be written:

$$2F_1 + F_2 = 5,000 \tag{a}$$

Since two unknowns are present, it is necessary to obtain another equation to effect a solution. This can be done by considering the deformations of the bars.

From the given data, all bars will have the same amount of deformation. Hence

$$\delta_1 = \delta_2, \quad \text{or} \quad \frac{F_1 l_1}{A_1 E_1} = \frac{F_2 l_2}{A_2 E_2}$$

Numerical values should be substituted into the equation above.

$$\frac{F_1 36}{0.2 \times 30,000,000} = \frac{F_2 36}{0.3 \times 15,000,000} \quad \text{or} \quad 3F_1 = 4F_2 \qquad (b)$$

Equations (a) and (b) should now be solved simultaneously to give

$$F_1 = 1,818 \text{ lb} \quad \text{and} \quad F_2 = 1,364 \text{ lb}$$

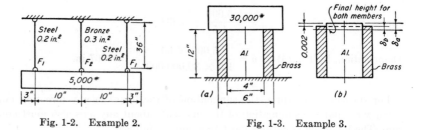

Fig. 1-2.　Example 2.　　　　　　　　　Fig. 1-3.　Example 3.

Example 3. In Fig. 1-3 a circular cylinder of aluminum is surrounded by a hollow circular cylinder of brass. Assume that the foundation beneath and the load on top are rigid. The fit between the parts is sufficiently loose to permit free lateral expansion.

(a) Find the load carried by the aluminum and by the brass.
(b) Suppose the aluminum is mistakenly machined 0.002 in. too long and that the parts are assembled. Find the force in each member.
(c) Suppose the parts are machined to the same length at the same temperature. Find the force carried by each should the temperature rise by 64 deg. F.

Solution. (a)

Area, aluminum:
$$A_a = \frac{\pi 4^2}{4} = 4\pi \text{ in.}^2$$

Area, brass:
$$A_b = \frac{\pi(6^2 - 4^2)}{4} = 5\pi \text{ in.}^2$$

By statics:
$$P_a + P_b = 30,000 \qquad (a)$$

By deformation:
$$\delta_a = \delta_b \quad \text{or} \quad \frac{P_a l_a}{A_a E_a} = \frac{P_b l_b}{A_b E_b}$$

$$\frac{P_a 12}{4\pi 10,000,000} = \frac{P_b 12}{5\pi 15,000,000} \quad \text{or} \quad 15P_a = 8P_b \qquad (b)$$

Combine Eqs. (a) and (b): $P_a = 10{,}435$ lb load in aluminum

$$P_b = 19{,}565 \text{ lb load in brass}$$

(b)

By deformation, see Fig. 1-3(b): $\delta_a = \delta_b + 0.002$

$$\frac{P_a 12}{4\pi 10{,}000{,}000} = \frac{P_b 12}{5\pi 15{,}000{,}000} + 0.002 \qquad (c)$$

Combine Eqs. (a) and (c): $P_a = 24{,}137$ lb load in aluminum

$$P_b = 5{,}863 \text{ lb load in brass}$$

(c) $\delta = \alpha l \, \Delta T$

Al $\delta = 0.0000128 \times 12 \times 64 = 0.00983$ in.

Brass $\delta = 0.0000102 \times 12 \times 64 = 0.00783$ in.

Net difference in length $= 0.00983 - 0.00783 = 0.002$ in.

Hence, the change in temperature has produced the same change in length and the same change in the forces as was produced by the error in machining of part (b).

As was illustrated by part (b) in the example above, the distribution of the forces in an indeterminate structure is sensitive to small variations in the dimensions of the parts. A small undetected error in machining a dimension can cause a large change in the distribution of the loads. Any calculations made by the designer will not be valid unless the fit of the parts can be rigidly maintained as originally planned.

A variation in temperature may change the values of the forces in an indeterminate system. If temperature causes a relative change between the lengths of the various parts of the assembly, the effect can be similar to that of the misfit of part (b) in the foregoing example. The designer must consider temperature variations as well as dimensional errors in his calculations for an indeterminate structure.

5. Center of Gravity

An equation for finding the center of gravity of an area can be derived from Fig. 1-4. The distance from the x-axis to the center of gravity is called $\bar{y}$, and the distance to an element dA parallel to the x-axis is called y. The moment arm for dA about a horizontal axis through the center of gravity C is equal to $(y - \bar{y})$. Mathematically, center of gravity means that the sum of the moments of the areas about the axis through C must be equal to zero as indicated

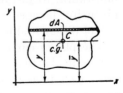

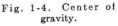

Fig. 1-4. Center of gravity.

by the following equation:

$$\int (y - \bar{y})dA = 0$$

or
$$\bar{y} = \frac{\int y\, dA}{\int dA} = \frac{\int y\, dA}{A} \qquad (5)$$

A similar equation can be written for the moments about the y-axis which permits $\bar{x}$ to be found.

A composite figure can usually be divided into simple areas, and Eq. (5) can be applied by making the numerator equal to the sum of the $\int y\, dA$ terms of the separate parts. The denominator is the total area. If the location of the center of gravity for each of the separate areas is known, it is not necessary to perform mathematical integrations. Each $\int y\, dA$ term can be replaced by the product of the area times the distance from the axis to its center of gravity as is shown in Fig. 1-5. Thus

$$\bar{y} = \frac{A_1\bar{y}_1 + A_2\bar{y}_2 + \cdots}{A_1 + A_2 + \cdots} \qquad (6)$$

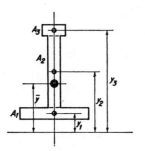

Fig. 1-5.   Center of gravity of composite section.

Example 4. Find the location of the center of gravity of the T-shaped cross section in Fig. 1-21(b).

Solution. Divide the area into two parts of 6 in.² and 4 in.² by extending the vertical sides of the stem to the bottom of the cross section. Let the axis of moments be taken along the bottom of the T.

In Eq. (6):
$$\bar{y} = \frac{6 \times 3 + 4 \times 0.5}{6 + 4} = 2 \text{ in.}$$

The center of gravity is located 2 in. up from the bottom.

6. Bending of Beams

Suppose a long, thin, straight beam is bent into a curve by moments M applied at the ends, as shown in Fig. 1-6(a). The beam and moments lie in the xy-plane with the origin at the left end and the y-axis positive downward. At distance x from the left end, the deflection of the beam is given by distance y, as shown. Figure 1-6(b) shows, enlarged, a slice AB of differential length dx cut from the beam at location x.

The planes cutting the right and left end surfaces of AB are taken perpendicular to the longitudinal axis of the originally straight beam. It is customary to assume that these cross sections will remain plane and perpendicular to the longitudinal elements of the beam after moments M

are applied. Laboratory experiments have in general verified this assumption. After bending, some of the elements have been lengthened, some have been shortened, and at one location, called the *neutral surface*, no change in length has taken place.

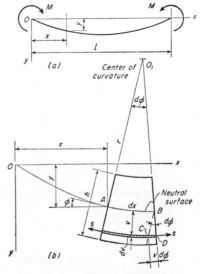

Fig. 1-6. Bending stress for beam loaded by moments at ends.

The loading of Fig. 1-6 is called *pure bending*. No shear or tangential stress will exist on the end surfaces of AB, and the only stress will be s, acting normally to the surfaces as shown. An equation can be derived for giving the value of this bending stress at any desired distance v from the neutral surface. Let O_1 be the center of curvature for slice AB of the deflected beam. Let $d\varphi$ be the small angle included between the cutting planes, and let r be the radius of curvature. Consider a horizontal element located a distance v below the neutral surface. Draw line BC parallel to O_1A. Angle AO_1B is equal to angle CBD and the following proportion can be written.

$$\frac{v}{r} = \frac{v\,d\varphi}{dx} = \epsilon \qquad (a)$$

Since the total deformation of the element $v\,d\varphi$ divided by the original length dx is the unit deformation or strain ϵ, Eq. (a) indicates that the elongation of the element varies directly with the distance v from the neutral surface. Let it be assumed that the material of the beam follows Hooke's law. Substitution of $\epsilon = s/E$ into Eq. (a) gives

$$\frac{s}{E} = \frac{v}{r} \qquad \text{or} \qquad s = \frac{E}{r}v \qquad (7)$$

Thus the stress also varies directly with the distance from the neutral surface, becoming larger as v increases. Equation (7) is of course valid only for stresses in the elastic range of the material. Above the neutral surface, for negative values of v, the stress is compressive and increases uniformly with the distance from the neutral surface. Equation (7), obtained from the geometry of the deformed beam, gives only a portion of the solution. It is now necessary to consider the equilibrium of the beam.

Figure 1-7(a) shows the beam after the left-hand portion has been removed by passing a single cutting plane at A. It will be observed that the stresses on the left-hand cross section are distributed in accordance with Eq. (7), and that the given moment M is acting at the right-hand end. A perspective of the stress system is shown in Fig. 1-7(b). The intersection of the neutral surface with the cross section upon which the stresses are acting is called the *neutral axis*.

The portion of the beam in Fig. 1-7(a) must be in equilibrium with respect both to forces and moments. Since the given loading M is a

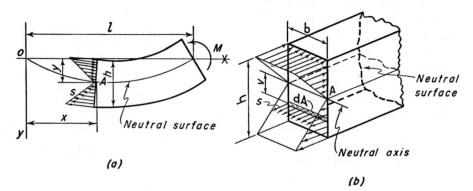

(a)

(b)

Fig. 1-7. Stress caused by bending moment.

pure moment, it is necessary that the forces acting on the left end surface be in equilibrium themselves. The force on an element of area dA, shown in Fig. 1-7(b), is equal to $s\,dA$. When this force is added up for the entire area, $\int s\,dA$, the result must be equal to zero. The value of s from Eq. (7) should now be substituted as follows:

$$\int s\,dA = \int \frac{E}{r} v\,dA = \frac{E}{r} \int v\,dA = 0 \qquad (b)$$

or
$$\int v\,dA = \bar{v}A = 0 \qquad (8)$$

The integral of Eq. (8) represents the total moment of area about the neutral axis. As was shown in Section 5, it can be set equal to the product of the area A of the cross section times the distance $\bar{v}$ of its center of gravity from the neutral axis. The only way in which this product can be zero is for $\bar{v}$ to have a zero value. It must therefore be concluded that the neutral axis passes through the center of gravity of the cross section.

Since the beam in Fig. 1-7(a) is in equilibrium, the moment of the stresses of the left-hand end surface must be equal to the applied moment load M. The force on an element of area, $s\,dA$, when multiplied by the distance v to the neutral axis, and integrated over the entire area, is equal to the moment M. Hence

$$M = \int sv \, dA = \int \frac{E}{r} v^2 \, dA = \frac{E}{r} \int v^2 \, dA = \frac{EI}{r} \qquad (9)$$

The integral $\int v^2 \, dA$ is customarily called the *moment of inertia of the area* and is represented by the letter I. This substitution has been made in the last form of Eq. (9). If the radius of curvature r is eliminated between Eqs. (7) and (9), it results in the important equation

$$s = \frac{Mv}{I} \qquad (10)$$

This equation gives the value of the bending stress at any distance v from the neutral axis. The greatest stress is found at the location on the cross section where v is the largest. This maximum value of v is usually denoted by c, and the equation for the maximum bending stress then becomes

$$s = \frac{Mc}{I} \qquad (11)$$

It should be noted that the magnitude of the stress s given by Eq. (11) is independent of the kind of material composing the beam. The ratio I/c is called the *section modulus of the cross section*.

Although Fig. 1-7 illustrates a rectangular beam, the foregoing theory is valid for any shape of cross section. The maximum stress is located on the boundary at the point farthest removed from the neutral axis.

According to the original assumption, this theory should be applied only to long, thin beams loaded in pure bending. However, under most conditions, the equations give satisfactory results for bending stress when the bending moment is caused by transverse forces applied to the beam. Transverse forces also cause compressive stress between the elements in the neighborhood of the loads.[1]

If the material in the beam does not follow Hooke's law, the magnitude of the stress is no longer proportional to the distance from the neutral axis. If Eq. (11) is applied to such beams, the results may only be approximate.

Example 5. Let the beam in Fig. 1-6 be 2 in. wide and 3 in. deep. Let the bending moment M at each end be equal to 40,000 in-lb. Find the value of the bending stress.

---

[1] See p. 146 of reference 9, Bibliography. Complete bibliographical information is given at end of each chapter,

Solution.

By Eq. (12): $I = \dfrac{bh^3}{12} = \dfrac{2 \times 3^3}{12} = 4.5$ in.⁴

By Eq. (11): $s = \dfrac{Mc}{I} = \dfrac{40,000 \times 1.5}{4.5} = 13,330$ psi

Example 6. A steel bandsaw blade is 0.028 in. thick. Find the value of the bending stress when the blade is passing around a pulley of 18 in. diameter. $E = 30,000,000$ psi.

Solution.

By Eq. (7): $s = \dfrac{Ev}{r} = \dfrac{30,000,000 \times 0.014}{9} = 46,670$ psi

7. Moment of Inertia

The integral $\int v^2\, dA$ appeared in connection with the bending theory of beams. For convenience in writing, this integral, as was mentioned in the foregoing section, is usually replaced by the symbol I and is called the

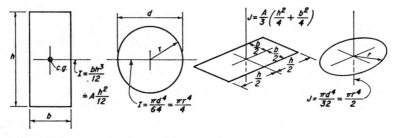

Fig. 1-8.   Moment of inertia and polar moment of inertia.

moment of inertia. Expressions for I for the commonly used geometric shapes of cross sections can be found in the mechanical engineering handbooks. See also Fig. 1-8.

If the integral is computed for a rectangle of width b and depth h about an axis parallel to side b through the center of gravity, as shown in Fig. 1-8, it is found to be equal to

$$I = \frac{bh^3}{12} \tag{12}$$

Width b is parallel to the axis about which the moment tries to rotate the cross section.

Another expression for the bending stress of a beam of rectangular cross section can be secured by substituting Eq. (12) into Eq. (11).

$$s = \frac{6M}{bh^2} \tag{13}$$

For a circle of diameter d or radius r about a diameter through the center, the value of the integral $\int v^2 \, dA$ becomes

$$I = \frac{\pi d^4}{64} = \frac{\pi r^4}{4} \tag{14}$$

When Eq. (14) is substituted into Eq. (11), the following expression for the bending stress of a beam of circular cross section is obtained.

$$s = \frac{32M}{\pi d^3} \tag{15}$$

Suppose that the moment of inertia for the shaded rectangle in Fig. 1-9 is desired about axis 1. Axis 0 should be drawn through the center of gravity parallel to axis 1 about which the moment of inertia is desired. The integral of distance squared times differential area then becomes

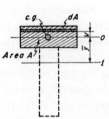

Fig. 1-9. Moment of inertia about parallel axis.

$$I_1 = \int (v + \bar{y})^2 \, dA = \int (v^2 + 2\bar{y}v + \bar{y}^2) dA \tag{a}$$

The integration can be made term by term and is to extend over the shaded area. The first integral, $\int v^2 \, dA$, is equal to the moment of inertia about axis 0 and may be written I_0. The second term, $2\bar{y}\int v \, dA$, is equal to zero since it represents merely the moment of the area about an axis through the center of gravity. The third term is seen to be equal to $A\bar{y}^2$, where A is the area. The moment of inertia for area A about axis 1 is then equal to

$$I_1 = I_0 + A\bar{y}^2 \tag{16}$$

This equation is known as the *parallel axis theorem*. The moment of inertia for a composite cross section can be found by dividing it into elementary parts, finding the moment of inertia about the desired axis for each by Eq. (16), and then adding the results together. Axis 0, however, must be taken through the center of gravity of the area under consideration and must be parallel to the axis about which the total value of I is desired.

The equation for moment of inertia is sometimes written

$$I = i^2 A \tag{b}$$

where i is called the *radius of gyration* for the area. It is the hypothetical distance at which the entire area A would have to be concentrated in order to give the same value for I as determined by the integral.

Example 7. Find the value of the moment of inertia of the T-shaped cross section of Fig. 1-21(b).

Solution. By Example 4, the center of gravity is located 2 in. up from the bottom.

By Eq. (16), for the stem: $I = \dfrac{1 \times 6^3}{12} + 6 \times 1^2 = 24 \text{ in.}^4$

By Eq. (16), for the T: $I = \dfrac{4 \times 1^3}{12} + 4 \times 1.5^2 = 9.33 \text{ in.}^4$

Total: $I = 24 + 9.33 = 33.33 \text{ in.}^4$

8. Principle of Superposition

Stresses and deformations are produced in a body by the forces which are exerted upon it. It is natural to assume that the resultant effect at any chosen point is the sum of the effects of the various loads. In general, experiments have shown that this is so. The idea that the resultant effect is the sum of the separate effects is known as the *principle of superposition*. In general, it is valid for cases of loading only where the magnitude of the stress and deflection is directly proportional to the load.

Example 8. Calculate and plot the distribution of stress over a cross section of the offset link shown in Fig. 1-10(a). The main body of the link is straight and is $\frac{3}{4}$ in. thick.

It is obvious that the loading of Fig. 1-10(a) produces both direct tension and bending stress on the cross section. The principle of superposition applies, and each stress can be computed separately. The two stresses can then be added algebraically to obtain the resultant.

At this point, good use may be made of a principle from statics whereby a given force may be resolved into a parallel force and a couple. By doing so, the equivalent loading on the cross section shown by Fig. 1-10(b) is secured. The moment arm is equal to the distance from the line of action of the force to the center of gravity of the cross section.

Solution. The computations are as follows.

$$A = \frac{3}{4} \times 2 = 1.5 \text{ in.}^2$$

$$I = \frac{bh^3}{12} = \frac{3}{4} \times 8 \times \frac{1}{12} = 0.5 \text{ in.}^4$$

In Eq. (1): $s = \dfrac{P}{A} = \dfrac{3,600}{1.5} = 2,400$ psi direct stress

The moment arm is the distance from the line of action of the force to the center of gravity of the cross-sectional area. $= c = $ dist from NA to farthest point

In Eq. (11): $s = \dfrac{Mc}{I} = \dfrac{3{,}600 \times 1.125 \times 1}{0.5} = 8{,}100$ psi bending stress

Superposition applies and the resultant stress is given by

$$s = \frac{P}{A} + \frac{Mc}{I}$$

On the inside edge: $s = 2{,}400 + 8{,}100 = 10{,}500$ psi tension

On the outside edge: $s = 2{,}400 - 8{,}100 = -5{,}700$ psi compression

Views (c) and (d) show the effect of moment and direct stress separately; the resultant stress on a cross section through the main body of the link is given by

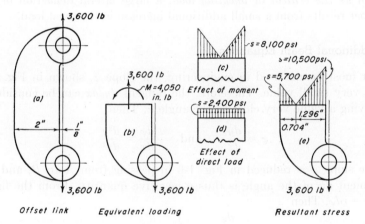

Fig. 1-10.   Offset link with tension load.

(e). Note that views (b) and (e) are in static equilibrium. Also note that the line of zero stress no longer passes through the center of gravity of the cross section.

Superposition cannot be applied if the loads produce deflections which are so great that the basic configuration of the system is thereby changed. Take, for example, the leaf spring with the load on the end shown in Fig. 1-11(a). Suppose, upon doubling the load, that the deflection, shown by the dashed outline, becomes so large that the moment arm of the loads is reduced. The stress and deflection will not be twice as great as for a single load.

Another example where the fundamental configuration of the system is changed by the application of a load is given in Fig. 1-11(b). A change in loading causes a change in deflection, which in turn causes a change in the length of the span. The load and deflection therefore are not proportional to each other.[2]

In general, superposition is not valid for slender members loaded in compression as shown in Fig. 1-11(c). After the load reaches a value

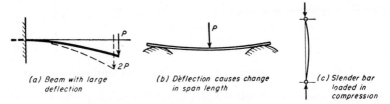

(a) Beam with large deflection   *(b) Deflection causes change in span length*   *(c) Slender bar loaded in compression*

Fig. 1-11.   Examples where deflection changes original geometry; superposition does not apply.

known as the *critical* or *buckling load*, a large lateral deflection of the member results from a small additional increase in the axial load.

9. Additional Beam Equations

For most beams used in engineering, the slope φ, shown in Fig. 1-6, has a very small value. Therefore, the tangent dy/dx can be considered as having a value very close to the angle φ. Then

$$\varphi = \frac{dy}{dx} \quad \text{and} \quad \frac{d\varphi}{dx} = \frac{d^2y}{dx^2}$$

The slope φ is reduced in Fig. 1-6 in passing from A to B, and the increment $d\varphi$ of the angle is thus a negative quantity. From the figure $dx = -r\,d\varphi$. Then

$$\frac{d\varphi}{dx} = -\frac{1}{r} = \frac{d^2y}{dx^2} \tag{17}$$

The negative sign is inserted because both dx and r are positive quantities. Substitution of Eq. (9) gives

$$\frac{d^2y}{dx^2} = -\frac{M}{EI} \tag{18}$$

Equation (18) is the fundamental equation of beam theory. For the general case of loading, moment M is a function of x and not a constant as in Fig. 1-6. If the beam has a large deflection, as, for example, a leaf spring in some types of service, the approximation $\varphi = dy/dx$ cannot be used, and the mathematics of the solution becomes very complicated.

When the bending moment of the beam is not constant, but varies with

[2] See pp. 4, 162, of reference 4, Bibliography.

x, the loading for slice AB is more complicated than in the case of pure bending previously considered. Shearing forces, as well as moments, exist on the end surfaces of the slice. In general the top surface of the beam is acted upon by transverse loads.

A slice from such a beam is shown in Fig. 1-12. The rate at which the bending moment is changing in value is equal to dM/dx, and the distance over which this change takes place in passing from A to B is dx. The change in value for the moment then is $(dM/dx)dx$. The moment on the right end is equal to the moment M of the left end plus the increment or change. Similarly, the shear force, as a function of x, changes from a value V on the left to the amount on the right, as shown. Should either the

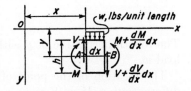

Fig. 1-12.   Element loaded by forces and moments.

moment or shear be decreasing with increasing x, the corresponding derivative would be negative, and would thus effect a reduction for the right-hand value. All shears and moments in Fig. 1-12 have positive directions. Note, however, that the arrows[3] have opposite directions on ends A and B.

Section AB of the beam in Fig. 1-12 is in equilibrium. The algebraic sum of the vertical forces must then be equal to zero. Hence,

$$V + \frac{dV}{dx}\,dx + w\,dx - V = 0 \qquad\qquad \text{(a)}$$

or

$$\frac{dV}{dx} = -w \qquad\qquad \text{(19)}$$

The derivative with respect to x of the expression for the shear is therefore the negative of the value of the load.

The moments also must be in equilibrium. The equation for moments about point A, for example, is

$$M + \frac{dM}{dx}\,dx - \left[V + \frac{dV}{dx}\,dx \right]dx - w\,dx \times \frac{dx}{2} - M = 0 \qquad \text{(b)}$$

When differentials of higher order are neglected, this equation reduces to

$$\frac{dM}{dx} = V \qquad\qquad \text{(20)}$$

The derivative of the moment, as a function of x, gives the expression for the shearing force. Differentiate Eq. (20) and substitute in Eq. (19)

$$\frac{d^2M}{dx^2} = -w \qquad\qquad \text{(21)}$$

[3] See also Section 13.

Differentiate Eq. (18) and substitute Eq. (20)

$$\frac{d^3y}{dx^3} = -\frac{V}{EI} \tag{22}$$

The third derivative of the equation for the deflection y gives an expression which is proportional to the shear. Finally, differentiate Eq. (22) and substitute Eq. (19) to obtain

$$\frac{d^4y}{dx^4} = \frac{w}{EI} \tag{23}$$

The fourth derivative of y with respect to x is thus proportional to the load w.

The location of the point of maximum bending moment is found by differentiating M with respect to x and setting the result equal to zero. However, dM/dx is equal to V by Eq. (20). Therefore, a maximum (or a minimum) value of the bending moment occurs at those points for which the shear V is equal to zero. The load w on the top surface of the beam may be uniform, may vary with x, or may be equal to zero except at the points where concentrated forces or moments are acting.

10. Deflection of Beams

The foregoing equations can be used for deriving equations for the deflections of beams. If the expression for the bending moment, as a function of x, is substituted in Eq. (18), and if two integrations are performed and the constants of integration are evaluated, the equation for the deflection y at location x is obtained. The process is illustrated by the following example.

Fig. 1-13. Example 9.

Example 9. Derive the equation for the deflection y for values of x located between the supports for the beam shown in Fig. 1-13.

Solution. By taking moments, the values of the reactions are found to be $R_1 = 3wl/8$ and $R_2 = 9wl/8$.

At location x:

$$M = \frac{3}{8}wlx - \frac{wx^2}{2}$$

In Eq. (18):

$$EI\frac{d^2y}{dx^2} = -M = -\frac{3}{8}wlx + \frac{wx^2}{2}$$

Integrate:

$$EI\frac{dy}{dx} = -\frac{3wlx^2}{16} + \frac{wx^3}{6} + C_1$$

Since the slope dy/dx is not known for any point on the beam, constant C_1 must be retained and evaluated later. Integrate:

$$EIy = -\frac{3wlx^3}{48} + \frac{wx^4}{24} + C_1x + C_2$$

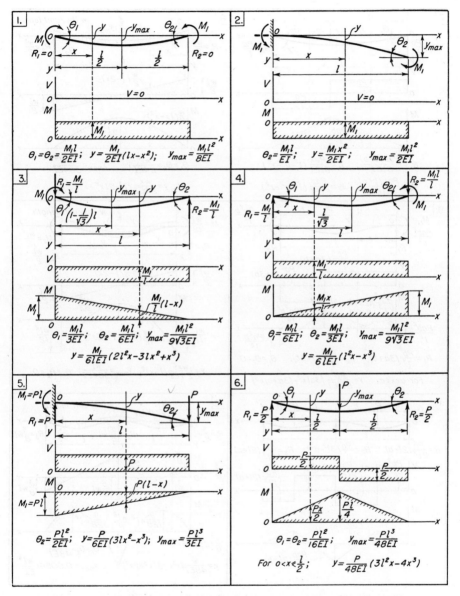

Fig. 1-14. Shear, moment, and deflection in beams of uniform cross section.

At the left end, $x = 0$ and $y = 0$. When these are substituted, $C_2 = 0$. At the right end, $x = l$ and $y = 0$. When these are substituted,

$$C_1 = \frac{wl^3}{48}$$

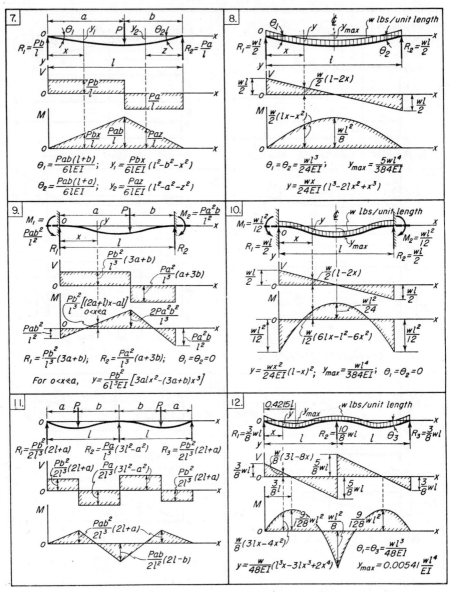

Fig. 1-15. Shear, moment, and deflection in beams of uniform cross section.

The equation for the deflection thus is

$$y = \frac{w}{48EI} (2x^4 - 3lx^3 + l^3x)$$

For indeterminate beams, when the expression for M as a function of x cannot be found by statics, the equation for deflection can still be secured, but the

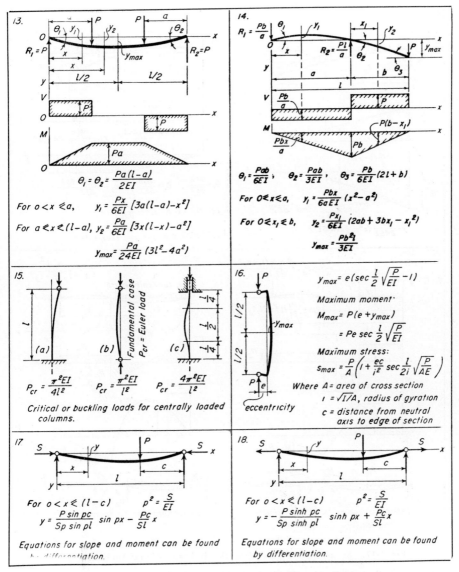

Fig. 1-16. Shear, moment and deflection in beams and columns.

integration process must be started with Eq. (23) and four constants of integration evaluated.

A transverse load on a beam causes a deflection or change in elevation at the point of application. However, a reaction generally remains fixed in elevation even though it carries a force.

Figures 1-14 to 1-17 inc. give the shears, moments, and deflections for a number of beams of various types of loads and conditions of support.

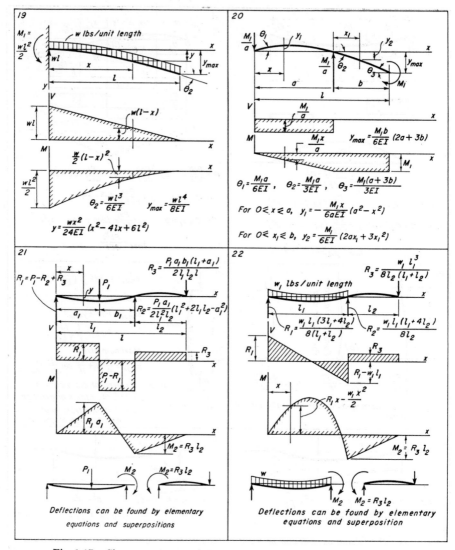

Fig. 1-17.   Shear, moment, and deflection in beams of uniform cross section.

In these figures, a simple support is assumed to offer no resistance to lateral motion or to rotation in the plane of the moments.

Example 10. Suppose it is specified that the deflection from its own weight at the center of a simply supported steel shaft should not exceed 0.010 in. per foot of span.

(a) Find the maximum permissible length for a 3 in. diameter shaft.

(b) Find the stress caused by the weight of the shaft. For steel, $\gamma = 0.283$ lb/in.³, $E = 30,000,000$ psi.

Solution. (a) By the conditions of the problem the deflection at the center is $0.010l/12$, where l is the length in inches. Hence by No. 8 of Fig. 1-15,

$$\frac{5wl^4}{384EI} = \frac{0.010l}{12} \quad \text{or} \quad l^3 = \frac{0.010 \times 384EI}{12 \times 5w}$$

By Eq. (14):

$$I = \frac{\pi d^4}{64} = \frac{\pi 3^4}{64} = 3.976 \text{ in.}^4$$

$$w = \gamma A = 0.283 \frac{\pi 3^2}{4} = 2.00 \text{ lb/in.}$$

Substitution of these values gives

$$l^3 = 3,817,000 \quad \text{or} \quad l = 156.3 \text{ in.} = 13.02 \text{ ft}$$

(b)

$$M = \frac{wl^2}{8} = \frac{2 \times 156.3^2}{8} = 6,106 \text{ in-lb}$$

$$s = \frac{Mc}{I} = \frac{6,106 \times 1.5}{3.976} = 2,300 \text{ psi}$$

If the beam has a cross-section width 8 or 10 or more times as great as the thickness, the beam is stiffer, and the deflection is less than that indicated by the equation for a narrow beam. The large cross-section width prevents the lateral expansion and contraction of the material, and the deflection is thereby reduced. A better value for the deflection of a "wide" beam is obtained by multiplying the result given in the equation for a narrow beam by $(1 - \mu^2)$ where μ is Poisson's ratio.

11. Effect of Ribs on Castings

Ribs are sometimes added to the webs of castings to give greater strength and rigidity. It is possible, however, that the addition of a shallow rib to a body loaded in bending may cause an increase in stress rather than a decrease. The low rib gives a small increase in the moment of inertia, but the distance from the neutral axis to the edge of the cross section becomes relatively greater, and the stress is accordingly increased. The situation is illustrated by the following example.

Example 11. Figure 1-18 represents the cross section through a simply supported beam 60 in. long that carries a 200 lb load at the center. $E = 15,000,000$ psi.

(a) Find the value of the bending stress and the deflection at the center if the ribs were omitted.

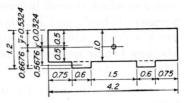

Fig. 1-18. Cross section for ribbed beam, Example 11.

(b) Find the value of the bending stress and the deflection at the center when the ribs are present.

Solution. (a)

$$I = \frac{bh^3}{12} = \frac{4.2 \times 1^3}{12} = 0.35 \text{ in.}^4$$

$$M = \frac{Pl}{4} = \frac{200 \times 60}{4} = 3,000 \text{ in-lb}$$

$$s = \frac{Mc}{I} = \frac{3,000 \times 0.5}{0.35} = 4,290 \text{ psi}$$

$$y = \frac{Pl^3}{48EI} = \frac{200 \times 60^3}{48 \times 15,000,000 \times 0.35} = 0.1714 \text{ in.}$$

(b) Area, $A = 4.2 \times 1 + 2 \times 0.2 \times 0.6 = 4.44 \text{ in.}^2$

To find $\bar{y}$, take the axis along top of the cross section.

$$4.44\bar{y} = 4.2 \times 0.5 + 0.24 \times 1.1 = 2.364$$

$$\bar{y} = 0.5324 \text{ in.}$$

For the main area: $I = \dfrac{bh^3}{12} + A\bar{y}^2 = 0.35 + 4.2 \times 0.0324^2 = 0.3544 \text{ in.}^4$

For the ribs: $I = \dfrac{1.2 \times 0.2^3}{12} + 0.24 \times 0.5676^2 = 0.0813 \text{ in.}^4$

Total: $I = 0.3544 + 0.0813 = 0.4357 \text{ in.}^4$

$$s = \frac{Mc}{I} = \frac{3,000 \times 0.6676}{0.4357} = 4,600 \text{ psi}$$

$$y = \frac{Pl^3}{48EI} = \frac{200 \times 60^3}{48 \times 15,000,000 \times 0.4357} = 0.1377 \text{ in.}$$

As shown above, shallow ribs cause an increase in the bending stress. The deflection, however, has been decreased. If the ribs are made somewhat larger, the stress would be decreased, and the beam would be stronger.[4]

Ribbed structures are frequently made of a brittle material such as cast iron which is weak in tension. If possible, the ribs should be in compression. When a cast iron body with parallel ribs is bent and the ribs are in tension, care must be exercised to make certain that all ribs are of the same height, or they may fail progressively beginning with the highest. Therefore, the full strength of the body cannot be realized.

[4] See references 10 and 11, Bibliography.

12. Shearing Stress

Suppose an element is loaded by shearing stresses acting tangentially to its sides as shown in perspective in Fig. 1-19(a) or in plan in Figs. 1-19(b) and (c). Such loading causes no change in the length of the sides of the element, but merely produces a distortion or change in the value of the 90° angles in the corners.

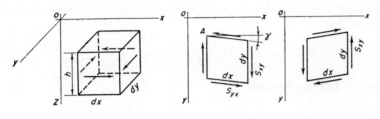

(a) Element loaded in shear   (b) Positive shear   (c) Negative shear

Fig. 1-19.   Element loaded by shearing or tangential stress.

Shearing stresses are usually denoted by double subscripts. The first subscript indicates the direction of the normal to the plane under consideration, and the second subscript indicates the direction of the stress. Hence stress s_{xy} lies in a plane whose normal is in the x-direction, while the stress acts in the y-direction. For similar reasons s_{yx} indicates that the stress is in a plane perpendicular to the y-axis, and is parallel to the x-axis. Since the element is in equilibrium, the moments of the forces about a point, say A, must add up to zero. The stress should be multiplied by the area and then by the moment arm to give

$$s_{xy}\, dx\, dy\, h - s_{yx}\, dx\, dy\, h = 0$$

or
$$s_{xy} = s_{yx} \tag{24}$$

Equation (24) shows that the shearing stresses in two perpendicular directions at a point are equal. Usually no distinction in notation is made, and both would be represented by the same symbol.

It should be noted, however, that four arrows are necessary to specify a state of shear for an element, and for equilibrium these arrows must be arranged either as in Fig. 1-19(b) for positive shear, or as in Fig. 1-19(c) for negative shear. Thus if the direction of one arrow is reversed, all four must be reversed. In other words, if shearing stress exists on one side of an element, then, in general, shearing stress must exist on all four sides, as shown in Fig. 1-19.

The shearing strain or angular deformation γ is proportional to the shearing stress for values within the elastic range, and Hooke's law for shear becomes

$$s_{xy} = \gamma G \tag{25}$$

The constant of proportionality, G, is called the *modulus of elasticity in shear*. It has dimensions of psi. In magnitude it would be equal to the stress which would cause the angular deformation to become equal to one radian, provided Hooke's law is valid for such imaginary loading. The mathematical relationship between the three elastic constants E, G, and μ is given by

$$G = \frac{E}{2(1 + \mu)}$$

where μ is Poisson's ratio.[5]

13. Transverse Shearing Stress in Beams

In addition to the bending stresses, the loads on a beam may also cause shearing stresses between the elements. The designer is interested in the magnitude of these stresses, since machine parts made of ductile materials are usually designed on the basis of shearing stress.

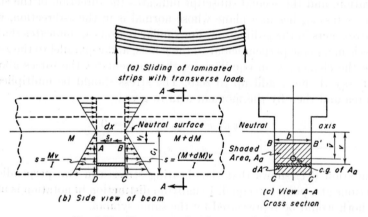

(a) Sliding of laminated strips with transverse loads

(b) Side view of beam

(c) View A-A Cross section

Fig. 1-20. Transverse shearing stress in beam.

If a vertical load is supported by a stack of laminated strips, the shearing effect is as shown in Fig. 1-20(a). In a solid beam the elements do not slide on each other, but the shearing stress tending to make them do so is present.

Figure 1-20(b) shows a portion $ABCD$ cut from a beam of uniform cross section by two adjacent vertical planes and a horizontal plane, lo-

[5] See p. 57 of reference 1, Bibliography.

cated at a distance v_1 below the neutral surface. Moment M is acting on the cross section of the left end of the slice, while moment $M + dM$ is acting on the right.

To maintain equilibrium in the horizontal direction, shearing stress s_s must act towards the left on surface AB. This shear is necessary because the normal stresses from the bending moment are assumed to be larger on surface BC on the right than on surface AD on the left.

An element of area dA on surface AD has the normal force $s\,dA$ or $Mv\,dA/I$ acting as shown in Fig. 1-20(b). The total force on the left end extending from A to D is then

$$\int_{v_1}^{c_1} \frac{Mv}{I}\,dA \tag{a}$$

Similarly, the total force on the right end BC is

$$\int_{v_1}^{c_1} \frac{(M + dM)v}{I}\,dA \tag{b}$$

The shearing force on the horizontal surface AB is $s_s b\,dx$, where b is the width of the beam at the location where the shear stress s_s is acting.

The equilibrium equation for horizontal forces for $ABCD$ is then

$$s_s b\,dx + \int_{v_1}^{c_1} \frac{Mv\,dA}{I} = \int_{v_1}^{c_1} \frac{(M + dM)v\,dA}{I} \tag{c}$$

or

$$s_s = \frac{1}{b}\int_{v_1}^{c_1} \frac{dM}{dx}\frac{v\,dA}{I} = \frac{V}{Ib}\int_{v_1}^{c_1} v\,dA \tag{26}$$

In the last form of Eq. (26), shear V has been substituted for dM/dx. In Eq. (26), $v\,dA$ represents the moment of the area of the element about the neutral axis. This is integrated over the entire surface from v_1, the location where the shearing stress s_s is desired, to the outer edge. This integral can also be written $\bar{v}A_a$, where A_a is the shaded area of view A-A, and $\bar{v}$ is the distance from its center of gravity to the neutral axis. Equation (26) can then be written

$$s_s = \frac{V}{Ib}\bar{v}A_a \tag{27}$$

As was proved in the preceding section, the shearing stress on the vertical end surfaces at distance v_1 from the neutral axis is also equal to the horizontal shear stress s_s as determined by Eqs. (26) or (27).

For composite cross sections it is convenient to divide area A_a into several parts, find $\bar{v}A_a$ for each of them, and then add together for the final result. For such beams, Eq. (27) is written

$$s_s = \frac{V}{Ib}\Sigma\,\bar{v}A_a \tag{28}$$

The total shear force on the cross section is represented by V. The distance from the neutral axis to the point where the shearing stress is desired is given by v_1.

Example 12. Find the transverse shear in the material 3 in. from the top surface for the beam of Fig. 1-21(a). Also find the value of the transverse shearing stress at the neutral axis.

Solution. As is shown in Example 4, the center of gravity of the cross section in Fig. 1-21(b) is found to be 2 in. up from the bottom. As shown in Example 7, the moment of inertia about the horizontal axis through the center of gravity is found to be 33.33 in.[4]

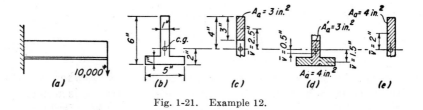

Fig. 1-21.   Example 12.

Referring to Fig. 1-21(c), it is seen for location 3 in. from the top that $\bar{v} = 2.5$ n. and $A_a = 3$ in.[2] Substitution in Eq. (27) gives

$$s_s = \frac{10,000}{33.33 \times 1} \times 2.5 \times 3 = 2,250 \text{ psi}$$

It is of course immaterial whether A_a is taken above or below the location at which the stress is desired. If taken below, the situation is as shown in Fig. 1-21(d). Equation (28) gives

$$s_s = \frac{10,000}{33.33 \times 1} (1.5 \times 4 + 0.5 \times 3) = 2,250 \text{ psi}$$

At the neutral surface, values of $\bar{v}$ and A_a shown in Fig. 1-21(e) are used, and the value of the shearing stress becomes

$$s_s = \frac{10,000}{33.33 \times 1} \times 4 \times 2 = 2,400 \text{ psi}$$

When Eq. (26) is applied to rectangular cross sections, $dA = b\,dv$ and $c_1 = h/2$. After making these substitutions and integrating, the following result is obtained.

$$s_s = \frac{V}{2I}\left(\frac{h^2}{4} - v_1^2\right) = \frac{3V}{2A}\left(1 - \frac{4v_1^2}{h^2}\right) \tag{29}$$

The transverse shearing stress in a rectangular beam thus varies as a second-degree parabola in v_1. Its value is proportional to the length of the arrows in Fig. 1-22(a). The maximum value occurs at the neutral axis, where $v_1 = 0$, and is equal to

$$s_s = \frac{3V}{2A} \tag{30}$$

The shear decreases both above and below the axis in accordance with Eq. (29) until at the upper and lower edges it becomes zero.[6] The end surface of the beam in Fig. 1-22(a) is also acted upon by the system of normal stresses caused by the bending moment, as shown by Fig. 1-7(b). In Fig. 1-22(a) these have been omitted for greater clarity.

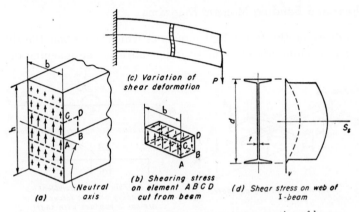

Fig. 1-22.   Distribution of shearing stress over cross section of beam.

Within reasonable limits, the presence of the shearing stress has no effect on the value of the bending stress, and vice versa.

The shearing deformation also varies over the surface of a cross section; it is maximum at the neutral axis and zero at the top and bottom. The shearing stress causes a warping of the cross sections which were originally plane and perpendicular to the longitudinal elements of the beam.[7] For a cantilever with a load on the end, the situation is as shown in Fig. 1-22(c).

For a solid circular cross section, Eq. (26) gives the following value for the maximum transverse shear which occurs at the neutral axis.[8]

$$s_{smax} = \frac{4}{3} \cdot \frac{V}{A} \tag{31}$$

---

[6] See p. 116 of reference 1, Bibliography.

[7] For deflection of beams caused by shear, see p. 170 of reference 1, Bibliography.

[8] A more exact analysis gives values of $1.38P/A$ and $1.23P/A$ for the shearing stress at the center and ends, respectively, of the neutral axis. See p. 290 of reference 2, Bibliography.

For a circular tube with very thin walls, the maximum transverse shear stress at the neutral axis is given by

$$s_{smax} = 2\frac{V}{A} \tag{32}$$

The distribution of transverse shear stress for an I-beam is shown in Fig. 1-22(d). The stress is practically uniform except in the regions near the top and bottom. A good approximate value for the stress is obtained by dividing the total shearing force V by the area of the web td with the web considered as extending the entire depth of the beam.

14. Shear and Bending Moment Diagrams

The effects of the forces and moments which act upon the different parts of a machine are of primary importance to the machine designer.

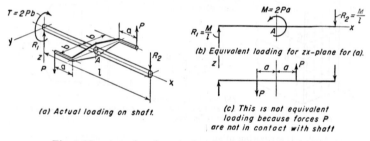

Fig. 1-23.   Actual and equivalent load diagram for shaft.

Forces arise from a variety of causes. A force may be due to weight or to inertia if a body is being accelerated. A force may be transmitted to the body by another member of the machine at the point where the two parts are in contact. It is common practice to represent forces by means of arrows on sketches in solving force problems. It is very important, except for gravity and inertia, to keep in mind that the body must have contact with the rest of the structure at the point where a force, represented by an arrow, is considered as acting. As an example, consider the shaft of Fig. 1-23(a). The entire loading occurs at point A, where the bracket is attached to the shaft. The equivalent loading diagram is shown in Fig. 1-23(b). The diagram of Fig. 1-23(c) is incorrect because forces P are not in contact with the shaft.

Moment loads such as those described in Fig. 1-23(b) frequently occur in machine parts. Thus in the tank shown in Fig. 1-24(a) the floor beam not only resists the vertical pressure of the fluid, but has moments applied to it at the ends by the uprights which are acted upon by the horizontal pressure of the fluid. The equivalent loading is shown in Fig. 1-24(b). In Fig. 1-24(c) the vertical bar is loaded at the base by the moment Wa as well as by the force P. The equivalent loading is shown in Fig. 1-24(d).

In solving most stress problems it is first necessary to find the reactions which the given loading produces. It is customary to make use of the following equations from statics.

$$\Sigma F_x = 0, \qquad \Sigma F_y = 0, \qquad \Sigma F_z = 0$$
$$\Sigma M_x = 0, \qquad \Sigma M_y = 0, \qquad \Sigma M_z = 0$$

According to these equations, the components of the forces, as well as the moments, in each of the three coordinate directions must add to zero.

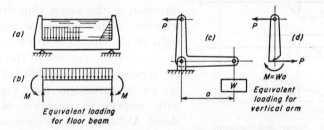

Fig. 1-24. Examples of beams with moment loads.

For static equilibrium, each of these equations must be satisfied. It should be noted that each is satisfied independently of the others. So far as the reactions are concerned, a force can be considered to be acting anywhere along its line of action, and a moment load can be considered to be acting anywhere in its plane. The state of stress in the material, however, is determined by the location, on the line of action, at which the force is considered to be applied.

The shearing force and bending moment, acting internally on the cross section of a beam at any point, are equal to the force and moment required for the equilibrium of each portion of the beam after it has been cut in two at the given point. For example, consider the simply supported beam, shown in Fig. 1-25(a), with load P and reactions R_1 and R_2. In (b) and (c), after cutting at distance x from the left end, shear V_1 and moment M_1 are required to maintain equilibrium of each portion. Reactions R_1 and R_2 in (b) and (c) are the same as in (a). Shear V_1 is found by summation of vertical forces. Moment M_1 is found by making a summatio 1 of moments, with the location of the cut taken as the moment center. The shear and moment diagrams shown in (d) and (e) are constructed by taking different values of x and finding V and M for each until a sufficient number of values has been found to plot the diagrams. It is generally assumed that a reaction does not change in elevation. Other transverse loads deflect the beam, and the elevations of the loads are thereby changed.

Moments and shears can, of course, be either positive or negative, depending on the direction in which they act. The shear and moment at point A for the beam shown in Fig. 1-25 are both positive. Positive directions for the arrows representing these quantities are accordingly shown in the figures. Even though both shear and moment are positive at A, note that a reversal in direction for both the V_1 and M_1 arrows occurs in (b) and (c). The direction of the arrow thus depends on whether the portion of the beam to the right of the cut, as in (b), is considered, or whether the portion to the left, as in (c), is considered. Note that both (b) and (c) are in agreement with Fig. 1-19(b) with respect to direction of positive shear. Although the y-axis is taken positive downward, both the V- and M-axes are taken positive upward.

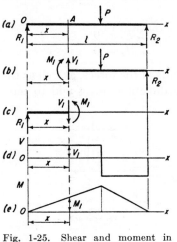

Fig. 1-25.   Shear and moment in beam.

Depending on the loading and method of supporting the beam, the shear at a cross section may have one sign, and the moment may have the opposite sign.

Another method for determining the sign of the moment is shown in Fig. 1-26. Here a moment tending to bow the beam concavely upward is considered positive, whereas a moment tending to make the beam concave downward is negative.

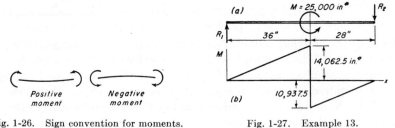

Positive   Negative
moment   moment

Fig. 1-26.   Sign convention for moments.   Fig. 1-27.   Example 13.

Example 13. A simply supported beam is loaded by a concentrated moment of 25,000 in-lb as shown in Fig. 1-27. Find values of reactions R_1 and R_2, and draw and dimension the bending moment diagram.

Solution. Reaction R_1 can be found by writing a moment equation for the entire beam with center of moments taken at R_2. The resulting equation is

$$64R_1 = 25,000; \qquad R_1 = 390.6 \text{ lb}$$

Reaction R_2 can be found by a moment equation with R_1 taken as the center.

$$64R_2 = 25,000; \qquad R_2 = 390.6 \text{ lb}$$

The moment diagram consists of segments of straight lines. Let it be assumed that the beam is cut just to the left of the point of application of the moment load. The bending moment is positive and is equal to

$$M = 36R_1 = 36 \times 390.6 = 14,062.5 \text{ in-lb}$$

Again let it be assumed that the beam is cut just to the right of the point of application of the load. The moment is negative.

$$M = 28R_2 = 28 \times 390.6 = 10,937.5 \text{ in-lb}$$

15. Slender Compression Members or Columns

When a short block is loaded in compression as in Fig. 1-28(a), the average compressive stress in the material is found by dividing the load

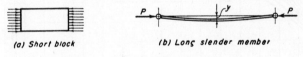

(a) Short block   (b) Long slender member

Fig. 1-28.   Bodies under compressive load.

by the cross-sectional area. However, when the member is long and slender, as that shown in Fig. 1-28(b), the situation is complicated by the possibility of lateral buckling. Buckling does not occur when the bar is straight and a load, smaller than the critical value, is centrally applied. Such a column is stable; the bar, if given a lateral deflection, returns to its originally straight condition upon removal of the lateral force.

Force P in Fig. 1-28(b) can be increased until the straight form of the bar becomes unstable, and the axial loads will then maintain the bar in a curved form. The smallest load capable of maintaining the bar in a slightly bent form is called the *critical or buckling load* P_{cr}. A load only slightly greater than P_{cr} causes a relatively large lateral deflection. After buckling the stress increases rapidly; in addition to the direct compression, a bending stress from moment Py is present.

Hence the phenomenon of stability or buckling is quite different from the phenomenon of bending. A beam with lateral load starts to deflect as soon as any load is present, and the deflection is directly proportional to the magnitude of the load. A slender member in compression, in contrast, exhibits no lateral deflection until the critical or buckling load has been reached. Any increase of load then causes a large increase of deflection with accompanying danger of failure. It is obvious that the principle of superposition does not apply to columns.

Sometimes only a portion of a stressed body is in compression, as, for example, the compression flange of a beam. The danger of buckling may be present here if sufficient lateral support is lacking.

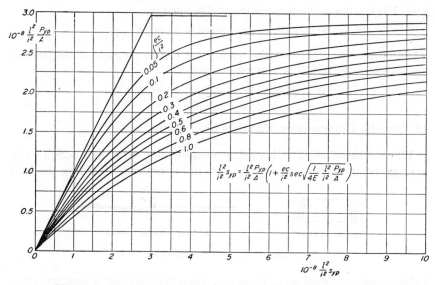

Fig. 1-29. Curves for designing steel columns by the secant equation.

The values of the critical or buckling loads for three cases of centrally loaded columns are given[9] in No. 15 of Fig. 1-16. Equations applicable to a column with eccentrically applied loads are given in No. 16 of Fig. 1-16. These are known as the secant equations. The permissible loading depends upon the slenderness ratio l/i, where $i = \sqrt{I/A}$, the radius of gyration for the cross section.[10]

As for other machine elements, a factor of safety must be used in column design. Because the stress is not proportional to the load, the factor of safety FS is applied to the load rather than to the stress. Let P_{yp} be the

---

[9] For derivation see books on strength of materials, e.g., references 2 and 5, Bibliography.

[10] Books sometimes represent radius of gyration by r. When this is done, care must be taken not to confuse radius of gyration with the radius r of a round cross section.

load on the column that causes the maximum stress to be equal to the yield point value s_{yp}. Let the working load P be equal to P_{yp} divided by the factor of safety.

$$P = \frac{P_{yp}}{FS} \tag{33}$$

The secant equation for stress can then be written

$$s_{yp} = \frac{P_{yp}}{A}\left[1 + \frac{ec}{i^2}\sec\frac{l}{2i}\sqrt{\frac{P_{yp}}{AE}}\right] \tag{34}$$

Equation (34) is difficult to use in design work. Results can be obtained much more easily by using curves that have been plotted from it. Figure 1-29 shows such a family of curves for steel columns ($E = 30,000,000$ psi) for various values of ec/i^2. It should be noted that it was necessary to multiply both sides of the equation by l^2/i^2 to obtain coordinates suitable for plotting.

Example 14. A steel column has an l/i value of 100 and an ec/i^2 value of 0.1. Find the value of the permissible working stress P/A if the factor of safety is to be 2.5. The yield point value for the material is 40,000 psi.

Solution.

$$\frac{l^2}{i^2}s_{yp} = 100^2 \times 40,000 = 4 \times 10^8$$

From Fig. 1-29:

$$10^{-8}\frac{l^2}{i^2}\cdot\frac{P_{yp}}{A} = 2.42$$

$$\frac{P_{yp}}{A} = 2.42\frac{10^8}{100^2} = 24,200 \text{ psi}$$

$$\frac{P}{A} = \frac{24,200}{2.5} = 9,700 \text{ psi}$$

Example 15. A load of 50,000 lb is to be carried by a solid circular column with hinged ends. The material is steel with a yield point value of 50,000 psi. The length of column is 36 in. with an assumed eccentricity in application of the load equal to $\frac{1}{40}$ of the diameter. The factor of safety is to be equal to 4. Find the required diameter of the column.

Solution. This type of problem is best solved by trial and error. A value for the area is chosen and the computations are carried out to see if the load capacity of the column is satisfactory.

$$i^2 = \frac{I}{A} = \frac{\pi d^4}{64} \times \frac{4}{\pi d^2} = \frac{d^2}{16}$$

$$\frac{ec}{i^2} = \frac{d}{40} \times \frac{d}{2} \times \frac{16}{d^2} = 0.2$$

$$P_{yp} = 4 \times 50,000 = 200,000 \text{ lb}$$

Assume: $A = 5.4 \text{ in.}^2$

$$d^2 = \frac{4A}{\pi} = 6.88 \text{ in.}^2$$

$$i^2 = \frac{d^2}{16} = \frac{6.88}{16} = 0.430 \text{ in.}^2$$

$$\frac{l^2}{i^2} s_{yp} = \frac{36 \times 36}{0.430} \times 50,000 = 1.51 \times 10^8$$

From Fig. 1-29: $10^{-8} \dfrac{l^2}{i^2} \cdot \dfrac{P_{yp}}{A} = 1.12$

$$\frac{P_{yp}}{A} = 1.12 \times \frac{0.430}{36 \times 36} \times 10^8 = 37,160 \text{ psi}$$

$$P_{yp} = 37,160 \times 5.4 = 200,700 \text{ lb}$$

Assumed value of A is satisfactory. Hence

$$d = \sqrt{6.88} = 2.622 \text{ in.}$$

For hinged or pin-connected ends, the assumption is made that there is no restraint against rotation at the ends of the column. For fixed ends, all rotation is prevented as shown by No. 15(c) of Fig. 1-16. The deflection curve consists of two quarter-waves and one-half-wave. Bending moments are present at the ends, but no moments act at the inflection points. Calculations are usually made by taking one-half the actual length for l in the equations for columns with hinged ends. For many practical cases, the end conditions are intermediate between being completely hinged and completely restrained.

An actual column under load may behave differently from an ideal column, and the design of this element therefore presents many difficulties. Uncertainties such as amount of restraint at the ends, eccentricity of the load, initial crookedness, nonhomogeneity of the material, and deflection caused by the load can produce large variations in the behavior of a column. The choice of a suitable value for the factor of safety also presents great difficulties.[11] Empirical equations are frequently used for column designing.[11] The possibility of buckling about both of the principal axes of the cross section should be investigated.

[11] See Chapter 3 of reference 5.

When the critical load $\pi^2 EI/l^2$ is substituted for P in the secant equation, an infinite value is obtained for the deflection. Although physically there can be no such deflection, it is characteristic of column equations to indicate the buckling phenomenon in this manner.

16. Stresses in Any Given Direction

The stresses in a body, as found by the equations of this chapter, have definite directions. It is sometimes necessary to have the stresses at directions other than those given by the equations.

Figure 1-30(a) shows an element of a plate with the vertical surfaces subjected to the general two-dimensional state of stress. The element has

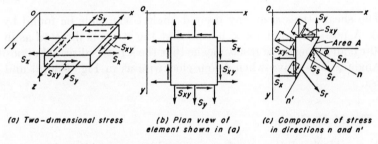

(a) Two-dimensional stress   (b) Plan view of element shown in (a)   (c) Components of stress in directions n and n'

Fig. 1-30.   Shear and normal stress on element at any angle φ.

been cut from a larger plate so that stresses s_x, s_y, and s_{xy} represent the effect of the surrounding material on the element. A plan view of the element is shown in Fig. 1-30(b). Suppose stresses s_x, s_y, and s_{xy} are known, and that it is necessary to find the values of the stresses on an inclined surface whose normal makes an angle φ with the x-axis as shown in Fig. 1-30(c). Angle φ is an arbitrarily chosen angle and determines the directions of the n- and n'-axes.

Assume that stress s_r must be applied to the cut surface in order to maintain equilibrium of the remaining portion of the plate. Resultant stress s_r can be resolved into the components of normal stress s_n and shear stress s_s as shown.

If the area of the inclined surface is A, then the area of the horizontal side of the body will be $A \sin \varphi$, and the area of the vertical side, $A \cos \varphi$. Since the plate of Fig. 1-30(c) is in equilibrium, the projections of the forces on the perpendicular to the inclined surface must be in equilibrium. Multiplication of stress by area and then by the appropriate trigonometric function gives the following equation for s_n.

$$s_n = 2s_{xy} \sin \varphi \cos \varphi + s_x \cos^2 \varphi + s_y \sin^2 \varphi$$

The trigonometric terms should be changed by the substitution of the equations involving the double angles. Hence,

$$s_n = \frac{s_x + s_y}{2} + \frac{s_x - s_y}{2} \cos 2\varphi + s_{xy} \sin 2\varphi \qquad (35)$$

Thus the normal stress in the plate at any desired angle φ can be found by means of Eq. (35). If a negative value is secured for s_n, the normal stress for that value of φ will be compression.

In a similar manner, s_s can be found by making the sum of the projections of all forces parallel to the cut surface equal to zero. Hence,

$$s_s = s_{xy} (\cos^2 \varphi - \sin^2 \varphi) - (s_x - s_y) \sin \varphi \cos \varphi$$

or $$s_s = s_{xy} \cos 2\varphi - \frac{s_x - s_y}{2} \sin 2\varphi \qquad (36)$$

The shear stress s_s at any desired angle φ can thus be found by Eq. (36). A positive result for s_s means that the stress is directed as in Fig. 1-30(c), and a negative result means that the stress is directed oppositely.

Angle φ is positive when taken clockwise as in Fig. 1-30(c) and vice versa.

17. The Mohr Circle

A graphical solution to the combined stress problem, known as the Mohr circle, will now be given. Use of this method rather than the previously derived equations usually effects a considerable saving in time. However, certain conventions regarding signs and directions must be understood and carefully followed.

Figure 1-31 shows the perpendicular axes s_n and s_s. Normal stresses, regardless of the inclination of the surface on which they act, are plotted horizontally—positive, or tension, to the right of the origin, and negative, or compression, to the left. Shear stresses are plotted vertically upward or downward on the diagram. The normal and shear stress at a point in the body thus become the coordinates of a point on the circle.

Stresses s_x and s_{xy} acting on the right and left edges of the plate in Fig. 1-30(b) locate point A in Fig. 1-31. Tension s_x is plotted to the right in accordance with the above-mentioned rule. Since shear stress s_{xy} tends to rotate the element in a clockwise direction, it is plotted upward. Stresses s_y and s_{xy} of the upper and lower edges of the plate shown in Fig. 1-30(b) locate point B in Fig. 1-31. Tension s_y is plotted to the right. Since shear stress s_{xy} on these surfaces tends to produce counterclockwise rotation, it is plotted downward. The Mohr circle is drawn with line AB as a diameter. Greater facility in the determination of angles will be obtained if radii AC and BC are marked x-axis and y-axis, respectively.

To find the stresses on an element oriented at angle φ, as shown in Fig. 1-31(c), the angle 2φ is laid off from CA, the x-axis of the circle, in the same direction as angle φ is turned in the body. Diameter DE is thus located.

The horizontal projection of CD has the value shown in the figure. When this is added to OC, the result is the value of s_n as given by Eq. (35).

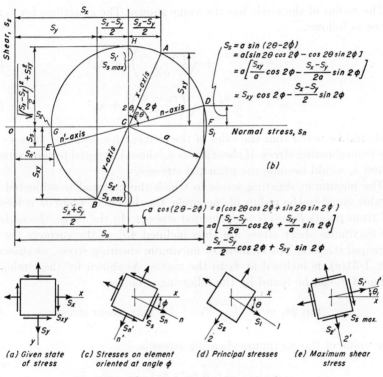

$$s_s = a \sin(2\theta - 2\phi)$$
$$= a[\sin 2\theta \cos 2\phi - \cos 2\theta \sin 2\phi]$$
$$= a\left[\frac{s_{xy}}{a} \cos 2\phi - \frac{s_x - s_y}{2a} \sin 2\phi\right]$$
$$= s_{xy} \cos 2\phi - \frac{s_x - s_y}{2} \sin 2\phi$$

Normal stress, S_n

(b)

$$a \cos(2\theta - 2\phi) = a(\cos 2\theta \cos 2\phi + \sin 2\theta \sin 2\phi)$$
$$= a\left[\frac{s_x - s_y}{2a} \cos 2\phi + \frac{s_{xy}}{a} \sin 2\phi\right]$$
$$= \frac{s_x - s_y}{2} \cos 2\phi + s_{xy} \sin 2\phi$$

(a) Given state of stress   *(c) Stresses on element oriented at angle ϕ*   *(d) Principal stresses*   *(e) Maximum shear stress*

Fig. 1-31.   Mohr circle for two-dimensional stress.

The vertical projection of CD has the value shown on the figure. This is equal to s_s as given by Eq. (36). It is plain that the coordinates of point D of the circle are equal to the normal and shear stresses as found by the combined stress equations.

Stresses $s_{n'}$ and s_s for the surface, in Fig. 1-31(c), whose normal lies at angle $(90° + \varphi)$ from the x-axis, are given by the coordinates of point E.

A clockwise angle φ on the body corresponds to a clockwise angle of 2φ on the circle, and vice versa.

Values of stresses s_n, $s_{n'}$, and s_s change as angle φ is changed. The maximum and minimum values of the normal stresses are called the principal stresses, and are designated s_1 and s_2, respectively. Their values can be found from the abscissas for points F and G in Fig. 1-31(b). The element for the principal stresses is oriented at angle θ to the x-axis as shown in Fig. 1-31(d). As shown by the circle, the value of θ can be found by the following equation.

$$\tan 2\theta = \frac{2s_{xy}}{s_x - s_y}, \quad \text{for principal stresses} \tag{37}$$

The radius of the circle has the value shown. The equations for s_1 and s_2 are as follows.

$$s_1 = \frac{s_x + s_y}{2} + \sqrt{\left(\frac{s_x - s_y}{2}\right)^2 + s_{xy}^2} \tag{38}$$

$$s_2 = \frac{s_x + s_y}{2} - \sqrt{\left(\frac{s_x - s_y}{2}\right)^2 + s_{xy}^2} \tag{39}$$

It should be noted that the sides of the element for principal stresses are free from shearing stress. If shear stress s_{xy} should be equal to zero, stresses s_x and s_y would become the principal stresses.

The maximum shearing stress to which the material is subjected has a value equal to the radius of the circle. On the circle, point H is located $90°$ from points F and G for principal stresses. In the body, the surfaces for maximum shear stress are thus inclined $45°$ to the surfaces for the principal stresses. The element of maximum shearing stress, as shown in Fig. 1-31(e), is inclined at θ_1 to the x-axis. As shown by the circle, the value of θ_1 can be found by the following equation.

$$\tan 2\theta_1 = -\frac{s_x - s_y}{2s_{xy}}, \quad \text{for max. shear stress} \tag{40}$$

The value of the maximum shearing stress is

$$s_{smax} = \sqrt{\left[\frac{s_x - s_y}{2}\right]^2 + s_{xy}^2} \tag{41}$$

Let the axes for maximum shear stress be called $1'$ and $2'$. In Fig. 1-31, the element for maximum shear stress has normal stresses on the sides of value

$$s_{1'} = s_{2'} = \frac{s_x + s_y}{2} \tag{42}$$

Another useful equation for maximum shear stress is obtained by subtracting s_2 from s_1.

$$s_{smax} = \frac{1}{2}(s_1 - s_2) \tag{43}$$

Example 17. Let the state of stress at some point in a body be defined as follows.

$$s_x = 20,000 \text{ psi}, \qquad s_y = -4,000 \text{ psi}, \qquad s_{xy} = 5,000 \text{ psi}$$

(a) Draw the view of the element for the given state of stress and mark values thereon.

(b) Draw the Mohr circle for the given state of stress and mark completely.

(c) Draw the element oriented 30° clockwise from x-axis and show values of all stresses.

(d) Draw the element correctly oriented for principal stresses and show values.

(e) Draw the element for maximum shear stress and mark values of all stresses.

Solution. The given state of stress and the Mohr circle are shown in Figs. 1-32(a) and (b), respectively.

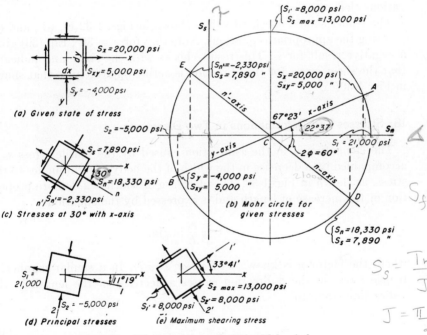

Fig. 1-32.   Solution of Example 17 by Mohr circle.

(c) Diameter ECD should be drawn at 60° clockwise to the x-axis of the circle, and stresses s_n and $s_{n'}$ scaled and placed on the element of Fig. 1-32(c). Since point D lies below the s_n-axis, shear stress s_s crosses the n-axis of Fig. 1-32(c) in the direction that causes a counterclockwise moment on the element. Likewise, since E lies above the s_n-axis, stress s_s crosses the n'-axis in sketch (c) in the direction that causes a clockwise moment on the element.

(d) Principal stresses s_1 and s_2, together with their angle of inclination, are scaled directly from the circle, and are shown acting on an element properly oriented in Fig. 1-32(d).

(e) The maximum shear stress $s_{s\,max}$ and the corresponding normal stress $s_{1'}$ are shown on the element of Fig. 1-32(e). The arrows are directed in accordance with the previously explained rules.

The advantages of the graphical method for solving combined stress problems should now be apparent. Not only is the method more rapid, but the state of stress for any direction can be scaled directly from the circle. When the equations are used for solving a problem, a separate computation must be made for each desired direction. The Mohr circle also aids in forming a mental picture of the state of stress in the body. In working problems, care must be exercised that all necessary information is placed on the drawing for the circle as well as on the views of the various elements.

The reader should check all values shown in Figs. 1-32(c), (d), and (e) by using the appropriate equations. Note that for $\varphi = 30°$, Eq. (36) gives a negative result for s_s. This result checks with the circle and indicates that the shear stress for this direction is acting oppositely to that shown in Fig. 1-30(c).

18. Stresses and Deformations in Two Directions

The elongation ϵ_x in the x-direction caused by the tensile stress s_x is accompanied by a decrease in the width of the body at right angles to the stress, as shown in Fig. 1-33. This decrease of width is a definite proportion of the increase of length and is expressed by the equation

$$\epsilon_y = -\mu \frac{s_x}{E} \text{ in./in.} \tag{44}$$

where the factor μ is known as *Poisson's ratio*. In a similar manner, a tensile stress in the y-direction causes a decrease of the length in the x-direction equal to

$$\epsilon_x = -\mu \frac{s_y}{E} \tag{45}$$

Conversely, a compressive stress causes an increase in the width at right angles to the stress. This result is confirmed by Eqs. (44) and (45), since compressive or negative stress values are substituted in the equations. For most metals in engineering service, μ has a value between 0.25 and 0.30.

Superposition of the stresses shown in Figs. 1-33 and 1-34 gives those shown in Fig. 1-35. Stress s_x causes an increase in length in the x-direction, whereas in this same direction a shortening occurs because of s_y. The net effect is given by

$$\epsilon_x = \frac{1}{E} (s_x - \mu s_y) \text{ in./in.} \tag{46}$$

In the y-direction a similar equation applies.

$$\epsilon_y = \frac{1}{E} (s_y - \mu s_x) \tag{47}$$

Equations (46) and (47) represent Hooke's law for two-dimensional

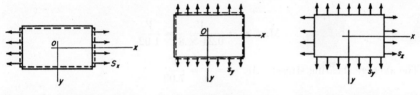

Fig. 1-33. Deflections due to   Fig. 1-34. Deflections due   Fig. 1-35. Tension in two
stress s_x.   to stress s_y.   directions.

stress. These equations can be solved simultaneously for the stresses to give

$$s_x = \frac{E}{1 - \mu^2} (\epsilon_x + \mu\epsilon_y) \tag{48}$$

$$s_y = \frac{E}{1 - \mu^2} (\epsilon_y + \mu\epsilon_x) \tag{49}$$

19. Deflection of Beam from Shearing Stress

In addition to the bending, warping of the cross sections, shown in Fig. 1-22(c), from the shearing stress causes additional deflection of a beam. The total deflection at the center for a simply supported beam carrying a uniform load w per unit length is given by

$$y = \frac{5wl^4}{384EI} \left(1 + \frac{25\alpha I}{l^2 A}\right) \tag{50}$$

The shear increment is represented by the second term of the parentheses. Here α represents the ratio of the maximum shearing stress to the average shearing stress, V/A, on the cross section. It therefore has the value 3/2 for rectangular cross sections and 4/3 for circular cross sections. For other shapes the value must be computed. In Eq. (50) it is assumed that there is no restraint to the free warping of the cross sections.

For a simply supported beam carrying a concentrated load P at the center, the equation is

$$y = \frac{Pl^3}{48EI}\left(1 + \frac{31.2\alpha I}{l^2 A}\right) \tag{51}$$

Example 18. Find the per cent of increase in deflection for a simply supported 8 in. I-beam with load P at the center. Area A is 7.09 in.^{2} The thickness of the web is 0.24 in. The moment of inertia I is 83.4 in.^{4} Length of the span is equal to 10 times the depth of the beam.

Solution. In accord with Section 13, the maximum shearing stress will be taken as the shear force V divided by the area of the web.

$$\text{Max. } s_s = \frac{V}{0.24 \times 8} = \frac{V}{1.92}$$

The average shearing stress: $Av. \; s_s = \frac{V}{A} = \frac{V}{7.09}$

Then: $\alpha = \frac{7.09}{1.92} = 3.69$

By Eq. (51): $y = \frac{Pl^3}{48EI}\left(1 + \frac{31.2 \times 3.69 \times 83.4}{80^2 \times 7.09}\right) = \frac{Pl^3}{48EI}(1 + 0.212)$

The deflection due to shear is thus 21.2 per cent as great as that due to bending.[12]

20. Principle of St. Venant

It was pointed out in Section 3 that equation $s = P/A$ was not applicable in the region close to the eye of the eyebar. At some distance away,

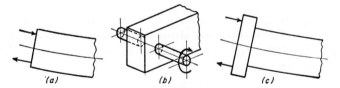

Fig. 1-36.   Methods for applying moment to end of beam.

however, the stress distribution becomes simple tension uniformly distributed, and the use of the equation for finding the value of the stress is justified.

A similar situation prevails for the use of equation $s = Mc/I$ for finding bending stress. The moments M in Fig. 1-6 could be applied to the

[12] For derivation of Eqs. (50) and (51) as well as for a more precise method for computing α, see Chapter **5**, reference 1, Bibliography.

beam in a number of ways as shown in Fig. 1-36. It is obvious that the state of stress near the end of the beam in Fig. 1-36(a) is not the same as that in Fig. 1-7(b), which represents the distribution for $s = Mc/I$. The same is true for Fig. 1-36(b). Equation (11) might be applied all the way to the end of the beam for sketch (c) because the basic assumption that the cross sections are planes is substantially fulfilled. At locations sufficiently far from the ends in Fig. 1-36(a) and (b), the use of Eq. (11) for finding the bending stress is satisfactory.

The remarks made above can be applied to the stress situation in the neighborhood of a concentrated force (either load or reaction). In Fig. 1-37 the stress situation for cross section OO' at the load is complicated by the vertical compressive stresses between the elements from the load. For cross section NN' located a distance equal to or greater than the depth of the beam from OO', the stress situation is approximately the same as that represented by Fig. 1-7(b) for bending stress and Fig. 1-22(b) for shear stress.

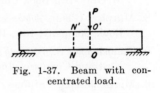

Fig. 1-37. Beam with concentrated load.

The phenomenon that the stress system tends to become regular at distances removed from the disturbance is known as the principle of St. Venant. This principle states that if the forces acting on a small region of the body are replaced by a different, but statically equivalent system, no change in the stress or deformation will be experienced at points sufficiently far removed from the loads.[13] It is valid for both normal and shear stress.

A sudden change in shape or form, arising from notches, holes, or fillets, causes the stresses to be increased beyond the values indicated by the equations of this chapter. This increase in stress is usually local in nature, and occurs in the immediate neighborhood of the discontinuity. It is taken care of in the computations by multiplying the stress, as given in the usual equation, by a stress concentration factor which will be explained in the following chapter.

BIBLIOGRAPHY

Volume number shown in **bold face** type. The number immediately following is the page on which the article begins.

1. Timoshenko, S., *Strength of Materials*, 2d ed., Vol. 1. New York: D. Van Nostrand Company, Inc., 1940.

2. Timoshenko, S., *Strength of Materials*, 2d ed., Vol. 2. New York: D. Van Nostrand Company, Inc., 1941.

[13] See p. 95, reference 3, Bibliography.

3. Timoshenko, S., *Theory of Elasticity.* New York: McGraw-Hill Book Company, Inc., 1934.

4. Southwell, R. V., *Theory of Elasticity,* 2d ed. New York: Oxford University Press, 1941.

5. Timoshenko, S., *Theory of Elastic Stability.* New York: McGraw-Hill Book Company, Inc., 1936.

6. Roark, Raymond J., *Formulas for Stress and Strain,* 2d ed. New York: McGraw-Hill Book Company, Inc., 1943.

7. Marin, Joseph, *Mechanical Properties of Materials and Design.* New York: McGraw-Hill Book Company, Inc., 1942.

8. Murphy, Glenn, *Advanced Strength of Materials.* New York: McGraw-Hill Book Company, Inc., 1946.

9. Timoshenko, S., *Strength of Materials,* 1st ed., Vol. 1. New York: D. Van Nostrand Company, Inc., 1930.

10. Marin, Joseph, "Stiffness of Ribbed Plates," *Machine Design,* **19,** May, 145 (1947).

11. Radich, E. A., "Strength and Stiffness of Ribbed Plates," *Machine Design,* **21,** Sept., 149 (1949).

PROBLEMS

See Table 2-1 of next chapter for mechanical properties of engineering materials.

1. The lower ends of the two hangers in Fig. 1-38 were at the same elevation before the loads were applied. The horizontal member is of uniform cross section. Find the value of length *l* if the horizontal member (assumed to be rigid) is horizontal after all loads are acting.   *Ans.* $l = 38.3$ in.

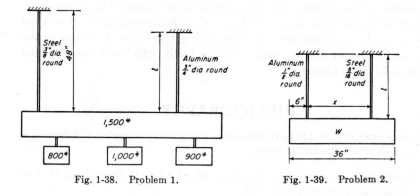

Fig. 1-38. Problem 1.   Fig. 1-39. Problem 2.

2. The bottom member in Fig. 1-39 is of uniform cross section and can be assumed to be rigid. Find the value of the distance *x* if the lower member is to be horizontal   *Ans.* $x = 22.2$ in.

3. The bottom member in Fig. 1-40 is of uniform cross section and can be assumed to be rigid. Its hinge is frictionless. Find the number of degrees of rotation of the lower member. *Ans.* $\varphi = 0.137°$.

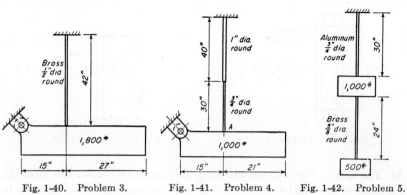

Fig. 1-40. Problem 3.   Fig. 1-41. Problem 4.   Fig. 1-42. Problem 5.

4. The bottom member in Fig. 1-41 is of uniform cross section. Its hinge is frictionless. The rods are of steel. Find the distance point A drops upon attachment of the weight. *Ans.* $\delta = 0.00475$ in.

5. In Fig. 1-42, find the drop of the 500 lb weight. *Ans.* $\delta = 0.0126$ in.

6. In Fig. 1-43 the lower member is of uniform cross section and can be assumed to be rigid. Find the angular rotation of the lower member in degrees.
Ans. $\varphi = 0.0286°$.

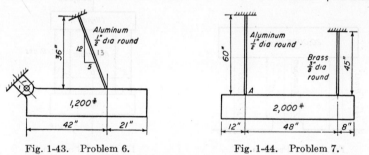

Fig. 1-43. Problem 6.   Fig. 1-44. Problem 7.

7. In Fig. 1-44 the lower member is of uniform cross section and can be assumed to be rigid. Find the change in elevation of the left end because of the stretch of the rods. *Ans.* Drop = 0.0352 in.

8. The members in Fig. 1-45 have a neat fit at the time of assembly. Find the force caused by an increase in temperature of 100 degrees F. Supports are immovable. *Ans.* $F = 25,050$ lb.

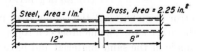

Fig. 1-45. Problem 8.

9. After being drawn up snug, the nut in Fig. 1-46 is given one-quarter additional turn. Find the force in the pipe and bolt. *Ans.* $F = 13{,}750$ lb.

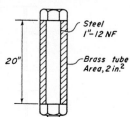

Fig. 1-46. Problem 9.

Fig. 1-47. Problem 10.

10. The bars in Fig. 1-47 are fitted top and bottom to immovable supports. The bars are of same material and have the same cross section. Find the force in each bar. *Ans.* Top, 11,430 lb; bottom, 8,570 lb.

11. In Fig. 1-48 the outer bars are symmetrically placed with respect to the center bar. The top member is rigid and located symmetrically on the supports. Find the load carried by each of the supports.

Ans. Center, 8,312 lb; outer, 5,844 lb.

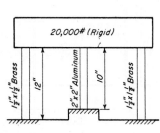

Fig. 1-48. Problem 11.

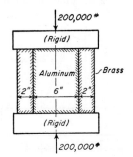

Fig. 1-49. Problem 12.

12. In Fig. 1-49, the hollow cylinder has a small amount of clearance with the inner cylinder. Both bodies have the same length at the time of assembly.

(a) Find the load carried by each member.

(b) What change in temperature must occur if each body is to carry one-half the load.

Ans. (a) Inner, 54,540 lb; outer, 145,460 lb;

(b) 85 deg F rise.

13. Because of an error in machining, the center strut in Fig. 1-50 was made 0.010 in. shorter than the other two. The members on top and bottom can be considered rigid. Bars are made of the same material and have equal cross sections. Find the load carried by each bar. Bars are 2″ × 2″ steel.

Ans. Outer, 173,330 lb; inner, 53,330 lb.

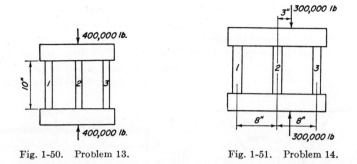

Fig. 1-50. Problem 13.

Fig. 1-51. Problem 14.

14. In Fig. 1-51, the struts are of the same material and have equal cross-sectional areas. Members on top and bottom can be considered rigid. Find the force in each bar. *Ans.* 43,750 lb, 100,000 lb, 156,250 lb.

15. Find the distance x in Fig. 1-52 that causes the 1,000 lb weight to remain level if the lower ends of the hanger are at the same elevation before the weight is applied. *Ans.* $x = 21.2$ in.

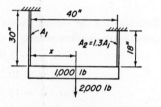

Fig. 1-52. Problem 15.

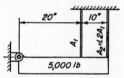

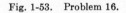

Fig. 1-53. Problem 16.

16. Find the force in each bar in Fig. 1-53. $E_1 = 2E_2$. The 5,000 lb weight can be considered rigid. *Ans.* $F_1 = 1,600$ lb; $F_2 = 1,440$ lb.

17. The rigid beam in Fig. 1-54 was level before the load was applied. Find the force in each hanger. *Ans.* Steel, 10,210 lb; aluminum, 7,660 lb.

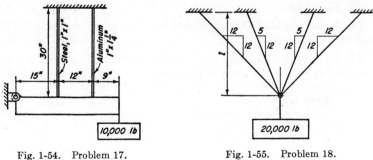

Fig. 1-54. Problem 17.

Fig. 1-55. Problem 18.

18. The bars in Fig. 1-55 are of the same material and have equal cross-sectional areas. There is no stress in the bars before the load is applied. Find the load carried by each bar. *Ans.* Outer, 4,390 lb; inner, 7,470 lb.

19. The bars in Fig. 1-56 have the same cross-sectional area. There is no stress in the bars before the load is applied. Each bar is 0.5 in. square.

    (a) Find the force in each bar.

    (b) Find the force in each bar if the temperature drops 100 deg F.

                             Ans. (a) Steel, 8,340 lb; brass, 5,560 lb;

                                       (b) Steel, 8,100 lb; brass, 5,970 lb.

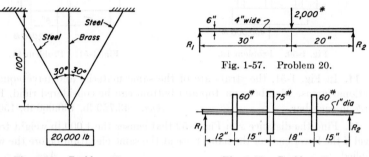

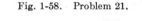

Fig. 1-57.   Problem 20.

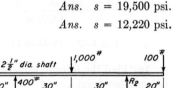

Fig. 1-56.   Problem 19.   Fig. 1-58.   Problem 21.

Draw the shear and bending moment diagrams for the beams shown in the following figures and find the values of the maximum bending stress.

  20. Figure 1-57.   *Ans.* $s = 1,000$ psi.

  21. Figure 1-58.   *Ans.* $s = 19,500$ psi.

  22. Figure 1-59.   *Ans.* $s = 12,220$ psi.

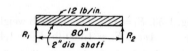

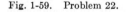

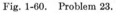

Fig. 1-59.   Problem 22.   Fig. 1-60.   Problem 23.

  23. Figure 1-60.   *Ans.* $s = 9,450$ psi.

  24. A steel saw blade 0.05 in. thick is bent into an arc of a circle of 2 ft radius. Find the bending stress.   *Ans.* $s = 31,250$ psi.

  25. Find the reactions and also the value of the bending stress at a point 5 ft from the left end for the beam of Fig. 1-61.   *Ans.* $s = 18,090$ psi.

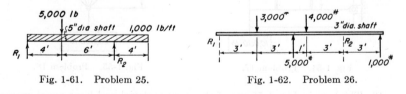

Fig. 1-61.   Problem 25.   Fig. 1-62.   Problem 26.

  26. Find the reactions and also the value of the bending stress at a point 6.5 ft from the left end for the beam in Fig. 1-62.   *Ans.* $s = 10,880$ psi.

27. Figure 1-63 illustrates the front side rod of a steam locomotive. Find the bending stress from inertia and dead weight for a train speed of 90 mph. Weight of steel equals 0.283 lb/in.³ Assume the rod to be a simply supported beam of uniform cross section *A-A*.   *Ans.* $s = 12{,}430$ psi.

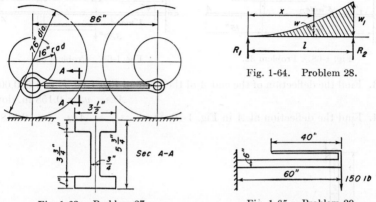

Fig. 1-64.   Problem 28.

Fig. 1-63.   Problem 27.   Fig. 1-65.   Problem 29.

28. The deflection of the beam shown in Fig. 1-64 is given by the equation

$$y = \frac{w_1}{360EIl^2} (x^6 - 5l^3x^3 + 4l^5x)$$

Find the expression for the load at any location *x*. Find the two reactions and the location of the maximum bending moment and its value.

Ans.   Max. $M = 0.039w_1l^2$.

29. Compute the change of elevation of the end of the light pointer attached to the beam of Fig. 1-65 upon the application of the load. The beam is 4 in. wide. $E = 1{,}500{,}000$ psi.

30. Moments M_1 and M_2 are applied to the ends of the simply supported beam shown in Fig. 1-66. Light pointers of lengths $2l/3$ and $l/3$ are attached to the ends as shown and are directed along the axis of the beam before applying the moments. If the distance *a* is measured, and if *E*, *I*, and *l* are known, show that moment M_1 is equal to $6EIa/l^2$.

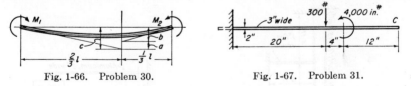

Fig. 1-66.   Problem 30.   Fig. 1-67.   Problem 31.

The idea of this problem can be used for finding the value of the unknown end moments acting on a beam. The pointers are clamped in position, and distance *a* is measured. Length *l* must be free from transverse loads.

31. Find the deflection at the end *C* of the beam in Fig. 1-67. $E = 1{,}600{,}000$ psi.

Ans. $y_c = 0.17$ in. up.

32. Find the deflection of the end A of the beam in Fig. 1-68. $E = 1,500,000$ psi.
Ans. $y_a = 0.126$ in. down.

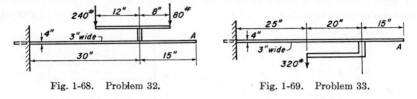

Fig. 1-68.   Problem 32.   Fig. 1-69.   Problem 33.

33. Find the deflection of the end A of the beam of Fig. 1-69. $E = 1,500,000$.
Ans. $y_a = 0.158$ in. down.

34. Find the deflection at A in Fig. 1-70. Steel.   *Ans.* $y = 0.518$ in.

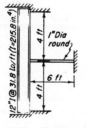

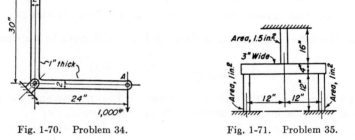

Fig. 1-70.   Problem 34.   Fig. 1-71.   Problem 35.

35. The supports top and bottom in Fig. 1-71 can be considered immovable. The upper strut was found to be $\frac{1}{32}$ in. too long to be assembled without stress. If this member is driven into place, what force will be induced therein? All parts are of steel.   *Ans.* $F = 27,040$ lb.

36. The steel bar in Fig. 1-72 was welded into place with a neat fit at time of assembly. Find the force in the bar if the temperature drops 120 deg F. Supports can be considered rigid.   *Ans.* $F = 9,510$ lb.

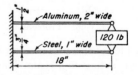

Fig. 1-72.   Problem 36.   Fig. 1-73.   Problem 37.

37. Find the deflection of the weight in Fig. 1-73.   *Ans.* $\delta = 0.185$ in.

38. The steel beams in Fig. 1-74 are $1\frac{1}{2}$ in. wide and 2 in. deep. Find the deflection of each beam. *Ans.* Top, 0.160 in.; bottom, 0.813 in.

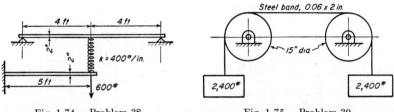

Fig. 1-74. Problem 38. Fig. 1-75. Problem 39.

39. Find the value of the stress in the steel band when it is passing around a pulley in Fig. 1-75. Pulley bearings are frictionless. *Ans.* $s = 140,000$ psi.

40. Compute the values of the transverse shear at points 1 in., 2 in., 3 in., and 4 in. below the top surface of the beam in Fig. 1-76 for cross sections to left of the load. The beam is 6 in. wide and 8 in. deep.

Ans. $s_s = 328$ psi, 563 psi, 703 psi, and 750 psi.

Find the value of the maximum transverse shear for the beams of the following figures:

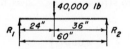

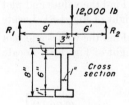

Fig. 1-76. Problem 40. Fig. 1-77. Problem 41.

41. Figure 1-77. *Ans.* $s_s = 1,170$ psi.

42. Figure 1-78. *Ans.* $s_s = 2,400$ psi.

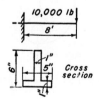

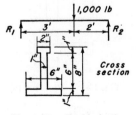

Fig. 1-78. Problem 42. Fig. 1-79. Problem 43.

43. Figure 1-79. *Ans.* $s_s = 99$ psi.

44. Find the thickness of the web required to make the value of the maximum transverse shearing stress equal to 600 psi for the beam in Fig. 1-80.

Ans. $t = 0.33$ in.

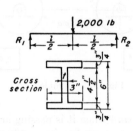

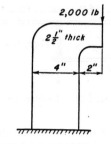

Fig. 1-80.   Problem 44.   Fig. 1-81.   Problem 48.

45. Utilizing Eq. (26), prove Eq. (31).

46. Find the maximum value of the transverse shear for a hollow circular shaft having outer and inner radii of r_1 and r_2 respectively.   *Ans.* $s_s = \dfrac{V(r_1{}^3 - r_2{}^3)}{3I(r_1 - r_2)}$.

47. Prove Eq. (32).

48. Find the values and plot the distribution of stress over the cross section of the upright of Fig. 1-81. Locate the point of zero stress.   *Ans.* $s_c = 1,400$ psi.

49. Find the values and plot the distribution of stress over the cross section of the upright of Fig. 1-82. Locate the point of zero stress.   *Ans.* $s_t = 6,860$ psi.

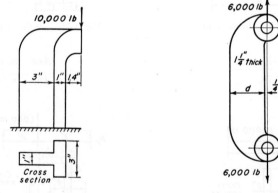

Fig. 1-82.   Problem 49.   Fig. 1-83.   Problem 50.

50. Determine the width d of the offset link of Fig. 1-83 if the permissible value of the working stress is 8,000 psi. Carry out the work in a manner similar to Example 8.   *Ans.* $d = 2.73$ in.

51. The loading and general arrangement of a link are the same as for Problem 50, but the cross section is shown in Fig. 1-84. Find width of flange b.

Ans. $b = 1.55$ in.

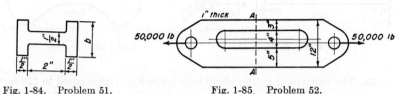

Fig. 1-84. Problem 51.   Fig. 1-85. Problem 52.

52. Cut the tension member shown in Fig. 1-85 along line A-A, plot the distribution of stress on the cut surface, and mark the four significant values.

Ans. Max. $s = 7,480$ psi.

53. Make a sketch showing the equivalent loading of axial force and moments about the x- and y-axes for the bar shown in Fig. 1-86. Compute and show on isometric sketches the distribution of stress on cross section $ABCD$ caused by each of the separate loads. Also make a sketch showing resultant distribution of stress and mark the value at each corner. Dimension the location of the neutral axis for the cross section.

Ans. Max. $s = 600$ psi.

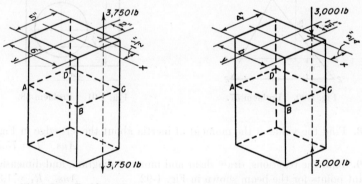

Fig. 1-86. Problem 53.   Fig. 1-87. Problem 54.

54. Make a sketch for the equivalent loading for the bar of Fig. 1-87. What must be the dimension b in order that the maximum stress on a typical cross section, such as $ABCD$, will be equal to 1,000 psi? Make sketches and mark values for the stresses due to the separate loads. Also make the sketch for the resultant stresses and mark values at corners. Dimension the location of the neutral axis.

Ans. $b = 4.29$ in.

55. The inclined load shown in view M-M, Fig. 1-88, is applied to the pin at the end of the beam. Resolve load into horizontal and vertical components and find the bending stress due to each. Add algebraically to get the stress at points A, B, C, and D.

Ans. at A, $s = 1,562.5$ psi.

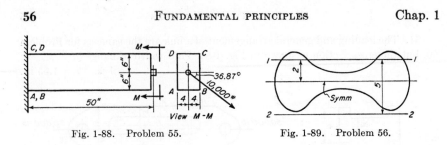

Fig. 1-88.   Problem 55.   Fig. 1-89.   Problem 56.

56. The moment of inertia about axis 1-1 in Fig. 1-89 is equal to 120 in.[4] The area is equal to 20 in.[2] Find the moment of inertia about axis 2-2.

Ans. $I_2 = 220$ in.[4]

57. The moment of inertia about axis 1-1 in Fig. 1-90 is equal to 540 in.[4] Area is equal to 60 in.[2] Find the moment of inertia about axis 2-2.

Ans. $I_2 = 1,440$ in.[4]

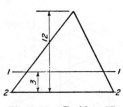

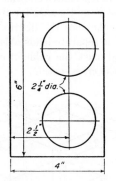

Fig. 1-90.   Problem 57.   Fig. 1-91.   Problem 58.

58. Find the value of the moment of inertia about the left edge in Fig. 1-91.

Ans. $I = 75.78$ in.[4]

59. Find the reactions, draw shear and moment diagram, and dimension significant points for the beam shown in Fig. 1-92.   *Ans.* $R_1 = 1,350$ lb.

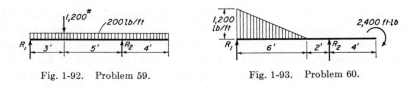

Fig. 1-92.   Problem 59.   Fig. 1-93.   Problem 60.

60. Repeat Problem 59 using the beam of Fig. 1-93. Does the curve for shear have a horizontal tangent at a point 6 ft from the left end? Why? Also find the value of the maximum bending moment and its location.

Ans.   Max. $M = 2,770$ ft-lb at 2.54 ft from left end.

61. Draw and dimension the bending moment diagram for the member shown in Fig. 1-94. *Ans.* Max. $M = 28,800$ in-lb.

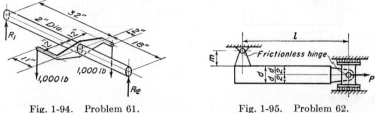

Fig. 1-94. Problem 61.

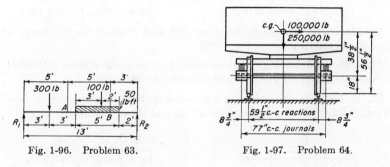

Fig. 1-95. Problem 62.

62. Repeat Problem 61 for Fig. 1-95.

63. Cut the *AB* portion of the beam of Fig. 1-96 free from the balance of the beam and place the shears and moments on the end surfaces which were acting before cutting. Is this portion of the beam now in equilibrium?

Fig. 1-96. Problem 63.

Fig. 1-97. Problem 64.

64. Figure 1-97 shows the loads and general dimensions of a freight car. The horizontal load is due to centrifugal effects in passing around a curve. If the car has four axles all equally loaded, make a force diagram showing the equilibrium of a unit consisting of one axle and two wheels. The centrifugal force is assumed to be applied to the axle at the inner bearing only, and to be resisted by the flange of the outer wheel only. Also draw and dimension the bending moment diagram for the axle. *Ans.* Max. $M = 832,800$ in-lb.

Draw and dimension the load and reaction diagram, the shear diagram, and the bending moment diagram for the beams shown in the following figures:

65. Figure 1-98.

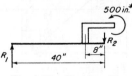

Fig. 1-98. Problem 65

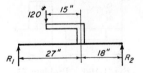

Fig. 1-99. Problem 66.

66. Figure 1-99.

67. Figure 1-100.

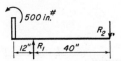

Fig. 1-100.   Problem 67.

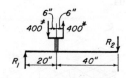

Fig. 1-101.   Problem 68.

68. Figure 1-101.

69. Figure 1-102.

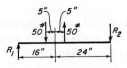

Fig. 1-102.   Problem 69.

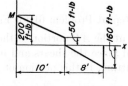

Fig. 1-103.   Problem 70.

70. Draw and dimension the shear and load diagram for the beam whose moment diagram is given in Fig. 1-103.

71. If the values in Fig. 1-104 represent pounds of shear, draw and dimension the corresponding load and moment diagrams for this beam.

72. If, however, the values in Fig. 1-104 represent foot-pounds of moment, draw and dimension the corresponding load and shear diagrams.

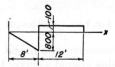

Fig. 1-104.   Problem 71.

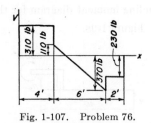

Fig. 1-105.   Problem 73.

73. Repeat Problem 71 using Fig. 1-105.

74. Repeat Problem 72 using Fig. 1-105.

75. Draw and dimension the load and moment diagrams for the beam whose shear diagram is represented by Fig. 1-106.

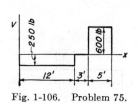

Fig. 1-106.   Problem 75.

Fig. 1-107.   Problem 76.

76. Repeat Problem 75 for the beam whose shear diagram is given in Fig. 1-107.

77. Draw and dimension the load and shear diagrams for the beam whose moment diagram is represented by Fig. 1-108.

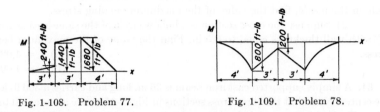

Fig. 1-108.   Problem 77.   Fig. 1-109.   Problem 78.

78. Repeat Problem 77 for the moment diagram shown in Fig. 1-109.

79. Make an exploded isometric view of the three portions of the beam of Fig. 1-110 and show all forces and moments necessary for equilibrium.

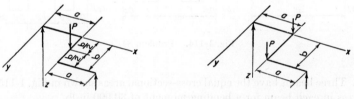

Fig. 1-110.   Problem 79.   Fig. 1-111.   Problem 80.

80. Repeat Problem 79 using Fig. 1-111.

81. Draw and dimension the bending moment diagram for the beam shown in Fig. 1-112. Find the location where the moment is maximum and find its value.

Ans. Max. M = 4,900 in-lb.

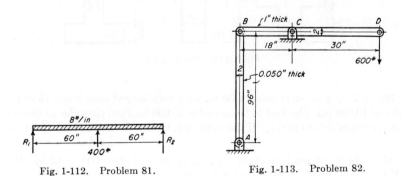

Fig. 1-112.   Problem 81.   Fig. 1-113.   Problem 82.

82. Find the deflection of point D in Fig. 1-113. All parts are steel.

Ans. 0.485 in. at D.

83. A simply supported beam is 60 in. long and carries a 5,000 lb load at the center.

(a) If the cross section is a hollow square 6 in. high on the outside and 5 in. high on the inside, find the value of the maximum bending stress.

(b) Suppose the cross section is a hollow circle of the same area as for part (a) with wall thickness equal to 0.5 in. Find the value of the maximum bending stress.   *Ans.* (a) $s = 4,020$ psi.

(b) $s = 4,090$ psi.

84. A simply supported cast iron beam is 36 in. long and carries a 300 lb load at the center. Note that the three cross sections in Fig. 1-114 have areas equal to each other. Find the stress and deflection at the center for each beam. $E = 15,000,000$.

Ans. (b) $s = 4,460$ psi; $y = 0.0472$ in.

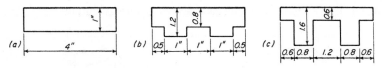

Fig. 1-114.   Problem 84.

85. Three beams have the equal cross-sectional areas shown in Fig. 1-115. Find the stress in each beam for a bending moment of 30,000 in-lb.

Ans. (b) $s = 8,820$ psi.

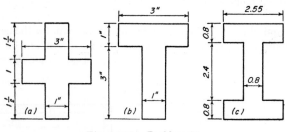

Fig. 1-115.   Problem 85.

86. A 2 by 2 in. steel column 60 in. long with hinged ends has a yield point value of 40,000 psi. The load to be carried is 35,000 lb. Find the value of the maximum permissible eccentricity if the column is to have a factor of safety of 2.5.

Ans. $e = 0.046$ in.

87. A 12 ft column is made of 4 in. standard steel pipe (OD = 4.5 in., ID = 4.03 in.), yield point = 36,000 psi, $FS = 10$.

(a) Find the permissible load if the column has hinged ends and the load centrally applied.

(b) Find the load for an eccentricity of 0.2 in.
Ans. (a) 10,250 lb; (b) 6,790 lb.

88. The material in a body is subjected to the following stresses: $s_x = -10,000$ psi, $s_y = -4,000$ psi, and $s_{xy} = 4,000$ psi. Draw the Mohr circle and mark all significant points. Draw a view of the element, properly oriented, for maximum normal stress and show values of all stresses. Do the same for the element with maximun shearing stress.
Ans. $s_1 = -2,000$ psi, $s_2 = -12,000$ psi, $s_{s\,max} = 5,000$ psi.

89. A uniformly distributed normal stress, either tension or compression, is applied to the edges of the plate of Fig. 1-116 in the x-direction, and a uniform tension or compression is also applied in the y-direction. The dimensions of the deformed plate are 15.010 in. and 9.996 in. Find the stresses s_x and s_y. $E = 30,000,000$ psi. Poisson's ratio $\mu = 0.3$.

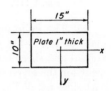

Fig. 1-116. Problem 89.

90. Draw the Mohr circle for a prismatic bar loaded in tension and prove the rule: "The maximum shearing stress is equal to one-half the axial stress and is located at 45° to the direction of the axial stress."

91. Draw the Mohr circle for an element loaded on pure shear, and determine the value of the maximum normal stress and its direction.

92. An element is acted upon by the following stresses: $s_x = 7,000$ psi, $s_y = -2,000$ psi, and $s_{xy} = 2,000$ psi.

(a) By means of the equations compute the stresses on the sides of an element oriented 30° clockwise with the x-axis.

(b) Find the value of φ for maximum and minimum normal stress and compute the values of these stresses.

(c) Repeat (b) for maximum shear.

(d) Make a view showing the given state of stress, and draw the corresponding Mohr circle. Scale the stresses for the element oriented 30° from the x-axis, and compare them with the results secured by use of the equations. Draw a view of this element with the stresses placed thereon.

(e) Scale the values of the maximum and minimum normal stress and represent them by arrows on an element oriented at the proper angle.

(f) Repeat for the element which is subjected to the maximum shearing stress. *Ans.* Max. $s = 7,420$ psi; max. $s_s = 4,920$ psi.

93. Repeat Problem 92 using given stresses of $s_x = 1,500$ psi, $s_y = 22,500$ psi, and $s_{xy} = -10,000$ psi. *Ans.* Max. $s = 26,500$ psi; max. $s_s = 14,500$ psi.

94. The total normal force uniformly distributed over edge AB of the plate of Fig. 1-117 is 15,000 lb, and the total shear force is 12,000 lb. For edge BC the normal and shear forces are 135,000 and 30,000 lb, respectively. Draw a view showing an element with the given state of stress and also draw the corresponding Mohr circle. Draw an element with sides parallel to the x- and y-axes and show the stresses acting on it. *Ans.* $s_x = -2,710$ psi.

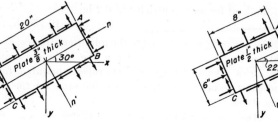

Fig. 1-117.   Problem 94.   Fig. 1-118.   Problem 95.

95. The uniformly distributed normal and shear forces for edge AB of the plate of Fig. 1-118 are 15,000 lb and 24,000 lb, respectively. For edge BC the normal and shear forces are 100,000 lb and 32,000 lb, respectively. Draw an element for the given state of stress; also draw the Mohr circle. Draw the element with sides parallel to the x- and y-axes and show the stresses which are acting on it.

Ans. $s_x = 5,050$ psi.

96. For the loading shown in Fig. 1-119, draw the element located at 45° from the x-axis and place the stresses thereon which are acting on it.

Ans. $s_s = 4,000$ psi.

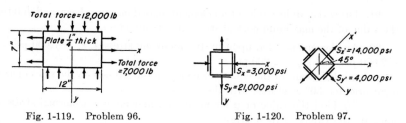

Fig. 1-119.   Problem 96.   Fig. 1-120.   Problem 97.

97. In Fig. 1-120 the elements show the normal stresses which are acting at the same point in a body. Determine the values of the shearing stresses for both elements and mark them with arrows properly directed.

98. Make a drawing for the element at A of the beam in Fig. 1-121 with horizontal and vertical sides, and show the stresses acting on it. Construct the corresponding Mohr circle. Draw the element for the principal stresses correctly oriented and show the stresses acting on it. Do the same for the element of maximum shear stress.   *Ans.*   Min. $s = -2,940$ psi; max. $s_s = 1,570$ psi.

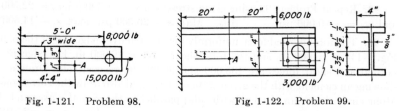

Fig. 1-121.   Problem 98.   Fig. 1-122.   Problem 99.

99. Repeat Problem 98 for the element at A of Fig. 1-122.

Ans.   Min. $s = -3,060$ psi; max. $s_s = 2,390$ psi.

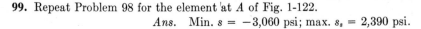

100. Draw a view of the element at A in Fig. 1-123 with horizontal and vertical sides and show all stresses acting on it. *Ans.* $s = 62.5$ psi.

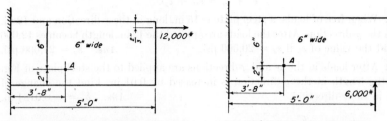

Fig. 1-123.   Problem 100.   Fig. 1-124.   Problem 101.

101. Draw a view of the element at A in Fig. 1-124 with horizontal and vertical sides and show all stresses acting on it.   *Ans.* $s = 750$ psi, $s_s = 140.6$ psi.

102. Draw a view of the element at A in Fig. 1-125 with horizontal and vertical sides and show all stresses acting on it. Draw the Mohr circle for this element and determine the value of the maximum normal stress and the maximum shear stress.

Ans. $s_{max} = 707$ psi, $s_{smax} = 382$ psi.

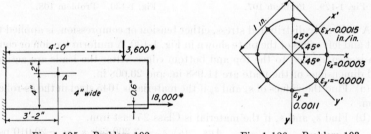

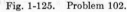

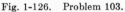

Fig. 1-125.   Problem 102.   Fig. 1-126.   Problem 103.

103. Strain gage measurements at a certain point on a body give the elongations shown by Fig. 1-126. Draw a view of the element with horizontal and vertical sides and show all normal and shear stresses acting on it. Do the same for the element whose sides are inclined 45° with the x-axis. Check all results with the Mohr circle. $E = 30,000,000$ psi; $\mu = 0.3$.

Ans. $s_x = 20,770$ psi; $s_y = 39,230$ psi; $s_{xy} = 18,460$ psi.

104. Repeat Problem 103 for the strain gage readings shown by Fig. 1-127.

Ans. $s_{x'} = 10,880$ psi; $s_{y'} = 6,260$ psi; $s_{x'y'} = 11,540$ psi.

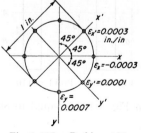

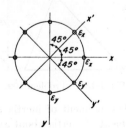

Fig. 1-127.   Problem 104.   Fig. 1-128.   Problem 105.

105. Prove that the strain measurements when taken as in Fig. 1-128 must fulfill the equation

$$\epsilon_x + \epsilon_y = \epsilon_{x'} + \epsilon_{y'}$$

106. When free of loads, a steel plate is 15 in. long in the x-direction and 12 in. long in the y-direction. After the loads are applied the 12 in. length becomes 12.006 in. Find the value of s_y if $s_x = 20,000$ psi.   *Ans.* $s_y = 21,000$ psi.

107. After loads in the x- and y-directions are applied to the steel plate of Fig. 1-129 the length in the y-direction is increased by 0.01 in. Find the change of length in the x-direction.   *Ans.* $\delta_x = -0.0184$ in.

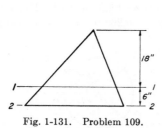

Fig. 1-129.   Problem 107.

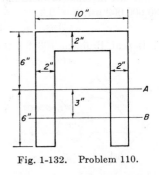

Fig. 1-130.   Problem 108.

108. A uniformly distributed stress, either tension or compression, is applied to the right and left edges of the plate shown in Fig. 1-130. A uniform tension or compression is also applied to the top and bottom edges. After the loads are acting, the final dimensions of the plate are 11.988 in. and 20.008 in.

    (a) Find the values of s_x and s_y if the material is 1045 steel in the as-rolled condition.

    (b) Find s_x and s_y if the material is Class 25 cast iron.

                     Ans.   (a) $s_x = 3,300$ psi; $s_y = -29,010$ psi

                              (b) $s_x = 1,560$ psi; $s_y = -13,730$ psi.

The following problems are presented without answers.

109. The moment of inertia about the 1-1 axis in Fig. 1-131 is equal to 4,320 in.[4] Area is equal to 120 in.[2] Find the moment of inertia about axis 2-2.

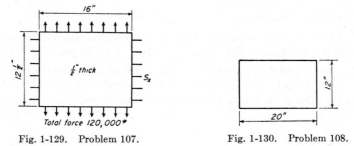

Fig. 1-131.   Problem 109.   Fig. 1-132.   Problem 110.

110. The moment of inertia about axis A in Fig. 1-132 is equal to 880 in.[4] Find moment of inertia about axis B.

111. The load shown on the beam of Fig. 1-133 is removed and replaced by a new load w uniformly distributed over the entire beam. The maximum bending moments for both loadings are the same. Find the value of w.

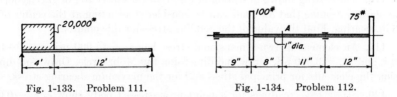

Fig. 1-133. Problem 111.   Fig. 1-134. Problem 112.

112. In Fig. 1-134 let the bearings be considered simple supports. The shaft is steel. Find the deflection at point A.

113. The pins in Fig. 1-135 are all at the same elevation. The bar is of spring steel. If the bar was originally straight, find the value of the maximum bending stress.

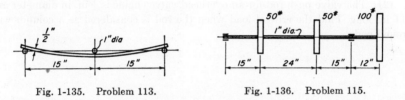

Fig. 1-135. Problem 113.   Fig. 1-136. Problem 115.

114. Let the cross section through an industrial car be similar to that of the car in Fig. 1-97. The loading for a single axle is 4,000 lb vertical and 1,000 lb horizontal. Rails are 36 in. center to center, and journals are 44 in. center to center. Wheels are 16 in. diameter. The center of gravity of load is 19 in. above the center of the axle. Draw and dimension the bending moment diagram for the axle.

115. Find the deflection at the midpoint between the bearings in Fig. 1-136. The shaft is steel.

116. In Fig. 1-137 assume that the forces in the oil films are symmetrically disposed about the center line of the bearing. Determine the value of the eccentricity e so that the slope assumed by the bearing is the same as the slope of the shaft at A. The shaft is steel. The bearing is Class 30 cast iron.

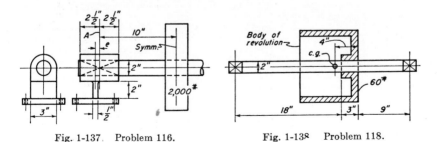

Fig. 1-137. Problem 116.   Fig. 1-138 Problem 118.

117. A 12 in. standard I-beam of 31.8 lb per ft has $I_x = 215.8$ in.[4] and $I_y = 9.5$ in.[4] The width of the flange is 5 in. Find the percentage increase in bending stress caused by changing a vertical load to one inclined at 1° to the vertical.

118. The casting shown in section in Fig. 1-138 has its center of gravity located as shown. Assume that all loads can be considered as acting at the center of the 3 in. bearing. Find the value of the bending stress for this point.

119. An element in two-dimensional stress has $s_x = 12,000$ psi, $s_y = -4,000$ psi, and $s_{xy} = 3,900$ psi. Draw and dimension the Mohr circle. Draw and dimension the elements for principal stress and for the maximum shearing stress.

120. Strain gage readings for a point in a stressed body show $\epsilon_x = -0.0006$ in./in., $\epsilon_y = .0026$ in./in., $\epsilon'_x = 0.0022$ in./in., and $\epsilon'_y = -0.0002$ in./in. Axes x and x' are at 45° to each other. $E = 30,000,000$ psi, $\mu = \frac{1}{3}$.

(a) Draw the view of an element with horizontal and vertical sides and show values of the stresses acting on it.

(b) Do the same for an element which is inclined 45°.

Check all results by making a Mohr circle.

121. The valve push rod for an overhead valve engine is $\frac{1}{4}$ in. in diameter and 14 in. long. Find the critical load when the rod is considered as a column with round ends.

2

Working Stresses

THE PROBLEM of mechanical strength is one of the most important features of the design of machine parts. Stress equations in general are applicable to idealized homogeneous materials subjected to steady loads. This chapter will extend the theories of designing to include cases of fluctuating loads where the fatigue strength of the material has an important influence on the success of the design. Machine parts should be shaped so that stress concentrations at points of high loading are avoided as much as possible. Suitable adjustments must also be made when the material carries loads in two directions. A distinction must be made between ductile and brittle materials. Lack of knowledge or appreciation of the behavior of engineering materials under actual service conditions has been the cause of many expensive failures.

FS, factor of safety
K, stress concentration factor
s_{av}, average stress
s_e, endurance limit stress for reversed bending
s_1, s_2, principal stresses

s_r, range stress
s_s, shear stress
s_{yp}, yield point stress, tension
s_{syp}, yield point stress, shear
s_{uc}, ultimate stress, compression
s_{ut}, ultimate stress, tension

1. Stress-strain Diagrams

Much useful information concerning the behavior of materials and their suitability for engineering purposes can be obtained by making tensile

tests and plotting a graph for the relationship between stress and strain.
The characteristic shape of the stress-strain diagram for low-carbon steel
is shown in Fig. 2-1(a). It should be noted that the material followed
Hooke's law until the loading became a little more than one-half of the
ultimate strength. This material has a well-defined *yield point* or stress at
which a marked increase in elongation occurs without increase in load.

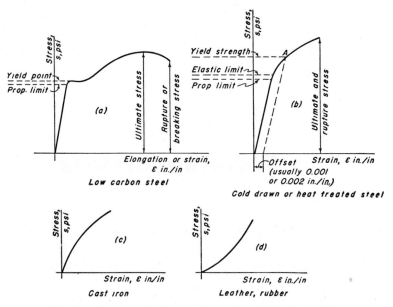

Fig. 2-1.   Stress-strain diagrams for various kinds of materials.

The *proportional limit* marks the maximum value of the stress for which
Hooke's law holds. The modulus of elasticity of the material can be found
from the slope, s/ϵ, of the straight-line portion of the curve, or from Eq. (3)
of Chapter 1, $E = s/\epsilon$.

After the ultimate stress is reached, soft steel specimens undergo a
marked reduction in diameter, called *necking*, at some point in the stressed
material. It is customary, however, to construct the diagram on the
basis of stresses computed by using the original cross-sectional area.
The ratio of the loss of cross-sectional area at failure to the original area
of the specimen is called the *reduction of area*. This quantity, together
with the elongation at failure, gives useful information concerning the
ductility of the material. The speed at which the load is applied affects
the shape of the diagram. The yield point and ultimate stresses become
higher as the speed of loading increases.

Many steels do not have a well-defined elastic limit, but yield gradually after passing the proportional limit, as shown in Fig. 2-1(b). If the loading were stopped at point A at a higher stress than the elastic limit, and if the specimen were then unloaded and readings taken, the curve would follow the dashed line, and a permanent set, or plastic deformation, would exist. For such materials, the stress corresponding to some given permanent set (usually 0.001 or 0.002 in./in.) is called the *yield strength*, and is taken as the limit of the engineering usefulness of the material.

Most materials do not exhibit a permanent set if loaded slightly beyond the proportional limit. The maximum value of such stress is known as the *elastic limit*, which is usually difficult to determine experimentally. *Proof loads* or *proof stresses* refer to loading which the material or part must sustain while fulfilling specified conditions relative to failure or deformation.

For ductile materials, the value of the yield strength in shear is equal to about 0.5 to 0.6 of the yield strength in tension.

Nonductile or brittle materials such as cast iron and concrete do not follow Hooke's law to any noticeable degree. The characteristic stress-strain diagram for either tension or compression is shown in Fig. 2-1(c) Leather and rubber have diagrams similar to that in Fig. 2-1(d).

Mechanical properties for a number of widely used engineering materials are given in Table 2-1.

TABLE 2-1
Average Values for Mechanical Properties of Engineering Materials

Material	Modulus of Elasticity		γ, Wt lb/in.^{3}	α, Coefficient of Linear Expansion in./in./deg F
	Tension, psi E	Shear, psi G		
Cast iron	See Table 14–13		0.256	0.000 0056
Steel	30,000,000	11,500,000	0.283	0.000 0065
Stainless steel, 18-8	28,000,000	10,000,000	0.295	0.000 0096
Brass, bronze	15,000,000	5,300,000	0.30–0.32	0.000 0102
Aluminum	10,000,000	3,850,000	0.100	0.000 0128
Magnesium	6,500,000	2,400,000	0.065	0.000 0145

Poisson's ratio, $\mu = 0.3$.
Variations in values shown in Table 2-1 are possible, depending on composition and method of manufacture.

Elementary elastic theories as discussed in Chapter 1 apply, in general, to bodies of uniform cross section and are unable to take account of the effect of a change in shape on the resulting stresses.

2. Stress Concentration Caused by Sudden Change in Form

Only rarely does the failure of a machine part occur because of the sudden application of a single heavy load. Breakage, in the great majority of cases, is caused by repeated or fatigue loading, and takes place at a point of stress concentration where an abrupt change in the form of the part occurs. Such failures can occur without warning or plastic deformation. The average stress for the cross section may be below the elastic limit for the material.

Consider, for example, the state of stress in the tension member of two widths illustrated in Fig. 2-2. Near each end of the bar the internal force

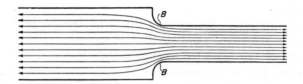

Fig. 2-2.   Stress concentration caused by sudden change in cross section.

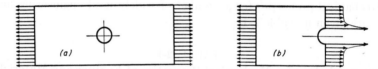

Fig. 2-3.   Stress concentration for bar with hole loaded in tension.

is uniformly distributed over the cross sections. The nominal stress in the right portion can be found by dividing the total load by the smaller cross-sectional area; the stress in the left portion can be found by dividing by the larger area. However, in the region where the width is changing, a redistribution of the force within the bar must take place. In this portion the load is no longer uniform at all points on a cross section, but the material near the edges in Fig. 2-2 is stressed considerably higher than the average value. The stress situation is thus more complicated, and the elementary equation P/A is no longer valid. The maximum stress occurs at some point on the fillet, as at B, and is directed parallel to the boundary at that point.

Another example is a bar in tension with a circular hole as shown in Fig. 2-3(a). If the bar is cut on the cross section of the hole, the tension stresses will be as shown in Fig. 2-3(b). The stress distribution along the cut surface is practically uniform until the neighborhood of the hole is reached, where it suddenly increases. High stresses such as these cause a fatigue crack to start under fluctuating loading.

This irregularity in the stress distribution caused by abrupt changes of form is called *stress concentration*. It occurs for all kinds of stress, axial, bending, or shear, in the presence of fillets, holes, notches, keyways, splines, tool marks, or accidental scratches. Inclusions and flaws in the material or on the surface also serve as stress raisers. The maximum value of the stress at such points is found by multiplying the nominal stress as given by the elementary equation by a stress concentration factor K which is defined as follows.

$$K = \frac{\text{highest value of actual stress on fillet, notch, hole, etc.}}{\text{nominal stress as given by elementary equation for minimum cross section}} \quad (1)$$

Values of stress concentration factors can be found experimentally by photoelastic analysis or direct strain gage measurement. For a number of cases, solutions have been obtained by mathematical analysis.

3. Stress Concentration Factors

Stress concentration factors have been determined for a wide variety of geometric shapes and types of loading. The factors for rectangular bars of two widths in tension or compression are given by the curves of Fig. 2-4.

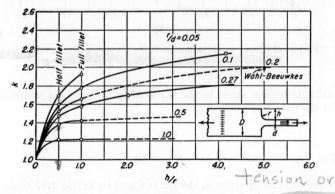

Fig. 2-4.　Factors of stress concentration for fillets of varying depths in tension or compression to be applied to the stress in the section of the plate of width d.

When such a bar is loaded in pure bending, the stress concentration factors can be obtained from Fig. 2-5. The use of such curves is illustrated by the following example.

Example 1. Let the minor width in Fig. 2-2 be 1.25 in., the major width be 2.25 in., and the radius of the fillet be 0.25 in.

(a) Find the value of the stress concentration factor when the bar is loaded in tension.

(b) Find the value of the stress concentration factor if the loading is a pure moment instead of tension.

Solution. (a) $d = 1.25$ in., $r = 0.25$ in., $h = 0.5$ in.

$$r/d = 0.2,   h/r = 2$$

From Fig. 2-4: $K = 1.80$

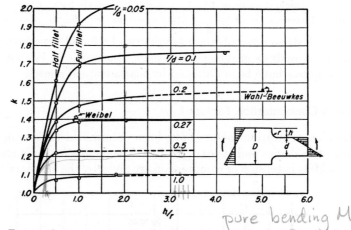

Fig. 2-5.   Factors of stress concentration for fillets of varying depths in pure bending to be applied to the bending stress in the plate of depth d.

The maximum tension stress in the bar is found by taking 1.80 times the P/A value for the narrower width.

(b)

From Fig. 2-5: $K = 1.52$

The maximum bending stress in the bar is found by taking 1.52 times the Mc/I value for the narrower width.

The stress concentration factor for this bar would be increased if the width of the left portion were increased. A decrease in fillet radius also causes an increase in the factor.

It is customary to represent the stress concentration factor by K. However Figs. 2-4 to 2-10 inc. are reproduced from technical literature in which the stress concentration factor was designated by k.

In general, a stress concentration factor is applied to the stress computed for the net or smallest cross section.

The effect of notches on the stresses for tension and bending can be

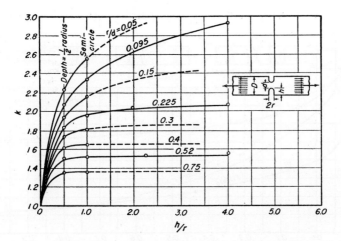

Fig. 2-6. Factors of stress concentration for grooves of varying depths in tension or compression to be applied to the stress in the section of the plate of width d.

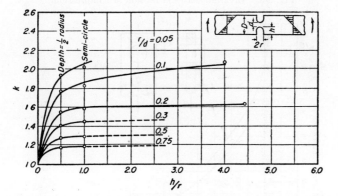

Fig. 2-7. Factors of stress concentration for grooves of varying depths in pure bending to be applied to the bending stress in the section of the plate of depth d.

found for Figs. 2-6 and 2-7, respectively. The stress concentration factors for a bar containing a circular hole[1] are shown in Fig. 2-8. If a circular hole in a plate contains a pin through which the load is applied, the stress concentration factors[2] will be as shown in Fig. 2-9.

The stress concentration factors for a T-head supported on the flange[3] are given in Fig. 2-10. Stress concentration factors for bodies of other shapes and loadings are given in references 6, 8, 20, and 31 of the Bibliography.

The curves for Figs. 2-4 to 2-10 inclusive were determined for flat plates or two-dimensional bodies. It should be noted that symbols d and

[1] See reference 2, Bibliography, for Figs. 2-4 to 2-8 inclusive.
[2] See reference 3, Bibliography.
[3] See reference 4, Bibliography

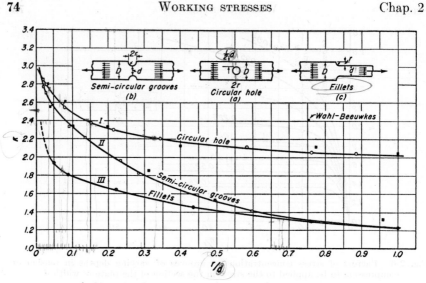

Fig. 2-8.   Invariant cases in tension or compression.

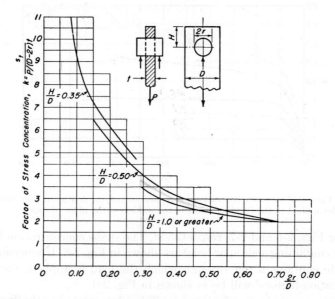

Fig. 2-9.   Stress concentration factors around a central circular hole in a plate loaded through a pin in the hole.

D have the meaning of width and not of diameter. It has been proved, however, that the curves for two-dimensional bodies can be used for three-dimensional members with but small errors which will be on the safe side.[4] For example, a shaft with an axial section similar to these figures

[4] See reference 7, Bibliography.

would have stress concentration factors for the given loading approximately equal to the values shown by the curves for flat plates.

Inspection of the curves in Figs. 2-4 to 2-10 inclusive indicates that stress concentration factors are reduced by the use of larger fillets or by

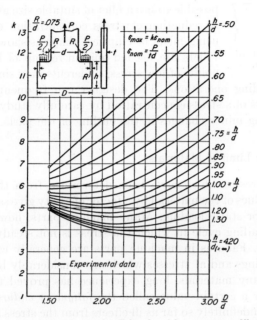

Fig. 2-10.　Stress concentration factor for T-heads with a constant fillet ratio of $R/d =$ 0.075.

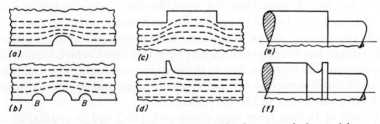

Fig. 2-11.　Reduction of stress concentration by removal of material.

more gradual transitions from cross sections of one size to those of another. Sometimes the designer can specify the removal of material in such a way as to secure a more gradual transition in size. Thus in Fig. 2-11(b) it is easy to visualize that the stress concentration would be less when the notches B are present than when the main notch stands alone. For the same reason, a bolt with a continuous thread shows less concentration effects than a bar with a single circumferential groove. The narrow projection of Fig. 2-11(d), into which the force cannot spread, has less increase in stress than the wide projection of Fig. 2-11(c). It may be beneficial to use a stress-relieving groove, as shown in Fig. 2-11(f), on a

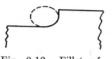

Fig. 2-12. Fillet of elliptical form.

shaft with a sudden change in diameter if it is not possible to use a fillet of suitable size at the junction.[5] A reduction of stress concentration can be had by using fillets of elliptical shape as shown in Fig. 2-12. Fillets are needed only in regions of high stress. At points of low stress, undercuts may simplify machining and grinding operations. The designer can frequently reduce the harmful effects of a stress concentration by carefully studying the details and by making minor changes in the outline of the parts.

4. Endurance Limit of Materials

Working stresses which have been determined from the ultimate or yield point values of the material by a factor of safety give safe and reliable results only for static loading. Many machine parts, however, are subjected to a loading cycle in which the stress is not steady but continuously varying. Failures in machine parts are generally caused by such repeated loadings and at stresses which are considerably below the yield point. For many materials, long experience has proved that when the stress is below a certain value called the *fatigue* or *endurance limit*, the part will last indefinitely so far as ill effects from the stress are concerned. However, for slightly greater values of the stress, failure can be expected after a certain number of repetitions of the stress cycle. Fracture occurs without perceptible stretching and resembles the failure of a brittle material. Although such breaks are called fatigue failures, no change has taken place in the material except in the immediate neighborhood of the fracture itself. Failure has been brought about by a tiny crack which started at a stress concentration or at a flaw in the material at a highly stressed point. The crack itself serves as a stress concentration, and grows continually larger until the failure of the part occurs.

Methods of testing have been developed which aid in evaluating the ability of a material to resist failure by fatigue. The rotating-beam test is in widest use. It applies a bending moment to the specimen, shown schematically in Fig. 2-13(a). As the specimen rotates, the bending stress varies continuously from a maximum tension to a maximum compression, which can be represented on the time-stress axes by the curve of Fig. 2-13(b). A record is kept of the number of cycles required to produce failure at a given stress, and the results are plotted as shown by the typical *S-N* or stress-cycle curves[6] of Fig. 2-14. The *endurance-limit stress* s_e is

---

[5] See p. 142, reference 8, Bibliography.
[6] See p. 21, reference 9, Bibliography.

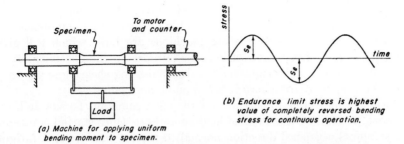

(a) Machine for applying uniform bending moment to specimen.

(b) Endurance limit stress is highest value of completely reversed bending stress for continuous operation.

Fig. 2-13. Rotating beam type of fatigue testing machine (schematic drawing).

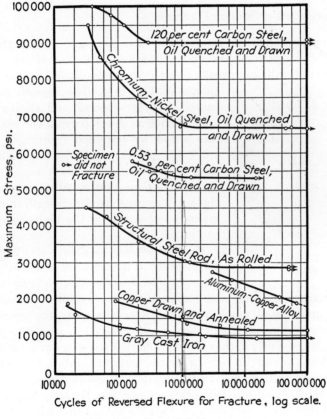

Fig. 2-14. Typical S-N curves.

defined as the maximum value of the completely reversed bending stress which a plain specimen can sustain for 10 million or more load cycles without failure. If a specimen of ferrous material lasts for this number of cycles, in general it can be assumed that it will last indefinitely.

Fatigue testing is also done for types of loading other than the completely reversed bending stress described above. Many kinds of stresses can be obtained by superposing a variable or fluctuating component on a static or steady stress. Testing machines are built which will give fluctuating axial stresses of various magnitudes to the specimen. It is customary to test spring materials with a pulsating shearing stress that varies continuously from zero to some maximum value.

Fatigue failures due to bending are the most common. Torsion failures are next, and failure due to axial loading are rare. Once started, a fatigue crack follows a general direction normal to the tension stress. A fatigue failure usually takes place across the crystals.

5. Interpretation of Service Fractures

The appearance of the fractured section gives information about the magnitude of the stress that caused the failure. For example, the fracture of a shaft in bending is usually composed of smooth and coarse areas as

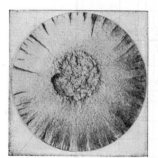

Fig. 2-15. Fatigue failure of shaft.

shown in Fig. 2-15. The smooth area was caused by the opening and closing of the crack during its development. The coarse area was caused by the final rupture. A fatigue crack starts under cyclic loading if the stress exceeds the strength of the weakest grain on a cross section. Continued operation causes the crack to grow as the strength of adjacent grains is exceeded by the high stress at the end of the crack.

If the stress was originally at a high value, the strength at a number of grains around the edge of the cross section was probably exceeded. Cracks started at these, and spread until they united with each other. The circumferential crack then progressed towards the center until final rupture occurred. It can therefore be concluded, when the ruptured area is near the center of the cross section, that the stress was considerably greater than the endurance limit for the material. Failure may have been caused by only a few hundred thousands of stress cycles.

When the final ruptured area is far to one side, the stress was probably only slightly above a safe value, so that the endurance limit was exceeded at but a single point on the boundary. Several million cycles may have been required to produce failure, and a small improvement may make the part safe for indefinite operation.[7]

A fatigue crack at approximately 45° to the axis indicates that the stress was mainly alternating torsion.

[7] See reference 10, and Chapter 13 of reference 1, Bibliography.

6. Factors Affecting Fatigue Strength

The value of the endurance limit is dependent on the condition of the surface of the specimen. The *endurance stress s_e* for ground and polished specimens, when no stress concentrations are present, is frequently found to be approximately equal to one-half the ultimate strength for wrought steels. For a somewhat rougher surface, as produced by machining, the endurance limit may be only 35 or 40 per cent of the ultimate strength. The endurance limit is further reduced if the surface is covered with scale from hot rolling or forging. Corrosion from water or acids may reduce the endurance limit to a very low value. The small pits which form on the surface act as stress raisers. The endurance limit is reduced for temperatures above room temperature. Carbon and alloy wrought steels give the most consistent results with respect to fatigue strength. For steel castings and cast iron, the endurance limit is about 40 per cent of the ultimate strength.

Unfortunately, information on the value of the endurance limit for steels with different types of surfaces is unavailable, or at best difficult to obtain. Hence, the designer is usually forced to estimate the value of this important quantity. The references in the bibliography will prove helpful. Apparently no relationship exists between the endurance limit and the yield point, impact strength, or ductility. Experiments have shown that the endurance limit for reversed torsion is about 0.56 of that for reversed bending.

Fatigue cracks can start not only at easily recognized changes of form, but also at frequently overlooked stress raisers such as file and tool marks, accidental and grinding scratches, quenching cracks, or part number and inspection stamps, which produce a high value for the stress and serve as the starting point for the progressive failure. The attention of the designer must therefore be focused on such "sore spots" whenever they are located in a region of high tension stress.

Since fatigue cracks are due to tensile stress,[8] a residual stress of tension on the surface of the part constitutes an additional fatigue hazard. Such a tensile stress, for example, may arise from a cold-working operation on the part without stress relieving. Parts which are finished by grinding frequently have an extremely thin surface layer, which is highly stressed in tension. Such residual stresses, combined with the tensile stress from the loading, may give a resultant stress sufficiently great to cause a fatigue crack to start.

Any residual surface tension should be removed, or better still, converted into a layer of compression. A prestressed surface layer of compression can be secured by such shop operations as shot blasting, peening,

[8] See reference 11, Bibliography

tumbling, or cold working by rolling between hardened steel rolls. When the surface layer is in compression, the resultant working stress in tension may have a low value. Sometimes the part can be subjected to an excessive load and the yield point stress exceeded in such a way that a residual stress of compression can be obtained at a point where the maximum working stress is tension. Any cold working of the part must, of course, be done under controlled conditions. Sand blasting must be avoided since the scratches serve as stress raisers. Carburized and nitrided parts have a compressive surface layer, which may account for the effectiveness of such parts in resisting fatigue. A finish grinding operation, however, may leave the surface in tension, as previously mentioned. Additional discussion of residual stress is given in Chapter 14.

A weak decarburized layer on the surface of a heat-treated part has a low endurance limit. This condition is especially harmful in springs. Reductions in strength are also brought about by residual stresses such as those produced by press and shrink fits. A press-fitted, antifriction bearing race also causes a reduction in the fatigue strength of the part to which it is fitted.[9] The rough surface of a weld or an internal void also serves as a stress concentration. A layer of hot-dipped galvanizing causes a considerable reduction in the fatigue strength. The same is true for chromium platings. Electroplated zinc coatings have been found to be harmless. Many nonferrous materials do not have a definitely defined endurance limit.

The par value for the material is the endurance limit for a plain polished specimen. Fatigue tests with various kinds of notches show how much of the potential strength is being sacrificed by a particular type of notch. It is usually difficult if not impossible to devise a notched specimen which has the same fatigue strength as a machine part of a particular shape.[10] Apparently such fatigue values can be obtained only from tests on the actual part. The results of tests on notched specimens may, however, serve as a better guide for the selection of a suitable steel than endurance tests made with plain specimens.

If proper attention has been given to the effect of stress concentration, failure in service is due mainly to accidental overload or abuse of the part which could not be anticipated by the designer. Thus the ability to withstand overload is a very desirable quality in engineering materials. Sometimes a material of low endurance limit exhibits better resistance to overloads in fatigue than do high-strength, heat-treated materials. The ability to resist crack propagation after a crack has started is another desirable quality.[11] Experiments have shown that killed steels are superior to

[9] See reference 12, Bibliography.
[10] See reference 13, Bibliography.
[11] See reference 14, Bibliography.

rimmed steels with respect to crack propagation.[12] Killed steels are de-oxidized in the furnace or ladle before being poured into the ingot mold. Rimmed steels are not so degasified.

The life of a part can be reduced by factors other than fatigue such as wear, corrosion, and high temperatures. If, for example, the useful life of a machine will be limited by wear of some of the parts, it would be uneconomical to design the other parts for infinite life in fatigue. The use of higher working stresses in fatigue can sometimes be justified in order to make the life of all the parts approximately equal. Precise information on the S-N curve for the material is required for such exact designing, and extensive testing must be conducted on the finished product. Ball bearings, and sometimes automotive parts, are designed on the basis of finite life.

7. Types of Failure. Ductile Materials and Brittle Materials

Two types of mechanical failures occur in materials: yielding and fracture. Yielding or permanent deformation is a pronounced sliding along certain angular planes in the material. It takes place without rupture. The engineering usefulness for most machine parts is ended after a sufficient amount of yielding has taken place. Therefore, yielding can properly be termed failure. Fracture is a separation failure that occurs on a cross section normal to the tension stress.

A ductile material can be defined as one whose resistance to sliding is smaller than its resistance to separation. Failure takes place by yielding. Many ductile materials have the same yield point value in compression as for tension.

A brittle material is one whose resistance to separation is less than its resistance to sliding. Failure takes place by fracture. A limit of about 5 per cent elongation is usually taken as the dividing line between ductile materials and brittle materials. Most brittle materials have a considerably higher value for the ultimate strength in compression than for tension.

Under certain conditions, a material ordinarily said to be ductile will undergo a fracture or separation failure similar to that of a brittle material. Some of these conditions are: (a) cyclic loading at normal temperatures (fatigue); (b) long-time static loading at elevated temperatures (creep); (c) impact or very rapidly applied loading, especially at low temperatures; (d) work hardening by a sufficient amount of yielding; (e) severe quenching in heat treatment if not followed by tempering; (f) a three-dimensional state of stress in which sliding is prevented, as at the bottom of the narrow

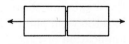
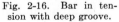

Fig. 2-16. Bar in tension with deep groove.

---

[12] See reference 15, Bibliography.

groove in the bar shown in Fig. 2-16. Internal cavities or voids in castings or forgings may have a similar effect.

8. Ductile Materials with Steady Stress

Under steady or static loading, a machine part made of a ductile material fails by yielding. The working stress is therefore based on the yield point stress.

It is possible for the yield point to be exceeded by the stress concentration as a result of a sudden change of form even though the elementary equation indicates that the average stress at the cross section has a safe value. In general, no damage occurs provided that the load is steady and the material is ductile. The material merely yields locally in the small overstressed regions, and the stress is thereby relieved. Hence, it is customary for designers to neglect the effects of stress concentration when the loads are steady and the material is ductile.

(a) *Simple Tension or Compression.* When the material is subjected to simple tension or compression the working stress s is given by the equation

Working stress: $$s = \frac{s_{yp}}{FS} \tag{2}$$

where FS is the factor of safety.

(b) *Pure Shear.* For pure shear loading, the equation for working stress in shear is

Working stress: $$s_{smax} = \frac{s_{syp}}{FS} \tag{3}$$

The expressions maximum stress or working stress are usually used interchangeably.

9. Maximum Shear Theory of Failure

Because ductile materials fail by shearing, the *maximum shear theory of failure* is in wide use by designers. The theory is applied by first finding the maximum shearing stress for the given loading and then dividing it into the yield point stress in shear to find the factor of safety. It is thus an application of Eq. (3).

The Mohr circle in Fig. 2-17 indicates that a body with simple tension stress s has shear stresses equal to one-half this value at directions 45° to the direction of s.

$$s_{smax} = \frac{1}{2} s \tag{4}$$

If stress s in this figure would be increased to the yield point value, the maximum shear theory postulates that the material will then be at the yield point value in shear.

Thus $$s_{syp} = \frac{1}{2} s_{yp} \qquad (5)$$

This can be substituted into Eq. (3) to give

$$s_{smax} = \frac{0.5 s_{yp}}{FS} \qquad \text{MAX SHEAR} \qquad (6)$$

Failure in shear is assumed to occur along the 45° directions of Fig. 2-18(a). Equations (5) and (6) are valid only when it is understood that the maximum shear theory of failure is being employed.

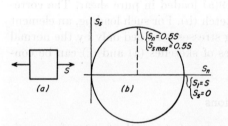

Fig. 2-17. Element in simple tension and corresponding Mohr circle.

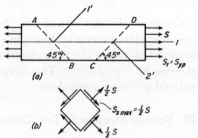

Fig. 2-18. Planes of maximum shear stress for bar with tensile load.

In addition to the shear stresses, an element oriented at 45° to the direction of s in Fig. 2-17(a) has normal stresses on all sides of $0.5s$. The complete loading for this element is then given by Fig. 2-18(b).

Example 2. Suppose the part of Example 1 is 0.5 in. thick and is loaded by a steady tensile force of 18,750 lb. The material is soft steel with a yield point value 45,000 psi. Find the value of the factor of safety based on the yield point.

Solution.

By maximum shear theory: $s_{syp} = 0.5 \times 45,000 = 22,500$ psi

$$A = 1.25 \times 0.5 = 0.625 \text{ in.}^2$$

In right portion: $$s = \frac{P}{A} = \frac{18,750}{0.625} = 30,000 \text{ psi}$$

By Eq. (4): $s_{smax} = 0.5 \times 30,000 = 15,000$ psi

By Eq. (3): $$FS = \frac{s_{syp}}{s_{smax}} = \frac{22,500}{15,000} = 1.5$$

As found in Example 1, the stress concentration factor for the fillets is equal to 1.8. The stress thus reaches the yield point value on the fillets, and local yielding occurs in these regions. The stress for the cross section as a whole, however, remains at a safe value. It is thus justified to neglect the effect of stress concentration for ductile materials and steady loads.

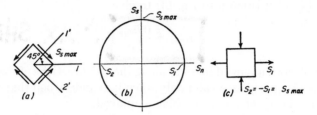

Fig. 2-19.   Elements and Mohr circle for pure shear stress.

Consider the element of Fig. 2-19(a) loaded in pure shear. The corresponding Mohr circle is shown in sketch (b). For such loading, an element oriented at 45° to the pure shearing stresses is loaded only by the normal stresses of Fig. 2-19(c). The stresses of sketches (a) and (c) can be considered as being equivalent.

10. Normal Stresses in Two Directions

For two- and three-dimensional states of stress, the failure of an engineering material is a complicated phenomenon. In addition, test data for combined loading is nearly always lacking, and the design must therefore be based solely on the yield point or ultimate strength values as found by the simple tension test. It is under such conditions that a theory of failure is most useful.

Let the theories for combined stress of Chapter 1 be applied to the case of general loading for stresses s_x, s_y, and s_{xy}, and thus obtain the principal stresses s_1 and s_2 of Fig. 2-20. For convenience, these are shown in the horizontal and vertical directions. The algebraically larger of the two stresses is designated s_1. If shear stress s_{xy} is equal to zero, s_x and s_y are principal stresses.

To arrive at suitable values for the working stresses, it is necessary to know how the element in Fig. 2-20 will fail. The presence of two stresses makes the situation more complicated than the case of simple tension of Fig. 2-17.

Figure 2-21 shows a perspective of the element in Fig. 2-20. Since all bodies are three-dimensional, three planes of failure must be investigated.

(1) Both stresses are tension as shown in Fig. 2-21. The weakest plane is $BADE$ because s_2 has no effect on this plane. Failure is determined solely by stress s_1. Equations (2) to (6) apply.

(2) Both stresses are compression as in Fig. 2-22. The weakest plane is *BCDF* because stress s_1 has no effect on this plane. Since s_2 is numerically the larger, failure is determined solely by stress s_2. Equations (2) to (6) apply.

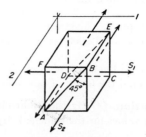

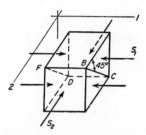

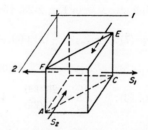

Fig. 2-20. Principal stresses in two dimensions.

Fig. 2-21. Plane of failure for two dimensional stress. All stresses tension.

Fig. 2-22. Plane of failure for two dimensional stress. All stresses compression.

Fig. 2-23. Plane of failure for two dimensional stress. s_1 tension, s_2 compression.

(3) Stress s_1 is tension, and stress s_2 is compression as in Fig. 2-23. The weakest plane is *ACEF*. Both stresses contribute to the shear stress on this plane. The value of the maximum shear stress is

$$s_{smax} = \frac{1}{2}(s_1 - s_2) = \sqrt{\left[\frac{s_x - s_y}{2}\right]^2 + s_{xy}^2} \qquad (7)$$

Equation (6) applies.

The maximum shear theory of failure is thus very easy to apply to two-dimensional stress problems.

11. Mises-Hencky or Distortion Energy Theory

Another criterion that fits experimental results closely is the *Mises-Hencky* or *distortion energy theory*. For two-dimensional stress the equation is

$$s^2 = s_1^2 + s_2^2 - s_1 s_2 \qquad (8)$$

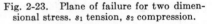

both principal stresses are assumed positive

(these must be principal stresses (point at no shear))

Substitution of Eqs. (38) and (39) of Chapter 1 for s_1 and s_2 gives

$$s^2 = s_x^2 - s_x s_y + s_y^2 + 3s_{xy}^2 \qquad (9)$$

Stress s can be considered as the equivalent working stress in simple tension, which makes it possible to apply Eq. (2) for the factor of safety.

Example 3. The stresses at a point in a body are $s_x = 13,000$ psi, $s_y = 3,000$ psi, and $s_{xy} = 12,000$ psi. The material tests $s_{yp} = 40,000$ psi.

(a) Find the factor of safety by the maximum shear theory of failure.
(b) Find the factor of safety by the Mises-Hencky theory.

Solution. (a) By the Mohr circle or the combined stress equations the following values for the principal stresses s_1 and s_2 are obtained.

$$s_1 = 21,000 \text{ psi}; \qquad s_2 = -5,000 \text{ psi}$$

The weakest shearing plane is the one to which both s_1 and s_2 contribute to the shearing stress as in Fig. 2-23. Hence

By Eq. (7): $\quad s_{smax} = \dfrac{1}{2}[21,000 - (-5,000)] = 13,000$ psi

By Eq. (5): $\quad s_{syp} = 0.5 \times 40,000 = 20,000$ psi

By Eq. (3): $\quad FS = \dfrac{20,000}{13,000} = 1.54$

(b)

By Eq. (8): $\quad s = \sqrt{21,000^2 + (-5,000)^2 - 21,000(-5,000)}$

$$= 23,900 \text{ psi}$$

Hence $\qquad FS = \dfrac{40,000}{23,900} = 1.67$

Example 4. The same body as that used in Example 3 has stresses $s_x = 20,000$ psi, $s_y = 4,000$ psi, and $s_{xy} = 6,000$ psi.

(a) Find the factor of safety by the maximum shear theory of failure.
(b) Find the factor of safety by the Mises-Hencky theory.

Solution. (a) The principal stresses are found to be

$$s_1 = 22,000 \text{ psi}; \qquad s_2 = 2,000 \text{ psi}$$

The weakest shearing plane is the one affected by s_1 alone as in Fig. 2-21. For this plane

By Eq. (4): $\quad s_{smax} = 0.5 \times 22,000 = 11,000$ psi

By Eq. (3): $\quad FS = \dfrac{20,000}{11,000} = 1.82$

(b)

By Eq. (8): $\qquad s = \sqrt{22,000^2 + 2,000^2 - 22,000 \times 2,000}$

$\qquad\qquad\qquad\qquad = 21,070$ psi

Hence $\qquad\qquad FS = \dfrac{40,000}{21,070} = 1.90$

Example 5. A 2 in. diameter shaft is loaded statically in pure torque at a shearing stress of 10,000 psi. Find the FS if the material is 4140 hot-rolled steel. Use the Mises-Hencky theory.

Solution.

By Fig. 2-19(c): $\quad s_{smax} = s_1 = -s_2 = 10,000$ psi

By Eq. (8): $\qquad\qquad s^2 = 10,000^2 + 10,000^2 - 10,000(-10,000)$

$\qquad\qquad\qquad\quad s = 10,000\sqrt{3} = 17,320$ psi

By Table 14-5: $\quad s_{yp} = 63,000$ psi

By Eq. (2): $\qquad\quad FS = \dfrac{s_{yp}}{s} = \dfrac{63,000}{17,320} = 3.64$

12. Ductile Materials with Completely Reversing Stress

As mentioned at the beginning of Section 8, local yielding under steady load takes place if the yield point is exceeded at certain points of stress concentration. However, when the load is fluctuating, such local relief cannot be obtained, and a suitable stress concentration factor K must be applied. Failure from such loading will be by fracture.

When the load is alternating or completely reversing, the endurance limit stress s_e, as determined by testing, is the criterion used for determining the factor of safety. For such loading, the working stress can be called the range stress s_r. Hence

$$FS = \frac{s_e}{Ks_r} \qquad\qquad (10)$$

A similar equation could be written for completely reversed shearing stress.

13. Ductile Materials with Combined Steady and Alternating Stress

In the great majority of strength problems, the major components of stress are static, with less accurately known alternating stresses superposed. Most failures originate with stresses of this type. The problem presents great difficulties because of the fundamentally different mechanisms of failure in the two sources of stress.

Suppose the tensile load P on the bar of Fig. 2-24(a) is continuously varying in magnitude as shown by the graph of Fig. 2-24(b). This load can be considered as being made up of two parts, the steady or average load P_{av}, and the variable or range load P_r. As illustrated by the figure, the maximum load is equal to the average load plus the range load; the minimum load is equal to the average minus the range load. Normal stresses s_{av} and s_r are found by dividing loads P_{av} and P_r by the cross-sectional area A. When the average stress is high, the material will safely

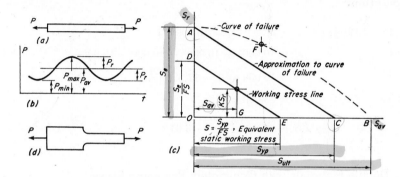

Fig. 2-24.   Working stress diagram for non-steady loading.

carry only a small additional range component. However, if the average stress is small, a larger range component can be permitted.

In order to take care of the unlimited number of combinations of range and average stress, the line of failure of the material must be used. Specimens are tested with fluctuating loads which are low enough to permit continuous operation but high enough so that any increase in either the average or range load will eventually cause failure. The s_{av} stress for the test is plotted as the abscissa, and the s_r stress as the ordinate. Thus, a typical point F is located, as in Fig. 2-24(c). After other combinations of s_{av} and s_r have been determined, the points are plotted to form a curve of failure. Point A, where the average stress is zero, represents the endurance limit for completely reversed stress as given by the s_e value of Fig. 2-13. Point B, where the range stress is zero, represents the static ultimate stress for the material.

Since experimental data for the line of failure are usually not at hand, it is customary to make the conservative approximation that it is a straight line.[13] To be still further on the safe side, the line is drawn from the endurance limit value at A to point C, representing the yield point,

[13] See reference 16, and Chapter 10 of reference 1, Bibliography.

rather than to point B for the ultimate stress. The line representing actual working stresses in the material is drawn after both s_e and s_{yp} have been divided by the factor of safety FS as shown in Fig. 2-24(c).

If a stress concentration exists, as illustrated by Fig. 2-24(d), at the cross section for which the stresses are computed, it is commonly neglected so far as the average stress s_{av} is concerned. However, since stress concentration must be taken into account for alternating stresses, the range stress s_r must be multiplied by the stress concentration factor K before plotting. If a point determined by s_{av} and Ks_r as coordinates falls on or below the working-stress line, the part is assumed to be safe for continuous operation.

The situation can be handled conveniently by equations as follows. All points along line DE can be assumed to be equally safe. This includes point E. Stress OE, or $s = s_{yp}/FS$, can then be considered as the static stress equivalent to the fluctuating stress $s_{av} \pm Ks_r$. By similar triangles, it is easy to show that GE is equal to $s_{yp}Ks_r/s_e$.

Then
$$s = s_{av} + \frac{Ks_{yp}}{s_e} s_r \tag{11}$$

This is sometimes called Soderberg's equation. When stress s is obtained, it can be used in Eq. (2) to determine the factor of safety.

Example 6.

(a) Find the area required for the safe continuous operation of a uniform bar in tension if $P_{max} = 50,000$ lb and $P_{min} = 20,000$ lb. Material tests $s_{ult} = 90,000$ psi and $s_{yp} = 60,000$ psi. Take the factor of safety FS equal to 1.5 based on the yield point. Let $s_e = 0.5s_{ult}$.

(b) Repeat (a) using the bar of two widths shown in Fig. 2-25(b). Let $r = h$, and $d = 2h$.

Solution. (a) $s_e = 0.5 \times 90,000 = 45,000$ psi. Divide s_{yp} and s_e each by factor of safety 1.5 and plot as shown. $P_{av} = 35,000$ lb and $P_r = 15,000$ lb. $s_{av} = 35,000/A$ and $s_r = 15,000/A$, where A is the required area.

By Eq. (11): $s = \dfrac{60,000}{1.5} = \dfrac{35,000}{A} + \dfrac{60,000}{45,000} \times \dfrac{15,000}{A}$

From which: $A = 1.375$ in.^{2}

(b) For $h/r = 1$ and $r/d = 0.5$, the value of K from Fig. 2-4 (also from Fig. 2-8, since $h/r = 1$) is 1.42.

Then: $s = \dfrac{60,000}{1.5} = \dfrac{35,000}{A} + \dfrac{60,000}{45,000} \times \dfrac{1.42 \times 15,000}{A}$

From which: $A = 1.585$ in.^{2}

The stress concentration caused by widening the left part has increased the possibility of failure so that the right portion must be increased also.

Although Eq. (11) refers to normal stress, the development could have been made equally well for shear stress. The equation for static shear stress s_s equivalent to the variable shear loading $s_{sav} \pm s_{sr}$ is

$$s_s = s_{sav} + \frac{Ks_{yp}}{s_e} s_{sr} \tag{12}$$

Stress s_s can be used in Eq. (3) for determination of the factor of safety. In the

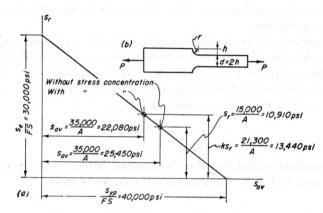

Fig. 2-25.   Working stress diagram for Example 6.

equation above ratio s_{yp}/s_e is taken as approximately equal to s_{syp}/s_{se} data for which is usually not available.

The case of fluctuating loading for combined normal and shear stress is discussed in Section 4 of the following chapter on shafting.

14. The Modified Goodman Diagram

Other types of diagrams have been devised for determining the values of the working stresses for parts subjected to fluctuating loads. The modified Goodman diagram is one of these. When the line for average stress is inclined at 45° as in Fig. 2-26(a), values for s_{max} and s_{min} can be scaled directly from the figure. Instead of drawing the complete figure, a diagram consisting only of line CBD can be drawn, as shown in Fig. 2-26(b). Such a diagram will give the same values for the average and range stress for a point such as E providing $A'B'$ is made equal to AB. This diagram permits somewhat higher stress values than Fig. 2-24 because line $C'B'$ is directed towards the ultimate stress rather than towards the yield point stress.

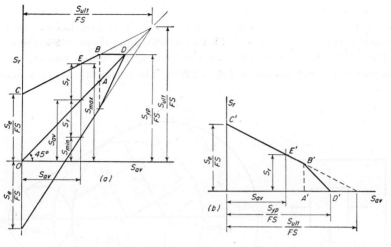

Fig. 2-26.   Modified Goodman diagram for fluctuating stress.

15. Brittle Materials with Steady Stress   SKIP

Failure in brittle materials takes place by fracture. The ultimate strength is used as the basis for determining the working stress. It is necessary to have separate equations for the factor of safety in tension and for the factor of safety in compression. Brittle materials are unable to yield locally at points of high stress caused by changes of form, and stress concentration factors are customarily applied even when the loading is steady.

(a) *Simple Tension or Compression.* The following equations can be written.

For tension, s_t
$$FS = \frac{s_{ut}}{K s_t} \qquad (13)$$

where s_{ut} represents the ultimate stress in tension.

For compression, s_c,
$$FS = \frac{s_{uc}}{K s_c} \qquad (14)$$

where s_{uc} represents the ultimate stress in compression.

(b) *Normal Stress in Two Directions.* Two cases must be considered.

(1) Both principal stresses of same sign. In accord with Figs. 2-21 and 2-22, failure is assumed to be due only to the principle stress of larger magnitude without regard to the stress at right angles thereto. Equations (13) and (14) apply.

(2) Principal stresses have opposite signs as shown in Fig. 2-27(a). The problem is as yet poorly understood. The best-known rational method is due to Mohr and is based on maximum shear stress theory.

The ultimate stress circles for the loading of simple tension s_1 and compression s_2 are shown in Fig. 2-27(b). The assumption is now made[14]

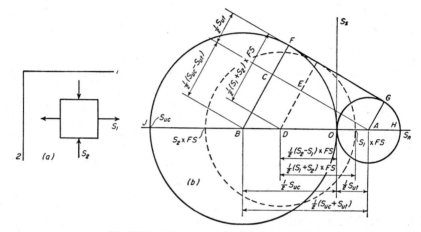

Fig. 2-27. Mohr circles for brittle materials.

that any stress condition at which failure is imminent can be represented by a circle that is somewhere tangent to FG. Suppose in Fig. 2-27(a) that the combination of working stresses of tension s_1 and compression s_2 represents the highest permissible state of stress for the material. When these stresses are multiplied by the factor of safety FS, the dashed circle tangent to FG in Fig. 2-27(b) results.

Triangles ABC and ADE are similar. If all lengths are considered positive, the following proportion of corresponding sides can be written.

$$\frac{DE}{AD} = \frac{BC}{AB} \quad \text{or} \quad DE \times AB = AD \times BC$$

Values of the terms from Fig. 2-27(b) can be substituted to give

$$\left[\frac{1}{2}(s_2 + s_1)FS - \frac{1}{2}s_{ut} \right] \frac{1}{2}(s_{uc} + s_{ut})$$

$$= \left[\frac{1}{2}(s_2 - s_1)FS + \frac{1}{2}s_{ut} \right] \frac{1}{2}(s_{uc} - s_{ut})$$

This equation, when reduced to lowest terms, becomes the following.

$$\frac{s_1}{s_{ut}} + \frac{s_2}{s_{uc}} = \frac{1}{FS} \tag{15}$$

[14] See p. 480 of reference 1, Bibliography.

In using this equation, s_{uc} must be substituted as a negative number. Stress concentration factors can be applied as shown in the following example.

Example 7. Assume that the computed stresses at a point in a cast iron body are as follows: $s_x = 2,000$ psi, $s_y = -6,000$ psi, and $s_{xy} = 3,000$ psi. The stress concentration factor is equal to 2 for all stresses. Material tests $s_{ut} = 20,000$ psi and $s_{uc} = -80,000$ psi. Find the value of the factor of safety.

Solution.

In Eq. (38), Chapter 1: $Ks_1 = 2(-2,000 + \sqrt{4,000^2 + 3,000^2}) = 6,000$ psi

In Eq. (39), Chapter 1: $Ks_2 = 2(-2,000 - \sqrt{4,000^2 + 3,000^2}) = -14,000$ psi

In Eq. (15): $\dfrac{6,000}{20,000} + \dfrac{-14,000}{-80,000} = \dfrac{1}{FS}$

$$FS = \frac{80}{38} = 2.1$$

The mechanism of failure for brittle materials is very complex, and the foregoing treatment must be considered only as a rough approximation.

(c) *Pure Shear*. Equation (15) is applicable for pure shear loading where $s_1 = -s_2 = s_s$ as indicated in Fig. 2-19. Let $s_{uc} = -C_1 s_{ut}$, where C_1 is a constant. Substitution in Eq. (15) gives the following.

$$\frac{s_s}{s_{ut}} + \frac{-s_s}{-C_1 s_{ut}} = \frac{1}{FS}$$

The equation above can be reduced to

$$\frac{C_1 + 1}{C_1} \cdot \frac{s_s}{s_{ut}} = \frac{1}{FS} \tag{16}$$

16. Brittle Materials with Fluctuating Loads

Although successful applications can be cited, brittle materials are usually considered unsatisfactory where the load is fluctuating. Large values for the factor of safety must be used.

17. Sensitivity to Stress Concentration

The actual reduction in fatigue strength, as indicated by the theoretical stress concentration factors, is approached only by large parts made of fine-grained heat-treated steels. The effect of stress concentration in coarse-grained annealed steels may be considerably less. Small specimens are affected less by stress concentration than much larger parts made of the same material. The size effect in steel is attributed mainly to the grain size of the material. When the crystal size is taken into account, it is seen that there is not complete geometric similarity between large and small specimens of the same material. Although a heat-treated part of expensive alloy steel may have a higher endurance limit than one made of a softer nonheat-treated material, the advantage may be largely lost in the presence of a stress concentration.

A wide variation exists in the *notch sensitivity* of different materials. For some quenched and tempered steels the effect of a sharp notch may be so great that a high strength material may be no better in fatigue than one of lower strength. Materials which work harden rapidly, such as the 18-8 stainless steels, may show great resistance to loss of fatigue strength due to notches. Notches have but little effect on the fatigue strength of cast iron, but may have a large effect as far as impact loads are concerned. However the impact strength of some steels is but little affected by notches.

A limited amount of data are available for making a quantitative estimate of the sensitivity of a steel to stress concentration,[15] but the methods are beyond the scope of this book. However, when the full theoretical stress concentration factor is applied to the fluctuating component, the result will be on the safe side.

18. Factor of Safety

It is sometimes hard to evaluate accurately all the different factors that are involved in an engineering design problem. It is particularly difficult, in some cases, to determine the magnitude of the various forces to which a machine part is subjected. Sometimes the shape of the part is such that no design equations are available for accurate computation of the stresses. Variations and nonuniformity in the strength of the material must be kept in mind, as well as the consequences that might result from failure of the part.

Engineers employ a so-called "factor of safety" to insure against uncertain or unknown conditions as mentioned above. The working stress is determined from the yield or ultimate strength of the material by means of a factor of safety, as demonstrated by the equations of this chapter. For columns and other elements where load and stress are not proportional, the factor of safety should be applied to the load on the member rather than to the stress.

Static loads can sometimes be determined accurately, but the values of fluctuating loads are more uncertain. The effects of impact loads and residual stress are particularly difficult to evaluate. Consideration must also be given to the long-term effects of corrosion and high temperatures.

[15] See references 10 and 17, also Chapter 4 of reference 30, Bibliography.

Sometimes the shape of the parts, or the method of support, can be modified in such a way that the design equations may fit the conditions more accurately. Perhaps a more uniform and reliable construction material can be used.

The strength of materials is usually obtained by laboratory tests. It must be kept in mind, however, that conventional laboratory tests rarely reproduce the conditions that the material must meet in service. Surface conditions in particular may be different for the test specimen than for an actual part. A much greater amount of knowledge of engineering materials, than is now available, must be gained before the designer will be able to apply test data to conditions that differ appreciably from the conditions of the test. The best method, whenever it is possible, is to make final adjustment in the proportioning of the components by tests on the completed product.

In general it is not economical to use safety factors large enough to eliminate all possibility of failure resulting from the worst possible combination of circumstances. The designer attempts to reduce the probability of failure to a suitable level which necessarily depends on each particular application. A failure that involves only a little inconvenience or loss of time might be allowed more frequently than one involving large financial loss or human life. Provision should be made for easy and rapid replacement of failed parts. If the product operates under conditions of frequent service inspection, smaller values for the factor of safety can sometimes be used. A more thorough and detailed analysis of the problem may show that smaller factors of safety can be used, and may justify the additional engineering expense involved.

When building one general product, the engineer usually does not think in terms of the factor of safety. He has learned from experience that certain materials under certain conditions, with working stresses of given values, will lead to satisfactory results. Although the determination[16] of suitable values for the factor of safety is a matter of great importance, the subject has been much neglected and is in an unsatisfactory state. Experience, which can only be accumulated as a result of a long period of trial and error, is the ultimate basis for the prediction of failure in engineering designs. Many failures are due to circumstances that the designer failed to consider.

BIBLIOGRAPHY

Volume number shown in **bold face** type. The number immediately following is the page on which the article begins.

1. Hetényi, M., editor, *Handbook of Experimental Stress Analysis*. New York: John Wiley & Sons, Inc., 1950.

[16] See reference 18, Bibliography.

2. Frocht, M. M., "Factors of Stress Concentration Photoelastically Determined," *Trans. ASME*, **57**, A-67 (1935).

3. Frocht, M. M., and Hill, H. N., "Stress-Concentration Factors Around a Central Circular Hole in a Plate Loaded Through Pin in the Hole," *Trans. ASME*, **62**, A-5 (1940).

4. Hetényi, M., "Some Applications of Photoelasticity in Turbine-Generator Design," *Trans. ASME*, **61**, A-151 (1939).

5. Lipson, Charles, Noll, G. C., and Clock, L. S., *Stress and Strength of Manufactured Parts*. New York: McGraw-Hill Book Company, Inc., 1950.

6. Neugebauer, G. H., "Stress Concentration Factors and Their Effect on Design," *Product Eng.*, **14**, 82, 168 (1943).

7. Peterson, R. E., and Wahl, A. M., "Two- and Three-Dimensional Cases of Stress Concentration and Comparison with Fatigue Tests," *Trans. ASME*, **58**, A-15 (1936).

8. Battelle Memorial Institute, *Prevention of Fatigue of Metals*. New York: John Wiley & Sons, Inc., 1941.

9. Moore, H. F., "Stress, Strain, and Structural Damage," *Proc. ASTM*, **39**, 549 (1939).

10. Peterson, R. E., "Stress Concentration Phenomena in Fatigue of Metals," *Trans. ASME*, **55**, APM-55-19, 157 (1933).

11. Almen, J. O., "Shot Blasting to Increase Fatigue Resistance," *SAE Journal* (Trans.) **51**, 249 (1943).

12. Peterson, R. E., and Wahl, A. M., "Fatigue of Shafts at Fitted Members, With a Related Photoelastic Analysis," *Trans. ASME*, **57**, A-1 (1935).

13. Almen, J. O., and Boegehold, A. L., "Rear Axle Gears," *Proc. ASTM*, **35**, Part 2, 99 (1935).

14. deForest, A. V., "The Rate of Growth of Fatigue Cracks," *Trans. ASME*, **58**, A-23, A-114 (1936).

15. Wilson, W. M., and Burke, J. L., "Rate of Propagation of Fatigue Cracks . . . ," *Bulletin 371*, University of Illinois Experiment Station, 1947.

16. Soderberg, C. R., "Factors of Safety and Working Stress," *Trans. ASME*, **52**(1), APM-13 (1930); **55**, APM-131 (1933); **57**, A-106 (1935).

17. Peterson, R. E., "Relation Between Life Testing and Conventional Tests of Materials," *ASTM Bull. 133*, March, 9 (1945).

18. Freudenthal, A. M., "The Safety of Structures," *Trans. ASCE*, **71**, 1157 (1945); **72**, 111 (1946); **73**, 208 (1947).

19. Timoshenko, S., *Strength of Materials*, 2d ed., Vol. 2. New York: D. Van Nostrand Company, Inc., 1941, Chap. 9.

20. Roark, Raymond J., *Formulas for Stress and Strain*, 2d ed. New York: McGraw-Hill Book Company, Inc., 1943.

21. Moore, H. F., *Materials of Engineering*, 6th ed. New York: McGraw-Hill Book Company, Inc., 1941.

22. Marin, Joseph, *Engineering Materials: Their Mechanical Properties and Applications.* Englewood Cliffs, N. J.: Prentice-Hall, Inc., 1950.

23. Smith, James O., "Effect of Range of Stress on the Fatigue Strength of Metals," *Bulletin 334,* University of Illinois Engineering Experiment Station, 1942.

24. Jacobsen, L. S., "Torsional Stresses in Shafts Having Grooves or Fillets," *Trans. ASME,* **47,** 619 (1925); **57,** A-154 (1935).

25. Poole, S. W., and Johnson, R. J., "A Review of Some Mechanical Failures of Steel Plant Machine Equipment," *Proc. Soc. Exptl. Stress Anal.,* **7, No. 2,** 17 (1949).

26. McFarland, F. R., "Experiences with Highly-Stressed Aircraft Engine Parts," *Proc. Soc. Exptl. Stress Anal.,* **3, No. 1,** 112 (1945).

27. Noll, G. C., and Lipson, C., "Allowable Working Stresses," *Proc. Soc. Exptl. Stress Anal.,* **3, No. 2,** 89 (1946).

28. Noll, G. C., and Erickson, M. A., "Allowable Stresses for Steel Members of Finite Life," *Proc. Soc. Exptl. Stress Anal.,* **5, No. 2,** 132 (1948).

29. Karpov, A. V., "Modern Stress Theories," *Proc. ASCE,* **62,** 1128 (1936). See also, *Metals & Alloys,* **10,** 346, 381 (1939).

30. Murray, Wm. M., editor, *Fatigue and Fracture of Metals.* New York: John Wiley and Sons, Inc., 1952.

31. Peterson, R. E., *Stress Concentration Design Factors.* New York: John Wiley and Sons, Inc., 1953.

32. Starkey, W. L., and Marco, S. M., "Effects of Stress-Time Cycles on the Fatigue Properties of Metals," *Trans. ASME,* **79,** 1329 (1957).

33. Findley, W. N., "Fatigue of Metals under Combinations of Stresses," *Trans. ASME,* **79,** 1337 (1957).

34. Frisch, J., and Thomsen, E. G., "Residual Grinding Stresses in Mild Steel," *Trans. ASME,* **73,** 337 (1951).

PROBLEMS

1. Find the value of the stress at each hole in Fig. 2-28.

   Ans. A, K_s = 29,710 psi; B, K_s = 31,330 psi; C, K_s = 35,680 psi.

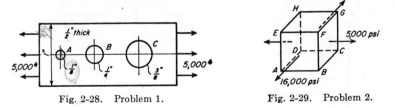

Fig. 2-28. Problem 1.   Fig. 2-29. Problem 2.

2. The loading on an element of 1045 steel in the as-rolled condition is shown in Fig. 2-29. Loads are steady and no stress concentrations are present. Assume maximum shear theory to be valid.

(a) Find the value of the *FS* for the *CDEF* plane.

(b) Find the value of the *FS* for the *ACGE* plane.

(c) Find the value of the *FS* for the *AFGD* plane.

      Ans. (a) *FS* = 3.75; (b) *FS* = 5.45; (c) *FS* = 12.

3. A plate of 1045 steel in the as-rolled condition is subjected to the following stresses: s_x = 3,300 psi; s_y = −29,000 psi; s_{xy} = 0.

(a) Find the value of the *FS* by the maximum shear theory.

(b) Find the value of the *FS* by the Mises-Hencky theory.

(c) Find *FS* if the plate is made of Class 25 cast iron.

     Ans. (a) *FS* = 1.86; (b) *FS* = 1.95; (c) *FS* = 2.37.

4. A machine part has a *FS* of 3 by the Mises-Hencky theory. The material is 4140 steel, hot rolled and annealed. If s_x is equal to 24,000 psi, find the value of s_y. s_{xy} = 0.   *Ans.* s_y = 15,000 psi or 9,000 psi.

5. A shaft is loaded by a torque of 40,000 in.-lb. The material has a yield point of 50,000 psi. *FS* is equal to 2.

(a) Find the required diameter by the maximum shear theory.

(b) Find the required diameter by the Mises-Hencky theory.

     Ans. (a) *d* = 2.535 in.; (b) *d* = 2.417 in.

6. A 15 by 15 in. plate of 1045 steel in the as-rolled condition has normal stresses only acting on all edges. Stress s_x is tension and s_y is compression. The length in the *y*-direction is reduced by 0.008 in. *FS* is equal to 2 by the maximum shear theory. Find the values of the stresses.

     Ans. s_x = 20,000 psi; s_y = −10,000 psi.

7. A 12 by 12 in. steel plate has normal stresses only acting on all edges. Stress s_x equals 12,000 psi tension. s_y is compression. Increase in length in the *x*-direction is 0.006 in. If *FS* is equal to 2.5 by the maximum shear theory, what is the yield point value for the material? *Ans.* s_{yp} = 55,000 psi.

8. A 15 by 15 in. plate of 1045 steel in the as-rolled condition has normal stresses only acting on all edges. Stress s_x equals 6,000 psi tension. s_y is compression. For a *FS* equal to 3 by the maximum shear theory, find the change in length in the *x*-direction.   *Ans.* δ_x = 0.0051 in.

9. The link shown in Fig. 2-30 is subjected to a completely reversing load of 20,000 lb. Find the maximum value of stress at each hole.

    Ans. Top, Ks_r = 17,880 psi; bottom, Ks_r = 17,540 psi.

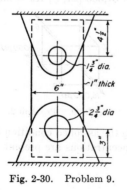

Fig. 2-30. Problem 9.

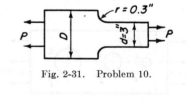

Fig. 2-31. Problem 10.

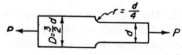

Fig. 2-32. Problem 11.

10. The plate shown in Fig. 2-31 is $\frac{1}{2}$ in. thick. Load P varies from 20,000 lb to 10,000 lb. Material tests $s_{yp} = 42{,}000$ psi; $s_e = 24{,}000$ psi. Factor of safety based on yield point is 2. Find the maximum permissible value of width D.

Ans. $D = 3.86$ in.

11. The plate of Fig. 2-32 is 1 in. thick. The load varies from 50,000 lb to 30,000 lb. Factor of safety $= 2$; $s_{yp} = 40{,}300$ psi; $s_e = 28{,}000$ psi. (a) Find the value of d. (b) Find d if the minimum load is 20,000 lb, other data remaining unchanged.

Ans. $d = 3.13$ in. and 3.45 in.

12. Find the diameter of the hole and the total width of the plate of Fig. 2-33 if the part is to be safe for continuous operation. The load varies from 36,000 lb to 20,000 lb. Use stress values of $s_{yp}/FS = 30{,}000$ psi and $s_e/FS = 18{,}000$ psi. The plate is 1 in. thick. 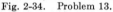 *Ans.* $D = 2.55$ in.

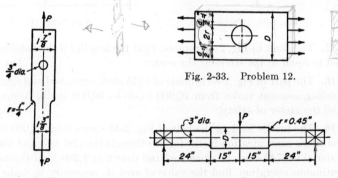

Fig. 2-33.   Problem 12.

Fig. 2-34.   Problem 13.   Fig. 2-35.   Problem 14.

13. A part is designed as shown in Fig. 2-34. Check the design by plotting the line of failure and points representing the stress values for the material at the hole and fillet. Is the part safe for continuous operation? The load varies from 12,000 lb to 2,000 lb. $s_{yp} = 41{,}000$ psi; $s_e = 28{,}500$ psi. Plate is $\frac{7}{16}$ in. thick.

14. Figure 2-35 shows a shaft with load P varying from 1,000 lb to 3,000 lb. The material tests $s_{yp} = 42{,}000$ psi, and $s_e = 24{,}000$ psi. Factor of safety is equal to 2. Find the permissible value for D if stress conditions at the fillets are to be satisfactory for continuous operation.   *Ans.* $D = 3.63$ in.

15. Material for the eyebolt of Fig. 2-36 tests $s_{yp} = 39{,}000$ psi and $s_e = 26{,}000$ psi. The factor of safety equals 2. Threads are American National. Let stress concentration factor for the threads be equal to 2.5. Upon assembly, the spring is given an initial stretch. During operation, the lower end of the spring moves 1 in. each way from its initial position. Find the permissible amount of initial stretch which may be given to the spring if eyebolt is to be safe for continuous operation.

Ans. 5.45 in.

16. The shaft of Fig. 2-37 rotates but carries no torque. For the material, $s_e = 28{,}500$ psi. Determine the value of the bending stress at the fillet. (a) Is the shaft safe for continuous operation? What is the value of the factor of safety? (b) Suppose in the turning operation the radius of the fillet is made $\frac{1}{8}$ in. and that the inspectors do not discover the mistake. Is the part now safe for continuous operation?   *Ans.*   (a) $FS = 1.32$.

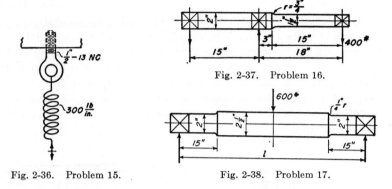

Fig. 2-37.   Problem 16.

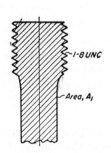

Fig. 2-36.   Problem 15.

Fig. 2-38.   Problem 17.

17. The shaft in Fig. 2-38 rotates. Find the length l if the bending stress at the fillet is equal to the stress at the center.   *Ans.* $l = 96.1$ in.

18. The part in Fig. 2-39 is made of 1045 steel, quenched and drawn at 1,000 F. Bending moment varies from 10,000 in.-lb to 50,000 in.-lb. Assume $s_e = 0.5s_{ult}$. Find the factor of safety.   *Ans.* $FS = 1.91$.

19. The tensile load on the bolt of Fig. 2-40 varies from 12,000 lb to 20,000 lb. The stress concentration factor for the threads is equal to 3 and for the fillet 1.2. Material is 8742 steel, oil quenched and drawn at 1,200 F. If threads are safe for continuous operation, find the value of area A_1 necessary to make the fillet safe for continuous operation.   *Ans.* $A_1 = 0.402$ in.^{2}

20. The beam shown in Fig. 2-41 is made of a brittle material. Find the value of the maximum bending stress at cross section A.   *Ans.* $s = 5,625$ psi.

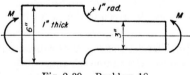

Fig. 2-41.   Problem 20.

Fig. 2-40.   Problem 19.

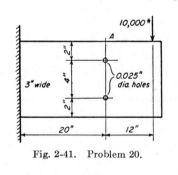

Fig. 2-39.   Problem 18.

21. The plates in Fig. 2-42 are made of a brittle material and are identical. The loading for (a) consists of a uniform tension applied at each end. In (b) the hole contains a pin that carries the load and a uniform tension is applied to the other end of the plate. Find the maximum tensile stress for each type of loading. Note that loading through a pin as for (b) gives a higher stress. H > D in Fig. 2-9.

Ans. (a) $Ks = 4,890$ psi; (b) $Ks = 6,110$ psi.

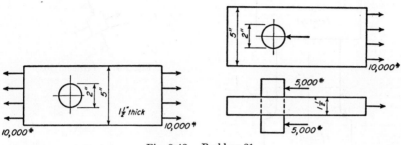

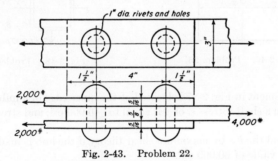

Fig. 2-42. Problem 21.

22. The plates shown in Fig. 2-43 are made of a brittle material. Assume each rivet transfers one-half the load. Find the value of the maximum tensile stress in the thicker plate.

Ans. $s = 8,740$ psi.

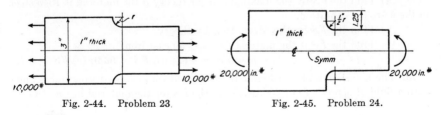

Fig. 2-43. Problem 22.

23. Find the value of the maximum stress on the fillet in Fig. 2-44 if the stress concentration factor is equal to 1.6. What is the FS if the part is made of Class 25 cast iron?

Ans. $FS = 3.12$.

Fig. 2-44. Problem 23.   Fig. 2-45. Problem 24.

24. Find the value of the maximum stress on the fillet in Fig. 2-45 if the stress concentration factor is equal to 1.75. What is the FS if the part is made of Class 30 cast iron?

Ans. $FS = 3.57$.

25. (a) Find the value of the *FS* if the part in Fig. 2-46 is made of 1045 steel in the as-rolled condition.

(b) Find the value of the *FS* if the same part in Fig. 2-46 is made of Class 20 cast iron.

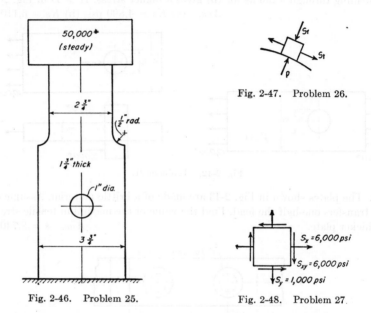

Fig. 2-47.   Problem 26.

Fig. 2-46.   Problem 25.

Fig. 2-48.   Problem 27.

26. The element in Fig. 2-47 is located at the inner edge of a hub that has been press fitted on a shaft. Stress s_r or p is equal to $-6,000$ psi, and stress s_t is equal to 10,000 psi.

(a) Find the *FS* by maximum shear theory if the hub is made of steel with a yield point value of 60,000 psi.

(b) Find the *FS* if the hub is made of Class 25 cast iron.

Ans.   (a) *FS* = 3.75; (b) *FS* = 2.17.

27. The state of stress for a material is shown in Fig. 2-48.

(a) Find the *FS* by the maximum shear theory if the material is 1045 steel in the as-rolled condition.

(b) Find the *FS* by the Mises-Hencky theory.

(c) Find the *FS* if the material is Class 30 cast iron.

Ans.   (a) *FS* = 4.62; (b) *FS* = 5.09; (c) *FS* = 2.77.

28. The hollow cylinder in Fig. 2-49 is made of Class 25 cast iron and is filled with a fluid at a pressure of 250 psi. Find the *FS* for the material in the wall.

Ans.   FS = 5.5.

29. The shaft in Fig. 2-50 is rigidly attached to the wall and is made of Class 25 cast iron. Stress concentration at the wall for bending and torsion is equal to 2. Find the value of the *FS*.   *Ans.   FS* = 3.08.

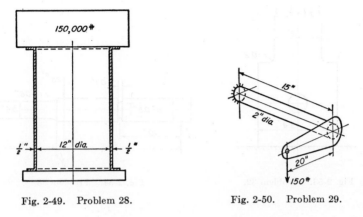

Fig. 2-49.   Problem 28.   Fig. 2-50.   Problem 29.

30. The hollow cylinder in Fig. 2-51 is fixed at the wall and has an OD of 6 in. and an ID of 4.5 in. Stress concentration factor at wall is equal to 3.

    (a) Find value of FS if material is Class 25 cast iron.

    (b) Find value of FS if material is 0.33 carbon cast steel normalized.

                              Ans.   (a) $FS = 4$; (b) $FS = 20.8$.

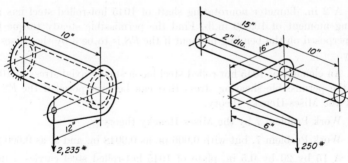

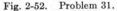

Fig. 2-51.   Problem 30.   Fig. 2-52.   Problem 31.

31. The shaft in Fig. 2-52 is made of Class 20 cast iron. The ends are simply supported, but are keyed against rotation. The stress concentration factor at bracket is equal to 2. Find the FS for the shaft on either side of the bracket.

                          Ans.   Left, $FS = 6.07$; right, $FS = 2.82$.

The following problems are presented without answers.

32. Find the diameter of the hole in Fig. 2-53 if the stress concentration factor there is to be the same as at the fillet.

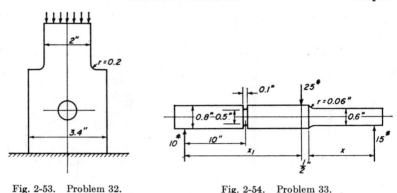

Fig. 2-53.   Problem 32.   Fig. 2-54.   Problem 33.

33. Find values of lengths x and x_1 in Fig. 2-54 if the bending stress at the groove and at the fillet are to be equal. Stress concentration should be taken into account.

34. In Fig. 2-50, let the 15 in. dimension become 12 in., and the 20 in. dimension become 10 in. The shaft is of 1045 hot-rolled steel. Find the permissible load at end of arm if FS by the Mises-Hencky theory is to be 2.5.

35. A steel plate 20 by 10 in. has normal stresses only on the four edges. After the loads are applied, the dimensions become 20.0066 in. and 9.9981 in. Material is 1035 cold-rolled steel. Find the FS by the maximum shear theory.

36. A 2 in. diameter nonrotating shaft of 1045 hot-rolled steel has a steady bending moment of 10,000 in.lb. Find the permissible steady torque that can be superposed on the bending moment if the FS is to be 3 by the Mises-Hencky theory.

37. An element of 1045 hot-rolled steel has a steady axial stress of 10,000 psi. Find the permissible shearing stress that can be superposed if the FS is to be 2.5 by the Mises-Hencky theory.

38. Work Problem 7 by the Mises-Hencky theory.

39. Work Problem 7, but with 0.006 in. as 0.0048 in. and s_x as 9,600 psi.

40. A 15 by 20 by 0.5 in. plate of 1045 hot-rolled steel carries a uniformly distributed tension of 90,000 lb on the 15 in. edge. Find the compressive stress on the 20 in. edge if the FS is 2 by the maximum shear theory. Find the dimensions of the plate after the loads are acting.

41. In Fig. 2-52, the 16 in. dimension becomes 8 in. with the load at the end of the bracket equal to 2,500 lb. The shaft material tests 54,000 psi yield and 90,000 psi ultimate. Find the FS by the maximum shear theory for an element on the top surface 4 in. to the left of the bracket. Do the same by the Mises-Hencky theory.

42. The part shown in Fig. 2-55 is made from 8742 steel quenched and tempered at 1,200 F. The load varies continuously from 30,000 lb to 50,000 lb. If the endurance limit is equal to one-half the ultimate strength, find the FS.

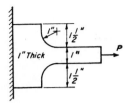

Fig. 2-55.   Problem 42.

43. A 2 in. diameter shaft carries a torque that fluctuates 25 per cent each way from the average value of 20,000 in-lb. The stress concentration factor is 2.5. The *FS* based on the yield point is 2. If the endurance limit in shear is equal to 0.6 of the yield point in shear, determine the minimum value of the yield point in shear which the material must have if the shaft is to be safe for continuous operation.

44. A body loaded by normal stresses s_1 and s_2 has a *FS* by the Mises-Hencky theory that is 10 per cent greater than the *FS* when computed by the maximum shear theory. If s_1 is 10,000 psi, find the value of s_2.

45. In Fig. 2-56, the leaf spring is straight and unstressed when the cam and shaft are removed. The material is cold drawn chrome-moly steel 4140. The stress concentration is zero. Assume s_e is equal to 0.5 of s_{ult}. If the cam rotates continuously, find *FS* for the spring.

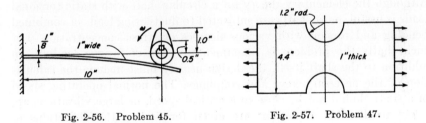

Fig. 2-56.   Problem 45.   Fig. 2-57.   Problem 47.

46. Work Problem 27(c) with $s_x = 17,000$ psi.

47. For a *FS* of 4, find the total force *P* in Fig. 2-57 if the material is Class 30 cast iron.

48. Work Problem 29, but find the *FS* for an element at the wall at midheight on the surface of the shaft on the side towards the observer.

49. A 10 by 20 in. plate of Class 50 cast iron has normal stresses only acting on the edges.

(a) Find the *FS* if the dimensions become 9.9981 by 20.0066 in. after the loads are applied.

(b) Do the same, but with dimensions of 10.0011 by 20.0048 in.

50. Find the relationship between s_{syp} and s_{yp} by the Mises-Hencky theory.

3

Shafting

SHAFTS are used in all kinds of machinery and mechanical equipment. Although the elementary theory for a circular shaft with static torsional loads is useful, most shafts are subjected to fluctuating loads of combined bending and torsion with various degrees of stress concentration. For such shafts the problem is fundamentally one of fatigue loading. In addition to the shaft itself, the design usually must include the calculation of the necessary keys and couplings. The normal operating speed of a shaft should not be close to a critical speed, or large vibrations are likely to develop. Equations are given for finding the deflections of shafts of nonuniform diameters. Machine parts with noncircular cross sections are sometimes loaded in torsion; the designer must therefore be able to determine the stresses and deformations sustained by such bodies.

d, diameter

E, modulus of elasticity

fpm, feet per minute

FS, factor of safety

G, modulus of elasticity in shear

hp, horsepower

I, moment of inertia

J, polar moment of inertia

K, stress concentration factor, normal stress

K_t, stress concentration factor, shear stress

l, length

M, bending moment

n, revolutions per minute

r, radius

rpm, revolutions per minute

s_e, endurance limit stress, reversed bending

s_s, shearing stress

s_{yp}, yield point stress, tension

SAE, Society of Automotive Engineers

T, torque

V, velocity, feet per minute

y, deflection

φ, (phi) angular deformation

ω, (omega) angular velocity, radians per second

106

1. Torsion of Circular Shaft

Figure 3-1 shows a circular shaft of uniform cross section loaded at the ends by the torques T which twist it about the longitudinal axis.

The shaft is assumed to be much longer with respect to the diameter than is indicated by the figure. It can be shown experimentally that cross sections perpendicular to the axis before loading remain plane and perpendicular to the axis after the loads T have been applied. The diameter of the bar is unchanged and radial lines remain straight and radial after twisting.

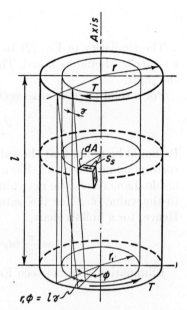

Fig. 3-1. Circular shaft twisted by torques at ends.

The only deformation in the bar is the rotation of the cross sections with respect to each other. As shown in Fig. 3-1, the bottom cross section has been rotated with respect to the top through the angle φ.

The sides of an element on the cylindrical surface of radius r_1 are unchanged in length, but the angles in the corners are changed by angle γ from their original 90° values. The element is thus stressed in pure shear. As shown by Fig. 3-1, $r_1\varphi = l\gamma$. Substitution of Hooke's law, $\gamma = s_s/G$, where G is the modulus of elasticity in shear, gives

$$s_s = \frac{\varphi G r_1}{l} \tag{1}$$

Since φ, G, and l are constants in Fig. 3-1, the value of the shearing stress s_s varies directly with the radius r_1.

If the portion of the bar above the element dA in Fig. 3-1 were removed, the torque of the shearing stress s_s, if integrated over the whole cross section, would be equal to the applied torque T. Hence,

$$T = \int_0^r s_s r_1 \, dA \tag{a}$$

The right side is multiplied and divided by r_1; by Eq. (1), ratio s_s/r_1 is a constant and can be removed from the integral. Thus

$$T = \int_0^r \frac{s_s}{r_1} r_1{}^2 \, dA = \frac{s_s}{r_1} \int_0^r r_1{}^2 \, dA = \frac{s_s}{r_1} J \tag{b}$$

In the last form of Eq. (b), the symbol J, called *polar moment of inertia*, has been substituted for the integral $\int r_1{}^2\, dA$.

The maximum value of the shearing stress occurs at the outer surface, where $r_1 = r$. Hence, from Eq. (b),

$$s_s = \frac{Tr}{J} = \frac{16T}{\pi d^3} \tag{2}$$

The similarity of Eq. (2) to Eq. (11) of Chapter 1 for bending stress, $s = Mc/I$, should be noted. The ratio J/r is called the *section modulus of the shaft*.

For a solid circular cross section,

$$J = \frac{\pi d^4}{32} = \frac{\pi r^4}{2} \tag{3}$$

It should be noted that the value of J for a circle is twice as great as the corresponding value of I. For a hollow shaft with outside diameter d_o and inside diameter d_i, the net value for the polar moment of inertia is equal to the value of J for the outer circle minus the J for the inner circle. Hence, for a hollow shaft,

$$J = \frac{\pi}{32}\left(d_o{}^4 - d_i{}^4\right) = \frac{\pi}{2}\left(r_o{}^4 - r_i{}^4\right) \tag{4}$$

Elimination of s_s between Eqs. (b) and (1) gives

$$\varphi = \frac{Tl}{JG} \tag{5}$$

This equation can be easily committed to memory when its analogy to Eq. (4), Chapter 1, $\delta = Pl/AE$, for axial deformation is noticed.

Angle φ is in radian measure. It should be recalled that $1°$ is equal to $\pi/180$ radian, or 1 radian $= 57.296°$.

In order that the foregoing equations may be valid in the neighborhood of the ends, moments T must be applied by means of stresses which vary in intensity with the distance from the axis. Since this condition rarely occurs in practice, Eq. (2) gives correct results only at cross sections somewhat removed from the points where loads T are applied.

Example 1. The shaft in Fig. 3-2 does not rotate; the loads are steady.

(a) Make a sketch for the element at A on the bottom surface of the shaft and show the values of the stresses.

(b) Do the same for the element at B at the elevation of the shaft axis.

Solution. (a) *Element at A.*

By Eq. (15), Chapter 1:

$$s = \frac{32M}{\pi d^3} = \frac{32 \times 3,500}{\pi 8} = 4,460 \text{ psi, tension}$$

By Eq. (2): $\quad s_s = \dfrac{16T}{\pi d^3} = \dfrac{16 \times 9,000}{\pi 8} = 5,730$ psi

If it is assumed that the shaft is cut at the right edge of the element, the given torque causes the shear stress s_s to have the direction shown in Fig. 3-2(b). The transverse shear stress for element A is equal to zero.

(b) *Element at B.* The torsional shear stress has the same value as in part (a). The transverse shear stress is found by Eq. (31) of Chapter 1.

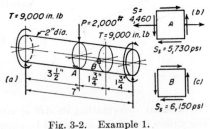

Fig. 3-2.   Example 1.

$$s_s = \frac{4V}{3A} = \frac{4 \times 1,000}{3\pi} = 420 \text{ psi}$$

If it is assumed that the shaft is cut at the right edge of the element, the transverse shear stress acting upon the element is directed upward. The total shear stress has the value shown in Fig. 3-2(c). The bending stress is zero for the element at B.

Example 2. A hollow shaft must carry a torque of 30,000 in-lb at a shearing stress of 8,000 psi. The inside diameter is to be 0.65 of the outside diameter. Find the value of the outside diameter.

Solution. $\qquad\qquad d_i = 0.65d_o$

In Eq. (4): $\qquad J = \dfrac{\pi}{32}(d_o{}^4 - 0.65^4 d_o{}^4) = 0.08065 d_o{}^4$

In Eq. (2): $\qquad J = \dfrac{30,000 \times 0.5 d_o}{8,000} = 0.08065 d_o{}^4$

$$d_o{}^3 = 23.2486$$

$$d_o = 2.854 \text{ in.}$$

Example 3. Suppose it is specified that the angular deformation in a shaft should not exceed $1°$ in a length of 6 ft. The permissible shearing stress is 12,000 psi. Find the diameter of the shaft. The material is steel.

Solution. $\qquad\qquad \varphi = 1° = \dfrac{\pi}{180}$ radian

By Eqs. (2) and (5): $\quad T = \dfrac{s_s J}{r} = \dfrac{\varphi J G}{l}$

or $\qquad\qquad r = \dfrac{s_s l}{\varphi G} = \dfrac{12,000 \times 72 \times 180}{11,500,000 \pi} = 4.305 \text{ in.}$

$$d = 8.609 \text{ in.}$$

Example 4. The shaft in Fig. 3-3 carries the torque of 10,000 in-lb at the location shown. If the ends of the shaft are fixed against rotation, find the values of the torque reactions T_1 and T_2.

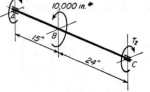

Solution.

Fig. 3-3. Example 4.

By Eq. (5), Ang. def. for AB: $\varphi_1 = \dfrac{15 T_1}{JG}$

By Eq. (5), Ang. def. for BC: $\varphi_2 = \dfrac{24 T_2}{JG}$

The angular deformation in AB is equal to the angular deformation in BC. The values for φ_1 and φ_2 should be equated.

$$15 T_1 - 24 T_2 = 0 \qquad\qquad (c)$$

By statics: $T_1 + T_2 = 10,000$

The equations above should now be solved simultaneously to give

$$T_1 = 6,154 \text{ in-lb}; \qquad T_2 = 3,846 \text{ in-lb}$$

2. Horsepower

Power is defined as the rate at which work is performed. The unit is the horsepower, which is equal to 33,000 ft-lb per minute. If a force of F pounds acts at a velocity of V feet per minute, the work done per minute is FV, and the equation for horsepower is

$$\text{hp} = \frac{FV}{33,000} \qquad\qquad (6)$$

In machinery where power is transmitted by shafting, it is necessary to transform Eq. (6) into angular dimensions. If force F is acting at radius r in. as shown in Fig. 3-4, the angular velocity, ω rad./sec, is equal to

$$\omega = \frac{V}{60} \times \frac{12}{r} = \frac{2\pi n}{60} \qquad\qquad (7)$$

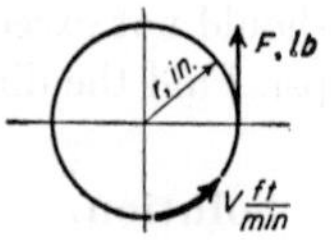

The value of V from Eq. (7) should now be substituted in Eq. (6) to give

Fig. 3-4. Relationships for deriving horsepower equations.

$$\text{hp} = \frac{T\omega}{12 \times 550} \qquad\qquad (8)$$

In Eq. (8) the product Fr has been replaced by torque T, which has dimensions in in-lb.

Velocity V in Fig. 3-4 is equal to

$$V = \frac{\pi dn}{12} \tag{9}$$

where n is rpm or revolutions per minute. When this substitution is made in Eq. (6) the following equation results.

$$\text{hp} = \frac{Tn}{63,025} \tag{10}$$

Torque T in this equation has dimensions in in-lb.

3. Maximum Static Shearing Stress

Many shafts carry combined loads of bending and torque. The bending moment M causes a normal stress in the axial direction of the shaft as shown by s in Fig. 3-5(a), and the torque T produces the shearing stress s_s. The normal stress in the y-direction, or at right angles to the shaft axis, is in general equal to zero. From the Mohr circle for this element, shown in Fig. 3-5(b), the value of the maximum shearing stress for static loading is given by the equation

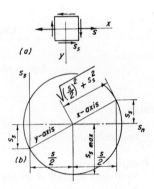

$$s_{smax} = \frac{0.5s_{yp}}{FS} = \sqrt{\left[\frac{s}{2}\right]^2 + s_s^2} \tag{11}$$

The equations for the stresses for a solid circular shaft,

Fig. 3-5.   Stresses on element of shaft surface.

$$s = \frac{32M}{\pi d^3} \quad \text{and} \quad s_s = \frac{16T}{\pi d^3} \tag{12}$$

should now be substituted into Eq. (11) to give the following equation for the maximum shearing stress for *static* loads.

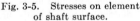

$$s_{smax} = \frac{0.5s_{yp}}{FS} = \frac{16}{\pi d^3}\sqrt{M^2 + T^2} \tag{13}$$

Substitution of $s_{smax} = 0.5s_{yp}/FS$ implies that the maximum shear theory of failure has been assumed to be applicable. This is in accord with Eq. (6) of Chapter 2.

4. ASME Code for Design of Transmission Shafting

Since the loads on most shafts in machinery are not constant, it is necessary to make proper allowance for the harmful effects of the fluctuation. The ASME Code for the Design of Transmission Shafting, B17c—1927, does this by inserting constants C_m and C_t into the equation for stress as follows:

$$s_{smax} = \frac{0.5s_{yp}}{FS} = \sqrt{\left(\frac{C_m s}{2}\right)^2 + (C_t s_s)^2} \tag{14}$$

or

$$s_{smax} = \frac{0.5s_{yp}}{FS} = \frac{16}{\pi d^3}\sqrt{(C_m M)^2 + (C_t T)^2} \tag{15}$$

where C_m = numerical combined shock and fatigue factor to be applied in every case to the computed bending moment

and C_t = the corresponding factor to be applied to the computed torque.

The recommended values for the shock and fatigue factors are given in Table 3-1. For rotating shafts, the bending stress s is not constant;

TABLE 3-1

Constants for ASME Code

Nature of Loading	Values for	
	C_m	C_t
Stationary shafts:		
Gradually applied load	1.0	1.0
Suddenly applied load	1.5–2.0	1.5–2.0
Rotating shafts:		
Gradually applied or steady load	1.5	1.0
Suddenly applied loads, minor shocks only	1.5–2.0	1.0–1.5
Suddenly applied loads, heavy shocks	2.0–3.0	1.5–3.0

it varies continuously from maximum tension to maximum compression as the shaft rotates. For steady loads, the table indicates that suitable compensation can be made for the alternating nature of the bending stress by using a value of 1.5 for C_m. If the shaft is hollow, factor $16/\pi d^3$ can be replaced by r/J, where r is the outside radius, and J is computed for the net area.

Example 5. Find the diameter by the ASME Code for a rotating shaft subjected to a maximum steady torque of 16,200 in-lb, and a steady bending moment of 27,000 in-lb. The shaft has a keyway.

Solution. $s_{smax} = 0.75 \times 8,000 = 6,000$ psi. See Section 20.

From Table 3-1: $C_m = 1.5$,   and $C_t = 1.0$

In Eq. (15): $d^3 = \dfrac{16}{6,000\pi} \sqrt{(1.5 \times 27,000)^2 + 16,200^2} = 37.026$

$$d = 3.333 \text{ in.}$$

Example 6. A 2 in. diameter rotating shaft carries a torque of 12,000 in-lb which may be applied suddenly and a bending moment of 8,000 in-lb which also may be applied suddenly. Material tests $s_{yp} = 70,000$ psi. Find the value of the FS by the ASME Code.

Solution. Assume $C_m = 2$ and $C_t = 1.5$.

By Eq. (15): $\dfrac{0.5 \times 70,000}{FS} = \dfrac{16}{\pi 2^3} \sqrt{(2 \times 8,000)^2 + (1.5 \times 12,000)^2}$

$$\frac{35,000}{FS} = \frac{2}{\pi} \times 24.083$$

or $FS = 2.28$

5. Maximum Shear Theory when Loads Are Fluctuating

It will now be shown[1] that the maximum shear theory of failure can be applied when the normal and shear stresses in a shaft are fluctuating. The loading for an element on the shaft surface is shown in Fig. 3-6. Stresses normal to the shaft axis are zero. It is assumed that the normal and shear stresses reach their maximum and minimum values simultaneously.

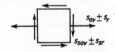

Fig. 3-6. Element loaded by fluctuating stresses.

Soderberg's Eq. (11), presented in Chapter 2, applied to the fluctuating normal stress of Fig. 3-6 gives the equivalent static normal stress s as

$$s = s_{av} + \frac{K s_{yp}}{s_e} s_r \tag{a}$$

The equivalent static shear stress s_s for Fig. 3-6 has the value

$$s_s = s_{sav} + \frac{K_t s_{yp}}{s_e} s_{sr} \tag{b}$$

Equations (a) and (b) are now substituted into Eq. (11) to give the resultant static shear stress s_{smax}.

$$s_{smax} = \frac{0.5 s_{yp}}{FS} = \sqrt{\frac{1}{4}\left(s_{av} + \frac{K s_{yp}}{s_e} s_r\right)^2 + \left(s_{sav} + \frac{K_t s_{yp}}{s_e} s_{sr}\right)^2} \tag{16}$$

or $s_{smax} = \dfrac{0.5 s_{yp}}{FS} = \dfrac{16}{\pi d^3} \sqrt{\left(M_{av} + \dfrac{K s_{yp}}{s_e} M_r\right)^2 + \left(T_{av} + \dfrac{K_t s_{yp}}{s_e} T_r\right)^2}$ (17)

[1] See reference 5, Bibliography; and p. 487 of reference 2.

Stress concentration factors for the appropriate change of form and type of loading can be determined from the curves of Chapter 2 and from Section 8 of this chapter.

The equations above apply to solid circular shafts. When a keyway is present at the section for which the calculations are made, the strength is reduced not only because of stress concentration but because of loss of cross section as well. A theoretical determination of this latter quantity would be very involved, but its magnitude may be estimated by the principles explained in Section 16. Perhaps the best way of taking care of the situation in a design is to use a lower value for the working stress in shear. Fortunately, the form of the equation is such that this correction could be considerably in error without causing very much difference in the resulting diameter of the shaft.

Example 7. Suppose the loads are the same as those given in Example 5 except $T_r = 0.1T_{av}$. Stress concentration is caused by a keyway and is equal to 1.35 for both bending and torque. Material tests $s_{ult} = 120,000$ psi; $s_{yp} = 100,000$ psi. The factor of safety equals 2. Let $s_e = 0.5s_{ult}$. Because of the keyway, let the working stress be reduced to 90 per cent of the value for a solid shaft. For an element on a rotating shaft, the average moment is zero.

Solution. $M_{av} = 0$, $M_r = 27,000$ in-lb

$$T_{av} = 16,200 \text{ in-lb}, \ T_r = 1,620 \text{ in-lb}$$

$$s_e = 0.5 \times 120,000 = 60,000 \text{ psi}$$

$$s_{smax} = 0.9 \frac{0.5 \times 100,000}{2} = 22,500 \text{ psi working stress}$$

In Eq. (17),

$$d^3 = \frac{16}{22,500\pi} \sqrt{\left[\frac{100}{60} \times 1.35 \times 27,000\right]^2 + \left[16,200 + \frac{100}{60} \times 1.35 \times 1,620\right]^2}$$

$$= \frac{16 \times 63,900}{22,500\pi} = 14.466$$

$d = 2.437$ in.

The use of a high-strength, heat-treated steel makes a considerable reduction in size possible. A smaller diameter shaft sometimes gives additional savings because smaller bearings can be used, and smaller hubs can be used as well on the shafts and pulleys. If the working stress is reduced to the extremely conservative value of 75 per cent of the stress for a solid shaft, the diameter for the example above comes out to be 2.589 in., or an increase of slightly more than $\frac{1}{8}$ in.

6. Mises-Hencky Theory for Shafting

For a shaft element loaded as in Fig. 3-6, Eq. (9) of Chapter 2 for average and range stress becomes

$$s'_{av} = \sqrt{s_{av}^2 + 3s_{sav}^2}$$

$$s'_r = \sqrt{s_r^2 + 3s_{sr}^2}$$

These are now substituted into Eq. (11) of Chapter 2 to obtain the equivalent static working stress in tension.

$$s = \frac{s_{yp}}{FS} = \sqrt{s_{av}^2 + 3s_{sav}^2} + \frac{Ks_{yp}}{s_e} \sqrt{s_r^2 + 3s_{sr}^2} \qquad (18)$$

Equations (12) are now substituted to give

$$s = \frac{s_{yp}}{FS} = \frac{16}{\pi d^3} \left[\sqrt{4M_{av}^2 + 3T_{av}^2} + \frac{Ks_{yp}}{s_e} \sqrt{4M_r^2 + 3T_r^2} \right] \qquad (19)$$

Example 8. Determine the required shaft diameter by the Mises-Hencky theory using the data in Example 7.

Solution. Substitution of the values for moments and torques should be made into Eq. (19).

Equivalent working stress in tension:

$$s = 0.9 \frac{s_{yp}}{FS} = \frac{0.9 \times 100,000}{2} = 45,000 \text{ psi}$$

Then,

$$d^3 = \frac{16}{45,000\pi} \left[\sqrt{3 \times 16,200^2} + \frac{1.35 \times 100}{60} \sqrt{4 \times 27,000^2 + 3 \times 1,620^2} \right]$$

$$= \frac{16}{45,000\pi} (28,060 + 2.25 \times 54,070) = 16.945$$

$$d = 2.569 \text{ in.}$$

7. Keys

Shafts and hubs are usually fastened together by means of keys. Several different kinds of keys are shown in Fig. 3-7. The square and flat type of keys are in wide use for general machine construction. Dimensions for square keys are given in Table 3-2. Kennedy keys are usually made tapered and are driven tightly into place upon assembly. They are adapted for rough, heavy service. The Woodruff key is much used in the

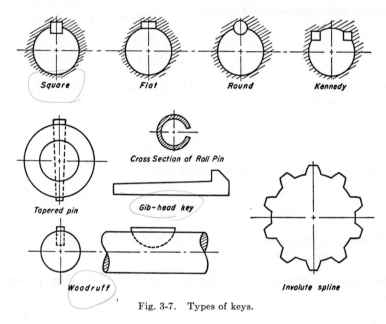

Fig. 3-7. Types of keys.

automotive and machine tool industries. The gib-head key facilitates removal, although the projecting head for some applications constitutes a hazard for workmen.

TABLE 3-2

Dimensions of Square Keys. ASA B17.1-1943

Dia. Shaft	Size Key	Dia. Shaft	Size Key	Dia. Shaft	Size Key
$\frac{1}{2}$ to $\frac{9}{16}$	$\frac{1}{8}$	$1\frac{7}{16}$ to $1\frac{3}{4}$	$\frac{3}{8}$	$3\frac{3}{8}$ to $3\frac{3}{4}$	$\frac{7}{8}$
$\frac{5}{8}$ to $\frac{7}{8}$	$\frac{3}{16}$	$1\frac{13}{16}$ to $2\frac{1}{4}$	$\frac{1}{2}$	$3\frac{7}{8}$ to $4\frac{1}{2}$	1
$\frac{15}{16}$ to $1\frac{1}{4}$	$\frac{1}{4}$	$2\frac{5}{16}$ to $2\frac{3}{4}$	$\frac{5}{8}$	$4\frac{3}{4}$ to $5\frac{1}{2}$	$1\frac{1}{4}$
$1\frac{5}{16}$ to $1\frac{3}{8}$	$\frac{5}{16}$	$2\frac{7}{8}$ to $3\frac{1}{4}$	$\frac{3}{4}$	$5\frac{3}{4}$ to 6	$1\frac{1}{2}$

In addition to a key, setscrews are usually employed to keep the hub from shifting axially on the shaft. Generally, two screws are placed in the hub: one screw bears on the key and the other bears on the shaft. For light service, rotation between shaft and hub may be prevented by setscrews alone.

Movement between shaft and hub can be prevented by a taper pin driven tightly into place. The so-called "roll pin" is not solid. It has the cross section shown in Fig. 3-7. It has sufficient flexibility to accommodate itself to small amounts of misalignment and variation in hole diameters, and will not come loose under vibrating loads.

For high-grade construction, and for cases where axial movement between shaft and hub is required, relative rotation is prevented by means of splines machined on the shaft and into the bore. One type of spline uses the involute curve as the outline. The spline on the shaft can be cut by a hobbing process similar to that used for cutting gears.

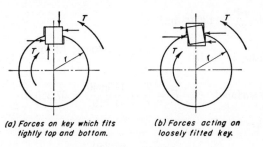

(a) Forces on key which fits   (b) Forces acting on
    tightly top and bottom.   loosely fitted key.

Fig. 3-8.   Forces on key.

Tables of dimensions for the foregoing machine elements may be found in engineering handbooks and catalogs of various supply houses.

The distribution of the force on the surfaces of a key is very complicated. It is dependent upon the fit of the key in the grooves of shaft and hub, as illustrated by Figs. 3-8(a) and (b), in which the distributed loads are represented by single arrows. In addition, the stresses are not uniform along the key in the axial direction; they are highest near the ends.

Because of many uncertainties, an exact analysis of the stresses usually cannot be made.[2] Engineers commonly assume that the entire torque is carried by a tangential force F located at the shaft surface. That is,

$$T = Fr \tag{20}$$

Shearing and compressive stresses are computed for the key from force F, and a sufficiently large factor of safety is employed.

Example 9. A $3\frac{7}{16}$ in. diameter shaft is made from material with a yield point value of 58,000 psi. A $\frac{7}{8}$ by $\frac{7}{8}$ in. key is to be used of material with a yield point value of 48,000 psi. Let $s_{syp} = 0.5s_{yp}$. The factor of safety is equal to 2.

Find the required length of key based on the torque value of the gross shaft.

[2] See reference 6, Bibliography.

Solution.

Shaft: $s_{yp} = 58,000$ psi, working stress, $s = \dfrac{58,000}{2} = 29,000$ psi

$s_{syp} = 29,000$ psi, working stress, $s_s = \dfrac{29,000}{2} = 14,500$ psi

Key: $s_{yp} = 48,000$ psi, working stress, $s = \dfrac{48,000}{2} = 24,000$ psi

$s_{syp} = 24,000$ psi, working stress, $s_s = \dfrac{24,000}{2} = 12,000$ psi

$$J = \frac{\pi d^4}{32} = 13.708 \text{ in.}^4$$

In Eq. (2), torque in shaft: $T = \dfrac{s_s J}{r} = \dfrac{14,500 \times 13.708}{1.719} = 115,650$ in-lb

Force at shaft surface: $F = \dfrac{T}{r} = \dfrac{115,650}{1.719} = 67,280$ lb

For length of key:

Based on bearing on shaft: $l = \dfrac{67,280}{29,000 \times 0.438} = 5.30$ in.

Based on bearing on key: $l = \dfrac{67,280}{24,000 \times 0.438} = 6.41$ in.

Based on shear in key: $l = \dfrac{67,280}{12,000 \times 0.875} = 6.41$ in.

8. Stress Concentration

Stress concentration factors[3] for a shaft with two diameters joined by fillets and loaded in torsion are given in Fig. 3-9. When a shaft has a transverse hole with a bending load, the stress concentration factors[4] are as shown in Fig. 3-10. The stress concentration factors[5] for a transverse hole and torsional loading are given in Fig. 3-11.

All stress concentration factors so far presented in this book are the geometric or full theoretical values. Section 17 of Chapter 2 discussed the fact that under fatigue loading the actual effect of stress concentration was usually less severe than indicated by the theoretical values.

[3] See reference 13, Bibliography.
[4] See reference 14, Bibliography.
[5] See reference 15, Bibliography.

The results of some tests to determine the fatigue strength reduction factors[6] for alternating bending stresses for shafts with keyways are given in Table 3-3. Two kinds of steel were used: a medium-carbon steel, and

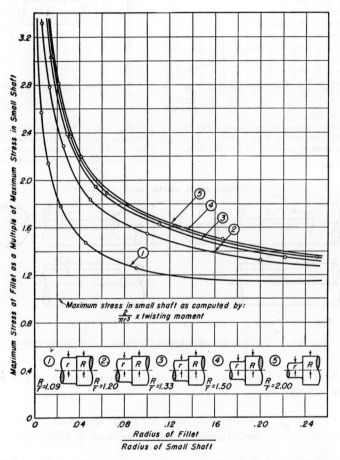

Fig. 3-9.   Torsional-stress concentrations in circular shafts of two diameters.

a heat-treated, chrome-nickel steel. Specimens tested were 1 in. in diameter with two types of keyways: sled runner and profile, which are shown in Fig. 3-12. In order to simulate conditions at an oil hole, tests were also made on carbon steel specimens with a $\frac{1}{4}$ in. transverse hole; the results are shown in Table 3-3.

[6] See reference 7, Bibliography.

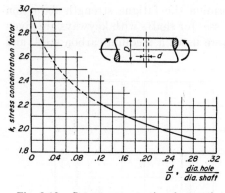

Fig. 3-10. Stress concentration factors for shaft with transverse hole loaded in bending. Based on section modulus of the net area.

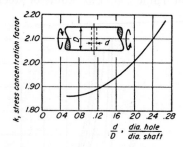

Fig. 3-11. Stress concentration factors for shaft with transverse hole. Torsional loading. Based on full cross-sectional area. No reduction for hole.

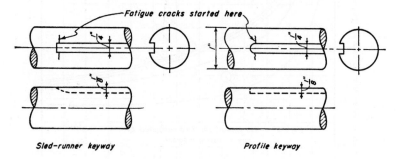

Fig. 3-12. Types of keyways tested for stress concentration effects.

For fluctuating loads, the fatigue stress concentration factor K is defined as follows:

$$K = \frac{\text{endurance limit for plain specimen}}{\text{endurance limit with keyway or hole}}$$

In these tests a fatigue crack started on the outer surface of the shaft near the end of the keyway. The results of the tests indicate that the sled runner keyway is preferable to the profile. It should also be noted that the heat-treated specimens had larger stress concentration factors than the plain carbon. As was mentioned in Section 17, Chapter 2, a heat-treated steel exhibits greater sensitivity to notch effects than does plain carbon steel. This fact unfortunately causes a reduction in the advantages which would otherwise be obtained by the use of a high-strength alloy steel. The tests also show that a designer should avoid locating an oil hole at a highly stressed point on a shaft.

TABLE 3-3

Fatigue Stress Concentration Factors in Bending for Shafts with Keyways Based on Section Modulus of Full Area

Steel	Tensile Strength, psi	Yield Strength, (Plastic Def. 0.2 per cent)	For Reversed Bending Stress	Chrome-Nickel Heat-treated		Medium-Carbon Normalized	
				Endurance Limit, psi	Stress Concentration Factor K	Endurance Limit, psi	Stress Concentration Factor K
Chrome-Nickel (About SAE 3140)	103,500	70,000	No keyway, or-dinary tapered specimen	58,000		37,000	
			Sled-runner key-way	36,000	1.61	28,000	1.32
Medium-Carbon (About SAE 1045)	80,000	45,000	Profile keyway	28,000	2.07	23,000	1.61
			$\frac{1}{4}$-in. transverse hole			12,100	3.06

Because of the lack of available data, Table 3-3 may also be used for the stress concentration factors for torsion in the equations of Sections 5 and 6.

9. Couplings (RIGID)

cannot take up angular missalienment

A wide variety of devices is available for connecting the ends of two shafts together. The solid coupling shown in Fig. 3-13 is a typical example. It is inexpensive and will withstand rough usage. Good alignment between the ends of the shafts is necessary, however, to avoid inducing bending stresses in the shafts or loads in the bearings.

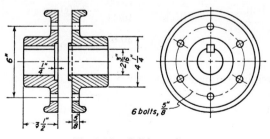

Fig. 3-13   Solid coupling.

Example 10. For the coupling shown in Fig. 3-13, the key is $\frac{1}{2}$ by $\frac{1}{2}$ in. The shaft carries a steady load of 50 hp at 150 rpm. For all parts, $s_{yp} = 60,000$ psi, and $s_{syp} = 30,000$ psi. Find the following stresses and the FS based on the yield point:

(a) Shear and bearing in key.
(b) Shear in bolts.
(c) Bearing on bolts in flange.
(d) Shear in flange at hub.

Solution. (a)

From Eq. (10): $\quad T = \dfrac{63,000 \text{ hp}}{n} = \dfrac{63,000 \times 50}{150} = 21,000$ in-lb

Tangential force at shaft surface: $\quad F = \dfrac{T}{r} = \dfrac{21,000}{1.094} = 19,200$ lb

Area in bearing for key $= 0.25 \times 3.25 = 0.8125$ in.^{2}

Compressive stress: $\qquad\qquad\qquad s_c = \dfrac{19,200}{0.8125} = 23,630$ psi

$$FS = \dfrac{60,000}{23,630} = 2.54 \text{ in bearing}$$

Area in shear for key $= 0.5 \times 3.25 = 1.625$ in.^{2}

Shearing stress in key: $\qquad\qquad s_s = \dfrac{19,200}{1.625} = 11,820$ psi

$$FS = \dfrac{30,000}{11,820} = 2.54 \text{ in shear}$$

(b) $\qquad$ Area in shear for bolts $= 6 \times \dfrac{\pi}{4} \times 0.625^2 = 1.841$ in.^{2}

Force at bolt circle: $\qquad\qquad F = \dfrac{21,000}{3} = 7,000$ lb

Shear stress in bolts: $\qquad\qquad s_s = \dfrac{7,000}{1.841} = 3,800$ psi

$$FS = \dfrac{30,000}{3,800} = 7.89$$

(c) $\qquad$ Area in bearing for bolts $= 6 \times 0.625 \times 0.625 = 2.344$ in.^{2}

Compressive stress on bolts: $\qquad s_c = \dfrac{7,000}{2.344} = 2,990$ psi

$$FS = \dfrac{60,000}{2,990} = 20.1$$

(d)   Area in shear at edge of hub $= 4.25\pi \times 0.625 = 8.345$ in.^{2}

$$\text{Force at edge of hub} = \frac{21,000}{2.125} = 9,880 \text{ lb}$$

Shear stress in web: $s_s = \dfrac{9,880}{8.345} = 1,180$ psi

$$FS = \frac{30,000}{1,180} = 25.4$$

Many types of flexible couplings are available which provide for some misalignment. Such couplings are often provided with springs or rubber inserts to cushion the shock of suddenly applied loads. Details, dimensions, and load ratings based on long experience may be found in the catalogs of the various manufacturers.[7] Information is also given in the mechanical engineering handbooks.

10. Bending Loads in Two Planes

Shafts are sometimes subjected to loads applied at different angles. To find the resulting bending moment at any cross section, it is necessary to have the components of the loads in two perpendicular axial planes. The following example illustrates a typical method for solving such problems.

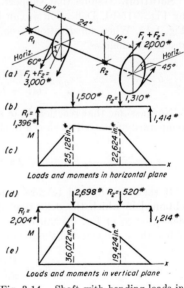

Example 11. Figure 3-14 shows a shaft with the belts making angles of 45° and 60° with the horizontal. Find the value of the maximum bending moment for the shaft.

Solution. The components of the belt forces in the horizontal plane and the corresponding bearing reactions are shown in Fig. 3-14(b). These loads give the bending moment diagram of sketch (c).

The loads and reactions for the vertical plane are given in Fig. 3-14(d), and the bending moment diagram is shown in sketch (e).

Fig. 3-14.   Shaft with bending loads in two planes. Example 11.

The maximum bending moment occurs at the left pulley and has the following value.

$$M_{max} = \sqrt{25,130^2 + 36,070^2} = 43.960 \text{ in-lb}$$

[7] See, for example, catalog pages listed under Couplings (Shaft) in reference 8, Bibliography. See also p. 152, reference 9.

11. Shaft on Three Supports

Shafts are sometimes supported on three bearings as illustrated in

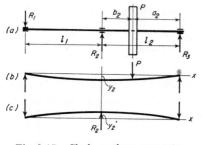

Fig. 3-15. Such a problem is statically indeterminate with three unknown reactions R_1, R_2, and R_3. It is possible to write only two independent equations from statics, one for the summation of the vertical forces and one for the summation of the moments. The additional equation required for a solution to the problem can be obtained by taking into account the deformation of the

Fig. 3-15.   Shaft on three supports.

body. This can be done in a variety of ways. The following example illustrates a typical method of solution.

Example 12. Derive the equation for reaction R_2 of Fig. 3-15.

Solution. Assume that support R_2 has been temporarily removed as shown by Fig. 3-15(b). Deflection y_2 can be found by the equation for y_1 in No. 7 of Fig. 1-15. When substitutions from Fig. 3-15(a) are made in this equation, the result is as follows.

$$y_2 = \frac{Pa_2l_1}{6(l_1 + l_2)EI} \, (l_2{}^2 + 2l_1l_2 - a_2{}^2) \tag{a}$$

Now assume that reaction R_2 of sketch (a) is acting, but that load P has been temporarily removed as shown in sketch (c).   Deflection y'_2 then is

$$y'_2 = \frac{2R_2l_1{}^2l_2{}^2}{6(l_1 + l_2)EI} \tag{b}$$

If sketches (b) and (c) are combined, the original shaft of Fig. 3-15(a) is obtained in which the deflection at R_2 is zero. In other words, the downward deflection y_2 of Eq. (a) must be equal to the upward deflection y'_2 of Eq. (b). When these are equated the following expression for R_2 results.

$$R_2 = \frac{Pa_2}{2l_1l_2{}^2} \, (l_2{}^2 + 2l_1l_2 - a_2{}^2) \tag{c}$$

Reactions R_1 and R_3, as well as other information concerning the shaft, can now be easily obtained by statics.

Example 13. In Fig. 3-15 let $a_2 = 20$ in., $l_1 = l_2 = 50$ in., $P = 300$ lb, and $EI = 26,000,000$ lb in². Find the value of R_2 if the elevation of the center bearing is made 0.05 in. lower than the others.

Solution. From the given conditions y'_2 in Fig. 3-15(c) will be 0.05 in. smaller than y_2 in Fig. 3-15(b). Hence

$$\frac{2R_2l_1{}^4}{6 \times 2l_1EI} + 0.05 = \frac{Pa_2l_1}{6 \times 2l_1EI} (l_1{}^2 + 2l_1{}^2 - a_2{}^2)$$

The given numerical data should now be substituted in this equation to give

$$R_2 = 108 \text{ lb}$$

When all bearings are at the same elevation, Eq. (c) gives a value for R_2 of 170.4 lb, a larger value than the 108 lb obtained above. Thus a small change in the geometry of the system made a relatively large change in the forces. This is characteristic of indeterminate structures, and care must be exercised in the manufacture and assembly of equipment where such a condition is present. This feature has been used to good advantage in the example above to effect a reduction in the force at the center bearing.

12. Crankshafts

In order to determine the stresses in a crankshaft, the loading on the separate parts of the mechanism must be secured. A typical example is shown in Fig. 3-16(a) which illustrates a single-cylinder, belt-driven air compressor. Suppose the dimensions of the machine are known, and it is desired to find the stresses in the cheek CD of the crankshaft. From the cylinder bore and the air pressure, the force on the piston can be found. By making a force triangle, the force in the connecting rod can be determined. This latter force also acts on the crankpin at A. As shown in Fig. 3-16(b), it is divided into components tangential and normal to the plane of the crank. The normal component gives the torque which the belt must exert at the given crank position. The forces in the tight and slack sides of the belt are now determined from the torque, and the sum is divided into components in the coordinate directions, as shown in Fig. 3-16(c).

The free-body diagram for the crank should now be made as shown in Fig. 16(d), utilizing the rod and belt forces, and with the bearing reactions determined by statics. It is customary to assume that the entire bearing load acts at the center of the bearing. The crank can now be cut apart, and the forces and moments for each portion can be determined in the usual way. Thus Fig. 3-16(e) shows the cheek after cutting at the mid-point between C and D with the various forces and moments that act on the cut surface.

Example 14. Let the bore of the compressor of Fig. 3-16 be 4.75 in., the stroke 6 in., and the length of rod 12 in. For a crank angle of 30°, the air pressure is 24.7 psi gage. The belt is horizontal with tension T_1 in the tight side three times as great as tension T_2 in the slack side. The coordinate system is as shown. Find the forces and moments for the cross section of the cheek midway between C and D.

Solution. Force on piston $= \dfrac{\pi}{4} \times 4.75^2 \times 24.7 = 437.7$ lb

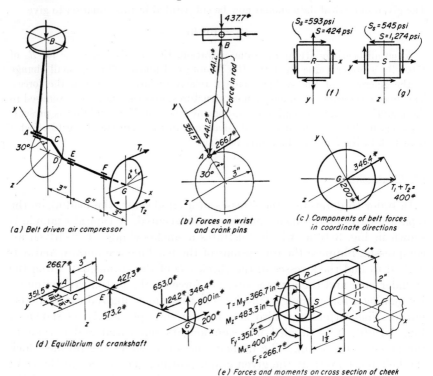

(a) Belt driven air compressor

(b) Forces on wrist and crank pins

(c) Components of belt forces in coordinate directions

(d) Equilibrium of crankshaft

(e) Forces and moments on cross section of cheek

Fig. 3-16.   Forces and moments for crankshaft. Example 14.

By taking components, the force in the rod is found to be 441.2 lb, as shown in Fig. 3-16(b). At the crank pin, the rod force divides into components 351.5 lb and 266.7 lb, tangential and normal, respectively, to the plane of the crank.

Torque on crank: $T = 266.7 \times 3 = 800$ in-lb

$$T = 4(T_1 - T_2) = 4(3T_2 - T_2) = 800 \text{ in-lb}$$

Hence $T_2 = 100$ lb

$T_1 = 300$ lb

The total belt load of 400 lb is now divided into components, as shown in Fig. 3-16(c).

The free-body diagram for the crank is shown in Fig. 3-16(d), in which the previously determined crank pin and belt loads are acting. The bearing reactions are determined in the usual way by taking moments.

The forces and moments for the desired cross section of the cheek are shown in Fig. 3-16(e). The reader should check the values shown thereon. Moment arms are the distances from the line of action of the force to the center of gravity of the cross section affected.

The arrows in Fig. 3-16(e) represent the resultant values for the forces and moments. Such loads actually are distributed as stresses in some fashion over the surface of the cheek where it was cut from the balance of the shaft. Because of the irregular shape of the crank, the stress equations previously derived may or may not be applicable. If the crank of Fig. 3-16 is of lightweight construction with relatively small-diameter pins, the equations might be valid for the cross section at the midpoint of the cheek. However, the stresses for large, massive crankshafts, such as those used in internal combustion engines, are usually determined experimentally by direct strain gage measurements.[8]

13. Critical Speed of Rotating Shaft

Rotating shafts become dynamically unstable at certain speeds, and large vibrations are likely to develop. The speed at which this phenomenon occurs is called a *critical speed*. It is shown in books on vibration theory that the frequency for free lateral vibration when the shaft is not rotating will be the same as its critical speed.

Vibration difficulties frequently arise at the lowest or fundamental critical speed. The equation[9] for finding this speed for a shaft on two supports is as follows.

$$f = \frac{1}{2\pi} \sqrt{\frac{g(W_1 y_1 + W_2 y_2 + W_3 y_3 + \cdots)}{W_1 y_1^2 + W_2 y_2^2 + W_3 y_3^2 + \cdots}} \text{ cycles/sec} \qquad (21)$$

where W_1, W_2, etc. represent the weights of the rotating bodies, and y_1, y_2, etc. represent the respective static deflections of the weights. The gravitational constant of 386 in./sec² is represented by g.

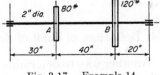

Example 15. Find the value of the fundamental critical speed for the shaft shown in Fig. 3-17. $E = 30,000,000$ psi.

Fig. 3-17 Example 14.

Solution. The static deflections at the weights can be found by the equations for No. 7 of Fig. 1-15.

$$I = \frac{\pi d^4}{64} = \frac{\pi}{4} = 0.7854 \text{ in.}^4$$

---

[8] See reference 10, Bibliography.
[9] See p. 92 of reference 16, Bibliography.

simply supported between weights otherwise this equation is no good.

At A, due to 80 lb: $y = \dfrac{80 \times 60 \times 30}{6 \times 90 \times 30,000,000 \times 0.7854} (90^2 - 60^2 - 30^2)$

$= 0.04074$ in.

At A, due to 120 lb: $y = \dfrac{120 \times 20 \times 30}{6 \times 90 \times 30,000,000 \times 0.7854} (90^2 - 20^2 - 30^2)$

$= 0.03848$ in.

Total deflection at A: $y = 0.04074 + 0.03848 = 0.07922$ in.

At B, due to 80 lb: $y = \dfrac{80 \times 30 \times 20}{6 \times 90 \times 30,000,000 \times 0.7854} (90^2 - 30^2 - 20^2)$

$= 0.02565$ in.

At B, due to 120 lb: $y = \dfrac{120 \times 20 \times 70}{6 \times 90 \times 30,000,000 \times 0.7854} (90^2 - 70^2 - 20^2)$

$= 0.03697$ in.

Total deflection at B: $y = 0.02565 + 0.03697 = 0.06262$ in.

In Eq. (21): $f = \dfrac{1}{2\pi} \sqrt{\dfrac{386(80 \times 0.07922 + 120 \times 0.06262)}{80 \times 0.07922^2 + 120 \times 0.06262^2}}$

$= 11.80$ cycles/sec

$n_{cr} = 11.80 \times 60 = 708$ rpm,   critical speed

The normal operating speed for a shaft should be considerably above or below the value of a critical speed.

It should be noted that Eq. (21) ignores the effect of the weight of the shaft and also assumes that all weights are concentrated. The equation does not take into account any effect of the flexibility of the bearings or supports. This additional flexibility may in some cases lower the value of the critical speed below that indicated by the equation.

A shaft will have as many critical speeds as there are rotating masses. The determination of the higher critical speeds is beyond the scope of this book.

14. Deflection of Shaft of Nonuniform Diameter

Another way to determine the deflection y of a shaft is by elastic energy. The equation is as follows.

$$EFy = \int \frac{M_p M_f \, dx}{I} \qquad (22)$$

As shown in Fig. 3-18, force F represents an auxiliary load placed on the shaft at point A where the deflection y is desired; M_p is the bending moment in terms of distance x for any general point B as caused by the actual loads P; M_f is the bending moment at B caused by the auxiliary load F. The modulus of elasticity of the material is represented by E; I is the moment of inertia of the cross section. The integration must extend throughout the entire volume of the shaft.

Equation (22) can be given a geometric interpretation[10] that eliminates the necessity of performing mathematical integrations. The integrand can be considered a solid with the three dimensions M_p/I, M_f, and dx, as shown in Fig. 3-19(a). If the moment diagrams for M_p and M_f consist of segments of straight lines, it is not necessary to consider a solid of thickness dx, but solids of finite lengths along the shaft can be taken and the

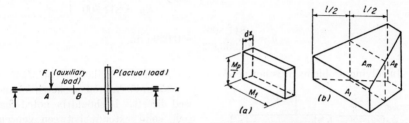

Fig. 3-18. Deflection of shaft by elastic energy.   Fig. 3-19. Deflection of shaft by elastic energy.

volumes found by solid geometry. When this is done for the full length of the shaft, the integration of Eq. (22) will have been performed.

Odd shaped solids will, in general, be present, and for these the prismoidal equation is useful.

$$\text{Vol.} = \frac{l}{6}\,(A_1 + 4A_m + A_2) \qquad (23)$$

As shown in Fig. 3-19(b), A_1 and A_2 refer to the end surfaces of the solid that are perpendicular to the centerline of the shaft. Length l refers to the distance between A_1 and A_2. Area A_m is the area of the cross section midway between A_1 and A_2. Note that in general it is not $(A_1 + A_2)/2$.

Equations (22) and (23) are especially useful when the shaft is non-uniform in diameter as illustrated by the following example.

Example 16. Find the deflection for point A where the diameter of the shaft of Fig. 3-20 changes. $E = 30,000,000$ psi.

Solution. The bending moment diagram for the P load is shown in Fig. 3-20(b). The values of the moments are divided by the corresponding values for I to give the M_p/I diagram of sketch (c). Let load F be taken as 1 lb acting at point A, as shown in sketch (d). This load has the bending moment diagram of sketch (e). The various solids formed by the M_p/I and M_f diagrams are given by sketch (f). The solid on each end is a pyramid with a volume equal to one-

[10] See reference 17, Bibliography.

third of the product of the base by the altitude. The prismoidal equation, however, must be applied to the solid in the middle. The calculations are as follows.

$$\frac{1}{3} \times 24 \times 31{,}280 = 250{,}250$$

$$\frac{18}{6} \, (18{,}340 + 4 \times 20{,}490 + 20{,}050) = 361{,}050$$

$$\frac{1}{3} \times 30 \times 20{,}050 = \underline{200{,}500}$$

$$Ey = 811{,}800$$

$$y = \frac{811{,}800}{30{,}000{,}000} = 0.0206 \text{ in.}$$

In solving problems, it is not necessary to make a sketch like (f). The M_pM_f/I values can be entered on sketch (e) and used directly. It should be noted that each solid extends between concentrated loads or points where the diameter changes.

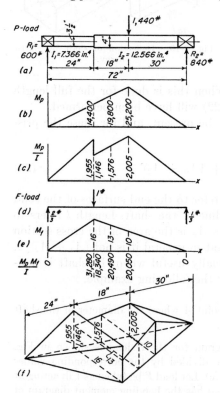

Fig. 3-20. Deflection of shaft of two diameters. Example 16.

15. Slope of Shaft by Elastic Energy

The slope of the shaft can also be found by elastic energy, but the auxiliary load must be a moment applied at the point where the slope is desired. Thus a moment M' is applied to the shaft at point A in Fig. 3-21. The M_f diagram is given by Fig. 3-21(c). Let θ be the rotation or change of slope at A caused

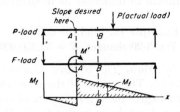

Fig. 3-21. Slope of shaft by elastic energy.

by load P. The external work from load M' due to rotation θ is then $M'\theta$. The expression for internal work is the same as that derived for Eq. (22).

The energy equation thus becomes

$$EM'\theta = \int \frac{M_p M_f \, dx}{I} \tag{24}$$

Moment M' is usually taken as 1 in-lb. Positive and negative signs must be observed as indicated by Fig. 3-21(c).

16. Torsion of Noncircular Shafts

It is sometimes necessary to make a design for a shaft of noncircular cross section. For example, the designer might have to know the torsional stress in the rectangular cheek of a crankshaft. Also, miscellaneous machine parts, such as brackets and supports, although not shafts, are sometimes loaded in torsion.

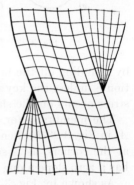

The theory of torsion for shafts of noncircular cross section is complicated because the assumptions which are valid for circular shafts do not apply. Cross sections are no longer plane and perpendicular to the shaft axis after twisting; rather, they are warped, as shown in Fig. 3-22, and the equations for the stresses are therefore more involved.

Complicated problems may be solved experi-

Fig. 3-22. Rectangular bar in torsion.

mentally by a method known as the *membrane analogy*.[11] A thin homogeneous membrane, such as a soap film, is stretched over a hole in a closed box. The hole is geometrically similar to the cross section of the shaft being studied. The film is slightly bowed by air pressure and the elevations of the resulting surface are measured. The measurements obtained will permit the contours, or lines of uniform elevations, to be plotted. For example, see Fig. 3-24(c). By mathematical analysis it can be shown that:

(1) The maximum shearing stress in the shaft has the same direction as the contour line at the corresponding point in the film.

(2) The maximum shearing stress at any point is proportional to the slope of the membrane at right angles to the contour at the corresponding point in the film.

(3) The torque carried by the shaft is proportional to twice the volume enclosed between the membrane and the plane of its base.

Although complicated problems can be solved by taking measurements on the membrane, experimental apparatus, which is rarely available to the designer, is required. Nevertheless, the idea of the membrane analogy is very useful since it gives a mental picture of the state of stress. The

[11] See p. 266 of reference 2; and p. 239 of reference 3, Bibliography.

designer can visualize the points of greatest slope, hence greatest stress, on the bowed film, and often, by making small changes in shape, can cause a reduction in stress.

For example, the membrane may have a steep slope, indicating a high stress at the internal corners of a keyway as shown in Fig. 3-23(a). The membrane analogy indicates that this stress concentration can be reduced

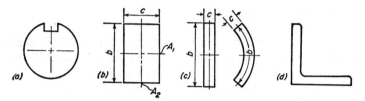

Fig. 3-23.   Typical cross sections of bars loaded in torsion.

by rounding off the bottom corners. However, as was mentioned in Section 8, unless the keyway runs the full length of the shaft, a still greater stress occurs on the shaft surface at the end of the keyway.

The membrane for a rectangular shaft has its greatest slope at point A_1 in Fig. 3-23(b); hence the stress is at a maximum at this point, and not at the corners, as is sometimes supposed. In the corner, the membrane has a zero slope along both edges, indicating a zero stress.

As shown by Fig. 3-23(c), the volume enclosed by the membrane for a thin, narrow, rectangular cross section is practically the same whether the rectangle is straight or formed into a curve. The torques carried by either section are the same. However, a slight concentration of stress will exist on the inner side of the curved section.

The volume enclosed by the membrane for a composite section, as in Fig. 3-23(d), is approximately equal to the sum of the volumes for the separate parts. Hence the membrane analogy permits the torque which such sections will carry to be found easily. However, a stress concentration will exist on the fillet in the re-entrant corner.

17. Torsion of Wide Rectangular Bar

As was previously mentioned, a mathematical solution for the stresses in a rectangular shaft is difficult to obtain. If the bar is very wide, however, the stress situation is much simplified. This is illustrated by Fig. 3-24(a), where it is assumed that side b of the cross section is much greater than width c. The membrane for this shaft has the contour lines shown in Fig. 3-24(c). These lines are practically straight and parallel to side b for almost the entire surface. Hence, except for small regions in the ends, the shearing stress is directed parallel to side b.

In accordance with the foregoing, the only stresses which act on an
element at an interior point A of the bar of Fig. 3-24(a) are those shown
in Fig. 3-24(b). The maximum value of the stress occurs on the long

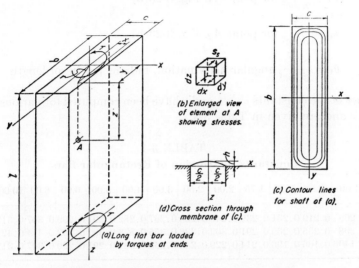

Fig. 3-24. Torsion of thin, wide, rectangular shaft.

side b of the cross section. It can be shown that the value of this stress
is given by the following equation.

$$s_{smax} = \frac{T}{0.333bc^2} \tag{25}$$

The angular rotation between two cross sections a unit distance apart is
given by the following equation

$$\theta_1 = \frac{T}{0.333Gbc^3} \tag{26}$$

One of the equations above should now be divided by the other, to
give

$$s_{smax} = Gc\theta_1 \tag{27}$$

Reference to Eq. (1) shows that the stress in the bar shown in Fig.
3-24(a) is twice as great as for a round bar of diameter c with equal **angular** deformation θ_1.

18. Torsion of Rectangular Bars, General Case

When side b of the cross section is not relatively great as compared with
width c, the foregoing equations cannot be used. For the bar in Fig. 3-22,

the general equations for stress and deformation may be written in the following forms:

$$s_s = \frac{T}{\alpha_1 bc^2} \text{ for point } A_1, \text{ Fig. 3-23(b)} \tag{28}$$

$$s_s = \frac{T}{\alpha_2 bc^2} \text{ for point } A_2, \text{ Fig. 3-23(b)} \tag{29}$$

$$\theta_1 = \frac{T}{\beta G bc^3} \text{ angular deformation, radians per in. of length} \tag{30}$$

Values of the constants α_1, α_2, and β have been computed for various ratios of b/c and are given in Table 3-4.

TABLE 3-4
Constants for Torsion of Rectangular Bars

b/c	1.00	1.20	1.50	1.75	2.00	2.50	3.00	4.00	5.00	6.00	8.00	10.00	∞
α_1	0.208	0.219	0.231	0.239	0.246	0.258	0.267	0.282	0.291	0.299	0.307	0.312	0.333
α_2	0.208	0.235	0.269	0.291	0.309	0.336	0.355	0.378	0.392	0.402	0.414	0.421	.....
β	0.1406	0.166	0.196	0.214	0.229	0.249	0.263	0.281	0.291	0.299	0.307	0.312	0.333

With the values from the table, computations can be made for the shear stress at the midpoint of both the long and the short sides, as well as the angular deformation, for rectangular cross sections starting from the square $b/c = 1$ to $b/c = \infty$. The maximum shear stress on the cross section occurs at the center A_1 of the long side, and is found by using α_1.

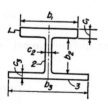

Fig. 3-25. Composite section loaded in torsion.

19. Composite Sections

The membrane analogy indicates that the torsional moment carried by a cross section consisting of a number of areas joined together is equal to the sum of the torques of the separate parts. The angle θ_1 applies to each of the parts as well as to the whole section. Therefore, the total torque T for the cross section of Fig. 3-25 is equal to the sum of the torques T_1, T_2, and T_3 for the separate parts 1, 2, and 3, respectively. Hence,

Torque carried by part 1: $T_1 = \theta_1 G \beta' b_1 c_1^3$

Torque carried by part 2: $T_2 = \theta_1 G \beta'' b_2 c_2^3$ \hfill (a)

Torque carried by part 3: $T_3 = \theta_1 G \beta''' b_3 c_3^3$

Adding: $T = \theta_1 G(\beta' b_1 c_1^3 + \beta'' b_2 c_2^3 + \beta''' b_3 c_3^3)$ \hfill (b)

Here β', β'', and β''' are the β values for parts 1, 2, and 3, respectively. It should be noted that the right-hand side of Eq. (b) will contain as many terms as there are rectangles in the cross section under consideration.

The maximum value of the shearing stress occurs in the bar of greatest width. Let this bar be No. 1 in Fig. 3-25. Hence, from Eq. (28),

$$s_{s1} = \frac{T_1}{\alpha_1 b_1 c_1^2} = \frac{\theta_1 G \beta' c_1}{\alpha_1} \tag{c}$$

Elimination of $\theta_1 G$ between Eqs. (b) and (c) gives

$$s_{s1} = \frac{T \beta' c_1}{\alpha_1 (\beta' b_1 c_1^3 + \beta'' b_2 c_2^3 + \beta''' b_3 c_3^3 + \cdots)} \tag{31}$$

The angular deformation per inch of length is found from Eq. (b).

$$\theta_1 = \frac{T}{G(\beta' b_1 c_1^3 + \beta'' b_2 c_2^3 + \beta''' b_3 c_3^3 + \cdots)} \tag{32}$$

As was previously mentioned, a concentration of stress exists at the re-entrant corners of a composite section. This factor depends upon the

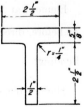

TABLE 3-5
Stress Concentration Factors for Structural Angle of Fig. 3-26*

r/c	0.125	0.25	0.50	0.75	1
K	2.5	2.25	2.00	1.85	1.80

* P. A. Cushman, Dissertation, University of Michigan, 1932.

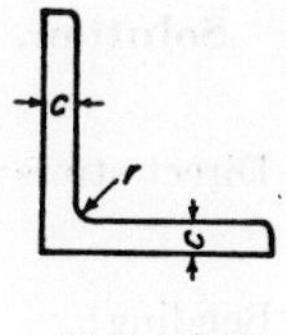

Fig. 3-26. Structural angle.

radius of the fillet and the width of the bars. Experimental data are very limited. However, stress concentration factors for the angle iron in Fig. 3-26 are given in Table 3-5.

Example 17. Find the torque which the long piece of T-bar shown in Fig. 3-27 can carry if the maximum shearing stress at the fillet is to be 12,000 psi. Approximate the stress concentration factor from Table 3-5.

Solution.

$$\frac{r}{c} = \frac{0.25}{0.625} = 0.4$$

From Table 3-5: $K = 2.10$

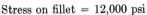

Stress on fillet = 12,000 psi

Fig. 3-27. T-bar. Example 17.

Stress on upper edge of horizontal bar: $s_s = \dfrac{12,000}{2.10} = 5,710$ psi

For horizontal bar: $\dfrac{b}{c} = \dfrac{2.5}{0.625} = 4$

Hence, $\alpha_1 = 0.282$ (from Table 3-4)

$\beta' = 0.281$ (from Table 3-4)

For vertical bar: $\dfrac{b}{c} = \dfrac{2.5}{0.50} = 5$

Hence, $\beta'' = 0.291$ (from Table 3-4)

In Eq. (31), $T = \dfrac{s_s \alpha_1 (\beta' b_1 c_1{}^3 + \beta'' b_2 c_2{}^3)}{\beta' c_1}$

$= \dfrac{5,710 \times 0.282(0.281 \times 2.5 \times 0.625^3 + 0.291 \times 2.5 \times 0.5^3)}{0.281 \times 0.625}$

$= 2,400$ in-lb

Example 18. Find the stresses at points R and S at the center of the sides of the cheek for the cross section midway between points C and D in Fig. 3-16.

Solution. Element at R:

Direct stress: $s = \dfrac{351.5}{2} = 176$ psi, compression

Bending: $s = \dfrac{6M}{bh^2} = \dfrac{6 \times 400}{1 \times 4} = 600$ psi, tension

The net tension of 424 psi is shown acting on the element in Fig. 3-16(f).

$$\frac{b}{c} = 2$$

From Table 3-4: $\alpha_2 = 0.309$

Shear stress, Eq. (29): $s_s = \dfrac{T}{\alpha_2 b c^2} = \dfrac{366.7}{0.309 \times 2 \times 1^2} = 593$ psi

This stress, properly directed, is also shown on the element in Fig. 3-16(f).
Element at S:

As before, direct stress. $s = 176$ psi, compression

Bending: $s = \dfrac{6M}{bh^2} = \dfrac{6 \times 483.3}{2 \times 1^2} = 1,450$ psi, tension

The net tension of 1,274 psi is shown on the element in Fig. 3-16(g).

$$\frac{b}{c} = 2$$

From Table 3-4: $\qquad\qquad\qquad \alpha_1 = 0.246$

Because of torque: $\quad s_s = \dfrac{T}{\alpha_1 bc^2} = \dfrac{366.7}{0.246 \times 2 \times 1^2} = 745$ psi

Because of transverse shear: $\quad s_s = \dfrac{3V}{2A} = \dfrac{3 \times 266.7}{2 \times 2} = 200$ psi

These shear stresses have opposite signs. The resultant, 545 psi, properly directed, is shown in Fig. 3-16(g).

20. Materials Used for Shafting

When service requirements are not too severe, the least expensive shaft material is hot-rolled, plain-carbon steel. For maximum machinability, a normalizing or annealing treatment may be necessary to improve the grain structure and to secure uniformity. Since hot-rolled bars as received from the mill are usually covered with scale, the shaft must be machined all over if a smooth surface is desired.

Cold drawn bars, in contrast, have a smooth, bright finish and have diameters held to tolerances of a few thousandths of an inch. This material is sometimes erroneously called cold rolled shafting. It is available in both plain carbon and alloy compositions, and is in wide use in the field of general power transmission, since the amount of machining required is a minimum. Cold drawing improves the physical properties; it raises the values for tensile strength and the yield point. When greater accuracy is required, shafting which has been turned and ground can be secured from the steel warehouses.

If greater strength is needed than can be secured by the use of a low-carbon steel in the as-rolled condition, a steel of somewhat higher carbon content can be used. After the machining has been completed, the tensile and yield strengths and hardness can be increased by a quenching and tempering heat treatment. To respond to quenching, the carbon content must be about 0.30 per cent or more. For forged shafts, such as are used in internal combustion engines and railroad cars, the carbon content is usually 0.45 per cent or 0.50 per cent. A widely used steel for such service is plain carbon steel 1045.

When service conditions are more severe, or when certain desirable physical properties are to be obtained, an alloy steel can be used. As a rule, such steels are not used unless the part is to be heat treated, since full advantage of the expensive alloying elements can be secured only in this way. When heat treated to high strength and hardness, alloy steels are tougher, more ductile, and better adapted to shock and impact loads than are plain carbon steels. The effect of the quenching penetrates deeper in alloy steels than in carbon steels, and a greater volume of the part is strengthened than if the hardening were confined to a shallow zone over the surface. Alloy steels warp and distort less in heat treatment, have less tendency to crack, and have smaller residual stresses than have carbon steels. Although practically all the alloy steels find application in the field of shafting, chromium-molybdenum steel 4140, and chromium-nickel-molybdenum steels 4340 and A8640 are in wide use as general purpose alloy steels.

For equal hardness, alloy steels are superior in machining qualities. Where considerable machining is required, shop costs can sometimes be reduced by use of a free cutting steel, such as 1137. This material is high in manganese and has a relatively high machinability rating for a heat-treating alloy steel.

If the service requirements demand resistance to wear rather than extreme strength, it is customary to harden only the surface of a shaft. The case hardening or carburizing process is in wide use. Carbon is absorbed by a relatively thin layer while the part is held at a red heat in the furnace. Low carbon alloy steels such as 4320, 4820, and A8620 are frequently used for carburizing. The cyaniding and nitriding processes are also used to produce a hard surface. Sometimes it is necessary to localize the wear to a relatively small area. The hardening treatment is applied to those surfaces requiring it; the remainder of the shaft is left in its original condition.

ASME Code B17c-1927 recommends that the working stress s_{smax} in shear be taken at 8,000 psi for "Commercial Shafting" but without any definite specifications for physical and chemical properties of the material. The ultimate strength of such steels may range from 45,000 psi to 70,000 psi. The corresponding elastic limits would be from 22,500 psi to 55,000 psi. When there is a keyway at the section for which the stress calculations are made, the working stress is to be reduced to 75 per cent of the value for a solid circular shaft. This reduction can be considered as making allowance for both loss of section and stress concentration.

For Diesel engine crankshafts "...we consider that 4500 is about the maximum allowable vibratory stress (for continuous running)...."[12]

BIBLIOGRAPHY

Volume number shown in **bold face** type. The number immediately following is the page on which the article begins.

1. Timoshenko, S., *Strength of Materials*, 2d ed., Vol. 1. New York: D. Van Nostrand Company, Inc., 1940.

2. Timoshenko, S., *Strength of Materials*, 2d ed., Vol. 2. New York: D. Van Nostrand Company, Inc., 1941.

[12] See Spaetgens, T. W., "Holzer Method for Forced-Damped Torsional Vibrations," *Trans. ASME*, **72**, APM 59 (1950).

3. Timoshenko, S., *Theory of Elasticity.* New York: McGraw-Hill Book Company, Inc., 1934

4. Roark, Raymond J., *Formulas for Stress and Strain,* 2d ed. New York: McGraw-Hill Book Company, Inc., 1943.

5. Soderberg, C. Richard, "Factor of Safety and Working Stress," *Trans. ASME,* **52**(1), APM-13 (1930); also **57,** A-106 (1935).

6. Solakian, Arshag G., and Karelitz, George B., "Photoelastic Study of Shearing Stress in Keys and Keyways," *Trans. ASME,* **54,** APM-97 (1932).

7. Peterson, R. E., "Fatigue of Shafts Having Keyways," *Proc. ASTM,* **32,** Part II, 413 (1932).

8 *ASME Annual Catalog and Directory.*

9 Nordenholt, Kerr, and Sasso, *Handbook of Mechanical Design.* New York: McGraw-Hill Book Company, Inc., 1942.

10. Gadd, C. W., and Van DeGrift, T. C., "A Short-Gage-Length Extensometer and Its Application to the Study of Crankshaft Stresses," *Trans. ASME,* **64,** A-15 (1942).

11. Norman C. A., and Stinson, K. W., "Angular Distortion of Crankshafts," *Bulletin 43,* Engineering Experiment Station, Ohio State University, 1928.

12. Timoshenko, S., "Torsion of Crankshafts," *Trans. ASME,* **44,** 653 (1922); also **45,** 449 (1923).

13. Jacobsen, L. S., "Torsional Stresses in Shafts Having Grooves or Fillets," *Trans. ASME,* **47,** 619 (1925); **57,** A-154 (1935).

14. Peterson, R. E., and Wahl, A. M., "Two- and Three-Dimensional Cases of Stress Concentration, and Comparison With Fatigue Tests," *Trans. ASME,* **58,** A-15, A-146 (1936). See also *Mech. Eng.,* **59,** 49 (1937).

15. Seely, F. B., and Dolan, T. J., "Stress Concentration at Fillets, Holes and Keyways as Found by the Plaster-Model Method," *Bulletin 276,* University of Illinois Experiment Station, 1935.

16. Timoshenko, S., *Vibration Problems in Engineering,* 2d ed. New York: D. Van Nostrand Company, Inc., 1937.

17. Spotts, M. F., "Critical Speeds of Shafts," *Product Engineering,* **12,** 20 (1941).

18. Macduff, J. N., and Felgar, R. P., "Vibration Design Charts," *Trans. ASME,* **79,** 1459 (1957).

PROBLEMS

1. A shaft carries a torque of 30,000 in-lb at a shearing stress of 8,000 psi. What is the diameter of the shaft? *Ans.* $d = 2.673$ in.

2. The torsional deformation of a steel shaft is to be 1° in a length of 2 ft when the shearing stress is equal to 10,000 psi. Find the diameter of the shaft.
Ans. $d = 2.392$ in.

3. Suppose it is specified that the deflection at the center of a simply supported shaft under its own weight should not exceed 0.010 in. per foot of span.

(a) Find the maximum permissible span for a 3 in. diameter steel shaft.

(b) Find the stress caused by its own weight when the span length is determined as in part (a).   *Ans.* $l = 13$ ft; $s = 2,300$ psi.

4. The bent bar $ABCDE$ in Fig. 3-28 lies in the horizontal plane and is simply supported at A and E. Angles at B and D are 90° each. Draw a view of the element lying on the top surface midway between C and D and show the values of the stresses. Mark the CD direction on your sketch. Dia. = 2 in.

           Ans. $s = 1,590$ psi; $s_s = 3,820$ psi.

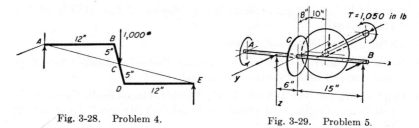

Fig. 3-28.   Problem 4.   Fig. 3-29.   Problem 5.

5. Make a free-body diagram for the unit consisting of shaft AB and disk C, see Fig. 3-29, and show all forces and torques necessary for equilibrium. Coefficient of friction $\mu = 0.3$. Sufficient force is exerted between the disks to develop the full coefficient of friction. The entire torque is carried by the torque reaction at A. Force reactions are applied at the bearings as shown.

6. Find the value of dimension b in Fig. 3-30 that causes the slope of the shaft to be zero at the bearings.   *Ans.* $b = 40$ in.

7. (a) Apply the equation for combined stress and find the value of the maximum shearing stress for the element at A in Fig. 3-2.

(b) If this shaft rotates, find the value of the maximum shearing stress by the ASME Code.   *Ans.*   (a) 6,150 psi; (b) 6,630 psi.

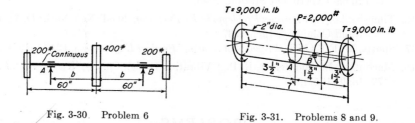

Fig. 3-30.   Problem 6   Fig. 3-31.   Problems 8 and 9.

8. Element at A in Fig. 3-31 is located on the bottom of the shaft; element at B is at the elevation of the shaft axis.

(a) Compute the value of the bending and shear stresses in directions parallel and perpendicular to the shaft axis for element at A. Draw a view of the element showing stress arrows and mark the value of each. Compute the value of the maximum shearing stress for this location on the shaft. Loads are steady and the shaft does not rotate.

(b) Repeat (a) for the element at B. Take into account the transverse shear for this location.

(c) Find the value of the maximum shear stress for the element at A for steady loads and a rotating shaft by ASME Code.　　　*Ans.* (c) 6,630 psi.

9. Work Problem 8 using Fig. 3-31 but with the length of the shaft not given. Find the value of length l which will make the maximum value of the shear stress at both elements equal. Take into account the transverse shear. The loads are steady and the shaft is nonrotating.　　　*Ans.* 7.05 in.

10. The shaft of Fig. 3-32 does not rotate, and is simply supported at A and B. The element at C is on the top surface; the element at D is at the elevation of the shaft axis.

(a) Draw a view of the element at C with sides parallel and perpendicular to the shaft axis; show arrows representing stresses, together with numerical values.

(b) Draw a view for the element at C, properly oriented with respect to the shaft axis, which has the maximum shearing stress. Show arrows and numerical values for all stresses acting.

(c) Work (b) for the element at D.　　　*Ans.* (b) $s_{smax} = 9,180$ psi.

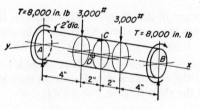

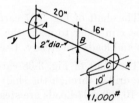

Fig 3-32.　Problem 10　　　　　　Fig. 3-33.　Problem 11.

11. The shaft of Fig. 3-33 is simply supported at A and B and is keyed against rotation at A.

(a) Draw a view of the element on the top surface of the shaft at B with sides parallel to the x- and y-axes. Show arrows and numerical values for all stresses acting.

(b) Draw the element at B properly oriented to give the maximum shearing stresses. Show arrows and numerical values for all stresses.
　　　　　　　　　　Ans. (b) $s_{smax} = 12,010$ psi.

12. Resistance-wire strain gages giving deformations at 45° with the shaft axis are attached at A and B in Fig. 3-34. Lead wires are carried from the gages through slip rings and brushes to electric instruments, which permit the deformations to be determined. The shaft carries torque only. Find its value if the elongation at A in x'-direction is 0.0006 in./in. positive, and if elongation at B in the y'-direction is the same amount but negative Draw a view of the element with sides parallel to the x- and y-axes and show stresses acting. Also draw a view for the element with sides parallel to x' and y'-axes $\mu = \frac{1}{3}$ $E = 30,000,000$ psi.
　　　　　　　　　　Ans $T = 21,200$ in-lb

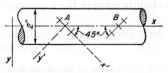

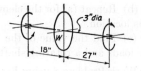

Fig. 3-34.   Problem 12.   Fig. 3-35.   Problem 13.

13. Find the permissible weight of the flywheel in Fig. 3-35 if the value of the maximum shearing stress in the shaft is to be 9,000 psi. The shaft rotates and carries a steady torque of 40,000 in-lb. Use ASME Code.   *Ans.* $W = 1,600$ lb.

14. How much torque will the shaft of Fig. 3-36 carry if the maximum shearing stress is not to exceed 8,000 psi? Loads are steady and the shaft rotates. Use ASME Code.   *Ans.* $T = 5,600$ in-lb.

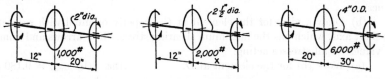

Fig. 3-36.   Problem 14.   Fig. 3-37.   Problem 15.   Fig. 3-38.   Problem 16.

15. The shaft of Fig. 3-37 carries a torque of 20,000 in-lb. What must be the distance x in order to make the maximum shearing stress 8,000 psi? The shaft rotates and loads are steady. Use ASME Code.   *Ans.* $x = 7.84$ in.

16. The shaft of Fig. 3-38 carries a torque of 50,000 in-lb. How large a hole may be drilled through the shaft so that the maximum shearing stress does not exceed 10,000 psi? Loads are steady and the shaft rotates. Use ASME Code.

Ans.   1.92 in.

17. A hollow shaft has a hole of diameter λd, where d is the outside diameter of the shaft, and λ is the appropriate constant. Show that the equation for the shearing stress by the ASME Code will be the same as Eq. (14) except that factor $(1 - \lambda^4)$ will appear in the denominator on the right-hand side.

18. What diameter hollow shaft is required to carry a bending moment of 16,200 in-lb together with a torque of 40,000 in-lb if the diameter of the hole is equal to 0.6 of the outside diameter of the shaft? Loads are steady and the shaft rotates. Maximum shearing stress equals 10,000 psi.   *Ans.* $d = 3.014$ in.

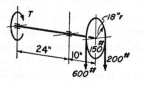

Fig. 3-39.   Problem 19.

19. Determine the required diameter for the hollow shaft of Fig. 3-39 having a hole diameter 0.6 as great as the shaft diameter. The maximum shear stress is to be 12,000 psi. The shaft rotates and loads are steady. Use ASME Code.   *Ans.* $d = 1.982$ in.

20. A hollow shaft has a hole of diameter λd_o, where d_o is the outside diameter and λ is a constant. Find the value of the ratio of d_o to the diameter d of a solid shaft for equal shearing stresses caused by the same torques for values of λ of 0.5, 0.55, and 0.6.   *Ans.* $d_o/d = 1.022$, 1.033, and 1.047.

21. What is the ratio of the weight of the hollow shaft per unit length to the weight of the solid for the foregoing values of λ? *Ans.* 0.783, 0.744, and 0.702.

22. Find the required shaft diameter (a) by the maximum shear theory, and (b) by the Mises-Hencky theory for the following conditions. The torque varies from zero to 12,000 in-lb. The bending moment varies from 6,000 to 10,000 in-lb. Stress concentration due to fillet for both bending and torque is equal to 2.5. The shaft does not rotate. The material tests $s_{ult} = 60,000$ psi and $s_{yp} = 40,000$ psi. Assume $s_e = 0.5s_{ult}$ and $s_{syp} = 0.5s_{yp}$. The factor of safety equals 2 based on yield point.   *Ans.* (a) 2.48 in., (b) 2.43.

23. The belt tensions for the pulleys of Fig. 3-40 fluctuate from the values shown in (a) to those given in (b). Details of shaft and hubs are shown in (c). Consider the stress concentration as being due to fillets only. Material tests $s_{yp} = 69,000$ psi and $s_{ult} = 104,000$ psi. Let $s_e = 0.5\ s_{ult}$, and $s_{syp} = 0.5\ s_{yp}$. Let $D/d = 1.33$ and $r/d = 0.125$. The factor of safety is 1.9 based on yield point.

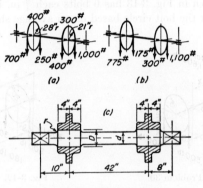

Fig. 3-40.   Problem 23.

Draw and dimension the bending moment diagram. Find the value of d (a) by the maximum shear theory, and (b) by the Mises-Hencky theory. Include the dead weight of the pulleys.   *Ans.* (a) 2.14 in., (b) 2.29 in.

24. Solve Problem 13, Fig. 3-35, by the maximum shear theory. Let the shaft be of uniform diameter, but let it have a keyway at the flywheel of the usual proportions with a stress concentration factor of 1.35. Let $s_e = 0.6s_{yp}$ for the shaft material. Take working stress equal to 90 per cent of the value for the shaft without a keyway.   *Ans.* $W = 640$ lb.

25. A $2\frac{1}{2}$ in. diameter shaft is made of 4140 steel normalized and tempered at 1000 F. The shaft rotates and carries a steady 2,500 lb load at the center of a 40 in. simply supported span. Average torque is 20,000 in-lb. Assume $T_r = 0.1T_{av}$. Let $K = K_t = 1.7$, and $s_e = 0.5s_{ult}$. On the basis of (a) the maximum shear theory and (b) the Mises-Hencky theory, find the FS for this shaft.
                              Ans. (a) $FS = 2.07$, (b) $FS = 1.75$.

26. A $2\frac{1}{2}$ in. diameter shaft has a key 0.625 by 0.625 in. The shaft material tests 60,000 psi at yield point. Let $s_{syp} = 0.5s_{yp}$. The factor of safety equals 2. The shaft fits into a cast-iron hub for which the working stress in compression is 18,000 psi. What length of key in the hub material will be required to carry the torque of the solid shaft? The key material is assumed to be amply strong.

                                                                    Ans. 6.55 in.

27. A 3 in. diameter shaft of material with a yield point value of 50,000 psi has a 0.75 × 0.75 × 5 in. key. What must the minimum yield point value be for the material in the key in order to transmit the torque of the shaft? The factor of safety equals 2. $s_{syp} = 0.5s_{yp}$.   *Ans.* 47,100 psi.

28. A square key has a diameter equal to one-fourth of the shaft diameter. The shaft and key are of materials which are equally strong with a yield point value in shear equal to one-half the yield point value in tension. Find the required length of the key in terms of shaft diameter necessary to transmit the shaft torque.   *Ans.* $l = 1.57d$.

29. A 3 in. diameter shaft is transmitting 400 hp at 600 rpm. A solid coupling similar to that shown in Fig. 3-13 has 6 bolts each $\frac{3}{4}$ in. in diameter. Find the required diameter of the bolt circle based on an average shearing stress of 4,000 psi in the bolts.   *Ans.* Dia. = 7.93 in.

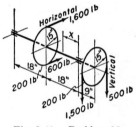

Fig. 3-41.   Problem 30.

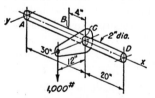

Fig. 3-42.   Problem 31.

30. Make the horizontal and vertical load and moment diagrams for the shaft shown in Fig. 3-41. Find the location and value of the minimum bending moment in the shaft for the portion lying between the left pulley and the right bearing.

                              Ans.   Min. $M = 17,050$ in-lb for $x = 7.88$ in.

31. Repeat Problem 30 for the shaft in Fig. 3-42. The minimum moment should be for the portion between the two pulleys.

                              Ans.   Min. $M = 10,540$ in-lb for $x = 19.96$ in.

32. The shaft shown in Fig. 3-43 is fixed at the ends. Find the reactions at the ends and the stresses in each portion of the shaft. Draw views of the elements for each portion and show the stresses acting.   *Ans.* $s_s = 17,190$ and 9,550 psi.

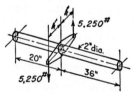

Fig 3-43   Problem 32

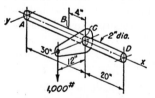

Fig. 3-44.   Problem 33.

33. The shaft in Fig. 3-44 is simply supported at A and D but is keyed against rotation at both points.

(a) Find reactions at the ends, and draw a view of the element at B on the top surface of the shaft. Show all stresses acting and their numerical values.

(b) Compute the value of the maximum shearing stress at B and the angle at which it acts. Make a view of the element properly oriented showing maximum shearing stresses acting as well as the normal stresses on all faces.

Ans. (a) $s_x = 13,240$ psi; $s_{xy} = 3,060$ psi.

34. The shaft in Fig. 3-45 is simply supported at A and C, but is keyed against rotation. Draw and dimension the bending moment diagram, and find all reactions at the ends.

Find the resultant stress from all causes for the elements on the top surface of the shaft at D and F. Do the same for the elements at E and G at the elevation of the center line. Draw sketches for the elements with arrows properly directed for the stresses and show numerical values.

Ans. At D, $s_s = 3,060$ psi; $s = 9,170$ psi.
At E, $s_s = 3,230$ psi; $s = 0$.

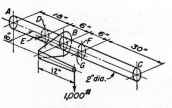

Fig. 3-45. Problem 34.

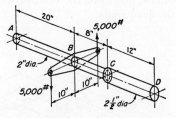

Fig. 3-46. Problem 35.

35. The shaft of Fig. 3-46 is built in at A and D. Find the value of the torque reactions at the ends. *Ans.* 39,230 in-lb; 60,770 in-lb.

36. The shaft of Fig. 3-47 is built in at A and D. Find the value of the torque reactions at A and D. *Ans.* 21,706 in-lb; 78,294 in-lb.

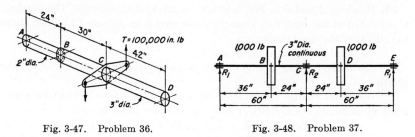

Fig. 3-47. Problem 36.

Fig. 3-48. Problem 37.

37. (a) Find the reactions, and draw and dimension the bending moment diagram for the shaft of Fig. 3-48. All bearings are on immovable supports at the same elevation. Include the effect of the dead load of the shaft. For the shaft, $E = 30,000,000$ psi; $\gamma = 0.283$ lb/in.³

(b) Find the values of the reactions if the bearing at C is $\frac{1}{8}$ in. lower than the others. Include the effect of the dead load of the shaft.

(c) Let the center support consist of a 6 in. I-beam, 12.5 lb per ft ($I = 21.8$ in.⁴), 12 ft long, simply supported with bearing C at its center. Find the reactions for the shaft, and draw and dimension the bending moment diagram. Neglect effects of the dead loads.

(d) What must the moment of inertia be for a beam supporting the bearing at C if the value of the bending moments, as caused by the 1,000 lb loads, at points B, C, and D, are to be equal? What will be the deflection of point C? Neglect effects of the dead loads.　　　　*Ans.*　(a) $R_1 = 253$ lb; $R_2 = 1,734$ lb.

(b) $R_1 = 460$ lb; $R_2 = 1,320$ lb.

(c) $R_1 = 398$ lb; $R_2 = 1,204$ lb.

(d) $I = 123$ in.⁴

38. (a) What moment of inertia would be required for the center beam of Fig. 3-49 if the bending moments for the shaft, as caused by the 1,000 lb loads, at points B, C, and D, are to be numerically equal? Neglect effects of the dead loads.

(b) If all three beams are 8 in. I-beams, 18.4 lb per ft, find the three bearing reactions, and draw the bending moment diagram for the shaft. Neglect effects of the dead loads.

Ans.　(a)　$I = 90.2$ in.⁴

(b) $R_1 = 278$ lb; $R_2 = 1,443$ lb.

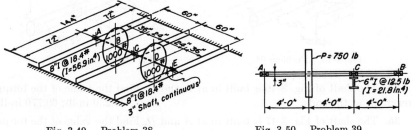

Fig. 3-49.　Problem 38.　　　　Fig. 3-50.　Problem 39.

39. Bearings A and B in Fig. 3-50 rest on unyielding supports. The bearing at C is located at the center of a simply supported 6 in. I-beam 12 ft long. Ignore the effects of the dead loads.

(a) Find reactions at A, B, and C.

(b) If the bearing at C is resting on an unyielding support, find the three reactions.

(c) What change in elevation of bearing C of part (b) must be made if bending moments in the shaft at load and at C are to be numerically equal?

Ans.　(a)　$R_a = 322$ lb; $R_c = 533$ lb; $R_b = 105$ lb downward.

(b) $R_a = 281$ lb; $R_c = 656$ lb; $R_b = 187$ lb downward.

(c) 0.039 in. higher.

40. A rotating shaft has the 1,000 lb centrifugal forces acting as shown in Fig. 3-51.

(a) Draw the bending moment diagram for the shaft. Note that large stresses are possible, even though bearing reactions are equal to zero.

(b) Suppose an additional bearing is placed in the center of the shaft. Find the reactions, and draw and dimension the bending moment diagram. Ignore the effect of the dead-load deflection. Note how the presence of the central bearing can affect the bearing loads of an engine crankshaft.

Ans. (b) Reactions; 427 lb downward, 854 lb upward, 427 lb downward.

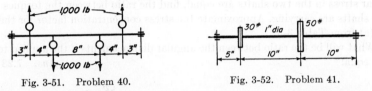

Fig. 3-51.   Problem 40.   Fig. 3-52.   Problem 41.

41. Find the lowest critical speed for the steel shaft shown in Fig. 3-52.
Ans. $n_{cr} = 1,700$ rpm.

42. The static deflection at the center of the steel shaft in Fig. 3-53 is equal to 0.0125 in. Find the value of the critical speed. *Ans.* $n_{cr} = 1,900$ rpm.

Fig. 3-53.   Problem 42.   Fig. 3-54.   Problem 43.

43. Find the value of the critical speed for the shaft of Fig. 3-54. Steel.
Ans. $n_{cr} = 617$ rpm.

44. Find the value of the critical speed for the shaft in Fig. 3-55. Steel.
Ans. $n_{cr} = 426$ rpm.

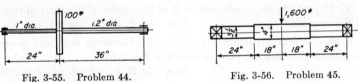

Fig. 3-55.   Problem 44.   Fig. 3-56.   Problem 45.

45. Find the deflection at the load and the slope at the end for the shaft shown in Fig. 3-56. Steel. *Ans.* $y_c = 0.0593$ in.; $\theta = 0.132°$.

46. Find the deflection at the load and the slope at the left end of the shaft in Fig. 3-57. Steel. *Ans.* $y = 0.0136$ in.; $\theta = 0.050°$.

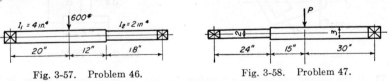

Fig. 3-57.   Problem 46.   Fig. 3-58.   Problem 47.

47. In Fig. 3-58, find the value of load P if the slope at the left bearing is 0.25°. Steel. *Ans.* $P = 776$ lb.

48. Find the torque which a long piece of $3 \times 3 \times \frac{1}{2}$ in. angle iron can carry if the maximum shearing stress at the fillet is 12,000 psi. The radius of the fillet is 0.5 in. *Ans.* $T = 2,880$ in-lb.

49. (a) What percentage more torque will a square shaft carry than a round shaft of the same diameter if both have the same unit stress?

(b) If the cost per pound is the same, what will be the percentage increase in cost of the square over the round shaft?   *Ans.* (a) 5.9%; (b) 27.3%.

50. Two pieces of shafting have the cross sections shown in Fig. 3-59. If the shear stress in the two shafts are equal, find the ratio between the torques which the shafts are carrying. Approximate the stress concentration factor for the shaft of (a) from Table 3-5.

What will be the ratio between the angular displacements if the applied torques are equal?   *Ans.* 7.23; 8.04.

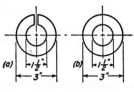

Fig. 3-59.   Problem 50.

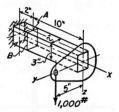

Fig. 3-60.   Problem 51.

51. The rectangular shaft in Fig. 3-60 is fixed at the wall.

(a) Cut the shaft at a point 2 in. from the wall, remove the portion to the right, and show all forces and moments on the end surface of the part that remains.

(b) Find the stresses from all causes on an element at A at the center of the top surface of the shaft at the cut. Take sides of the element parallel to the coordinate axes.

(c) Repeat (b) for an element at B at the center of the vertical side of the cut on the near side.   *Ans.* At A, $s_s = 1{,}550$ psi; $s = 3{,}330$ psi.

52. Work Problem 51, using Fig. 3-60, with the same data and dimensions except that shaft is now oriented as shown in Fig. 3-61.

Ans. At B, $s_s = 2{,}020$ psi; $s = 2{,}500$ psi.

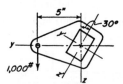

Fig. 3-61.   Problem 52.

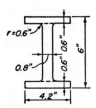

Fig. 3-62.   Problem 53.

53. If the torque applied to a long bar having the cross section shown in Fig. 3-62 is equal to 5,000 in-lb, find the value of the maximum shearing stress.

Ans. $s_s = 5{,}760$ psi.

54. The beam shown in Fig. 3-63 is simply supported but is keyed at the ends to prevent rotation.

(a) Find all reactions at the ends.

(b) Find the value of the maximum shearing stress due to torque.

(c) Find the angular rotation of the bracket in degrees.

$Ans.$ $s_s = 10,450$ psi; $\varphi = 0.416°$.

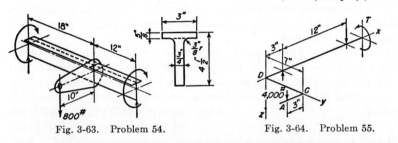

Fig. 3-63.   Problem 54.   Fig. 3-64.   Problem 55.

55. (a) Make an isometric drawing of the crankshaft shown in Fig. 3-64, and place all reactions thereon which are necessary for equilibrium.

(b) Cheek CD is rectangular in cross section, 2 in. wide in the x-direction, and 3 in. deep in the z-direction. Cut the cheek midway between C and D, and show all forces and moments acting on the cut surface.

(c) Draw the element at R lying at the midpoint of the top surface of the cheek with sides parallel to the coordinate axes, and show all stresses acting. Mark directions of the axes on the sketch.

(d) Repeat (c) for the element at S at the center of the near side vertical surface of the cheek.

(e) Suppose the loading consists of a force of 3,000 lb in the xy-plane acting to the left at A parallel to the y-axis. Find the bearing reactions for the shaft. Cut the cheek midway between C and D, and show all forces and moments acting on the cut surface.

(f) Draw the element at R showing all stresses acting.

(g) Draw the element at S showing all stresses acting.

$Ans.$ (c) $s = 4,667$ psi; $s_s = 3,717$ psi.

(d) $s = 0$; $s_s = 5,329$ psi.

56. The stroke of the air compressor shown in Fig. 3-65 is 3 in., and the length of the connecting rod is 5 in. Crank cheek CD is circular in cross section and is 1 in. in diameter. If the torsional shearing stress in the cheek is equal to 12,000 psi, find the value of the gas force on the piston. $Ans.$ Gas force = 3,320 lb.

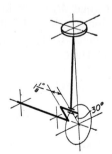

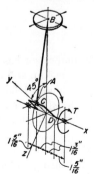

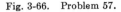

Fig. 3-65.   Problem 56.   Fig. 3-66.   Problem 57.

57. (a) The bore of the air compressor of Fig. 3-66 is 4 in., and the stroke is 6 in. The value of the air pressure is 300 psi gage for a crank angle of 45°. The length of the rod is 11 in. Axes x, y, and z are mutually perpendicular. The shaft is turned by a pure torque applied at the right bearing as shown. Make sketches similar to Figs. 3-16(b), (d), and (e) for this problem, and place the value of all necessary forces and moments thereon.

(b) The cheek is $\frac{7}{8}$ in. wide in the x-direction and $1\frac{3}{4}$ in. deep in the z-direction. Make an enlarged sketch for the element with sides parallel to the x- and y-axes lying at the center of the top surface of the cheek. Show all stresses acting.

(c) Repeat (b) for the element lying at the center of the right vertical side of the cheek. *Ans.* (b) $s = 15{,}370$ psi; $s_s = 5{,}060$ psi.

(c) $s = 6{,}990$ psi; $s_s = 7{,}910$ psi.

58. A belt-driven air compressor has the crank mechanism shown in Fig. 3-67. The axes x, y, and z are mutually perpendicular. The bore is 4 in.; stroke is 5 in.; length of the rod is 9 in. For a crank angle of 30° the air pressure is 100 psi gage.

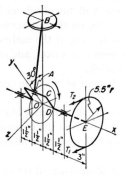

Fig. 3-67. Problem 58.

The belts are perpendicular to the axis OB of the cylinder. The tight-side tension is three times that of the slack side.

Make sketches similar to Figs. 3-16(b), (c), (d), and (e) for this problem, and place all necessary forces and moments thereon.

Ans. Axial force, $F_y = 322$ lb.

Transverse shear, $F_z = 698$ lb.

Moment, $M_x = 1{,}080$ in-lb.

Torque, $M_y = 797$ in-lb.

Moment, $M_z = 1{,}549$ in-lb.

59. An air compressor has a crank arrangement similar to that shown in Fig. 3-16. The stroke is 4 in. and length of the rod is 7 in. The crank cheek is circular in cross section, and is 1 in. in diameter. Distance AC is equal to $1\frac{1}{8}$ in. If the torsional shearing stress at the midlength of the cheek is equal to 10,000 psi for a crank angle of 30°, find the value of the gas force on the piston.

Ans. Gas force $= 2{,}792$ lb.

60. Find the deflection of the weight in Fig. 3-68. The bending moments are negligible since bearings are located close to the crank arms. Shafts and cranks lie in a horizontal plane. Ignore the effect of bending in cranks. The material is steel.

Ans. $\delta = 0.146$ in.

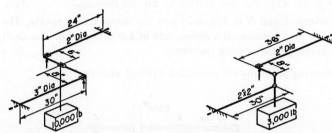

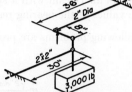

Fig. 3-68. Problem 60.   Fig. 3-69. Problem 61.

61. Find the deflection of the weight in Fig. 3-69. The shaft and beam lie in horizontal planes, and are built in at the walls. Bending in crank and shaft is negligible, as is the extension in link connecting the members together. All joints are frictionless. The material is steel.   *Ans.* $\delta = 0.244$ in.

62. Work Problem 61 but with the connection between the end of the crank and the beam replaced by a flexible member with a spring rate equal to 16,000 lb/in.   *Ans.* $\delta = 0.309$ in.

63. Find the three reactions for the shaft in Fig. 3-70. Assume the effect of the dead-load deflection of the beam to be negligible.

Ans. $13wl/16$; $33wl/16$; $wl/8$.

64. If reactions R_1, R_2, and R_3 of Fig. 3-70 have values of $15wl/16$, $27wl/16$, and $3wl/8$, respectively, find the amount that support R_2 is lower than R_1 and R_3. Ignore the effect of dead-load deflection of the shaft.   *Ans.* $\delta = wl^4/6EI$.

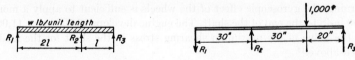

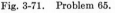

Fig. 3-70. Problems 63 and 64.   Fig. 3-71. Problem 65.

65. The three supports in Fig. 3-71 are all at the same elevation. Ignore the dead load of the shaft. Find the values of the three reactions.

Ans. $R_1 = 175$ lb, down; $R_2 = 680$ lb, up; $R_3 = 495$ lb, up.

66. The three supports in Fig. 3-72 are all at the same elevation. Ignore the dead load of the shaft. Find the values of the three reactions.

Ans. $R_1 = 422$ lb, down; $R_2 = 1{,}063$ lb, up; $R_3 = 359$ lb, up.

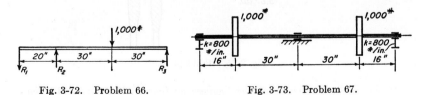

Fig. 3-72. Problem 66.   Fig. 3-73. Problem 67.

67. The center bearing in Fig. 3-73 rests on an immovable support. End bearings rest on structural beams with the spring rates shown. For the shaft, $EI =$ 7,200,000 lb in.[2] Find the load carried by an end bearing.   *Ans.*   391 lb.

68. Bearings A and B in Fig. 3-74 rest on immovable supports. The bearing at C rests on an I-beam with a spring rate of 5,000 lb per in. The shaft is steel. Find the values of the bearing reactions.   *Ans.* $R_3 = 295$ lb.

The following problems are presented without answers.

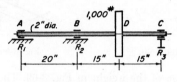

Fig. 3-74.   Problem 68.

69. Work Problem 19 except with the 10 in. dimension as 12 in. and 18 in. radius as 15 in.

70. Make a figure like that in Fig. 3-45 except that the 12 in. length becomes 16 in., and the 8 in. length becomes 7 in. Mark numerical values for all the reactions on the drawing. Draw and dimension the bending moment diagram for the shaft.

71. Work Problem 37(c) but with only one pulley, on the right, present. Find the values of the bearing loads.

72. Figure 3-75 shows a jet engine shaft with two overhung turbine wheels each weighing 85 lb. However, due to vertical acceleration, the shaft loading from the wheels should be considered as ten times as great. In addition, because of turning, the gyroscopic effect of the wheels is sufficient to apply a moment of 89,000 in-lb to the end of the shaft. The engine develops 16,500 hp at 11,000 rpm. Find the value of the maximum shearing stress in the shaft for the loading described above.[13]

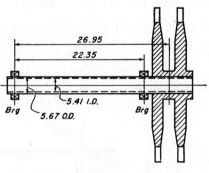

Fig. 3-75.   Problem 72.

[13] See Lewis, R. W., *General Motors Engineering Journal*, May–June, 40 (1955).

73. A Diesel locomotive weighing 250,000 lb is carried by four axles like those shown in Fig. 3-76. The material has a yield point of 48,000 psi and an endurance limit of 34,000 psi. Assume the locomotive is running on a straight level track. Let the torque in the shaft be determined from the tractive effort equal to the coefficient of friction of 0.3 times the weight equally distributed to all wheels. Assume the torque fluctuates plus and minus 10 per cent each way from the mean value. Wheel diameter is 40 in. If the stress concentration factor for the wheel seat fillet is 1.5, find the factor of safety for this point by the maximum shear theory of failure.[14]

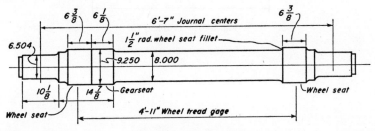

Fig. 3-76. Problem 73.

74. Find the deflection at point A in Fig. 3-77. Consider the bearings as simple supports.

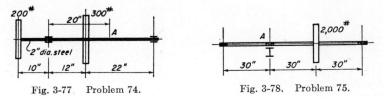

Fig. 3-77. Problem 74. Fig. 3-78. Problem 75.

75. In Fig. 3-78 the end bearings rest on immovable supports. The steel shaft, $I = 4$ in.[4] The beam is 9 ft long, simply supported, with the bearing at the center, $I = 18$ in.[4] Find the bearing load at A.

76. The numerical values for the bending moments at B, C, and D in Fig. 3-79 are equal. Find the difference in elevation between the bearing at C and those at A and E.

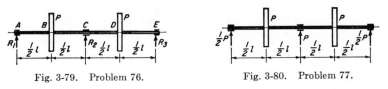

Fig. 3-79. Problem 76. Fig. 3-80. Problem 77.

77. The shaft of Fig. 3-80 has the bearing reactions shown. Find the change in elevation of the center bearing with respect to those at the ends.

[14] See Petersen, L., and Moreau, R. A., *General Motors Engineering Journal*, 2⅗ (May–June 1955).

78. Show that the deflection at the center of the shaft of Fig. 3-81 is given by the following equation.

$$y = \frac{P}{24E}\left[\frac{4a^3}{I_1} + \frac{b}{I_2}(8a^2 + 4ab + l^2)\right]$$

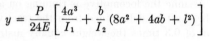

Fig. 3-81.   Problem 78.

4

Springs

WHEN flexibility or deflection in a mechanical system is specifically desired, some form of spring can be used. Otherwise, the elastic deformation of an engineering body is usually a disadvantage. Springs are employed to exert forces or torques in a mechanism or to absorb the energy of suddenly applied loads. Springs frequently operate with high

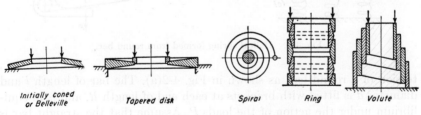

Initially coned   Tapered disk   Spiral   Ring   Volute
or Belleville

Fig. 4-1. Various types of springs.

values for the working stresses, and with loads which are continuously varying.

Helical and leaf springs are in widest use. A number of other types[1] such as Belleville, disk, spiral, ring, and volute springs are shown in Fig. 4-1.

[1] For design theories of such spring reference 3, Bibliography.

A, Area

c_1, spring index

d, diameter of wire

FS, factor of safety

E, modulus of elasticity

G, modulus of elasticity in shear

I, moment of inertia

J, polar moment of inertia

K_c, stress concentration factor due to curvature

k, spring rate

N, number of active coils

P, load

R, mean radius of helix

s_{yp}, yield point stress in tension

s_{ult}, ultimate tensile stress

s_s, shearing stress

s_{syp}, yield point stress in shear

$s_s'{}_e$, endurance limit in shear, zero to maximum stress

T, torque

δ, (delta) deflection of helical spring

1. Helical Springs

The equations for the stress and deformation of a closely coiled helical spring are derived directly from the corresponding equations for the

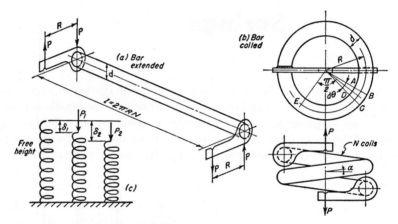

Fig. 4-2.   Helical spring formed from round bar.

torsion of a round bar, as shown in Fig. 4-2(a). The bar of length l and diameter d is fitted with brackets at each end of length R, and is in equilibrium under the action of the loads P. Assume that the straight bar is bent into the helix of N coils of radius R as shown in Fig. 4-2(b). The coiled bar is in equilibrium under the action of the two equal and opposite forces P.

The stress in the straight bar is shear caused by a torque equal to PR. The principal stress in the helix is also torsional shearing stress. From Eq. (2) of the preceding chapter, the stress in Fig. 4-2 is

$$\text{Torsional shearing stress} = \frac{Tr}{J} = \frac{16PR}{\pi d^3} \qquad \text{(a)}$$

After being coiled into the helix, the cross sections have an additional stress from the transverse shear. An exact analysis shows that this stress at the midheight has the value $1.23P/A$. Then

$$\text{Transverse shearing stress} = 1.23\frac{P}{A} = \frac{16PR}{\pi d^3} \times \frac{0.615}{c_1} \qquad \text{(b)}$$

where

$$c_1 = \frac{2R}{d} \qquad \text{(1)}$$

The total shearing stress s_s on the inside of the coil at the midheight from static load P is given by the sum of Eqs. (a) and (b).

$$s_s = \frac{16PR}{\pi d^3}\left(1 + \frac{0.615}{c_1}\right) \qquad \text{(2)}$$

By substitution of Eq. (1), this equation assumes the forms

$$s_s = \frac{8Pc_1}{\pi d^2}\left(1 + \frac{0.615}{c_1}\right) \qquad \text{(3)}$$

$$s_s = \frac{2Pc_1^3}{\pi R^2}\left(1 + \frac{0.615}{c_1}\right) \qquad \text{(4)}$$

The deflection of the spring can be found by considering the rotation of the cross sections with respect to each other caused by the torque PR. Assume temporarily that element $ABCD$ in Fig. 4-2(b) is flexible, but that the remainder of the spring is rigid. Thus, from Eq. (5), Chapter 3, the rotation $d\varphi$ of section CD with respect to the adjacent cross section AB is equal to

$$d\varphi = \frac{PR\,dl}{JG}$$

This rotation of the differential length of the spring causes point E, located 90° away, to be moved an amount equal to

$$d\delta = R\,d\varphi = \frac{PR^2\,dl}{JG}$$

The total deflection caused by the torque when the entire spring is elastic is found by integration of this equation over the entire length of the spring.

$$\delta = \frac{PR^2 l}{JG} = \frac{64PR^3N}{d^4G} \qquad \text{(5)}$$

The last form of Eq. (5) is obtained by substituting the equivalent values for l and J.

Substitution of Eq. (1) causes the equation above to assume the additional forms:

$$\delta = \frac{8Pc_1{}^3N}{dG} = \frac{4Pc_1{}^4N}{GR} \qquad (6)$$

An equation for the spring rate k, or the force required for a deflection of one inch, can be had by considering Fig. 4-2(c).

$$k = \frac{P_1}{\delta_1} = \frac{P_2}{\delta_2} = \frac{P_2 - P_1}{\delta_2 - \delta_1} \qquad (7)$$

Another equation for k can be had from Eqs. (5) and (6) by replacing P by k and δ by unity.

$$k = \frac{d^4G}{64R^3N} = \frac{dG}{8c_1{}^3N} = \frac{GR}{4c_1{}^4N} \qquad (8)$$

Example 1. A helical compression spring is made from 0.225 in. diameter wire, and has an outside coil diameter of 2 in. There are 8.6 active coils. Find the static load that will cause a shearing stress of 50,000 psi. Find the deflection of the spring.

Solution. $R = \frac{1}{2}(2.0 - 0.225) = 0.8875$ in.

By Eq. (1): $\quad c_1 = \dfrac{2R}{d} = \dfrac{2 \times 0.8875}{0.225} = 7.89$

By Eq. (2): $\quad 50{,}000 = \dfrac{16P0.8875}{\pi 0.225^3}\left(1 + \dfrac{0.615}{7.89}\right) = 428P$

$$P = 116.9 \text{ lb}$$

By Eq. (5): $\quad \delta = \dfrac{64 \times 116.9 \times 0.8875^3 \times 8.6}{0.225^4 \times 11{,}500{,}000} = 1.526$ in.

No allowance is made in the design for stress concentration because of curvature caused by loads which are static or by loads which may fluctuate only a small number of times during the expected life of the spring.

The average value of G for steels used for springs is equal to 11,500,000 psi.

Torsion bar springs similar to Fig. 4-2(a) are sometimes used. For example, the springs of motor buses can be arranged to run longitudinally along the sides of the bus beneath the floor.

If a helical compression spring is relatively long as compared with its diameter, danger of column action or lateral buckling may exist at loads smaller than the desired working load. Sometimes it is practical to prevent the buckling of a long compression spring by placing it over a loosely fitting bar or in a tube, which serves as a guide. Calculations for buckling loads can be made, but the theory is beyond the scope of this book.

2. Effect of End Turns for Compression Springs

Several different types of end turns used for helical compression springs are shown in Fig. 4-3. The equations are derived for springs assuming that the loading is axial—a condition difficult to secure in practice. The end coils produce an eccentric application of the load, increasing the stress on one side of the spring. Under certain conditions, especially where the number of coils is small, this effect must be taken into account.[2]

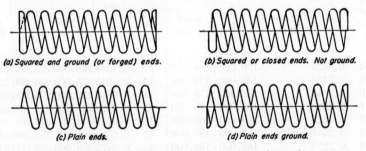

(a) Squared and ground (or forged) ends.   (b) Squared or closed ends. Not ground.

(c) Plain ends.   (d) Plain ends ground.

Fig. 4-3. Types of end turns used for compression springs.

The nearest approach to an axial load is secured by the spring shown in Fig. 4-3(a), where the end turns are squared and then ground perpendicular to the helix axis.

Equation (5) for the deflection requires the use of the proper number of active coils N. A deduction must be made from the total number of coils to take care of the turns at the ends which do not affect the deflection. It is impossible to say definitely just how much this deduction should be. However, an average value for the number of active coils, based on experimental results, is found by deducting 1.75 turns from the total number, tip to tip, when both ends are squared and ground as shown in Fig. 4-3(a). For plain ends, Fig. 4-3(c), the deduction from the total turns should be approximately one-half turn; and for plain ends ground, Fig. 4-3(d), the deduction should be one turn.

3. Properties of Spring Materials

Helical springs are either cold formed or hot formed depending on the size of the wire. Small sizes are wound cold, but when the bar has a diameter larger than about $\frac{3}{8}$ in., the spring is wound from a heated bar.

[2] See p. 159 of reference 3, Bibliography.

Three types of materials, as given in Table 4-1, are in wide use for cold-formed springs wound from prehardened wires. The material is plain carbon steel with a rather high carbon content. The effect of the drawing or heat treatment is more pronounced on the smaller sizes, as is reflected in the values for tensile strength. After winding, the spring is

TABLE 4-1

Diameters and Minimum Tensile Strengths of Steel Spring Wire for Cold-Formed Springs

W. & M. Gage No.*	Diam- eter in.	Min. Tensile Strength, psi			W. & M. Gage No.	Diam- eter in.	Min. Tensile Strength, psi		
		Music Wire	Oil Tem- pered	Hard Drawn			Music Wire	Oil Tem- pered	Hard Drawn
000	0.3625		180,000	168,000	12	0.1055	269,000	225,000	216,000
00	0.3310		182,000	172,000	13	0.0915	275,000	230,000	221,000
0	0.3065		183,000	175,000	14	0.0800	282,000	235,000	227,000
1	0.2830		184,000	178,000	15	0.0720	287,000	241,000	232,000
2	0.2625		185,000	180,000	16	0.0625	293,000	247,000	237,000
3	0.2437		187,000	183,000	17	0.0540	301,000	253,000	243,000
4	0.2253		188,000	186,000	18	0.0475	306,000	259,000	248,000
5	0.2070		190,000	190,000	19	0.0410	314,000	266,000	255,000
6	0.1920		195,000	192,000	20	0.0348	323,000	273,000	261,000
7	0.1770		200,000	195,000	21	0.0317	327,000	280,000	265,000
8	0.1620		205,000	200,000	22	0.0286	332,000		271,000
9	0.1483	253,000	210,000	203,000	23	0.0258	337,000		
10	0.1350	258,000	215,000	206,000	24	0.0230	343,000		
11	0.1205	263,000	220,000	210,000	25	0.0204	349,000		
Yield strength in tension		0.60 to 0.75 of tensile strength	0.70 to 0.85 of tensile strength	0.60 to tensile strength	These values are in approximate agreement with the following specifications. For music wire, ASTM Spec. A228-51 For oil-tempered wire, ASTM Spec. A229-56 For hard drawn wire, ASTM Spec. A227-47				

For torsion, use 0.60 of corresponding value for tensile strength.
* Washburn and Moen gage is used for steel spring wire.

given a stress-relieving heat treatment at about 525 F for 30 minutes. Music wire is usually used when the wire diameter is less than 0.032 in. Cold-formed springs are generally wound with values for the spring index c_1 between 5 and 10.

Information on the torsional properties of spring materials is usually lacking, and the designer is forced to base his calculations on the tensile strength. A reasonable figure is to take 0.6 of the tensile yield point for the yield point stress in torsion.[3] A factor of safety of 1.5, based on the torsional yield point, has been recommended for helical springs with static or infrequently repeated loading under normal temperatures. This factor might be made somewhat more or less depending on the conditions prevailing for each particular design.

Long experience with springs has shown that higher stresses can be used with smaller size wires because of the relatively deeper penetration of the hardening due to drawing. Recommended working-stress values for helical springs of good-quality spring steel are given in Table 4-2.[4]

TABLE 4-2

Recommended Working Stresses in Shear, psi, Steel Helical Compression Springs

Wire Diameter, in.	Severe Service	Average Service	Light Service
Up to 0.085	60,000	75,000	93,000
0.085 to 0.185	55,000	69,000	85,000
0.186 to 0.320	48,000	60,000	74,000
0.321 to 0.530	42,000	52,000	65,000
0.531 to 0.970	36,000	45,000	56,000
0.971 to 1.500	32,000	40,000	50,000

For phosphor bronze use 50 per cent of the foregoing.

Stress concentration factors must be employed when these stress values are used. Values from the table do not apply under conditions of corrosion and high temperatures. Severe service covers fatigue conditions of continuously varying load where the maximum stress is at least twice the minimum. However, if the spring carries a steady load, or is subjected to but few stress cycles during its normal life, the service would be considered light. The values in Table 4-2 are conservative, and might be increased somewhat if it is known definitely that overloads cannot be imposed on the spring, and if no other harmful condition is present.

Example 2. A helical compression spring of oil-tempered wire is to carry a maximum load of 40 lb. The mean radius of the helix is 0.5 in. The factor of safety is 1.5. Find a suitable standard size diameter of wire. Assume $s_{yp} = 0.75s_{ult}$ and $s_{syp} = 0.6s_{yp}$.

Solution. Assume tentatively a No. 11 wire.

By Table 4-1, $d = 0.1205$ in., $s_{ult} = 220,000$ psi

$$s_{syp} = 0.75 \times 0.60 \times 220,000 = 99,000 \text{ psi}$$

[3] See reference 11, Bibliography.
[4] See reference 11, Bibliography.

Permissible stress: $\qquad s_s = \dfrac{s_{syp}}{FS} = \dfrac{99,000}{1.5} = 66,000$ psi

By Eq. (1): $\qquad c_1 = \dfrac{2R}{d} = \dfrac{1}{0.1205} = 8.3$

By Eq. (2), actual stress: $\quad s_s = \dfrac{16 \times 40 \times 0.5}{\pi 0.1205^3} \left(1 + \dfrac{0.615}{8.3}\right) = 62,530$ psi

The assumed wire size is satisfactory.

Example 3. A helical compression spring of music wire has a maximum load that is 4 lb greater than the minimum load. The deflection under the maximum load is 0.25 in. greater than the deflection under the minimum load. Assume tentatively that the number of active coils is 10. Let $s_{yp} = 0.6 s_{ult}$ and $s_{syp} = 0.6 s_{yp}$. The factor of safety is 1.5. $R = 0.25$ in.

Determine a suitable standard size wire, and find the exact number of active coils. Find the initial deflection of the spring.

Solution.

By Eq. (7): $\quad k = \dfrac{4}{0.25} = 16$ lb per in.

By Eq. (8): $\quad d^4 = \dfrac{64 \times 0.25^3 \times 10 \times 16}{11,500,000} = 0.0000128, \quad d = 0.0598$ in.

By Table 4-1, use No. 16 wire, $d = 0.0625$ in., $s_{ult} = 293,000$ psi.

$$s_{syp} = 0.6 \times 0.6 \times 293,000 = 105,500 \text{ psi}$$

Working: $\qquad s_s = \dfrac{105,500}{1.5} = 70,320$ psi, working stress

By Eq. (1): $\qquad c_1 = \dfrac{0.50}{0.0625} = 8$

By Eq. (2): $\quad 70,320 = \dfrac{16P_2 0.25}{\pi 0.0625^3} \left(1 + \dfrac{0.615}{8}\right) = 5,616P_2$

$$P_2 = 12.5 \text{ lb}, \quad P_1 = 8.5 \text{ lb}.$$

By Eq. (8): $\qquad N = \dfrac{d^4 G}{64 R^3 k} = \dfrac{0.0625^4 \times 11,500,000}{64 \times 0.25^3 \times 16} = 11.0$ active coils

By Eq. (7): $\qquad \delta_1 = \dfrac{P_1}{k} = \dfrac{8.5}{16} = 0.532$ in.

Cold-formed springs can also be wound from plain carbon or alloy steel wire in the annealed condition. Afterwards the spring is heat treated to develop suitable strength values.

Compression springs are sometimes wound with considerably greater free height and pitch of coil than is desired. They are then compressed solid several times, which permanently sets the final height at the desired position. This operation is known as presetting or cold setting, and reduces the tendency of the spring to take a permanent set in service. The yield point is exceeded, and residual stresses are retained in the material with a sign opposite to those produced by normal operation. Such a residual stress permits a spring to carry larger loads than one in which the material was originally stress free.

Helical springs made of $\frac{3}{8}$ in. bar and larger are usually hot wound to avoid the high residual stresses which would be induced by cold forming.

TABLE 4-3

Tensile Strength of Heat-Treated Steels for Hot-Formed Springs. $1\frac{5}{8}$ in. Diameter Specimens Quenched and Drawn at Temperatures Shown

Draw Temp. F	1095 Plain Carbon		6150 Chromium-Vanadium		8660 Chromium-Nickel-Molybdenum		9262 Silico-Manganese	
	Ultimate	Yield	Ultimate	Yield	Ultimate	Yield	Ultimate	Yield
850	192,000	128,000	220,000	203,000	206,000	193,000	243,000	212,000
950	188,000	120,000	198,000	185,000	190,000	170,000	214,000	182,000
1050	172,000	107,000	180,000	168,000	171,000	150,000	188,000	156,000
1150	151,000	92,000	162,000	152,000	150,000	129,000	167,000	137,000

For torsion, use 0.60 of corresponding tensile value.

After forming, the spring is heat treated by quenching and tempering to produce the desired physical properties. Both plain carbon and alloy steels are used for hot-formed springs. The materials in widest use[5] are shown in Table 4-3. Compositions for these steels are given in Chapter 14.

Plain carbon steel 1095 is in wide use because of its availability and low cost. This material, however, is shallow hardening, and sections larger than $\frac{3}{8}$ in. will not harden completely through. To obtain depth of hardening and a material with a higher yield point, an alloy steel must be used, even though the cost is greater. Silico-manganese steel 9262 has been widely used as a low-priced alloy spring material. It has the disadvantages of being subject to decarburization in heat treatment and of being inclined to have excessive quantities of nonmetallic inclusions as well as a poor surface. Because of its higher cost, chromium-vanadium steel 6150 is being supplanted by other steels. Use of chromium-nickel-molybdenum steel 8660 is increasing because of its many desirable quali-

[5] See references 6 and 12, Bibliography.

ties such as good impact resistance, freedom from decarburization and surface defects, and relatively low cost. Alloy steels in general undergo less permanent set in service than plain carbon steels, and are better suited to impact conditions, especially for service conditions where the surface of the spring becomes scratched and pitted.

Since most failures are caused by fatigue, a poor surface is the worst handicap of hot formed springs. Figure 4-4 shows a typical fatigue failure of a helical spring. A fatigue crack usually starts at a surface imperfection in a region of stress concentration. The endurance-limit stress for steel bars in the as-rolled condition may be from 30,000 to 45,000 psi for both plain carbon and low alloy steels. If the surface is badly pitted, the endurance limit may be as low as 18,000 psi to 20,000 psi. These values for actual springs are thus seen to be much lower than the endurance limit for the same material when polished specimens are tested in the laboratory. A layer of decarburized material on the surface, resulting from the heat treatment, is also a source of weakness since the endurance limit for the surface may then be less than the working stress for the spring. Decarburization can be avoided if the heat treatment is conducted in a controlled atmosphere. Corrosion, even in a mild form, greatly reduces the fatigue strength. Cadmium plating offers some degree of relief against corrosion.

Fig. 4-4. Fatigue failure of helical spring. (*From Wahl*, "Mechanical Springs," *Penton Publishing Co. p. 31.*)

Shot peening, which leaves the surface in compression, has proved to be very successful in raising the fatigue life of springs.[6] A good surface can also be secured by the use of ground stock and controlled atmospheres, but the costs are relatively high. Such a surface, however, will be spoiled if the spring is subjected to rough usage.

If the spring operates under conditions of elevated temperature, there is a danger of creep or permanent deformation unless very low stress values are used.[7] Such effects become noticeable above 350 F, and the ordinary spring steels cannot be used at temperatures above 400 F. Stainless steel of the 18-8 type resists high temperature better than other spring steels. For temperatures of 500 to 800 F, high-speed steel (18W, 4Cr, 1V) must be used.

For low-temperature service, the alloy steels, listed in Table 4-3, are

[6] See reference 7, Bibliography.
[7] See reference 8, Bibliography.

in use. Failure under impact loads at low temperatures can frequently be guarded against by providing a stop to limit the deflection to a safe value.

Many special type springs for appliances and other products are stamped from flat stock.[8] For high stresses and severe service conditions, the sheared edges of flat springs must be polished to prevent the formation of fatigue cracks.

Springs are also made from a variety of nonferrous metals.[9] Some of these materials have the desirable qualities of good electric conductivity and resistance to corrosion. Mechanical properties for such materials are given in Chapter 14.

4. Design for Fluctuating Loads

If the loading on the spring is continuously fluctuating, due allowance must be made in the design for fatigue and stress concentration. The

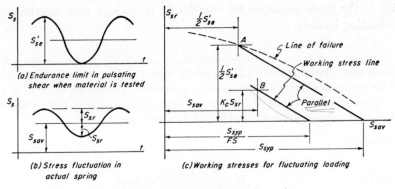

Fig. 4-5. Working stress diagram for springs.

working-stress triangle, as explained in Chapter 2, is modified because spring materials are usually fatigue tested, not in reversed bending, but in pulsating shear s'_{se}, zero to maximum, as shown in Fig. 4-5(a). For such test loading, the range stress is equal to the average, which is one-half the value of the maximum stress. Thus the straight line approximating the line of failure can be drawn from point A in Fig. 4-5(c). The line giving actual working stresses is parallel to this line and can be drawn after dividing the yield point stress in shear s_{syp} by the factor of safety FS

[8] See reference 14, Bibliography.
[9] See reference 15, Bibliography.

The stress concentration factor K_c for curvature can be calculated by the following equation.[10]

$$K_c = \frac{4c_1 - 1}{4c_1 - 4} \tag{9}$$

The range stress s_{sr} as determined by Eqs. (2), (3), or (4) for range load P_r is multiplied by K_c before plotting in Fig. 4-5(c).

As is customary when designing for fluctuating loading, stress concentration is ignored when the average stress s_{sav}, as determined by the average load P_{av}, is plotted. It is also assumed that the residual stresses from coiling and from eccentric application of the load are small enough to be neglected.

By making a proportion of corresponding sides of similar triangles in Fig. 4-5, the following equation can be written.

$$\frac{K_c s_{sr}}{\frac{s_{syp}}{FS} - s_{sav}} = \frac{\frac{1}{2}s'_{se}}{s_{syp} - \frac{1}{2}s'_{se}} \tag{10}$$

This is the basic equation for the design of springs with continuously fluctuating loading.

Example 4. A helical compression spring, made of No. 4 wire, carries a fluctuating load. Material tests[11] 120,000 psi for torsional yield strength, and 100,000 psi for endurance limit in shear, zero to maximum. The spring index is 6, and the factor of safety is 1.5. If the average load on the spring is 180 lb, find the permissible values for the maximum and minimum loads.

Solution.

From Eq. (1):
$$R = \frac{6 \times 0.2253}{2} = 0.676$$

By Eq. (9):
$$K_c = \frac{4 \times 6 - 1}{4 \times 6 - 4} = 1.15$$

By Eq. (2):
$$s_{sav} = \frac{16 \times 180 \times 0.676}{\pi 0.2253^3}\left(1 + \frac{0.615}{6}\right)$$
$$= 59{,}730 \text{ psi}$$

By Eq. (10):
$$\frac{1.15 s_{sr}}{\dfrac{120{,}000}{1.5} - 59{,}730} = \frac{50{,}000}{120{,}000 - 50{,}000}$$

From which:
$$s_{sr} = 12{,}590 \text{ psi}$$

---

[10] See Chapter 2 of reference 3, Bibliography.
[11] See reference 5, Bibliography.

Then:
$$P_r = \frac{s_{sr}}{s_{sav}} P_{av} = \frac{12,590}{59,730} \times 180 = 37.9 \text{ lb}$$

Then:
$$P_2 = 180 + 37.9 = 217.9 \text{ lb}$$
$$P_1 = 180 - 37.9 = 142.1 \text{ lb}$$

The reader should plot a figure similar to Fig. 4-5(c) for this problem and check the stress values above by measuring lengths on the diagram.

5. Vibration or Surging of Helical Springs

A sudden compression of the end of a helical spring may form a compression wave that travels along the spring and is reflected at the far end. The material in the compressed wave is subjected to higher stresses which may cause early fatigue failure. The natural frequency[12] for a round trip of the wave is given by the following equation.

$$f = \frac{d}{2\pi R^2 N} \sqrt{\frac{Gg}{32\gamma}} \quad \text{cycles/sec} \qquad (11)$$

Here g represents the acceleration constant of gravity, 386 in./sec², and γ represents the weight in lb per cu in. for the material of the spring.

For a steel spring, $G = 11,500,000$ psi and $\gamma = 0.285$ lbs/in.³ The equation above then becomes

$$f = \frac{3,510d}{R^2 N} \quad \text{cycles/sec} \qquad (12)$$

Example 5. Find the lowest natural frequency for a valve spring of No. 4 steel wire with 10 active coils and mean diameter of helix of 2 in.

Solution.　　　　$R = 1$ in.

By Table 4-1:　　　$d = 0.2253$ in.

In Eq. (12):　　　$f = \dfrac{3,510 \times 0.2253}{1^2 \times 10} = 79.1$ cycles/sec

$$= 4,745 \text{ cycles/min}$$

A spring can exhibit higher modes of vibration whose frequencies are $2, 3, 4 \cdots$, times the value given by Eqs. (11) and (12).

6. Commercial Tolerances

Sizes of helical springs are not standardized. They must therefore be made to order. Production costs can be kept low if liberal tolerances for

12 See Chapter 13 of reference 3, Bibliography.

dimensions and loading are allowed. Tolerances for commercial grade springs are rather wide and can be found by the following equations;[13] the necessary constants are given in Table 4-4. Free height is represented by l_1.

$$\text{Free length tolerance} = \pm T_1 c_1 l_1 \tag{13}$$

$$\text{Coil diameter tolerance} = \pm 2 T_2 R \tag{14}$$

$$\text{Spring rate tolerance} = \pm (T_3 + T_4) K \tag{15}$$

$$\text{Load tolerance} = \pm (T_4 + T_5) P \tag{16}$$

$$\text{Squareness tolerance} = \psi, \text{ degrees}$$

The use of the equations above is illustrated by the following example.

TABLE 4-4

Constants for Computing Tolerances of Commercial Springs

l_1	T_1	d	T_2	T_4	N	T_3	$\dfrac{l_1}{\delta}$	T_5	$\dfrac{4R^2}{l_1 d}$	ψ, deg
0.4	0.0092	0.010	0.0485	0.0490	2	0.0560	1.1	0.0200	0.5	1.62
0.7	0.0073	0.020	0.0367	0.0435	3	0.0480	1.5	0.0269	0.7	1.72
1.0	0.0063	0.030	0.0314	0.0405	4	0.0430	2	0.0353	1	1.84
1.5	0.0054	0.040	0.0278	0.0385	5	0.0395	3	0.0512	2	2.09
2	0.00477	0.060	0.0238	0.0360	6	0.0368	4	0.0675	3	2.24
3	0.00405	0.080	0.0210	0.0342	8	0.0330	5	0.083	4	2.36
4	0.00362	0.100	0.0194	0.0330	10	0.0303	6	0.098	5	2.45
5	0.00332	0.150	0.0164	0.0307	15	0.0260	8	0.129	6	2.54
6	0.00306	0.200	0.0147	0.0293	20	0.0233	10	0.159	8	2.66
7	0.00288	0.300	0.0125	0.0273	25	0.0214	13	0.203	10	2.76
8	0.00274	0.400	0.0113	0.0260	30	0.0200	16	0.247	12	2.85
10	0.00250	0.500	0.0103	0.0250	40	0.0180	20	0.303	15	2.96

Data by Spring Manufacturers' Association, Inc.

Example 6. A spring of No. 11 steel wire is wound with a mean diameter helix of 1 in. Free height is to be 3.75 in. and the spring rate is 35 lb per in. Find the tolerances on the dimensions and on the spring rate. Spring must operate at loads of 17.5 and 61 lb. Find the expected tolerances for these loads.

Solution. By Table 4-1: $\qquad d = 0.1205$ in.

By Eq. (8): $\qquad N = \dfrac{d^4 G}{64 R^3 k} = \dfrac{0.1205^4 \times 11,500,000}{64 \times 0.5^3 \times 35} = 8.66$ coils

By Eq. (1): $\qquad c_1 = \dfrac{2R}{d} = \dfrac{2 \times 0.5}{0.1205} = 8.3$, spring index

[13] See reference 16, Bibliography.

By Table 4-4· $T_1 = 0.0037$, $T_2 = 0.018$, $T_3 = 0.032$, $T_4 = 0.032$

By Eq. (13):   Free length tol. $= \pm 0.0037 \times 8.3 \times 3.75 = \pm 0.115$ in.

By Eq. (14):   Coil diameter tol. $= \pm 2 \times 0.018 \times 0.5 = \pm 0.018$ in.

By Eq. (15):   Spring rate tol. $= \pm (0.032 + 0.032) \times 35 = \pm 2.24$ lb/in.

For 17.5 lb load: $\delta = \dfrac{P}{k} = \dfrac{17.5}{35} = 0.5$ in., $\dfrac{l_1}{\delta} = \dfrac{3.75}{0.5} = 7.5$, $T_5 = 0.122$

By Eq. (16),   Load tol. $= \pm (0.032 + 0.122) \times 17.5 = \pm 2.70$ lb

For 61 lb load: $\delta = \dfrac{61}{35} = 1.743$ in., $\dfrac{l_1}{\delta} = \dfrac{3.75}{1.743} = 2.15$, $T_5 = 0.038$

By Eq. (16):   Load tol. $= \pm (0.032 + 0.038) \times 61 = \pm 4.27$ lb

$$\frac{4R^2}{l_1 d} = \frac{4 \times 0.5^2}{3.75 \times 0.1205} = 2.21$$

By Table 4-4: $\psi = 2.1°$, squareness tolerance

Tolerances should be specified as widely as the proper functioning of the spring permits, especially for those dimensions that are not critical. Tolerances must be greater for large hot-wound springs. Loads should always be specified at a fixed length, not for a given deflection. Testing mechanisms function in this manner. Testing to a definite load with tolerance on the deflection is slow and costly. The modulus of elasticity in shear, particularly for nonferrous materials, may vary over a considerable range. The diameters of spring wires are also subject to variations as shown in Table 4-5.

TABLE 4-5
Spring Wire Diameter Tolerances, Plus or Minus, Inches

Diameter, in.	Music Wire	Hard Drawn Oil Tempered
0.026 and under	0.0003	
0.027 to 0.063	0.0005	
0.028 to 0.075		0.001
0.064 to 0.250	0.001	
0.076 ot 0.375		0.002
0.376 and up		0.003

Example 7. Suppose a helical spring is wound from commercial wire which is found to be 3 per cent larger than the specified diameter d. Spring index $= 5$.

(a) To what radius helix must the spring be wound in order to maintain the original value of the deflection? What will the shearing stress be in the resulting spring?

(b) Suppose, in using this 3 per cent oversize wire, it had been desired to retain the original shearing stress. Find the radius of helix to which the spring should be wound, and the resulting deflection.

Solution. (a) Let the new radius of helix be called R_1, and the new diameter of wire be called d_1, where $d_1 = 1.03d$.

From Eq. (5):
$$\frac{64PR^3N}{d^4G} = \frac{64PR_1^3N}{d_1^4G}$$

$$R_1^3 = \frac{d_1^4}{d^4} R^3 = \frac{(1.03d)^4}{d^4} R^3 \quad \text{or,} \quad R_1 = 1.04R$$

New spring index:
$$c'_1 = \frac{2R_1}{d_1} = \frac{2 \times 1.04R}{1.03d} = 1.01c_1 = 5.05$$

Original stress:
$$s_s = \frac{16PR}{\pi d^3}\left(1 + \frac{0.615}{5}\right) = 5.7194\frac{PR}{d^3}$$

New stress:
$$s'_s = \frac{16PR_1}{\pi d_1^3}\left(1 + \frac{0.615}{c'_1}\right) = \frac{16P1.04R}{\pi(1.03d)^3}\left(1 + \frac{0.615}{5.05}\right)$$

$$= 5.4386\frac{PR}{d^3}$$

$$\frac{\text{Original } s_s}{\text{New } s_s} = \frac{5.4386}{5.7194} = 0.95$$

The radius of helix must thus be made 4 per cent larger than the original radius, which gives a stress 95 per cent as great as the original.

(b)

New spring index:
$$c'_1 = \frac{2R_1}{d_1} = \frac{2R_1}{1.03d} \times \frac{R}{R} = \frac{c_1R_1}{1.03R} = 4.8544\frac{R_1}{R}$$

Stresses are equal:
$$\frac{16PR_1}{\pi d_1^3}\left(1 + \frac{0.615}{c'_1}\right) = \frac{16PR}{\pi d^3}\left(1 + \frac{0.615}{c_1}\right)$$

$$\frac{R_1}{(1.03d)^3}\left(1 + \frac{0.615R}{4.8544R_1}\right) = \frac{R}{d^3}(1 + 0.123)$$

$$R_1 + 0.1267R = 1.2271R$$

$$R_1 = 1.10R$$

In Eq. (5):
$$\delta = \frac{64P(1.10R)^3N}{(1.03d)^4G} = 1.18\frac{64PR^3N}{d^4G}$$

In order to maintain the original stress, the helix radius must be made 10 per cent greater, which gives 18 per cent larger deflection than the original design.

This example illustrates how a small revision of design dimensions can easily make allowance for variation in the diameter of commercially available wire.

7. Helical Extension Springs

In helical tension springs, the shape of the hooks or end turns for applying the load must be designed so that the stress concentration effects

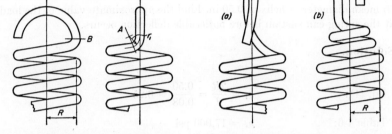

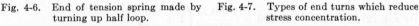

Fig. 4-6.   End of tension spring made by   Fig. 4-7.   Types of end turns which reduce
turning up half loop.   stress concentration.

caused by the presence of sharp bends are decreased as much as possible. In Fig. 4-6 the end of the tension spring has been formed by merely bending up a half-loop. If the radius of the bend is small, the stress concentration at cross section A will be large.

The most obvious method for avoiding these severe stress concentrations is to make the radius r_1 of the bend larger. Figure 4-7(a) shows one method of doing this. Here the end has been formed by turning up a complete loop in a gradual sweeping curve; stress concentration has been greatly reduced. Another expedient is to reduce the radius of the end turns gradually from the maximum value R, as shown in Fig. 4-7(b). Although the curvature of the end turns has been increased, the moment arm for the force has been correspondingly reduced.

Special hooks or loops on the ends of tension springs, as well as the grinding of the ends of compression springs, add to the cost of manufacture and should be avoided whenever possible.[14]

For computing the deflection of a tension spring, the end shown in Fig. 4-6 should be counted as about 0.1 turn for each of the hooks, and the full loop of Fig. 4-7(a) should count as 0.5 turn for each end so formed.

TABLE 4-6

Shear Stress Induced by Initial Tension in Helical Extension Spring*

$c_1 = 2R/d$	Shear stress, s_s (psi)
4	20,000
5	18,550
6	17,300
7	16,100
8	14,950
9	14,000
10	13,100
11	12,450
12	12,000

* Data by Spring Mfrs'. Assn., Inc.

[14] See reference 4, Bibliography.

Another feature of helical tension springs is the initial tension which is induced at the time the spring is coiled. Such springs are wound solid and will not deflect until this initial tension is overcome. Table 4-6 gives average values of shear stress as caused by initial tension for springs produced on standard coiling machines.

Example 8. A helical extension spring is wound from 0.080 in. diameter wire with mean diameter of helix of 0.50 in. Find the approximate value of the load P that the spring can sustain before noticeable deflection occurs.

Solution.

By Eq. (1):
$$c_1 = \frac{2R}{d} = \frac{0.50}{0.08} = 6.25$$

By Table 4-6:
$$s_s = 17,000 \text{ psi}$$

By Eq. (2):
$$17,000 = \frac{16P0.25}{\pi(0.08)^3}\left(1 + \frac{0.615}{6.25}\right)$$

$$P = 6.22 \text{ lb}$$

Working stresses for helical extension springs are usually about 75 per cent as great as for corresponding compression springs.

8. Helical Springs of Rectangular Wire

When rectangular wire is used for helical springs, the value of the shearing stress can be found by use of the equations for rectangular shafts. For the springs of Figs. 4-8(a) and (b) the stresses at points A_1 and A_2 are found by Eqs. (28) and (29) of Chapter 3, which are as follows:

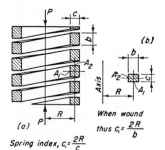

Spring index, $c_i = \frac{2R}{c}$

Fig. 4-8. Helical spring of rectangular wire.

$$s_s = \frac{PR}{\alpha_1 bc^2} \quad \text{for point } A_1 \quad (17)$$

$$s_s = \frac{PR}{\alpha_2 bc^2} \quad \text{for point } A_2 \quad (18)$$

Values of α_1 and α_2 for various b/c ratios are found in Table 3-4.

To these stresses must be added the transverse shearing stress of $1.5P/A$ to point A_1 in Fig. 4-8(a) and Point A_2 in Fig. 4-8(b).

An equation for deflection may be derived from Eq. (30) of Chapter 3 by substituting $\theta_1 = \delta/Rl$, and $l = 2\pi RN$. Hence,

$$\delta = \frac{2\pi PR^3 N}{\beta Gbc^3} \tag{19}$$

Since a rectangular bar tends to become trapezoidal in cross section after it is wound into a spring, equations for the stresses and deflections for the true shape are more complicated. The equations above are only approximate since it is assumed that the cross section remains rectangular.

Example 9. Find the stresses at points A_1 and A_2 of the spring of Fig. 4-8(b) for $b = \frac{3}{4}$ in., $c = \frac{1}{2}$ in., and $R = 1.2$ in. The static load on the spring is 2,500 lb. Find the deflection if the number of active coils is 6.

Solution. $\qquad c_1 = \dfrac{2R}{b} = \dfrac{2 \times 1.2}{\frac{3}{4}} = 3.2$ in.

From Table 3-4: $b/c = 1.50$; $\alpha_1 = 0.231$; $\alpha_2 = 0.269$; $\beta = 0.196$

By Eq. (17): $\qquad s_s = \dfrac{PR}{\alpha_1 bc^2} = \dfrac{2,500 \times 1.2}{0.231 \times 0.75 \times 0.5^2} = 69,270$ psi for point A_1

By Eq. (18): $\qquad s_s = \dfrac{PR}{\alpha_2 bc^2} = \dfrac{2,500 \times 1.2}{0.269 \times 0.75 \times 0.5^2} = 59,480$ psi for point A_2

Total stress at A_2: $s_s = 59,480 + 1.5\,\dfrac{2,500}{0.75 \times 0.5} = 69,480$ psi

In Eq. (19): $\qquad \delta = \dfrac{2\pi \times 2,500 \times 1.2^3 \times 6}{0.196 \times 11,500,000 \times 0.75 \times 0.5^3} = 0.771$ in.

For fluctuating loads, the design can be made as in Section 4, with the stress concentration factor K_c estimated by Eq. (9).

9. Helical Springs with Torsional Loading

A helical spring can be loaded by a torque about the axis of the helix. Such loading, as shown in Fig. 4-9(a), is similar to the torsional loading of a shaft. The torque about the axis of the helix acts as a bending moment on each section of the wire as shown in Fig. 4-9(b). The material is thus stressed in flexure, and the usual equation for bending stress can be used.

Because of the curved shape, the stress is larger on the inner edge of the coil and smaller on the outer edge. The adjustment can be made by multiplying the stress, as given by $s = Mc/I$, by an appropriate stress concentration factor. For wire of rectangular cross section, these factors are

$$K_1 = \frac{3c_1{}^2 - c_1 - 0.8}{3c_1(c_1 - 1)} \text{ for inner edge} \quad (20) \quad K_2 = \frac{3c_1{}^2 + c_1 - 0.8}{3c_1(c_1 + 1)} \text{ for outer edge} \quad (21)$$

where $c_1 = 2R/h$; h is the depth of section perpendicular to the axis.

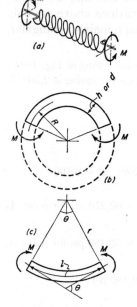

(a)

(b)

(c)

Fig. 4-9. Loading and angular deformation of torsional spring.

For circular cross sections, the stress concentration factors are

$$K_3 = \frac{4c_1{}^2 - c_1 - 1}{4c_1(c_1 - 1)} \text{ for inner edge} \quad (22)$$

$$K_4 = \frac{4c_1{}^2 + c_1 - 1}{4c_1(c_1 + 1)} \text{ for outer edge} \quad (23)$$

where $c_1 = 2R/d$.

Cold forming leaves a residual stress of compression in the outer region of the cross section. The normal loading of the spring should therefore be such as to cause it to wind up and thus produce tensile stress in the outer portion of the wire. If the spring is mounted over an arbor, sufficient clearance must be provided to allow for the decrease in radius of the helix as the spring is wound. For fluctuating loads, care should be exercised in the design of the end turns or hooks to avoid stress concentration caused by sharp bends.

For commonly used values of the spring index, the curvature has no effect on the angular deformation. The deformation of the wire in the spring is the same as for a straight bar of the same length l. By No. 1 of Fig. 1-14 the total angular deformation θ between tangents drawn at the ends of the bar, as shown in Fig. 4-9(c), is

$$\theta = \frac{Ml}{EI} \quad (24)$$

Angle θ in some cases may amount to a number of revolutions.

Example 10. A torsional window shade spring is made from No. 17 music wire. The mean diameter of helix is 0.875 in. and number of coils is 400. Assume $s_{yp} = 0.6s_{ult}$ and $FS = 2$ based on the yield point. Compute stresses on the inside of helix, taking into account the stress concentration due to curvature. Find the torque that the roller can exert after unwinding 12 revolutions from the most highly stressed condition.

Solution.

By Table 4-1: $d = 0.0540$, $s_{ult} = 301,000$ psi

$$c_1 = \frac{2R}{d} = \frac{0.875}{0.054} = 16.2$$

By Eq. (22): $K_3 = \dfrac{4 \times 16.2^2 - 16.2 - 1}{4 \times 16.2(16.2 - 1)} = 1.048$

$$s_{yp} = 0.6 \times 301,000 = 180,600 \text{ psi}$$

$$K_3 s = \frac{s_{yp}}{FS} = \frac{180,600}{2} = 90,300 \text{ psi}$$

$$s = \frac{90,300}{1.048} = 86,140 \text{ psi}$$

$$I = \frac{\pi d^4}{64} = \frac{\pi \times 0.054^4}{64} = 0.0000004174 \text{ in.}^4$$

At max. stress: $M = \dfrac{sI}{c} = \dfrac{86,140 \times 0.0000004174}{0.027} = 1.3317 \text{ in-lb}$

$$l = 2\pi RN = \pi \times 0.875 \times 400 = 1,100 \text{ in.}$$

At max. stress.
by Eq. (24): $\theta = \dfrac{1.3317 \times 1,100}{30,000,000 \times 0.0000004174} = 116.94 \text{ radians}$

Deflection, after
unwinding 12
revolutions: $= 116.94 - 12 \times 2\pi = 41.54 \text{ radians}$

Remaining torque,
by Eq. (24): $M = \dfrac{30,000,000 \times 0.0000004174 \times 41.54}{1,100} = 0.473 \text{ in-lb}$

10. Leaf Springs

The stresses and deformations of rectangular leaf springs for small
deflections can be found by the appropriate
equations for beams as given in Chapter 1.
For cases where the width of cross section is
large compared with the thickness, it is
necessary to multiply the deflection as given
by the equation for a narrow beam by
$(1 - \mu^2)$, where μ is Poisson's ratio, as explained in Section 10 of Chapter 1.

Example 11. Find the sidewise deflection of
the spring-mounted table shown in Fig. 4-10.

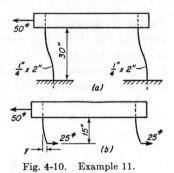

Fig. 4-10.   Example 11.

The steel springs are fixed at top and bottom so that tangents at the ends remain vertical at all times.

Solution. The springs are deformed into symmetrical curves with points of inflection at the mid-height. A point of inflection has a zero value for the bending moment because the moment changes sign at such a point. If the springs are cut at the mid-heights, shear forces only are present as shown in the free body diagram of Fig. 4-10(b). Hence,

$$I = \frac{bh^3}{12} = \frac{2}{64 \times 12} = \frac{1}{384} \text{ in.}^4$$

$$y = (1 - \mu^2) \frac{Pl^3}{3EI} = \frac{(1 - 0.3^2) \times 25 \times 15^3 \times 384}{3 \times 30,000,000} = 0.3276 \text{ in.}$$

Total deflection of table = $2 \times 0.3276 = 0.6552$ in.

Multiple-leaf springs are in wide use, especially in motor car and railway service. An exact analysis of this type of spring is complicated. An approximate solution can be obtained if the shorter leaves are tapered to a sharp point, and if it is assumed that the leaves remain in contact with each other throughout their length when the spring deflects. If these conditions are fulfilled, the curvature, and therefore the stress, may be obtained by replacing the actual spring shown in Fig. 4-11(a) by the trapezoid in Fig. 4-11(b). To form this trapezoid, it is assumed that each of the shorter leaves has been split along its center, that each half has been placed on either side of the longest leaf, and that all edges have then been welded together. The width b_o at the support is equal to the width of each leaf multiplied by the number of leaves. When the trapezoid deflects under the load, the leaves on either side of a welded edge have the same deflection and curvature, and hence the same stress.

For small deflections, the equation for the cantilever trapezoid with a load on the end is as follows.[15]

$$\delta = K_1 \frac{Pl^3}{3EI_o} \tag{25}$$

Factor K_1 depends on the ratio of the widths b/b_o, and is given by the curve of Fig. 4-12. The moment of inertia I_o refers to the section at the wall and is equal to $b_o h^3/12$, where h is the thickness of the leaf. If b is large in comparison with h, the previous remark relative to the deflection of wide beams should be observed.

When the deflection is large compared to the thickness, the usual equations for small deflections of beams can no longer be used. The theory is complicated and beyond the scope of this book.[16]

---

[15] See p. 287 of reference 3, Bibliography.
[16] See reference 23, Bibliography.

Leaf springs frequently have a hole through the leaves for the tie bolt. This reduction of area, together with the stress concentration, usually occurs at the point of maximum bending stress and is frequently the cause of fatigue failures. The stress concentration factor for a hole, and also for semicircular notches, may be taken from Fig. 2-8 for a bar in tension. Another harmful effect is due to the clamping pressure used in attaching the spring. This compression also usually occurs at the location of maximum bending stress and causes a reduction in the fatigue strength.

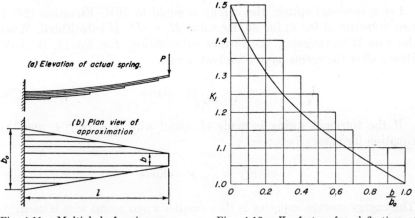

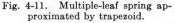

Fig. 4-11. Multiple-leaf spring approximated by trapezoid.

Fig. 4-12. K_1 factor for deflection of trapezoidal spring.

Materials suitable for leaf springs are listed in Table 4-3. The previous remarks concerning condition of surface and decarburized surface layer apply equally well to leaf springs. If sharp bends occur in the region of high stress, the concentration must be taken into account, particularly for nonsteady loading.

11. Energy Storage by Springs

Springs are frequently used for storing energy in spring motors, or for absorbing the energy of shock or impact loads. When the force and deformation of a spring are proportional, the energy stored is equal to $\frac{1}{2}P\delta$, where P is the load and δ is the deformation. This equation assumes that the spring was carrying no load at the time P was applied.

From Eq. (5) for the deflection of a helical spring of round wire, and the value for s_s from Eq. (a), Section 1, the expression for the energy for static loads can be written, after rearrangement of terms, as

$$\text{energy} = \frac{1}{2}P\delta = \frac{s_s^2}{4G} \times \text{volume} \qquad (26)$$

For a given stress, some types of springs can store more energy, per unit volume of material, than other types can. For the purpose of comparing the helical spring with other kinds, Eq. (26) will be transformed into units of axial stress. Within the elastic range $s_s = 0.5s$ and $G = E/2(1 + \mu)$, where $\mu = 0.3$. These substitutions are made in Eq. (26) to give

$$\text{energy} = \frac{s^2}{6.15E} \times \text{volume} \tag{27}$$

For a torsional spring, the energy is equal to $\frac{1}{2}\theta M$. Equation (24) is now substituted for θ; for M, its value $M = sI/c$ is substituted. When the wire is rectangular, the further substitution, $I = bh^3/12$, is made. Hence after the terms have been rearranged,

$$\text{energy} = \frac{s^2}{6E} \times \text{volume} \tag{28}$$

If the torsional spring is made of round wire, $I = \pi d^4/64$, and the equation for energy becomes

$$\text{energy} = \frac{s^2}{8E} \times \text{volume} \tag{29}$$

The energy storage capacity is thus smaller when round wire is used.

For a rectangular cantilever with load P on the end, the deflection is $Pl^3/3EI$, and the expression for the energy in terms of the maximum stress which occurs at the support is

$$\text{energy} = \frac{s^2}{18E} \times \text{volume} \tag{30}$$

If the cantilever is triangular ($b/b_o = 0$) the deflection, from Eq. (25) and Fig. 4-12, is equal to $1.5Pl^3/3EI_o$, and the equation for the energy becomes

$$\text{energy} = \frac{s^2}{6E} \times \text{volume} \tag{31}$$

Since the multiple-leaf spring may be approximated as the triangular cantilever, Eq. (31) indicates that such a spring is efficient from the standpoint of energy storage.

12. Rubber Springs

Rubber springs and cushioning devices are finding an increasing range of application in industry. Knowledge of the behavior of rubber under

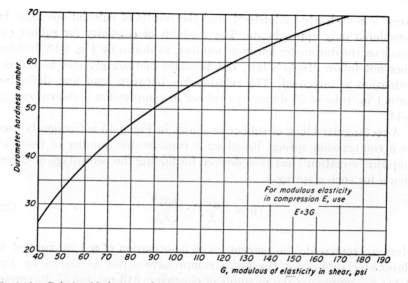

Fig. 4-13.   Relationship between durometer hardness number and modulus of elasticity for rubber.

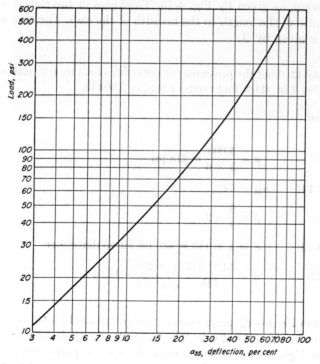

Fig. 4-14.   Load deflection curve for 1 in. cube of 55 durometer rubber between steel plates bonded to the rubber.

stress is not clearly understood, and the results of calculations must be considered only approximate. The modulus of elasticity for rubber depends on the durometer hardness number, as shown by Fig. 4-13. Rubber does not follow Hooke's law, but becomes increasingly stiff as the deformation is increased. The relationship between load and deflection for a 1 in. cube of 55 durometer rubber in compression is shown by Fig. 4-14.

A rectangular block of rubber as shown in Fig. 4-15 is frequently used as a compression spring. Based on a considerable number of tests, an empirical equation[17] has been derived for finding the percentage of deflection α for such a spring.

$$\alpha = \frac{\alpha_{55} E_{55}}{E} \cdot \frac{(h\beta)^{2/3}}{\sqrt{A}} \tag{32}$$

Here α_{55} represents the percentage of deformation of a 1 in. cube of 55 durometer rubber for the given compressive stress as shown by Fig. 4-14; E_{55} represents the modulus of elasticity, 313 psi, for 55 durometer rubber; modulus E refers to the durometer hardness of the slab under consideration, as given by Fig. 4-13. Thickness of the slab is h in., and β is the ratio of the length to the breadth of the slab. The area normal to the load is given by A.

Example 12. Find the percentage of deflection of a 3 by 6 in. slab of 65 durometer rubber 1 in. thick that carries a load of 5,000 lb.

Solution.

Unit load: $\qquad p = \dfrac{5,000}{3 \times 6} = 278$ psi

By Fig. 4-14: $\qquad \alpha_{55} = 54\%$

$$\beta = \frac{6}{3} = 2$$

By Fig. 4-13: $\qquad E = 3 \times 145 = 435$ psi for 65 durometer

In Eq. (32): $\qquad \alpha = \dfrac{54 \times 313}{435} \dfrac{(1 \times 2)^{2/3}}{\sqrt{3 \times 6}} = 14.54\%$

A load-deflection diagram can be plotted for a rubber spring by finding the value of α for other loads. The foregoing discussion assumes that the rubber in Figs. 4-14 and 4-15 is bonded to metal plates top and bottom.

---

[17] See reference 25, Bibliography.

Figure 4-16 shows a simple shear spring of two blocks of rubber. Hooke's law holds reasonably well for rubber in shear, and the following equation can be used for the shearing deformation γ

$$\gamma = \frac{s_s}{G} = \frac{P}{2AG} \tag{a}$$

where A represents the area of one of the surfaces in shear.

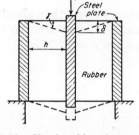

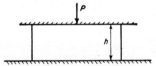

Fig. 4-15.   Rubber block spring with com-   Fig. 4-16.   Simple rubber shear spring
pression loading.

Deformation δ is equal to $h \tan \gamma$, and for moderate values of γ the angle can be substituted for the tangent which gives $\delta = h\gamma$. Substitution should now be made for γ in Eq. (a) to obtain an approximate equation for the deflection δ.

$$\delta = \frac{Ph}{2AG} \tag{33}$$

A shear spring of cylindrical form is shown in Fig. 4-17. The rubber is bonded to a steel ring on the outside and a steel shaft in the center. Shear stress in the rubber at radius r is equal to

$$s_s = \gamma G = \frac{P}{2\pi rh} \tag{b}$$

Deformation angle γ is then equal to

$$\gamma = \frac{P}{2\pi rhG} = \frac{b}{r} \tag{c}$$

where

$$b = \frac{P}{2\pi hG} \tag{d}$$

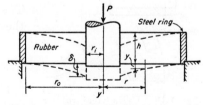

Fig. 4-17.   Cylindrical rubber spring with shear loading.

The slope of the deformed rubber at radius r is given by

$$\frac{dy}{dr} = \tan \gamma = -\tan \frac{b}{r} \tag{e}$$

The minus sign is due to the fact that the slope is negative for the chosen coordinate system. The tangent term should now be expanded into a series and integrated term by term.

$$\frac{dy}{dr} = \frac{-b}{r} - \frac{b^3}{3r^3} - \cdots \qquad \text{(f)}$$

$$y = -b \log_e r + \frac{b^3}{6r^2} + \cdots + C \qquad \text{(g)}$$

When $\tan \gamma$ is less than about 0.4, only the $b \log_e r$ term need be retained. The constant of integration C can be evaluated from the condition that $y = 0$ when $r = r_o$. Then

$$C = b \log_e r_o \qquad \text{(h)}$$

and
$$y = b \log_e \frac{r_o}{r} \qquad \text{(i)}$$

The maximum value of y or δ occurs for $r = r_i$. Hence,

$$\delta = b \log_e \frac{r_o}{r_i} = \frac{P}{2\pi hG} \log_e \frac{r_o}{r_i} \qquad \text{(34)}$$

A cylindrical spring loaded in torsional shear is shown in Fig. 4-18. At radius r the area in shear is $2\pi rh$. The shear force is this area multiplied by shearing stress s_s, and the torque or moment is the force multiplied by the radius r.

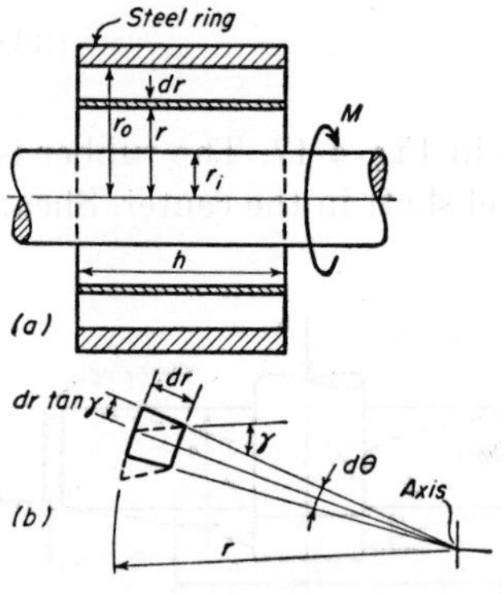

$$M = 2\pi r^2 h s_s \qquad \text{or} \qquad s_s = \frac{M}{2\pi r^2 h} \qquad \text{(j)}$$

The shear stress has a maximum value for the minimum value of r. Hence,

$$s_{smax} = \frac{M}{2\pi r_i^2 h} \qquad \text{(35)}$$

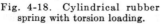

Fig. 4-18. Cylindrical rubber spring with torsion loading.

Figure 4-18(b) shows, to an enlarged scale, the deformation angle γ for the element at radius r from the axis. Since $r \, d\theta = dr \tan \gamma$, the contribution $d\theta$ to the total angular rotation of the shaft, given by the element at radius r, is

$$d\theta = \frac{dr \tan \gamma}{r} \qquad \text{(k)}$$

Angle γ can be found by the following equation.

$$\gamma = \frac{s_s}{G} = \frac{M}{2\pi r^2 hG} = \frac{c}{r^2} \tag{1}$$

where

$$c = \frac{M}{2\pi hG} \tag{m}$$

This value of γ should now be substituted in Eq. (k), and the tangent term expanded into a series. The resulting equation should be integrated term by term.

$$d\theta = \frac{1}{r}\left[\tan\frac{c}{r^2}\right]dr = \frac{1}{r}\left[\frac{c}{r^2} + \frac{c^3}{3r^6} + \cdots\right]dr \tag{n}$$

$$\theta = \left[-\frac{c}{2r^2} - \frac{c^3}{18r^6}\right]_{r_i}^{r_o} \tag{o}$$

This series converges rapidly, and the first term will usually be sufficient. When the limits for r are substituted, the following equation for θ is obtained.

$$\theta = \frac{M}{4\pi hG}\left[\frac{1}{r_i^2} - \frac{1}{r_o^2}\right] \tag{36}$$

The equations for many other types of rubber springs can be found in the literature.[18]

Working stresses are generally limited to 25 to 50 psi in shear. For rubber compression springs, the deformation should not be greater than 10 to 20 per cent of the free height to avoid excessive creep. Under fatigue loading even smaller values should be used. For satisfactory curing during vulcanization the maximum thickness should be limited to 2 in., with a preferred thickness of not over 1 in.

BIBLIOGRAPHY

Volume number shown in **bold face** type. The number immediately following is the page on which the article begins.

1. Timoshenko, S., *Strength of Materials*, 2d ed., Vol. 1. New York: D. Van Nostrand Company, Inc., 1940.

2. Timoshenko, S., *Strength of Materials*, 2d ed., Vol. 2. New York: D. Van Nostrand Company, Inc., 1941.

3. Wahl, A. M., *Mechanical Springs*. Cleveland: Penton Publishing Company, 1944.

4. Conrad, W. C., "How to Get Springs that Satisfy," *Elec. Mfg.*, July, 1939.

[18] See, for example, reference 25, Bibliography.

5. Weibel, E. E., "The Correlation of Spring-Wire Bending and Torsion Fatigue Tests," *Trans. ASME*, **57**, 501 (1935).

6. Keysor, H. C., "Carbon and Alloy Steel Materials for Hot-Formed Springs," *Product Eng.*, **17**, Nov., 86 (1946).

7. Zimmerli, F. P., "How Shot Blasting Increases Fatigue Life," *Machine Design* **12**, Nov., 62 (1940).

8. Zimmerli, F. P., "Effect of Temperature on Coiled Steel Springs Under Various Loadings," *Trans. ASME*, **63**, 363 (1941).

9. Almen, J. O., "Improving Fatigue Strength of Machine Parts," *Mech. Eng.*, **65**, 553 (1943).

10. Johnson, J. B., "Fatigue Characteristics of Helical Springs," *Iron Age*, **133**, Mar. 15, 12; Mar. 22, 24 (1934).

11. Wahl, A. M., "Helical-Spring Design Stresses for a Standard Code," *Trans. ASME*, **64**, 476 (1942).

12. Bittner, E. T., "Alloy Spring Steels," *Trans. ASM*, **40**, 263 (1948).

13. Sayre, M. F., "Laws of Elastic Behavior in Metals," *Trans. ASME*, **56**, 555 (1934).

14. Zimmerli, F. P., "Carbon and Alloy Steel Materials for Cold-Formed Springs," *Product Eng.*, **17**, Oct., 119 (1946).

15. Zimmerli, F. P., "Nonferrous Alloy Materials for Mechanical Springs," *Product Eng.*, **17**, Dec., 85 (1946).

16. *Standards for Mechanical Springs*, The Spring Manufacturers' Association, Inc., Bristol, Conn., 1949.

17. Tatnall, R. R., "Factors in the Fatigue of Helical Springs," *Mech. Eng.*, **62**, 289 (1940).

18. Simi, H. E., "Torsional Rod Springs and How They Are Designed," *Product Eng.* **13**, 710 (1942).

19. Burdick, W. E., Chaplin, F. S., and Sheppard, W. L., "Deflection of Helical Springs Under Transverse Loadings," *Trans. ASME*, **61**, 623 (1939).

20. Clurman, S. P., "The Design of Nonlinear Leaf Springs," *Trans. ASME*, **73**, 155 (1951).

21. Rouverol, W. S., "Accurate Spring Counterbalancing," *Trans. ASME*, **73**, 141 (1951).

22. Ryan, J. J., "Characteristics of Dished-Plate (Belleville) Springs as Measured in Portable Recording Tensiometers," *Trans. ASME*, **74**, 431 (1952).

23. Bisshopp, K. E., and Drucker, D. C., "Large Deflection of Cantilever Beam," *Quart. Applied Math.*, **3**, No. 3, Oct., 272 (1945). See also *Product Eng.*, **21**, March, 163 (1950).

24. Mackenzie, B., "Automobile Suspension Springs," *Proc. Inst. Mech. Engs.*, *Automobile Div.*, Part 3, 122 (1947–1948).

25. Smith, J. F. D., "Rubber Mountings," *Trans. ASME*, **60**, A-13 (1938); **61**, A-159 (1939).

26. Marsh, S. W., "Rubber as a Stress-Carrying Material and Some Design Considerations," *Proc. Inst. Mech. Engrs., Automobile Div.*, Part 2, 25 (1948–1949).

27. Chilton, E. G., "Large Deflections of an Elastic Solid," *Trans. ASME*, **70**; *Appl. Mech.*, 362 (1948).

28. McPherson, A. T., and Klemin, A., *Engineering Uses of Rubber*, New York: Reinhold Publishing Corp., 1956.

29. Gardnier, F. J., and Carlson, H. C. R., "The Spring Back of Coil Springs," *Mechanical Engineering*, **80**, April 74 (1958); Disc. Nov. 140.

30. Hinkle, R. T., and Morse, I. E., Jr., "Design of Helical Springs for Minimum Weight, Volume, and Length," *Trans. ASME*, **81**, 37 (1959).

PROBLEMS

Spring material for the problems is steel.

1. A helical spring must sustain a static load of 100 lb at a deflection of 1 in. Spring index is equal to 6. Find the value of the maximum stress if the spring is made of No. 8 wire. Find the required number of active coils. *Ans.* $N = 10.8$.

2. A helical spring is made of No. 4 wire and has 10 active coils. Spring index is equal to 6. Find the stress when the deflection is equal to 1 in.

Ans. 49,760 psi.

3. A helical spring is made of No. 8 wire with spring index equal to 6. Load is steady and spring rate is 150 lb/in. Maximum stress is 60,000 psi. Find the number of active coils. *Ans.* $N = 7.2$ coils.

4. A helical spring of rate 60 lb/in. is mounted on top of another spring of rate 42 lb/in. Find the force required to give a total deflection of 2 in.

Ans. $F = 49.4$ lb.

5. The outer of two concentric helical springs has a rate of 2,400 lb/in. The inner spring has a rate of 1,750 lb/in. The outer spring is $\frac{1}{2}$ in. longer than the inner. If the total load is 8,000 lb, find the weight carried by each spring.

Ans. Outer = 5,132.5 lb; inner = 2,867.5 lb.

6. The larger of two concentric helical springs is made of $1\frac{1}{2}$ in. diameter round bar stock and is 9 in. OD of helix, and has 6 active coils. The inner spring is of 1 in. bar and is $5\frac{1}{2}$ in. OD helix and has 9 active coils. The free height of the outer spring is $\frac{3}{4}$ in. more than the inner. Find the deflection of each spring for a load of 20,000 lb. Find the load carried by each spring.

Ans. $P_o = 13,242$ lb; $\delta_o = 4.606$ in.

7. A compression spring is to be made of 0.120 in. diameter wire with 10 active coils, and 1 in. mean diameter of helix. Commercial limits for the wire diameter are 0.1185 and 0.1215 in. Helix diameter may vary from 0.980 to 1.020 in. The number of active coils may vary from $9\frac{3}{4}$ to $10\frac{1}{4}$. The modulus may vary from 11,400,000 psi to 11,800,000 psi. Find the spring rate when all variables tend to give the weakest spring. Find the spring rate when all variables tend to give the stiffest spring. *Ans.* $k = 25.8$ lb/in.; $k = 35.0$ lb/in.

8. A helical spring must be capable of exerting a force of 150 lb after being released 0.4 in. from its most highly compressed position. No. 3 wire is used; spring index is equal to 6. Loading is static. Maximum stress is 60,000 psi. Find the required number of active coils.   *Ans.* $N = 10.5$ coils.

9. A helical compression spring is made from No. 3 wire and carries a static load of 250 lb. The maximum shearing stress is to be 60,000 psi. Find the radius of the helix and the number of active coils for a deflection of $\frac{3}{4}$ in.
Ans. $R = 0.607$ in.; $N = 8.50$ coils.

10. A helical spring is subjected to a continuously varying load. The length varies between $2\frac{1}{2}$ in. and $2\frac{3}{4}$ in. with corresponding loads of 114 lb and 78 lb. The spring is made of No. 7 wire and has a mean helix diameter of 1 in. Material tests 98,000 psi yield point in shear. The endurance limit (zero to maximum shear) is 70,000 psi. Find the value of the factor of safety and the number of active coils. Find the free height of the spring.   *Ans.* $FS = 1.44$; $N = 9.8$ coils.

11. A helical spring is subjected to a continuously varying load. It is made of No. 3 wire with mean radius of helix equal to $\frac{3}{4}$ in. In the least compressed position, the load is 110 lb. Range of compression is $\frac{1}{4}$ in. The number of active coils is 8; the factor of safety is 1.5. Material tests 90,000 psi yield point in shear. Find the required value which the material must have in pulsating shear (zero to maximum).   *Ans.* $s'_{se} = 48,300$ psi.

12. A helical spring is subjected to a continuously varying load. No. 7 wire is used with a mean radius of helix of $\frac{1}{2}$ in. In the most compressed condition the force is 92 lb. After 0.32 in. of release the minimum force is 48 lb. Material tests 90,000 psi yield point in shear, and 60,000 psi endurance limit in pulsating shear, zero to maximum. Find the factor of safety and the number of active coils.
Ans. $FS = 1.46$; $N = 10.3$ coils.

13. A helical spring is made from rectangular wire $\frac{1}{2}$ by $\frac{1}{4}$ in. with the narrow side parallel to the helix axis. Mean helix radius is 1.5 in. The static load is 150 lb.

(a) Find the value of the maximum stress, and the deflection, if the number of active coils is 8.

(b) Repeat (a) with the spring wound with the long side of the cross section parallel to the axis.   *Ans.* (a) $s_s = 29,270$ psi, $\delta = 1.24$ in.

14. A helical spring carries a static load of 250 lb. There are 10 active coils, and the radius of the helix to the center of the wire is 1 in.

(a) What size square wire must be used and what will be the stress if the deflection is to be 2 in.?

(b) If this spring is made of round wire, find the required diameter and the stress. What percentage of weight of material is saved by the use of round wire?
Ans. (a) $c = 0.264$ in.; $s_s = 70,700$ psi.

15. A torsional helical spring for a 30 in. door, see Fig. 4-19, is to have a pull at the handle of 1 lb when the door is closed, and a pull of 3 lb after the door has rotated through 180°. No. 6 wire is to be used, and maximum stress is 150,000 psi. Find the required diameter of helix, the required initial angular deformation, and the number of active coils in the spring. Take into account the stress concention. *Ans.* Dia. helix = 1.047 in.; θ_0 = 90°; N = 31.8.

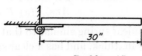

Fig. 4-19. Problem 15.

16. How many coils must there be in a window-shade spring that is to exert a pull on the shade of 3 lb after being wound up 15 revolutions? The spring is made of 0.0475 in. square wire. Helix diameter is 0.75 in. center to center of coils, and roller diameter is 1.25 in. What is the value of the maximum flexural stress?

Ans. N = 272; s = 109,600 psi.

17. A flexible coupling has an active element in the form of a torsional helical spring. Twenty-five horsepower is transmitted at 900 rpm. To what radius of helix must the spring be wound if made of $\frac{3}{4}$ in. square wire, and if the permissible stress is 30,000 psi? How many active coils must there be if the torsional deflection is not to exceed 5°? *Ans.* R = 1.47 in.; N = 4.27.

18. A torsional spring is to be located within the hub of the reel for raising the weight shown in Fig. 4-20. The spring is wound from $\frac{5}{16}$ in. square wire. OD of helix is $6\frac{1}{2}$ in. Ignore the effect of curvature on stress. The number of active coils is 20.

(a) Find the initial angular deformation required by the spring in order to support the load in the upper position.

(b) Find the additional force which must be applied to the weight in order to hold it in the lower position.

(c) Using Eq. (29), compute the strain energy stored in the spring because of lowering the weight; check the result by totaling the work done by the external forces. *Ans.* θ_o = 3.47 radians; force = 81.5 lb.

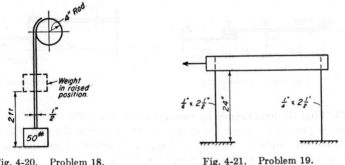

Fig. 4-20. Problem 18.   Fig. 4-21. Problem 19.

19. (a) Find the force F necessary to move the top of the shaking table shown in Fig. 4-21 a distance of 1.75 in. to one side of the midposition. Tangents to the springs at the top and bottom remain vertical at all times. Find the value of the bending stress in the springs.

(b) Repeat (a) except that the right spring is now $\frac{5}{16}$ in. thick. The left spring remains $\frac{1}{4}$ in. thick.   *Ans.* (a) $F = 326$ lb.; (b) $F = 481$ lb.

20. A cantilever, multiple-leaf spring similar to that in Fig. 4-11 is composed of five leaves $2\frac{1}{2}$ in. wide and $\frac{1}{2}$ in. thick, and has a clear span to the point of application of the load of 20 in. Assume that the shorter leaves are of the proper length and end taper to permit the spring to be approximated as a trapezoid. What static load will the spring support at a stress in the material of 60,000 psi? What will be the deflection of the load?   *Ans.* $P = 1,560$ lb; $\delta = 1.40$ in.

21. A spring mount for a machine is built up of steel plates and rollers as shown in Fig. 4-22. Find the deflection caused by the load and the bending stress in the plates.   *Ans.* $y = 1.084$ in.; $s = 11,850$ psi.

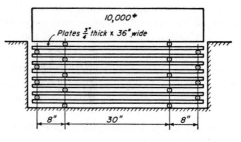

Fig. 4-22.   Problem 21.

22. Find the value of force P if the force between the contact points in Fig. 4-23 is to be 3 lb. Find the deflection of point B. Leaves are steel, 0.03 in. thick and 0.40 in. wide. Neglect effects of any friction.   *Ans.* $P = 5$ lb; $y = 0.369$ in.

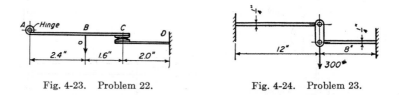

Fig. 4-23.   Problem 22.   Fig. 4-24.   Problem 23.

23. Find the load carried by each spring in Fig. 4-24. The left spring is trapezoidal in plan, 2 in. wide at the hinge, and 10 in. wide at the wall. The right spring has a uniform width of 3 in. Assume hinges are frictionless and that the connecting link is inextensible. Find the deflection of the load.
                Ans.   Left $= 129$ lb; right 171 lb; $\delta = 0.2267$ in.

24. Forces R in Fig. 4-25 are just sufficient to bring the ends of the upper spring into contact with the lower spring. The material is steel. Find the value of R.
                Ans. $R = 941$ lb.

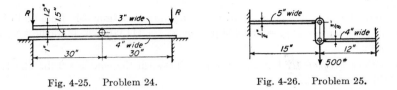

Fig. 4-25.   Problem 24.   Fig. 4-26.   Problem 25.

25. Find the deflection of the load in Fig. 4-26. Springs are of steel. Assume that hinges are frictionless and that connecting link is inextensible.

Ans. $y = 0.1975$ in.

26. A cantilever spring has a load at the end. The spring is of uniform thickness, but is triangular in plan. Prove that the bending stress is the same for all cross sections.

27. Let the expression for the strain energy U for a simply supported leaf spring with load P in the center be given by $\frac{1}{2}Py$, where y is the deflection. Prove that stress $s = c \sqrt{6EU/Il}$ where c is the distance from the neutral axis to the edge of the cross section. Use this relationship to prove that for a rectangular cross section the energy absorbed for a constant stress s is the same regardless of whether the long or short dimension is vertical.

The following problems are presented without answers.

28. A helical spring is to carry a static load of 100 lb at a stress of 70,000 psi. Spring index equals 6. Find the theoretical diameter of the wire.

29. A steel helical spring of 9 active coils is to have a deflection of $\frac{5}{8}$ in. under a static load of 50 lb. Spring index equals 5. Find the theoretical diameter of the wire.

30. A steel helical spring of index 4 has 10 active coils. Deflection is 1.5 in. when the stress is 70,000 psi. Find the static load the spring is carrying and the mean radius of the helix.

31. A steel helical spring must exert a force of 2.5 lb after being released 0.10 in. from its most highly compressed condition. No. 19 wire is used with a spring index of 6. Find the static loading for a maximum stress of 60,000 psi. Find the number of active coils.

32. The maximum and minimum static loads on a steel helical spring are 86 lb and 71 lb respectively. These loads cause a change in the deflection of 0.25 in. Spring index is 8, and maximum stress is 70,000 psi. Find the theoretical value of d. Also find R and N.

33. Find the *FS* for a spring with the same data as Problem 12 except that R equals 0.6 in.

34. An engine valve spring must exert a force of 60 lb when the valve is closed and 100 lb when the valve is open. The lift is $\frac{5}{16}$ in. Material tests $s_{syp} = 98,000$ psi and $s'_{se} = 68,000$ psi. $FS = 1.4$. If the spring index is 6, find the theoretical wire diameter. Also find the number of active coils and the initial compression of the spring.

35. A helical spring of Swedish valve spring wire,[19] $d = 0.125$ in., has a mean helix diameter of $\frac{5}{8}$ in. The load on the spring varies continuously from 50 lb to 100 lb. Material tests $s_{syp} = 139,000$ psi and $s'_{s_e} = 111,000$ psi. Find the *FS* for the spring.

36. Work Problem 22 but with the force between the contacts 2 lb. The 1.6 dimension becomes 2.4 in.

37. In Fig. 4-27 each steel spring has 10 active coils of No. 12 wire. Mean radius of helix is 0.3 in. The right spring has a free height 0.5 in. greater than the left spring. When the load is acting, the bar is level. Find the distance x.

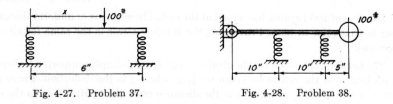

Fig. 4-27.   Problem 37.   Fig. 4-28.   Problem 38.

38. In Fig. 4-28 assume the bar to be rigid and weightless, and the joint at the left to be frictionless. Each steel spring has 10 active coils of No. 10 wire wound with a spring index of 5. Springs are stress free when the bar is level. Find the force carried by each spring and the deflection of the weight.

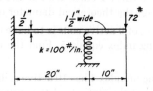

Fig. 4-29.   Problem 39.

39. The bar in Fig. 4-29 is made of steel. Find the force in the spring.

[19] See reference 5, Bibliography.

5

Screws

Bolts and screws are used to fasten the various parts of an assembly together. The designer should be familiar with the different kinds of threads in commercial use and with the method of specifying the desired tolerances for the fit between screw and nut. He should understand the reasons for the increase of fatigue strength obtained by the application of initial tension in the bolt. Power screws are employed in machines for obtaining motion of translation and also for exerting forces.

1. Kinds of Threads

For general service in bolts and studs, two systems of threads are in use: the Unified and the American National. The Unified thread represents the agreement of standardization committees of Canada, Britain, and the United States.[1] During the transition period required for replacement of tools and gages, the American National form of thread is being retained as a standard. Bolts and nuts of these systems are interchangeable with each other. The systems differ only in minor details, mainly in the arrangement of the tolerances. The included angle of the thread is 60°. The basic form of the thread is shown in Fig. 5-1(a), although actual threads are made with a rounded root. The crest is flat in the American National and may be either flat or rounded in the Unified thread. The Whitworth

[1] See reference 4, Bibliography.

191

thread, shown in Fig. 5-1(b), is standard in Great Britain, but is being replaced by the Unified Thread.

For lead screws and power transmission the Acme screw shown in Fig. 5-1(c) is in wide use. It has an included angle of thread of 29°. The standard proportions of the American National Pipe[2] Thread are given in Fig.

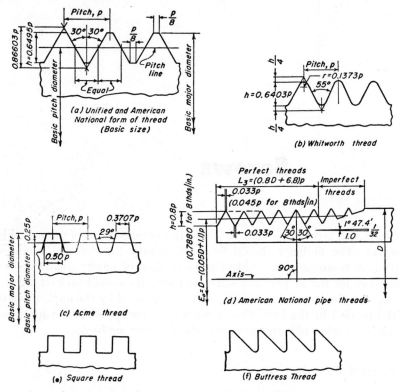

Fig. 5-1.   Standard types of screw threads.

5-1(d). The taper, together with the smaller flat at crest and root, assists in producing a fluid-tight joint. Square and buttress threads shown in Figs. 5-1(e) and (f) are used to a limited extent for power transmission.

If an imaginary cylinder, coaxial with the screw, intersects the thread at the height which makes the width of thread equal to the width of space, the diameter of this cylinder is called the *pitch diameter* of the screw. See Fig. 5-1(a). The distance measured parallel to the axis from a point on one thread to the corresponding point on the adjacent thread is called the *pitch*. A screw made by cutting a single helical groove on the cylinder is

[2] See reference 2, Part II, Bibliography.

called a *single-thread* screw. If the helix angle is somewhat steeper, and a second thread is cut in the space between the grooves of the first, a *double-threaded* screw is formed. For certain applications, triple and quadruple threads are in use. For multiple-threaded screws the *lead* is the distance the nut advances in one revolution. The pitch is defined as for a single-thread screw. The helix may be cut either right hand or left hand. The screw shown in Fig. 5-10 is a right-hand screw.

2. Standardized Threads

Table 5-1 gives a summary of the various sizes and pitches for Unified and American National forms of threads. The size of a screw refers to the major diameter, or the size of the stock upon which the helix is cut. It should be noticed that sizes less than $\frac{1}{4}$ in. are designated by number. In general, there are two pitches, coarse and fine, that may be cut on each diameter. For certain sizes, there is also an extra fine series of pitches. Complete information on sizes, pitches, tolerances, and allowances is given in *Unified and American Screw Threads, ASA B1.1-1949*, published by the American Society of Mechanical Engineers.[3] There are three additional series of threads of 8, 12, and 16 threads per inch which may be cut on a wide variety of diameters.

Example 1. Compute the basic pitch diameter for a 1 in. coarse thread series screw. Find the value of the helix angle α.

Solution. By Table 5-1, the 1 in. coarse series has 8 threads per inch. The basic pitch diameter is equal to the nominal outside diameter minus the height of thread h.

By Fig. 5-1(a): $\qquad\qquad h = 0.6495p = 0.6495 \times \frac{1}{8} = 0.0812$ in.

Basic pitch diameter: $\qquad d = 1.0000 - 0.0812 = 0.9188$ in.

Circumference of pitch circle: $\quad \pi d = 0.9188\pi = 2.8865$ in.

For helix angle: $\qquad\qquad \tan \alpha = \dfrac{0.125}{2.8865} = 0.04331$

$$\alpha = 2°29'$$

Since it is impossible to manufacture parts exactly to a specified size, tolerances have been placed on the dimensions of the screw and nut. Such tolerance zones are illustrated in Figs. 5-2 and 5-3. When the measured

---

[3] See also reference 3, Bibliography.

TABLE 5-1
Dimensions of Unified and American National Screw Threads*

Size†	Outside or Major Dia., in.‡	Coarse Thread Series			Fine Thread Series			Extra Fine Thread Series			Hex. Nut, Width Across Flats, in.#
		Thds. per in.	Basic Pitch Dia., in.§	Stress Area, in.²‖	Thds. per in.	Basic Pitch Dia., in.§	Stress Area, in.²‖	Thds. per in.	Basic Pitch Dia., in.§	Stress Area, in.²‖	
0	0.0600				80	0.0519	0.0018				
1	0.0730	64	0.0629	0.0026	72	0.0640	0.0027				
2	0.0860	56	0.0744	0.0036	64	0.0759	0.0039				
3	0.0990	48	0.0855	0.0048	56	0.0874	0.0052				
4	0.1120	40	0.0958	0.0060	48	0.0985	0.0065				
5	0.1250	40	0.1088	0.0079	44	0.1102	0.0082				
6	0.1380	32	0.1177	0.0090	40	0.1218	0.0101				
8	0.1640	32	0.1437	0.0139	36	0.1460	0.0146				
10	0.1900	24	0.1629	0.0174	32	0.1697	0.0199				
12	0.2160	24	0.1889	0.0240	28	0.1928	0.0257	32	0.1957	0.0269	
1/4	0.2500	20	0.2175	0.0317	28	0.2268	0.0362	32	0.2297	0.0377	7/16
5/16	0.3125	18	0.2764	0.0522	24	0.2854	0.0579	32	0.2922	0.0622	9/16
3/8	0.3750	16	0.3344	0.0773	24	0.3479	0.0876	32	0.3547	0.0929	5/8
7/16	0.4375	14	0.3911	0.1060	20	0.4050	0.1185	28	0.4143	0.1270	3/4
1/2	0.5000	13	0.4500	0.1416	20	0.4675	0.1597	28	0.4768	0.1695	13/16
9/16	0.5625	12	0.5084	0.1816	18	0.5264	0.2026	24	0.5354	0.2134	7/8
5/8	0.6250	11	0.5660	0.2256	18	0.5889	0.2555	24	0.5979	0.2676	15/16
3/4	0.7500	10	0.6850	0.3340	16	0.7094	0.3724	20	0.7175	0.3855	1 1/8
7/8	0.8750	9	0.8028	0.4612	14	0.8286	0.5088	20	0.8425	0.5352	1 5/16
1	1.0000	8	0.9188	0.6051	12	0.9459	0.6624	20	0.9675	0.7095	1 1/2
1 1/8	1.1250	7	1.0322	0.7627	12	1.0709	0.8549	18	1.0889	0.8993	1 11/16
1 1/4	1.2500	7	1.1572	0.9684	12	1.1959	1.0721	18	1.2139	1.1216	1 7/8
1 3/8	1.3750	6	1.2667	1.1538	12	1.3209	1.3137	18	1.3389	1.3684	2 1/16
1 1/2	1.5000	6	1.3917	1.4041	12	1.4459	1.5799	18	1.4639	1.6397	2 1/4
1 3/4	1.7500	5	1.6201	1.8983				16	1.7094	2.2382	2 5/8
2	2.0000	4½	1.8557	2.4971				16	1.9594	2.9501	3
2 1/4	2.2500	4½	2.1057	3.2464							
2 1/2	2.5000	4	2.3376	3.9976							
2 3/4	2.7500	4	2.5876	4.9326							
3	3.0000	4	2.8376	5.9659							
3 1/4	3.2500	4	3.0876	7.0992							
3 1/2	3.5000	4	3.3376	8.3268							
3 3/4	3.7500	4	3.5876	9.6546							
4	4.0000	4	3.8376	11.0805							

* Data from references 1 and 2 Bibliography.
† Sizes 0 to 12 inc. American National. Other sizes are both Unified and Am. National.
‡ Tolerances for OD depend on class of fit.
†† These are basic pitch diameters.
§ Assumed area of bolt used for computing tensile stress.
‖ Semifinished.

dimension of a part falls within the tolerance zone, it is accepted as meeting the dimensional specifications.

The term *maximum metal* refers to the screw of largest pitch diameter and the nut of smallest pitch diameter. Similarly, *minimum metal* refers to the screw of smallest pitch diameter and the nut of largest pitch diameter. Allowance is the clearance between the pitch diameters of screw and nut when both parts of the assembly are at the maximum metal condition.

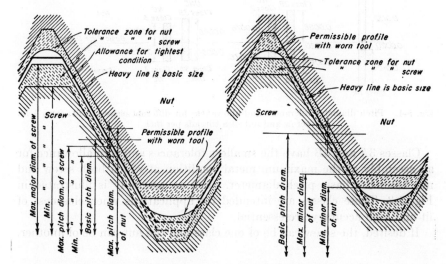

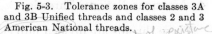

Fig. 5-2. Tolerance zones and allowances for classes 1A, 1B, 2A and 2B Unified Threads.

Fig. 5-3. Tolerance zones for classes 3A and 3B Unified threads and classes 2 and 3 American National threads.

In general, the quality of a product is highest when the tolerance zones are smallest. Manufacturing costs, however, rise as tolerance zones are made smaller.

Unified and American National threads are divided into various classes which depend on the size of the tolerance zones. Figure 5-1(a) illustrates the manner in which the basic size is obtained for both screw and nut.

3. Unified Threads

Unified threads are divided into classes 1A, 2A, and 3A for external threads and classes 1B, 2B, and 3B for internal threads.

Classes 1A and 1B are provided when bolts and nuts of the largest tolerances and the largest clearance after assembly are required. An assembly of such parts is illustrated in Fig. 5-2. The pitch diameter of the maximum metal nut is at the basic size, and the pitch diameter of the maximum metal screw is smaller than basic. Bar diagrams representing the tolerances and allowances for a typical screw are shown in Fig. 5-4.

Classes 2A and 2B are similar to classes 1A and 1B but have smaller tolerances and a smaller clearance after assembly. These classes are well suited for the vast majority of bolts.

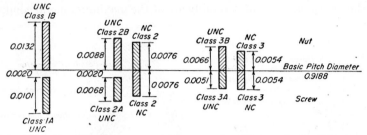

Fig. 5-4. Pitch diameter tolerances and allowances for different classes of fits for a 1 in. screw and nut of 8 threads per inch.

Classes 3A and 3B have the smallest tolerances and zero allowance for an assembly at the maximum metal condition at which both screw and nut have the basic pitch diameter. Such an assembly is illustrated in Fig. 5-3. These classes are intended for applications when closeness of fit and high accuracy are essential.

If desired, the screw can be of one class and the nut can be of another.

4. American National Threads

These threads are divided into classes 2 and 3 for screws and nuts.

Class 2 has the larger tolerances for screw and nut but no allowance for a maximum metal assembly as shown in Fig. 5-3.

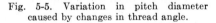

Fig. 5-5. Variation in pitch diameter caused by changes in thread angle.

Fig. 5-6. Variation in pitch diameter caused by difference in lead.

Class 3 has smaller tolerances and produces tighter fits upon assembly. At the maximum metal condition there is no allowance between screw and nut as shown in Fig. 5-3.

It should be noted that Classes 2A and 2B Unified threads have an allowance but that Class 2 American National does not.

As illustrated in Fig. 5-5, a variation in the thread angle of a screw causes a change in its pitch diameter. As shown in Fig. 5-6, a screw and nut, if made with slight differences in lead, may still be assembled if the extent of engagement is limited, and if the two parts have a difference in pitch diameter.

The tolerance on the pitch diameter permitted by the standards must provide for errors from all causes. The effects of angle and lead variation must be included, as well as discrepancies in the pitch diameter itself.

5. Identification Symbols

Following are examples of approved identification symbols for use on drawings, tools, and specifications.

(a) Unified coarse thread series, $\frac{1}{2}$ in. diameter external thread, 12 threads per inch, class 2A fit:

$$\tfrac{1}{2}''\text{–}12\text{UNC–2A}$$

(b) American National coarse thread series, $\frac{1}{2}$ in. diameter, 13 threads per inch, class 2 fit:

$$\tfrac{1}{2}''\text{–}13\text{NC–2}$$

(c) Unified fine thread series, 1 in. diameter internal thread, 12 threads per inch, class 1B fit:

$$1''\text{–}12\text{UNF–1B}$$

For a left-hand thread the designations above should be followed by the letters LH.

6. Effect of Initial Stress

Figure 5-7 shows a load P carried by the part which is attached to the support by means of a bolt. The bolt center is located at the center of gravity of the cross section of the part. Let it be assumed that the nut is merely made snug against the part but with no initial tension in the bolt. Also let it be temporarily assumed in Fig. 5-7 that the part is welded to the support, making it possible for both bolt and part to carry tensile loads.

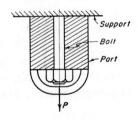

Fig. 5-7. Bolted part carrying load.

When load P is placed on the assembly, the part immediately stretches, and since it is in contact with the nut, the bolt is stretched also. Both part and bolt have tension stresses, because load P divides and is carried partly by the bolt and partly by the part. In finding the portion of load carried by each, it is convenient to work with the so-called "spring constants" of these members. The spring constant k is the value of the force required to give a deformation of one inch. It may be found by using the equation for deformation, $\delta = Pl/AE$, and letting P be equal to k when δ becomes equal to unity. When these substitutions are made, the equations for k_b for the bolt and k_p for the part become

$$k_b = \frac{A_b E_b}{l_b}; \quad \text{and} \quad k_p = \frac{A_p E_p}{l_p} \tag{1}$$

where subscripts b and p refer to bolt and part, respectively, and where A is the cross-sectional area, E is the modulus of elasticity, and l is the length in the direction of the force. If the thread stops immediately above the nut, the gross area of the bolt must be used in computating k_b, since it is the unthreaded portion which is stretched by the load.[4]

Let P_b be the portion of load P which is carried by the bolt, and P_p be the remainder which is taken by the part. The deformation of the bolt is equal to P_b/k_b, and of the part, P_p/k_p. Because of the arrangement of the members in Fig. 5-7, these deformations are equal, and the following equation can be written.

$$\frac{P_b}{k_b} = \frac{P_p}{k_p} \tag{a}$$

Substitution of $P - P_b$ for P_p gives

$$P_b = \frac{k_b}{k_b + k_p} P \tag{b}$$

Similarly,

$$P_p = \frac{k_p}{k_b + k_p} P \tag{c}$$

Suppose now that the nut is tightened to the extent that an additional tensile load equal to F_o is placed in the bolt. The total tension in the bolt is now

$$F_b = \frac{k_b}{k_b + k_p} P + F_o \tag{2}$$

At the same time that the bolt was receiving the additional tension F_o from the tightening, the part was receiving an equal and opposite force of compression F_o. The resultant force in the part now is

$$F_p = \frac{k_p}{k_b + k_p} P - F_o \tag{3}$$

It is usual practice to induce force F_o initially upon assembly of the parts before load P is applied. Equations (2) and (3) are, of course, unaffected. Initial force F_o is always made sufficiently large to keep force F_p

[4] When a greater length of bolt is threaded, suitable allowance must be made for the increased flexibility which thereby results.

for the part negative or compression, and the assumed welding is thus not required. Should P be so great as to remove all the initial compression from the part, then neither Eq. (2) nor Eq. (3) can be used, for the bolt will then be carrying the total load P.

The use of sufficient initial tension is very advantageous in reducing the fatigue effects in the bolt if load P is not steady but fluctuating. For varying load, the maximum bolt force is found by substituting the maximum value of P in Eq. (2), and the minimum bolt force is obtained by use of the minimum value of P. Whereas the maximum value of the bolt force is somewhat larger than if no initial force were used, the presence of F_o gives a considerably larger value of the minimum bolt force than if no tightening-up tension were used. The resultant effect is to give a much smaller range of variation in the bolt force F_b than takes place in the applied load P, and the fatigue effects, which depend on the extent of the variation of the stress, are correspondingly reduced.[5]

Example 2. Let the bolt in Fig. 5-7 be $\frac{1}{2} \times 13$UNC. Bolt and part are of same length; the threads stop immediately above the nut. Bolt material has a yield point value of 50,000 psi with an endurance limit of 30,000 psi. Take the stress concentration factor for the threads as 3. The steel part has a net area of 0.5 in.[2] The load fluctuates continuously between zero and 2,400 lb.

(a) Find the FS for the bolt when no initial force is present.

(b) Find the minimum required value of F_o to prevent loss of compression in the part.

(c) Find the FS for the bolt when F_o is taken as 2,500 lb.

(d) Find the minimum force in the part for the given loading and F_o equal to 2,500 lb.

Solution. (a). By Table 5-1, stress area = 0.1416 in.[2]

$$P_{av} = 1,200 \text{ lb} \qquad s_{av} = \frac{1,200}{0.1416} = 8,475 \text{ psi}$$

$$P_r = 1,200 \text{ lb} \qquad Ks_r = \frac{1,200}{0.1416} \times 3 = 25,420 \text{ psi}$$

When s_{av} and Ks_r are plotted as in Fig. 5-8, it is seen that the bolt loading is unsafe.

(b). For bodies of equal lengths and moduli, the spring constants are proportional to the cross-sectional areas.

$$\text{Gross area of bolt} = \frac{\pi}{4}\left(\frac{1}{2}\right)^2 = 0.1964 \text{ in.}^2$$

[5] See references 5 and 6, Bibliography.

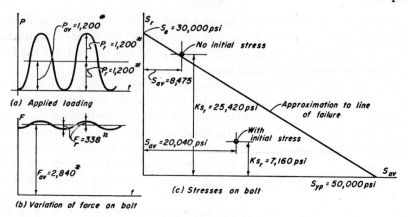

(a) Applied loading

(b) Variation of force on bolt

(c) Stresses on bolt

Fig. 5-8.   Loads and stresses in bolt. Example 2.

When the part has zero compression:

$$F_o = \frac{k_p}{k_b + k_p} P_{max} = \frac{0.5}{0.6964} \times 2,400 = 1,720 \text{ lb}$$

This is the theoretical minimum value for F_o.

(c).

$$F_{bav} = \frac{k_b}{k_b + k_p} P_{av} + F_o = \frac{0.1964}{0.6964} \times 1,200 + 2,500 = 2,840 \text{ lb}$$

$$s_{av} = \frac{2,840}{0.1416} = 20,040 \text{ psi}$$

$$F_{br} = \frac{k_b}{k_b + k_p} P_r = \frac{0.1964}{0.6964} \times 1,200 = 338 \text{ lb}$$

$$s_r = \frac{338}{0.1416} = 2,390 \text{ psi}$$

By Eq. (11), Chapter 2:

$$\frac{50,000}{FS} = 20,040 + \frac{3 \times 50 \times 2,390}{30} = 20,040 + 11,940 = 31,980 \text{ psi}$$

$$FS = \frac{50,000}{31,980} = 1.56$$

(d).

$$F_{pmin} = \frac{k_p}{k_b + k_p} P_{max} - F_o = \frac{0.5}{0.6964} \times 2,400 - 2,500 = -780 \text{ lb}$$

It should be noted that the use of initial stress has changed the situation to the extent that the bolt now has a reasonable value for the factor of safety.

Equations can also be derived for the case where the bolt is located eccentrically to the center of gravity of the part[6] and where the bolt and the part are made of different materials.

7. Effect of Spring Washers and Gaskets

Spring washers and gaskets are frequently incorporated in bolted assemblies. Their effect must be taken into account in the design, since the resulting assembly may be made either weaker or stronger.

Consider first the bolt in Fig. 5-9(a). If the area of the part is very large as compared with the cross section of the bolt, the value of k_p in

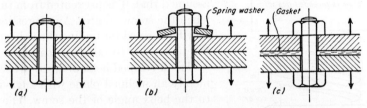

Fig. 5-9.   Various types of bolted assemblies.

Eq. (2) will be much larger than k_b, and variations in load P will have but small effect on the value of F_b. The force in the bolt remains substantially constant at the value F_o as long as initial compression is retained by the part. Although this is a desirable feature, it must be remembered, when the part is rigid, that the lengthening of the bolt required to induce force F_o is a very small quantity. Should the loading cause any creep or recession at the high spots of the contact surfaces, the initial stretch of the bolt may be lost and force F_o will disappear. Shortening of the part may also be caused by corrosion, wear, or displacement of platings and coatings.

The situation can be improved by the use of a spring washer under the nut, as shown in Fig. 5-9(b). The deformation sustained by the washer from force F_o may be many times as great as the stretch of the bolt. Any small shortening of the part during service then has but small effect in reducing the value of F_o, and the initial force can be expected to be retained. It is assumed that the washer is acting in its elastic range and is not compressed solid. Ordinary lock washers, which are compressed solid upon assembly, are of no help in reducing the fluctuations of the load in the bolt. In fact, such devices may constitute an additional hazard from loss of initial stress, caused by plastic flow at high spots or burrs on the surfaces.

A gasket is shown between the parts in Fig. 5-9(c). The stiffness of

[6] See reference 7, Bibliography.

the gasket, hard or soft, influences the over-all value of k_p in Eq. (2). A soft gasket reduces the value of k_p and causes a larger proportion of the load P to be taken by the bolt. It should be kept in mind that any set or permanent deformation of the gasket may cause a loss of the initial force F_o.

8. Power Screws

A power screw can be used for raising weights or exerting forces in machines.[7] The weight W shown in Fig. 5-10, into which the supporting screw is threaded, can be raised or lowered by the rotation of the screw. It is, of course, assumed that W is prevented from turning when the screw rotates. An expression will now be derived for finding the value of the torque needed to raise the load.

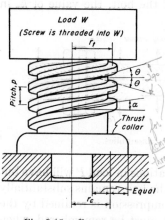

Fig. 5-10.   Power screw.

The developed helix of a screw becomes merely an inclined plane with angle equal to the helix angle of the screw. The force analysis is made from this viewpoint. In Fig. 5-11(a), the lower triangular block represents the screw with the helix angle α computed at the pitch line of the thread; the upper block, in dotted outline, represents the weight. Let force F be just sufficient to cause motion to the left of the lower block. The frictionless rollers at the left cause the upper block to move upward as force F moves the lower block to the left. During rotation of the screw, friction forces occur which oppose the motion on the surface between weight and screw and also on the surface between the collar and the supporting base. This latter friction force in Fig. 5-11(a) is equal to $\mu_2 W$, where μ_2 is the coefficient of friction for this surface.

The situation is shown in perspective in Fig. 5-11(c). Here plane OAB is an axial section through the screw with OB normal to the intersection of the plane and the thread. Line OB is thus inclined to the vertical by angle θ. Plane OAC is tangent to the pitch cylinder with OC normal to the helix. Line OC is thus inclined to the vertical by angle α. The inclination of F_n to the vertical is the resultant effect of angles θ and α. Component OC is equal to $F_n \cos \theta_n$, where θ_n is the angle between F_n and the tangential plane.

$$\tan \theta_n = \frac{CD}{OC} = \frac{AB}{OC} \tag{a}$$

[7] See reference 20, Bibliography.

But
$$AB = AO \tan \theta \tag{b}$$

and
$$OC = \frac{AO}{\cos \alpha} \tag{c}$$

Equations (b) and (c) should now be substituted into Eq. (a) to give

$$\tan \theta_n = \tan \theta \cos \alpha \tag{4}$$

The vector for force F_n has the various components shown. If μ_1 is the

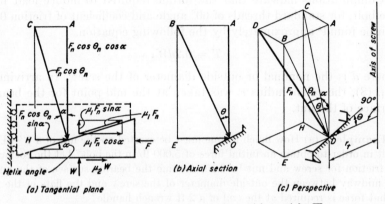

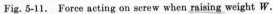

Fig. 5-11.   Force acting on screw when raising weight W.

coefficient of friction for the thread surface, the total friction force is $\mu_1 F_n$ in Fig. 5-11(a). This force is also divided into horizontal and vertical components.

Summation of the vertical forces gives

$$F_n \cos \theta_n \cos \alpha = \mu_1 F_n \sin \alpha + W \tag{d}$$

or
$$F_n = \frac{W}{\cos \theta_n \cos \alpha - \mu_1 \sin \alpha} \tag{5}$$

All thread forces, as well as force F, act at the pitch radius of the thread r_t. The force of the collar friction acts at radius r_c to the midpoint of the collar surface. The torque required to raise the load is found by multiplying the horizontal forces by the appropriate radii. Hence,

$$T = Fr_t = r_t(F_n \cos \theta_n \sin \alpha + \mu_1 F_n \cos \alpha) + r_c \mu_2 W$$

Substitution of the above value for F_n gives

$$T = r_t W \left[\frac{\cos \theta_n \sin \alpha + \mu_1 \cos \alpha}{\cos \theta_n \cos \alpha - \mu_1 \sin \alpha} + \frac{r_c}{r_t} \mu_2 \right] \tag{6}$$

or
$$T = r_t W \left[\frac{\cos \theta_n \tan \alpha + \mu_1}{\cos \theta_n - \mu_1 \tan \alpha} + \frac{r_c}{r_t} \mu_2 \right] \tag{7}$$

see fig 5-10 & 5-11

Equations (6) and (7) give the value of the torque required to raise the load when friction for both thread and collar are included. Sometimes the collar consists of an antifriction bearing, in which case μ_2 may be sufficiently small to be neglected. The equations then contain the μ_1 terms only.

For standard screws that have small values for the helix angle α, Eq. (4) indicates that θ_n has almost the same value as θ. When this is so, θ_n can be replaced by one-half the thread angle in the foregoing equations.

Computations indicate that the torque required to induce load W in the bolt, for standard threads of 60° angle and coefficient of friction 0.15, can be found[8] approximately by the following equation.

$$T = 0.2dW \tag{8}$$

where d is the nominal or outside diameter of the screw. In arriving at Eq. (8), the collar radius r_c was taken at the mid-point for the bearing surface of the nut.

Example 3. (a) How much torque must be exerted on the nut of a 1″–8UNC bolt in order to obtain an initial force of 5,000 lb in the bolt? Let the coefficient of friction for screw and nut be 0.15. Assume the bearing surface of the nut to be midway between the outside diameter of the screw and the flats of the nut. What force is required at the end of a 2 ft wrench handle?

(b) What is the value of the torque by the approximate equation?

Solution. (a)

For helix angle: $\tan \alpha = \dfrac{0.125}{0.9188\pi} = 0.04331$

$\alpha = 2°29'$.

Cosine α is very close to unity, so that θ_n can be taken equal to θ in Eq. (4).

Radius of thread: $r_t = \dfrac{1}{2} \times 0.9188 = 0.4594$ in.

By Table 1, the outside diameter of the collar can be taken as 1.5 in.

The radius of the collar: $r_c = \dfrac{1.5 + 1}{2 \times 2} = 0.625$ in.

By Eq. (7): $T = 0.4594 \times 5,000 \left[\dfrac{0.866 \times 0.043305 + 0.15}{0.866 - 0.15 \times 0.043305} + \dfrac{0.625}{0.4594} \times 0.15 \right]$

$= 2,297 \left[\dfrac{0.1875}{0.8595} + 0.2041 \right] = 970$ in-lb

At the end of the wrench handle: $F = \dfrac{970}{24} = 40$ lb

(b) By Eq. (8), $T = 0.2 \times 1 \times 5,000 = 1,000$ in-lb

[8] See reference 9, Bibliography.

If the weight is being lowered by the application of force F acting to the right in Fig. 5-11, the sign of F, together with the signs of all the friction terms, are reversed. The torque required to lower the load then becomes

$$T = r_t W \left[-\frac{\cos \theta_n \tan \alpha - \mu_1}{\cos \theta_n + \mu_1 \tan \alpha} + \frac{r_c}{r_t} \mu_2 \right] \tag{9}$$

If the helix angle is sufficiently great, the screw will overhaul, or the weight will revolve the screw. The inclined plane in Fig. 5-11(a) will then move to the right and force F must act to the left to preserve uniform motion. The torque equation for the overhauling screw is found to be

$$T = r_t W \left[\frac{\cos \theta_n \tan \alpha - \mu_1}{\cos \theta_n + \mu_1 \tan \alpha} - \frac{r_c}{r_t} \mu_2 \right] \tag{10}$$

If all friction could be eliminated in both screw and collar, Eq. (7) shows that the torque required to raise the load would be

$$T' = r_t W \tan \alpha \tag{11}$$

The efficiency of a power screw with collar friction when it is raising the load is equal to the ratio of the torques of Eqs. (7) and (11). Hence for both screw and collar,

$$\text{efficiency} = \frac{T'}{T} \tag{12}$$

If the collar friction is negligible, the following equation for the efficiency of the screw alone results.

$$\text{efficiency} = \frac{\cos \theta_n - \mu_1 \tan \alpha}{\cos \theta_n + \mu_1 \cot \alpha} \tag{13}$$

Efficiencies, as given by Eq. (13), have been plotted in Fig. 5-12 for several values of μ_1. It should be noted that the power screw has very low mechanical efficiency when the helix angle is in the neighborhood of either 0° or 90°.

The friction between the threads and between the nut and the abutment depends on a variety of factors such as surface finish, degree of lubrication, alignment, materials, plating, burrs, and the like. Calculations for the induced force in the bolt will therefore vary as these factors affect the coefficient of friction. The torque wrench, although widely used, is not considered a very reliable means for obtaining an accurate value of the induced force.

A better way is to measure the bolt elongation when this is possible. The angle of twist of the nut can also be used. The nut is first firmly tightened to seat the parts on each other. It is then loosened and made

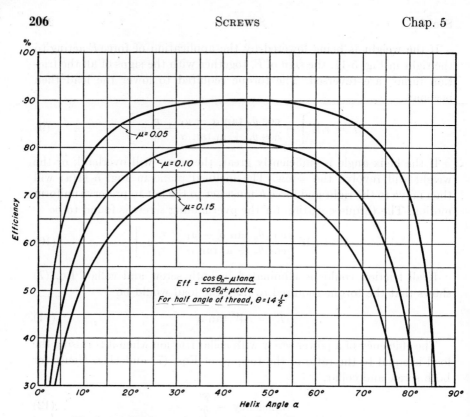

Fig. 5-12. Efficiency of power screw when collar friction is negligible.

finger tight. The nut is then turned through a specified angle which has been calculated to give the desired axial force in the bolt.

9. Stress Due to Impact Load

these are ball-park equations

not on test

Bolts are sometimes subjected to suddenly applied or impact loads. The stress caused by such loads can be found from the energy of impact U that the bolt must absorb.

The force-deformation diagram for a bolt under a tensile load is a triangle, as shown in Fig. 5-13. The area represents the strain energy U stored in the bolt. Thus

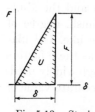

Fig. 5-13. Strain Energy diagram for bolt.

$$U = \frac{1}{2} F \delta \qquad (14)$$

where F is the force caused by impact, and δ is the corresponding deformation. Deformation δ is equal to

F/k, where k is the spring constant for the bolt, AE/l. Substitution for δ gives

$$U = \frac{F^2}{2k} \tag{15}$$

The stress in the bolt is equal to force F divided by the smallest cross-sectional area. For a threaded bolt, this area is the root area of the threaded portion.

Example 4. A $\frac{1}{2}''$–13UNC $\times$ 12 in. long steel bolt must carry an impact load of 40 in-lb.

(a) Find the stress in the root area for a standard bolt.
(b) Find the stress if the entire body of the bolt between head and nut is reduced to that of the root area.

Solution. (a) If the threads stop adjacent to the nut, the full $\frac{1}{2}$ in. diameter is stretched by the impact force. Hence,

$$A = \frac{\pi}{4}\left(\frac{1}{2}\right)^2 = 0.1964 \text{ in.}^2 \quad \text{root area}$$

$$U = \tfrac{1}{2}FS$$

$$k = \frac{AE}{l} = \frac{0.1964E}{12} = 0.01637E$$

$$S = \frac{FL}{AE}$$

In Eq. (15): $\quad F = \sqrt{2kU} = \sqrt{2 \times 0.01637 \times 30{,}000{,}000 \times 40}$

$$U = \tfrac{1}{2}\frac{F^2 L}{AE}$$

$$= 6{,}267 \text{ lb}$$

By Table 5-1:

$$\text{stress area} = 0.1416 \text{ in.}^2$$

In root area: $\qquad\qquad\qquad s = \dfrac{6{,}267}{0.1416} = 44{,}260 \text{ psi}$

It is possible for stress concentration to cause a large increase in the stress above.

(b) The value of k now depends on the root area; hence,

$$k = \frac{AE}{l} = \frac{0.1416E}{12} = 0.01180E$$

In Eq. (15) $\quad F = \sqrt{2 \times 0.01180 \times 30{,}000{,}000 \times 40} = 5{,}320$

$$s = \frac{5{,}320}{0.1416} = 37{,}580 \text{ psi}$$

By careful attention to details, this reduced diameter can be gradually blended into the threaded portion and the stress concentration factor reduced practically to unity.

This example illustrates how a smaller impact stress results from increasing the flexibility by making the diameter equal to the root diameter of the thread. Flexibility can also be increased by using a longer bolt. If the bolt is made of a ductile material, and the yield point is exceeded by the impact force, some permanent stretching results.

10. Friction of Screws

Test results for the coefficients of friction for screw threads and thrust collars for various materials are given in Table 5-2. A number of different speeds and loadings were used in obtaining these average values. The lubricant was a medium-weight engine oil.

TABLE 5-2

Coefficient of Friction for Square, Acme, and American National Screw Threads and Thrust Collars*

Steel Screw and Bronze or Cast-iron Nut		Thrust Collar Friction		
Conditions	Average coefficient of running friction, μ_1	Material	Coefficient of friction, μ_2	
			Starting	Running
High grade materials and workmanship and best running conditions.	0.103	Soft steel on cast iron.	0.170	0.121
Average quality of materials and workmanship and average running condition.	0.126	Hardened steel on cast iron.	0.147	0.092
		Soft steel on bronze.	0.101	0.084
Poor workmanship or very slow and infrequent motion with indifferent lubrication or newly machined surfaces.	0.154	Hardened steel on bronze.	0.081	0.063
Average ratio of starting to running friction, 1.376.				

* From reference 11, Bibliography.

The values in Table 5-2 demonstrate the marked effect which the condition of the surface has on the coefficient of friction. It is also affected by the type of lubricant present. Since rigid control cannot always be exercised over these conditions, too much reliance should not be placed on computations which involve the coefficient of friction.

11. Stress Concentration

A stress concentration is present in the screw when the load is transferred through the nut to the adjoining member. Under ideal conditions, the tension in the screw and the compression in the nut should be reduced uniformly, starting from full load at the bearing surface of the nut. The tension increases the pitch in the screw, and the compression decreases the pitch in the nut. If contact is to be everywhere maintained, the pitches for screw and nut must be initially different. As this is not the case in practice, the load is concentrated toward the base of the nut where the major portion of the force is transferred. Most bolt failures occur in the first or second thread of engagement. Beyond this point, the load decreases very rapidly. The stress concentration is partially relieved by bending of the threads and expansion of the nut.[9] In addition, the load is not uniformly distributed over the root area but increases towards the edge where it is being transferred to the threads of the nut.

Stress concentration factors for threads with static loads are usually determined by photoelastic analysis. When an actual thread is tested in fatigue loading, it is more correct to speak of a stress reduction factor. This factor is defined as the ratio of the endurance limit of the material for a plain specimen to the endurance limit for a specimen with threads. Some test results for screw threads are given in Table 5-3. Other investigators have reported higher values.[10] These experiments show that heat-treated alloy steel is more sensitive to changes of form than plain carbon steel. Stress concentration factors as determined by photoelasticity are somewhat higher than the values given by fatigue tests on actual screws.

Experience has shown that stress concentration is the cause of most bolt failures, especially for fluctuating and impact loads. As was previously mentioned, failure usually occurs in the bolt at the first or second thread of engagement with the nut where the load is localized. Various methods are used for increasing the flexibility of the nut and thus increasing the area over which this transfer of force takes place. A tension nut or a nut with a tapered lip,[11] as shown in Fig. 5-14(a), has been successfully used in fatigue service. The reduced cross-sectional area of the lip deforms with the bolt more than the conventional nut, and the load is accordingly spread over a greater number of threads. The cross section of the bolt can also be reduced over the engaged length. Another method is to cut the thread of the nut on a very small taper, thus reducing the contact area for the first few threads. Since these threads will bend and

---

[9] See references 23 to 28, Bibliography.

[10] See references 3 and 29, Bibliography.

[11] See reference 26, Bibliography.

TABLE 5-3

Stress Concentration Factors for Screw Threads

Tests on Actual Screw, $\frac{3}{8}$ in. $\times$ 16 Threads per Inch*					Stress Conc. Factor by Photo-elasticity	
Material	Tensile Strength, psi	Thread	Endurance Limit, 0-Max., Tension psi	Stress Conc. Factor	Conventional*	Three Dimensional†
0.3% C, as rolled	57,400	No thread	37,000			
0.3% C, as rolled		Am. National	13,000	2.84	5.62	
0.3% C, as rolled		Whitworth	21,000	1.76	3.86	2.72
0.3% C, cold worked	74,000	No thread	43,000			
		Rolled	20,000	2.15		
SAE 2320, heat treated	109,000	No thread	73,000			
SAE 2320, heat treated		Am. National	19,000	3.85		
SAE 2320, heat treated		Whitworth	22,000	3.32		

* See reference 12, Bibliography.
† See reference 22, Bibliography.

carry less load, additional threads must come into service. This method is expensive because of the close dimensional tolerances required. Nuts made of a material with a modulus smaller than the bolt have also been successful in spreading the load over a larger area. The material in the

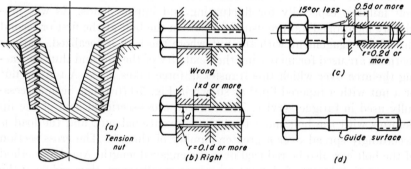

Fig. 5-14. Typical methods for increasing the strength of bolts.

nut, however, must have a sufficient reserve of ductility to deform without breaking.

An increase in the flexibility of the bolt is also beneficial under fatigue conditions.[12] Accordingly, there should be a considerable length of free thread beyond that required for engagement of the nut, as shown in Fig. 5-14(b). A radius between shank and head is helpful in reducing the stress concentration at this point. The run-out angle for the thread should have a small value, as shown in Fig. 5-14(c), since the stress concentration is highest at the first threads. For the same reason, a stress-relieving groove is shown on the right end of this stud. It should have a diameter equal to that of the root of the thread or slightly less, and should be merged to the shank by radii of considerable size. A large radius causes less stress concentration in transferring the load from the larger to the smaller cross section. In addition, if the stud is bent because of misfits in assembly of the parts, the smaller diameter will produce a smaller bending stress in the material. Flexibility of the bolt is increased by reducing the entire length between the head and the threads to the root diameter. If the bolt is holding two or more members together, short lengths of the original diameter must be left at each junction to serve as guide surfaces for the bolted parts, as shown in Fig. 5-14(d).

(a) Castellated nut, drilled bolt and cotter.

(b) Upper part of nut is tapered. Segments press against bolt.

(c) Threads in section above slot are deformed to provide friction grip.

(d) Nylon or fiber insert exerts friction grip on threads.

(e) Nylon plug staked in flat of nut applies friction to bolt threads.

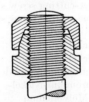

(f) Upper nut contracts the slotted projection of lower nut against bolt.

Fig. 5-15.   Several forms of locknuts.

12. Locknuts

Many different types of locknuts have been devised to prevent a nut from loosening in service due to vibration. Several different forms of locknuts are illustrated in Fig. 5-15. The speed nut, shown in Fig. 5-16,

[12] See reference 23, Bibliography.

Fig. 5-16. Standard flat-type speed nut.

acts as a single-thread nut of spring steel strip. This type of nut can be rapidly assembled. When tightened, the prongs press against the stud, and the strip acts as an arched spring lock.

Many kinds of lock and spring washers, placed beneath an ordinary nut, are also in use. Success depends on the type of washer and the conditions of the particular application.

Self-tapping[13] and drive screws are available for fastener service in sheet metal, plastics, nonferrous metals, and other materials.

13. Materials and Methods of Manufacture

Bolts and screws may be turned on automatic screw machines, using bar stock of the same dimensions as the head, or they may be cold- or hot-headed from stock of the same diameter as the shank. A number of typical steels for bolts and screws are shown in Table 5-4. Free-cutting screw

TABLE 5-4
Typical SAE Steels for Bolts and Screws

Steel	Automatic Screw Machine		Cold Heading	Hot Heading
	Material	Machinability		
Free-cutting screw stock	1113	135% Cold drawn		
Free-cutting screw stock	1112	100% Cold drawn		
Free-cutting screw stock	1117	85% Cold drawn		
Free-cutting screw stock	1137	73% Cold drawn		
Plain-Carbon	1015 to 1035	57% Cold drawn	1010 to 1045	1010 to 1045
Nickel	2330	61% Annealed	2330	2330
Nickel-Chromium	3140	57% Annealed	3140	3140
Chromium-Molybdenum	4140	61% Annealed	4140	4140
Chromium-Nickel-Molybdenum	A8640	55% Annealed	A8640	A8640

stock is preferred for use on automatic screw machines because the chips break short and, as a result, there is less danger of fouling the working parts of the machine. These advantages are indicated by the high machinability ratings for these materials. Steels 1112 and 1113 are Bessemer steels of high sulphur and phosphorous content; 1117 and 1137 are high-manganese, open-hearth steels. Alloy steel bolts are used for severe service conditions where the properties of high strength and ductility

[13] See reference 16, Bibliography.

are required. Bolts of alloy steels are usually heat treated to secure the benefits of the alloy content of the material.

Turned bolts generally have good dimensional control and concentricity between head and shank. The threads are cut as one of the screw machine operations. A considerable waste of material results from this method in turning the shank from material that was originally the size of the head. Because of this loss, the automatic screw machine is in widest use for bolts of about $\frac{1}{4}$-in. diameter and less.

The cold-heading process uses slightly oversize stock which is first drawn through a die to secure dimensional uniformity and to cold work the surface. The forging machine then upsets a round head which is afterwards trimmed to a square or hexagonal shape by a shearing operation. The low-carbon steels, because of better workability, give longer die life than alloy steels. The threads on cold-headed bolts are usually formed by rolling the shank between dies which depress part of the steel to form the root and which force the remainder up to make the top of the thread. The outside diameter of the thread thus is larger than the stock on which it was rolled. If the threaded portion of the bolt is to have the same diameter as the unthreaded part, the rolling must be done on a reduced diameter. Forging machines form this portion of smaller cross section at the same time that the head is upset. Rolled threads, because of favorable grain structure at the root of the thread, are stronger than cut threads in fatigue and impact.

For larger size heads and more complicated shapes, hot heading is generally employed. Hot heading is especially suitable for the tougher and less ductile alloy steels. The process is more expensive than cold heading because of the operations involved in heating the end of the bar to the forging temperature. Bolts and screws of nonferrous materials are produced in large quantities by the same methods used for steel.

BIBLIOGRAPHY

Volume number shown in **bold face** type. The number immediately following is the page on which the article begins.

1. *Unified and American Screw Threads, ASA B1.1-1949.* New York: American Society of Mechanical Engineers.

2. *Screw-Threads for Federal Services, Handbook H28.* Washington: U. S. Government Printing Office, 1957.

3. Den Hartog, J. P., "The Mechanics of Plate Rotors for Turbo Generators," *Trans. ASME,* **51,** APM 1 (1929).

4. Tucker, S. A., "What the New Screw Thread Standard Means to Designers," *Product Eng.,* **20,** May, 81 (1949).

5. Almen, J. O., "On the Strength of Highly Stressed, Dynamically Loaded Bolts and Studs," *SAE Journal (Trans.)*, **52**, April, 151 (1944). See also *Machine Design*, **15**, Aug., 133 (1943); **16**, Feb., 158 (1944).

6. Dolan, T. J., "Load Relations in Bolted Joints," *Mech. Eng.*, **64**, 607 (1942).

7. Dolan, T. J., and McClow, J. H., "Influence of Bolt Tension and Eccentric Tensile Loads on the Behavior of a Bolted Joint," *Proc. Soc. Exptl. Stress Anal.*, **8**, No. 1, 29 (1950).

8. Lipson, C., "Strength Considerations in the Bolt Fastening Design," *Proc. Soc. Exptl. Stress Anal.*, **1**, No. 2, 101 (1943).

9. Lenzen, K. H., "Strength and Clamping Force of Bolts," *Product Eng.*, **18**, Dec., 130 (1947).

10. Stang, A. H., "Tensile Forces in Tightened Bolts," *Product Eng.*, **22**, Feb., 118 (1951).

11. Ham, C. W., and Ryan, D. G., "An Experimental Investigation of the Friction of Screw Threads," *Bulletin 247*, University of Illinois Engineering Experiment Station, 1932.

12. Moore, H. F., and Henwood, P. E., "Strength of Screw Threads Under Repeated Tension," *Bulletin 264*, University of Illinois Engineering Experiment Station, 1934.

13. Whittemore, H. L., Nusbaum, G. W., and Seaquist, E. O., "Impact and Static Tensile Properties of Bolts," *J. Research*, **14**, 139 (1935).

14. Pickel, Wm. F., "Tightening Characteristics of Nut and Stud Assemblies," *Product Eng.*, **20**, Jan., 98 (1949).

15. Millard, A. C., "Machine Screws," *Mech. Eng.*, **65**, 701 (1943).

16. Millard, A. C., "Self-Tapping Screws," *Mech. Eng.*, **68**, 935 (1946).

17. Johnson, E., "Some Experiments in Tapping," *Proc. Inst. Mech. Engs.*, **164**, 46 (1951).

18. Eatough, C., "Screws and Screwing," *Proc. Inst. Mech. Engrs.*, **164**, 52 (1951).

19. Brunot, A. W., and Schmittner, W. G., "Stress Study of a Fabricated Steam Chest," *Proc. Soc. Exptl. Stress Anal.*, **4**, No. 1, 49 (1946).

20. Atwood, G. H., "A New Type of Screw-Luffing Crane for Shipbuilding," *Mech. Eng.*, **66**, 569 (1944).

21. Goodier, J. N., and Sweeney, R. J., "Loosening by Vibration of Threaded Fastenings," *Mech. Eng.*, **67**, 798 (1945).

22. Hetényi, M., "A Photoelastic Study of Bolt and Nut Fastenings," *Trans. ASME*, **65**, A-93 (1943).

23. Arnold, S. M., "Effect of Screw Threads on Fatigue," *Mech. Eng.*, **65**, 497 (1943).

24. Goodier, J. N., "Distribution of Load on the Threads of Screws," *Trans. ASME*, **62**, A-10 (1940).

25. Heywood, R. B., "Tensile Fillet Stresses in Loaded Projections," *Proc. Inst. Mech. Engrs.*, **159**, 384 (1948).

26. Sopwith, D. G., "Distribution of Load in Screw-Threads," *Proc. Inst. Mech. Engrs.*, **159**, 373 (1948).

27. Almen, J. O., "Fatigue Durability of Prestressed Screw Threads," *Product Eng.*, **22**, April, 153 (1951).

28. Thurston, R. C. A., "Fatigue Strength of Threaded Connections," *Trans. ASME*, **73**, 1085 (1951).

29. Brown, A. F. C., and Hickson, V. M., "A Photoelastic Study of Stresses in Screw Threads," *Proc. Inst. Mech. Engrs.*, (*B*), **1 B**, 605 (1952–53).

30. Stoeckly, E. E., and Macke, H. J., "Effect of Taper on Screw Thread Load Distribution," *Trans. ASME*, **74**, 103 (1952).

31. *Guide to World Screw Thread Standards*, Lynton Works, Bedford, England: W. H. A. Robertson & Co. Ltd.

PROBLEMS

In problems 1 to 5 inclusive, let it be assumed that the threads stop immediately above the nut.

1. In an assembly with loading arrangement equivalent to Fig. 5-7, the bolt is $\frac{3}{4}''$=16UNF, and the total load varies from 2,000 lb to 10,000 lb. The material in the bolt tests $s_{yp} = 100,000$ psi and $s_e = 60,000$ psi, with stress concentration factor for the threads equal to 3. Let the factor of safety based on the yield point be 2, and let E for both part and bolt be equal to 30,000,000 psi. Bolt and part each are 5 in. long; the cross-sectional area of the part is equal to 1.25 in.^{2}

(a) Draw the working-stress triangle for the bolt material, and plot the stresses when there is no initial stress in the bolt.

(b) If the initial force in the bolt is 8,000 lb, plot the stress values for the bolt on the working-stress triangle.

It will be necessary to determine whether or not the part will have a compressive force when the maximum load is acting. Should all the initial compression be removed, the force in the bolt will have the same value as the load.

(c) Repeat (b) with an initial bolt force of 13,000 lb. Note the effect of excessive initial stress.

(d) Suppose the bolt is made of steel, but the part is made of aluminum. $E = 10,000,000$ psi. Plot the stress values for the bolt if other data are the same as in (b).

(e) Suppose the bolt were turned to the root diameter of the thread over its entire length except for the nut. Plot the stress values for the bolt; other data are the same as in (b).

Ans. (a) $s_{av} = 16,110$ psi; $Ks_r = 32,220$ psi.

(b) $s_{av} = 25,690$ psi; $Ks_r = 8,420$ psi.

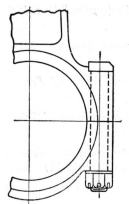

Fig. 5-17.   Problem 2.

2. The connecting rod bolt of Fig. 5-17 is $\frac{3}{8}''$–24UNF and is drawn up to an initial force of 3,500 lb. The bolt material has a yield-point value of 90,000 psi, and an endurance limit of 58,000 psi. The average cross-sectional area of the bolted parts is equal to 0.50 in.² Stress concentration factor for the threads is equal to 3. The load for the part varies continuously from zero to 2,500 lb. Find the value of the factor of safety for the bolt. Find the value of the minimum force in the part. Material of the part has the same modulus as the bolt.

Ans. FS = 1.65.

3. Let the bolt in Fig. 5-7 be $1''$–12UNF and be made of material with a yield point of 90,000 psi and an endurance limit of 55,000 psi. The factor of safety is to be 2. The part is made of steel with cross-sectional area equal to 1.2 in.² The maximum applied load is 20,000 lb. The minimum load is 10,000 lb. Because of the threads, stress concentration factor equals 2. Find the maximum value of F_o if the bolt is to be safe for continuous operation.   *Ans. F_o = 17,400 lb.*

4. Let the bolt in Fig. 5-7 be $\frac{3}{4}''$–10UNC and be made of material with a yield point of 90,000 psi and an endurance limit of 55,000 psi. The factor of safety is to be 2.5. The part is made of steel with a cross-sectional area of 1 in.² Because of the threads, stress concentration factor equals 2. The initial force is 8,000 lb. The average value of the stress at the stress area is 30,000 psi. Find the maximum and minimum values of the applied load P. Find the minimum force in the part.

Ans. P_{max} = 8,590 lb; P_{min} = 4,590 lb.

5. (a) In Fig. 5-7 let the part undergo a permanent shortening in length equal to ϵ after the bolt has been tightened to an initial force of F_o. Derive an equation for the new value F'_o for the initial force in the bolt.

(b) Find the value of F'_p for the bolt of Problem 1(b) if the part for some reason should shorten 0.0003 in.

$$Ans. \quad (a) \ F'_o = F_o - \frac{\epsilon k_b k_p}{k_b + k_p}, \quad (b) \ F'_p = -23 \text{ lb.}$$

6. Find the force of tension in a $\frac{5}{16}''$–24NF bolt if it is tightened by a wrench with a torque equal to 240 in-lb. Assume the coefficient of friction for the screw and the collar to be the same, and make computations for coefficients of 0.10, 0.15, and 0.20. Take the outer collar diameter as being equal to 0.50 in.

Ans. For μ = 0.10, F_0 = 5,510 lb.

7. A load of 10,000 lb is carried by a 2.5-in. single-thread Acme screw of standard proportions. The pitch is $\frac{1}{3}$ in. and the pitch diameter is $2\frac{1}{3}$ in. The OD of the collar is equal to 4 in., and the ID is equal to 1.25 in.

(a) For $\mu_1 = \mu_2 = 0.15$, find the horsepower required to rotate the screw if the weight is to be raised at the rate of 10 fpm.

(b) What is the efficiency when friction of both screw and collar is considered? What is the efficiency if the collar friction were made negligible by use of an anti-friction bearing?

(c) Find the horsepower required to lower the load at the same rate.

(d) What horsepower will raise the load at the given rate when the collar is supported on a ball thrust bearing for which $\mu_2 = 0.003$? Let the collar radius be the same as for the plain bearing. What will now be the efficiency?

(e) Find the pitch of the thread at which overhauling will take place, using a ball thrust bearing. The pitch diameter is the same.

(f) Suppose the screw is made with pitch just sufficient to overhaul. What will be the efficiency for the screw alone?

(g) If the minimum major diameter of the screw is 2.483 in. and the maximum minor diameter of the nut is 2.183 in., find the minimum length of the nut which must be engaged if the compressive stress on the projected area of the threads is equal to 600 psi.

(h) If the minimum minor diameter of the screw is 2.130 in., find the average value of the compressive stress at the root of the thread. What is the bearing pressure for the collar?   *Ans.*   (a) hp = 24.7; (b) eff. = 12.3% and 22.5%; (e) p = 1.16 in.; (g) length = 5.05 in.

8. (a) Write the expression for tan α for a square thread with negligible collar friction at which the maximum efficiency will occur.

(b) What is the value of the maximum efficiency, and the angle at which it occurs, for $\mu_1 = 0.1$.   *Ans.*   tan $\alpha = -\mu_1 + (1 + \mu_1^2)^{1/2}$; eff. = 81.9%.

9. What pitch must be provided on a square thread power screw to raise a 2,000 lb weight at 40 fpm with power consumption of 4 hp? The pitch diameter is 1.375 in., μ_1 is 0.15, and collar friction is negligible.   *Ans.* p = 1.106 in.

10. A square thread screw has an efficiency of 65 per cent when raising a load. The coefficient of friction for the threads is 0.15 with collar friction negligible. Pitch diameter is 2.75 in. When lowering a load, a uniform velocity is maintained by a brake mounted on the screw. If the load is equal to 10 tons, what torque must be exerted by the brake?   *Ans.* T = 4,550 in-lb.

11. A square thread screw has an efficiency of 70 per cent when raising a weight. The coefficient of friction $\mu_1 = 0.12$ with collar friction negligible. The load is 8,000 lb and the pitch diameter is 1.15 in. Find the torque which a brake mounted on the screw must exert when lowering the load at a uniform rate.

Ans. T = 890 in-lb.

12. A square thread screw, 0.9 in. pitch diameter, has an efficiency of 70 per cent when raising a 4,000 lb weight. The coefficient of friction for the threads is 0.10, with collar friction negligible. Find the torque that a brake mounted on the screw must exert when the load is being lowered at a constant rate.

Ans. T = 270 in-lb.

13. A square thread screw has a pitch diameter of 1.5 in. and a lead of 1 in. The screw consumes 4 hp when raising a 2,800 lb weight at the rate of 30 fpm. Collar friction is negligible. Find the coefficient of friction for the threads.

Ans. μ_1 = 0.113.

14. A square thread screw is at the point of overhauling when at rest. When raising a 1,000 lb weight at 15 fpm the input is 0.93 hp. Find the pitch of the screw if the pitch diameter is 0.8 in. Collar friction is negligible.

Ans. p = 0.377 in.

The following problems are presented without answers.

15. A screw of 9 threads per inch is to be cut on a $1\frac{3}{16}$ in. diameter bar. Proportions are similar to the Unified Thread. Find the value of the basic pitch diameter. If the screw is made double thread, find the helix angle.

16. The minimum major diameter of a $1''$–8UNC screw is 0.9755 in. The maximum minor diameter of the nut is 0.8797 in. Find the required length of nut that must be engaged with the screw if the tensile load is 8,000 lb and the permissible bearing stress on the projected area of the threads is 10,000 psi.

17. The OD of the aluminum part in Fig. 5-7 is 1.00 in. The bolt is steel, $\frac{1}{2}$ in. in diameter. The nut is torqued to 600 in-lbs by the approximate equation. Find the maximum load P that can be placed on the part without losing all the initial compression in the part. Threads stop immediately above the nut. Part and bolt are of equal length.

18. A square thread power screw has μ_1 equal to 0.14 and negligible collar friction. When holding a load, it is just at the point of overhauling. What is the efficiency for this screw when raising a load?

19. Work Problem 11, but with the efficiency at 75 per cent.

20. Work Problem 13, but with the horsepower of 4.5.

21. Work Problem 14, but with the input horsepower of 0.95.

22. A square thread screw is at the point of overhauling. Its efficiency when raising a load is 0.49. What is the coefficient of friction for the threads if the collar friction is negligible?

23. A square thread screw has an efficiency of 60 per cent when mounted with an anti-friction collar. The helix angle is 12°. Find the torque required to exert a 2,000 lb force if the pitch diameter of the screw is 2 in.

6

Belts, Clutches, Brakes

BELTS, brakes, and clutches are examples of machine elements that employ friction for transfer of energy. Although individual electric motor drives have become increasingly popular, the use of belts in industry will undoubtedly remain important in the power transmission field for many years to come. Design calculations for devices that depend on friction are subject to uncertainties brought about by changes in the value of the coefficient of friction. Such changes arise from variations in the operating conditions of the machine, especially those of temperature and moisture. In addition, the capacity of a brake to absorb energy is generally limited by the maximum permissible temperature of the lining material.

A, area
b, width of belt or brake lining
c, center distance
CCW, counterclockwise
CW, clockwise
d, diameter
$e = 2.718$, base of natural logarithms
fpm, feet per minute
fps, feet per second
F_n, normal force
$g = 32.2$ ft/sec^2 = 386 in./sec^2 acceleration due to gravity
hp, horsepower
l, length of belt

M_f, moment due to friction forces
M_n, moment due to normal forces
n, rpm, revolutions per minute
p, pressure, psi
P, force
r, radius
R, reaction
s, stress
T, torque, in-lb
T_0, initial force in belt
T_1, force in tight side
T_2, force in slack side
V, velocity, fpm
V_s, velocity, fps

v, velocity, in./sec
w, weight per ft of belt
α, (alpha) arc of contact for belt or brake lining

β, (beta) active arc for belt
δ, (delta) wear, in.
ϵ, (epsilon) elongation in./in.
μ, (mu) coefficient of friction

1. Forces in Flat Belts

Power can be transmitted from one shaft to another by means of a belt and pulleys as shown in Fig. 6-1. It is necessary for the belt to have an initial tension T_0, which is secured by making the belt slightly under length, or by providing a take-up screw at one of the pulleys to increase the

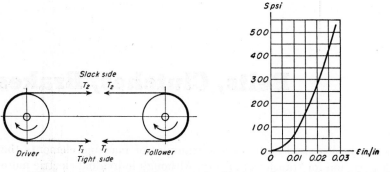

Fig. 6-1. Forces in flat belt.

Fig. 6-2. Stress-strain curve for leather.

center distance. When transmitting power, the tension force T_1 of the tight side is greater than the tension force T_2 of the slack side.

For belt materials such as leather, the stress is not proportional to the strain. A typical stress-strain curve is shown[1] in Fig. 6-2, which indicates that the elongations become smaller with increase of stress.

The relationship between stress s and elongation ϵ can be approximated by an equation of the form

$$s = C_1{}^2\epsilon^2 \tag{1}$$

where C_1 is a constant. A commonly used value of C_1 for leather is 830, which has been used for plotting the curve of Fig. 6-2.

Let it be assumed, when transmitting power, that the total stretch of the belt is the same as when it is at rest. In other words, the increase of stretch on the tight side is equal to the decrease of stretch on the slack side. On this assumption, the total stretch of the belt from the unstressed condition is given by the following equation.

$$\frac{1}{2}l\epsilon_1 + \frac{1}{2}l\epsilon_2 = l\epsilon_0 \tag{2}$$

[1] See reference 1, Bibliography.

where ϵ_1 and ϵ_2 are the elongations for the tight and slack sides, respectively, ϵ_0 is the initial elongation, and l is the total length of the belt.

Equation (1) should now be substituted and each term multiplied by the cross-sectional area of the belt, to give

$$\sqrt{T_1} + \sqrt{T_2} = 2\sqrt{T_0} \tag{3}$$

where T_1, T_2, and T_0 are tight side, slack side, and initial forces of the belt, respectively.

The horsepower transmitted by a belt is $T = tension$

$$\text{hp} = \frac{(T_1 - T_2)V}{33,000} = \frac{(T_1 - T_2)V_s}{550} \tag{4}$$

where V is the velocity of the belt in feet per minute, and V_s is the velocity in feet per second.

Example 1. The belt shown in Fig. 6-1 is made of $\frac{5}{16}$ by 8 in. leather and is to transmit 25 hp at 200 rpm of the driving pulley. The center distance for the pulleys is 18 ft, and diameter of each pulley is 54 in. Let the take-up screws be adjusted until the center distance is increased $5\frac{1}{4}$ in. beyond the point where the slack had been removed. Find the value of the tight, slack, and initial belt forces. $C_1 = 830$.

Solution.

Velocity of the belt: $\quad V = \frac{54}{12}\pi \times 200 = 2827.4 \text{ fpm} = 47.12 \text{ fps}$

In Eq. (4): $\quad T_1 - T_2 = \dfrac{33,000 \text{ hp}}{V} = \dfrac{33,000 \times 25}{2827.4} = 291.8 \text{ lb}$ $\tag{a}$

One-half length of belt $= 27\pi + 18 \times 12 = 301$ in.

Initial elongation: $\quad \epsilon_0 = \dfrac{5.25}{301} = 0.01745 \text{ in./in.}$

In Eq. (1): $\quad s_0 = C_1{}^2\epsilon_0{}^2 = 830^2 \times 0.01745^2 = 209.7 \text{ psi}$

Initial force: $\quad T_0 = \dfrac{5}{16} \times 8 \times 209.7 = 524.3 \text{ lb}$

$$2\sqrt{T_0} = 45.8$$

In Eq. (3): $\quad \sqrt{T_1} = -\sqrt{T_2} + 45.8$

Squaring: $\quad T_1 = T_2 - 91.6\sqrt{T_2} + 2097.8$ $\tag{b}$

Equations (a) and (b) should now be solved simultaneously to give

$$T_1 = 680.4 \text{ lb}; \qquad T_2 = 388.6 \text{ lb}$$

It should be noted in the example above that it was necessary to take the deformations into account in order to find the values of the belt forces. A further investigation is necessary to determine if the friction forces on the pulleys are sufficient to transmit the given power.

2. Action of Belt on Pulley

The fact that T_1 is greater than T_2 implies that the belt has a small relative movement, called creep, on the surface of the pulley. This occurs because the change in tension from T_1 to T_2 must be accompanied by a

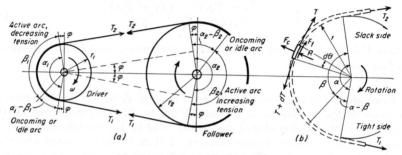

Fig. 6-3. Action of belt on pulleys.

change in the elongation of the belt material. The tight side has the maximum elongation because of the higher value of force T_1, and the slack side has the minimum elongation because of the smaller force T_2. The belt must therefore creep on the surface of the pulley to compensate for these different elongations.

Except when the drive is delivering its maximum power, creep occurs only on a portion β of the total arc of contact α as shown in Fig. 6-3(a). No creep takes place[2] on the oncoming or idle arc $\alpha - \beta$. The magnitude of the idle arc decreases if the belt is called upon to transmit more power. The maximum output of the drive is reached when creep is taking place over the entire arc of contact.

Figure 6-3(b) shows the forces acting on an element of the belt cut by two radii an angle $d\theta$ apart. The tension in the tight side is equal to the tension T on the slack side plus an increment dT. If the tangential velocity of the pulley is V_s, fps, and if the weight per foot of the belt is w, the centrifugal force F_c acting on the element is equal to

$$F_c = \frac{wr\,d\theta}{g} \cdot \frac{V_s^2}{r} = \frac{wV_s^2}{g}\,d\theta \tag{a}$$

The total inward component of the forces T and $T + dT$ is equal to $T\,d\theta$. The reaction R of the pulley on the belt is equal to the difference

[2] See reference 2, Bibliography.

between $T\,d\theta$ and F_c. The friction force F_f is then equal to

$$F_f = \mu R = \mu(T\,d\theta - F_c) \tag{b}$$

where μ is the coefficient of friction.

Summation of the forces in the tangential direction gives

$$T + dT = T + \mu\left[T\,d\theta - \frac{wV_s{}^2}{g}\,d\theta\right]$$

or

$$\frac{dT}{T - (wV_s{}^2/g)} = \mu\,d\theta$$

Integration over the active arc from 0 to β gives

$$\log\left[T - \frac{wV_s{}^2}{g}\right]_{T_2}^{T_1} = \mu\theta\,\Big|_0^\beta$$

or

$$\frac{T_1 - (wV_s{}^2/g)}{T_2 - (wV_s{}^2/g)} = e^{\mu\beta} \tag{5}$$

where e is 2.718, the base for the system of natural logarithms.

The output of a belt is decreased by the centrifugal effects which tend to lift it from the pulley and prevent the full value of the tangential friction force from being developed. With increase of speed, Eq. (5) indicates that a velocity will be reached at which no power can be transmitted. Since experiments have shown that even at high speeds considerable power is carried, the equation should be considered conservative and on the safe side, particularly for heavy belts.

Term $wV_s{}^2/g$ has the dimension force. Values of the exponential function $e^{\mu\beta}$ are given in Table 6-1.

TABLE 6-1
Values of Exponential $e^{\mu\beta}$

$\mu\beta$	$e^{\mu\beta}$	$\mu\beta$	$e^{\mu\beta}$	$\mu\beta$	$e^{\mu\beta}$	$\mu\beta$	$e^{\mu\beta}$	$\mu\beta$	$e^{\mu\beta}$	$\mu\beta$	$e^{\mu\beta}$	$\mu\beta$	$e^{\mu\beta}$
0.30	1.350	0.45	1.568	0.60	1.822	0.75	2.117	0.90	2.460	1.05	2.858	1.20	3.320
0.31	1.363	0.46	1.584	0.61	1.840	0.76	2.138	0.91	2.484	1.06	2.886	1.21	3.354
0.32	1.377	0.47	1.600	0.62	1.859	0.77	2.160	0.92	2.509	1.07	2.915	1.22	3.387
0.33	1.391	0.48	1.616	0.63	1.878	0.78	2.181	0.93	2.535	1.08	2.945	1.23	3.421
0.34	1.405	0.49	1.632	0.64	1.896	0.79	2.203	0.94	2.560	1.09	2.974	1.24	3.456
0.35	1.419	0.50	1.649	0.65	1.916	0.80	2.226	0.95	2.586	1.10	3.004	1.25	3.490
0.36	1.433	0.51	1.665	0.66	1.935	0.81	2.248	0.96	2.612	1.11	3.034	1.26	3.525
0.37	1.448	0.52	1.682	0.67	1.954	0.82	2.270	0.97	2.638	1.12	3.065	1.27	3.561
0.38	1.462	0.53	1.699	0.68	1.974	0.83	2.293	0.98	2.664	1.13	3.096	1.28	3.597
0.39	1.477	0.54	1.716	0.69	1.994	0.84	2.316	0.99	2.691	1.14	3.127	1.29	3.633
0.40	1.492	0.55	1.733	0.70	2.014	0.85	2.340	1.00	2.718	1.15	3.158	1.30	3.669
0.41	1.507	0.56	1.751	0.71	2.034	0.86	2.363	1.01	2.746	1.16	3.190	1.31	3.706
0.42	1.522	0.57	1.768	0.72	2.054	0.87	2.387	1.02	2.773	1.17	3.222	1.32	3.743
0.43	1.537	0.58	1.786	0.73	2.075	0.88	2.411	1.03	2.801	1.18	3.254	1.33	3.781
0.44	1.553	0.59	1.804	0.74	2.096	0.89	2.435	1.04	2.829	1.19	3.287	1.34	3.819

Example 2. (a) Find the size of the active arc for the belt described in Example 1. The weight of the leather is 0.035 lb/in.[3] Coefficient of friction, $\mu = 0.3$.

(b) For the same value of active arc, what would be the horsepower if centrifugal effects are neglected?

Solution. (a) $\qquad w = 0.035 \times \dfrac{5}{16} \times 8 \times 12 = 1.05$ lb/lineal ft

From Example 1: $\quad V_s = 47.12$ fps, $\quad T_1 = 680.4$ lb, $\quad T_2 = 388.6$ lb

$$\frac{wV_s^2}{g} = \frac{1.05 \times 47.12^2}{32.2} = 72.5 \text{ lb}$$

In Eq. (5): $\qquad \dfrac{680.4 - 72.5}{388.6 - 72.5} = 1.9231 = e^{\mu\beta}$ $\hfill$ (a)

The value of $\mu\beta$ can be found from Table 6-1, or can be computed as follows Take the logarithm of both sides of Eq. (a).

$$\mu\beta \log_{10} e = \log_{10} 1.9231$$

$$0.43429\mu\beta = 0.28400$$

$$\mu\beta = \frac{0.28400}{0.43429} = 0.65394$$

$$\beta = \frac{0.65394}{0.3} = 2.18 \text{ radians}$$

$$= 2.18 \times 57.296 = 124.9°$$

(b)

From Eq. (5): $\qquad\qquad \dfrac{T_1}{T_2} = e^{\mu\beta} = 1.9231$

$$T_1 = 1.9231 T_2$$

This equation should be solved simultaneously with Eq. (b) of Example 1.

$$T_1 = 708 \text{ lb}; \qquad T_2 = 368 \text{ lb}$$

By Eq. (4): $\qquad \text{hp} = \dfrac{(708 - 368) \times 47.12}{550} = 29.1$

The action of a belt on a pulley when transmitting power is complicated, and there are a number of factors which the design equations are unable to take into account. However, experimental results from various investigators are in agreement in showing that the power transmitted, up to a certain limit, increases as the creep or slip between pulley and belt increases.

The relationship between the net tension $T_1 - T_2$ and the creep and slip has been plotted for the idealized case in Fig. 6-4. The net tension increases uniformly with the creep from A to B until the entire arc of contact is transmitting power. Should the attempt be made to transmit more power, a uniform slip B to C, in addition to the creep, will occur over the entire arc of contact. The location of the knee of the curve at B varies somewhat for different belt and pully materials, but it is usually located at a value for the creep of 1 per cent to 3 per cent of the total movement of the belt. Experimental curves are sometimes more rounded in the neighborhood of point B and may have a slight upward slope for the BC portion. This latter feature may be explained if it is assumed that the coefficient of friction is not constant for belt materials but increases somewhat with the increase of slip.[3]

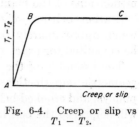

Fig. 6-4. Creep or slip vs $T_1 - T_2$.

3. Coefficient of Friction and Working Stresses

The coefficient of friction depends on the kind of material for belt and pulley, and also on the condition of the surfaces, since moisture or grease tends to reduce the coefficient. Table 6-2 gives average values for various materials.

TABLE 6-2

Coefficients of Friction for Belts and Pulley Materials*

Belt Material	Pulley Material					
	Iron-Steel	Wood	Paper	Wet Iron	Greasy Iron	Oily Iron
Oak-tanned leather	0.25	0.30	0.35	0.20	0.15	0.12
Mineral-tanned leather	0.40	0.45	0.50	0.35	0.25	0.20
Canvas stitched	0.20	0.23	0.25	0.15	0.12	0.10
Balata	0.32	0.35	0.40	0.20	—	—
Cotton woven	0.22	0.25	0.28	0.15	0.12	0.10
Camel-hair	0.35	0.40	0.45	0.25	0.20	0.15
Rubber-friction	0.30	0.32	0.35	0.18	—	—
Rubber-covered	0.32	0.35	0.38	0.15	—	—
Rubber on fabric	0.35	0.38	0.40	0.20	—	—

* *Machinery*, **37**, 560-a (1931).

Long-duration experiments have shown that low working stresses greatly increase the useful life of a belt. However, when the stresses are low, the belt must be larger, and the initial cost is then greater. The designer must compromise between these two considerations. A

[3] See references 2, 5, and 28, Bibliography.

conservative value of the working stress for leather is 250 psi; a value of 300 psi should not be exceeded. For other belting materials, the recommendations of the manufacturer should be followed.

Leather belting weighs from 0.035 to 0.045 lb/in.[3] Other materials weigh approximately the same, but the manufacturers' catalogs should be consulted for exact values.

The assembly of the various elements composing a drive is subject to geometric imperfections such as skewed or nonparallel shafts, staggered pulleys, and crooked belts or belt joints. A camber or crown on the pulley will help keep the belt in place. The central half of the pulley face should

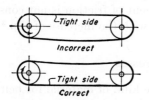

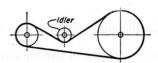

Fig. 6-5. Tight side of belt should be on   Fig. 6-6. Flat belt with idler pulley.
bottom.

be cylindrical, and the portions on either side should be given slight tapers, either straight or curved.[4]

It is general practice to operate line shaft and machine belting at speeds of from 1,000 to 3,000 fpm. Higher speeds sometimes require the use of excessively large pulleys and careful attention to alignment and mechanical details. Leather belting manufacturers should be consulted concerning drives operating at speeds of 5,000 or 6,000 fpm.[5]

For horizontal drives where a considerable distance exists between the pulley centers, the weight of the belt is of great value in helping to maintain the tension. This advantage is lost when the belt is vertical or steeply inclined. Horizontal drives should be arranged to run with the tight side on the bottom, as indicated in Fig. 6-5. The pulley size should be as large as practical, providing the belt speeds are not excessive. Since a large pulley produces less flexing of the belt, the fatigue effects are correspondingly reduced, and the belt life is prolonged. Various devices are in use for increasing the pressure between belt and pulley or increasing the arc of contact in order that a larger friction force can be developed and more power transmitted. One device of this kind is an idler pulley, shown in Fig. 6-6. Although the power output is increased, the idler causes a flexing in the reverse direction which may seriously shorten the belt life. Belt life is also reduced if the loads are unsteady or

---

[4] See reference 3, Bibliography.
[5] See reference 6, Bibliography.

subject to shocks. A leather belt which is new and stiff will not develop its full output until it is broken in.

4. Design of Belts by Tables

Although the above-mentioned factors exert a large influence on belt performance, they are not taken into consideration by the design equations previously derived. Consequently, tables of loads and service factors have been prepared for the design of belts. Table 6-3 gives the horsepower per inch of width for various speeds and thicknesses of belt.[6] The effects of pulley diameter and center distance are given by the service factors of Table 6-4. Correction factors for condition of surface, angle of belts, pulley material, and type of load are shown in Table 6-5. The horsepower per inch of width is found by taking the appropriate value from Table 6-3, and multiplying by the factors from Tables 6-4 and 6-5.

Example 3. By use of the tables, find the horsepower which the belt of Example 1 can transmit. The tight side is on the bottom and the atmospheric conditions are normal. Pulleys are cast iron. Service is continuous and loads are jerky.

Solution. Constant from Table 6-3: 8.27; constant from Table 6-4: 1.00; successive constants from Table 6-5: 1, 1, 1, 0.8, 0.8.

Per inch of width: hp $= 8.27 \times 1 \times 1 \times 1 \times 1 \times 0.8 \times 0.8 = 5.29$

Total: hp $= 8 \times 5.29 = 42.3$

This example shows that the capacity of a belt, as determined by the tables, may be considerably different from the results obtained by the use of equations. In general, it is necessary for the designer to decide whether the most economical drive consists of a large belt operating at low stresses and long life, or whether it is better to use a smaller and cheaper belt with consequent higher stresses and shorter life.

5. Pivoted Motor Drive

The belt pulley of an electric motor is characterized by high angular velocity, which necessitates a small-diameter pulley if the belt speed is not to be excessive. Floor space is often at a premium so that drives of long center distance cannot be used. With a large speed reduction, the smaller pulley has a reduced angle of contact. A short center drive usually has insufficient elasticity in the belt to retain the initial tension for the desired interval between adjustments. However, if the base is pivoted[7]

[6] See reference 7, Bibliography.
[7] See references 4 and 10, Bibliography.

TABLE 6-3*
Horsepower per Inch of Width

Belt Speed Feet per Min.		Single Ply		Double Ply			Triple Ply	
		$\frac{11}{64}''$	$\frac{13}{64}''$	$\frac{18}{64}''$	$\frac{20}{64}''$	$\frac{23}{64}''$	$\frac{30}{64}''$	$\frac{34}{64}''$
		Med.	Heavy	Light	Med.	Heavy	Med.	Heavy
600		1.1	1.2	1.5	1.8	2.2	2.5	2.8
800		1.4	1.7	2.0	2.4	2.9	3.3	3.6
1000		1.8	2.1	2.6	3.1	3.6	4.1	4.5
1200		2.1	2.5	3.1	3.7	4.3	4.9	5.4
1400		2.5	2.9	3.5	4.3	4.9	5.7	6.3
1600		2.8	3.3	4.0	4.9	5.6	6.5	7.1
1800		3.2	3.7	4.5	5.4	6.2	7.3	8.0
2000		3.5	4.1	4.9	6.0	6.9	8.1	8.9
2200		3.9	4.5	5.4	6.6	7.6	8.8	9.7
2400		4.2	4.9	5.9	7.1	8.2	9.5	10.5
2600		4.5	5.3	6.3	7.7	8.9	10.3	11.4
2800		4.9	5.6	6.8	8.2	9.5	11.0	12.1
3000		5.2	5.9	7.2	8.7	10.0	11.6	12.8
3200		5.4	6.3	7.6	9.2	10.6	12.3	13.5
3400		5.7	6.6	7.9	9.7	11.2	12.9	14.2
3600		5.9	6.9	8.3	10.1	11.7	13.4	14.8
3800		6.2	7.1	8.7	10.5	12.2	14.0	15.4
4000		6.4	7.4	9.0	10.9	12.6	14.5	16.0
4200		6.7	7.7	9.3	11.3	13.0	15.0	16.5
4400		6.9	7.9	9.6	11.7	13.4	15.4	16.9
4600		7.1	8.1	9.8	12.0	13.8	15.8	17.4
4800		7.2	8.3	10.1	12.3	14.1	16.2	17.8
5000		7.4	8.4	10.3	12.5	14.3	16.5	18.2
5200		7.5	8.6	10.5	12.8	14.6	16.8	18.5
5400		7.6	8.7	10.6	12.9	14.8	17.1	18.8
5600		7.7	8.8	10.8	13.1	15.0	17.3	19.0
5800		7.7	8.9	10.9	13.2	15.1	17.5	19.2
6000		7.8	8.9	10.9	13.2	15.2	17.6	19.3
Minimum Pulley Diameter	Belts Under 8" Wide	3"	5"	6"	8"	12"	20"	24"
	Belts 8" and Over Wide			8"	10"	14"	24"	30"
	Wide	These are the minimum allowable pulleys for the above thickness belts.						

* Tables 6-3, 6-4, and 6-5 are reproduced by permission of the American Leather Belting Association, 41 Park Row, New York 7, N. Y.

TABLE 6-4

Correction Factor for Small Pulley Diameter

Diameter Small Pulley Inches	Center Distance in Feet							
	Up to 10'		15'		20'		25' and Over	
	Tight Side		Tight Side		Tight Side		Tight Side	
	Above	Below	Above	Below	Above	Below	Above	Below
2"	.37	.37	.38	.41	.37	.43	.37	.44
$2\frac{1}{2}$"	.41	.41	.43	.46	.41	.48	.42	.49
3	.45	.45	.48	.52	.48	.54	.48	.55
$3\frac{1}{2}$"	.49	.49	.53	.57	.53	.59	.53	.60
4"	.53	.53	.58	.63	.59	.65	.59	.66
$4\frac{1}{2}$"	.56	.56	.61	.66	.62	.68	.62	.70
5"	.59	.59	.65	.70	.66	.72	.66	.74
6"	.62	.62	.68	.74	.69	.76	.70	.78
8"	.66	.66	.72	.78	.73	.80	.74	.82
9"	.67	.67	.73	.79	.74	.81	.75	.83
10"	.68	.68	.75	.81	.76	.83	.77	.85
12"	.70	.70	.77	.83	.78	.86	.79	.88
14"	.72	.72	.79	.85	.80	.88	.81	.90
16"	.74	.74	.80	.87	.81	.89	.82	.91
18"	.75	.75	.82	.89	.83	.91	.84	.93
20"	.75	.75	.83	.90	.84	.92	.85	.94
24"	.77	.77	.85	.92	.86	.94	.87	.96
30"	.79	.79	.87	.94	.88	.96	.89	.98
36"	.80	.80	.88	.95	.89	.98	.90	1.00

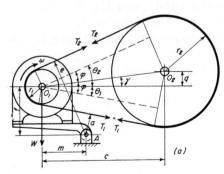
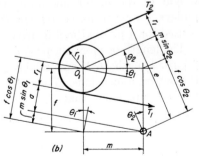

Fig. 6-7.   Pivoted motor drive.

TABLE 6-5
Service Correction Factors
Select the one appropriate factor from each of the five divisions in Table 6-5

Atmospheric Condition	Clean, scheduled maintenance on large drives............	1.2
	Normal..	1.0
	Oily, wet or dusty.....................................	.7
Angle of Center Line	Horizontal to 60 degrees from horizontal................	1.0
	60 to 75 `"` `"` `"`	.9
	75 to 90 `"` `"` `"`	.8
Pulley Material	Fibre on motor and small pulleys.......................	1.2
	Cast iron or steel.....................................	1.0
Service	Temporary or infrequent...............................	1.2
	Normal..	1.0
	Important or continuous...............................	.8
Peak Loads	All electric motor drives,	
	motor pulley diameters— 3″ to $3\frac{1}{2}$″................	.5
	4″ to $4\frac{1}{2}$″................	.55
	5″ to $5\frac{1}{2}$″................	.58
	6″ to 10″...............	.6
	11″ to 13″...............	.63
	14″ to 17″...............	.65
	18″ to 23″...............	.68
	24″ to 30″...............	.7
	All other drives—	
	Steady belt loads...............................	1.0
	Jerky belt loads................................	.8
	Shock and reversing belt loads....................	.6

as shown in Fig. 6-7, the motor weight W maintains an initial tension in the belt. A moment equation can be written by multiplying forces T_1, T_2, and W by their respective arms measured from the pivot at A. Hence,

$$Wm = T_1a + T_2e \qquad (6)$$

This equation should be solved simultaneously with Eq. (5). Since the weight of the motor maintains the belt in intimate contact with the pulleys, the terms for centrifugal force are usually neglected when Eq. (5) is used for a pivoted motor drive.

The length of moment arms a and e can be found by reference to Fig. 6-7(b). Length O_1O_2 and angles γ and φ can be easily calculated from the given dimensions. Then $\theta_1 = \varphi - \gamma$, and $\theta_2 = \varphi + \gamma$. Reference to the figure shows that

$$a = f \cos \theta_1 - m \sin \theta_1 - r_1 \qquad (7)$$

$$e = f \cos \theta_2 + m \sin \theta_2 + r_1 \qquad (8)$$

High rotative speeds increase the number of stress cycles, and the fatigue effects are correspondingly greater. To reduce the effects of

flexing around the small pulley, the belt should be thin and correspondingly wider. The largest possible pulleys consistent with reasonable belt
speeds should be used. The tight side should be on the bottom, and, if
the belt is wide, no camber should be placed on the small pulley.

Example 4. Let the belt in Fig. 6-7 be of oak-tanned leather. The smaller
pulley is of wood, 9 in. in diameter, and turns 1,150 rpm. The motor weighs 765 lb;
$f = m = 11.5$ in.; $c = 30$ in.; $q = 5.5$ in. Find the horsepower capacity of the
drive. $r_2 = 15$ in.

Solution. $O_1O_2 = \sqrt{30^2 + 5.5^2} = 30.5$ in.

$$\tan \gamma = \frac{5.5}{30} = 0.18333; \qquad \gamma = 10°23'$$

$$\sin \varphi = \frac{10.5}{30.5} = 0.34426; \qquad \varphi = 20°8'$$

$$\theta_1 = 20°8' - (10°23') = 9°45'$$

$$\theta_2 = 20°8' + (10°23') = 30°31'$$

By Eq. (7): $a = 11.5 \times 0.98556 - 11.5 \times 0.16935 - 4.5 = 4.886$ in.

By Eq. (8): $e = 11.5 \times 0.86148 + 11.5 \times 0.50779 + 4.5 = 20.246$ in.

By Eq. (6): $4.886T_1 + 20.246T_2 = 765 \times 11.5 = 8797.5$ (a)

By Table 6-2: $\mu = 0.3$

$$\beta = 180° - 2(20°8') = 139°44' = 2.4388 \text{ radians}$$

$$\mu\beta = 0.3 \times 2.4388 = 0.7316$$

By Table 6-1: $e^{\mu\beta} = 2.0785$

$$\frac{T_1}{T_2} = e^{\mu\beta} = 2.0785; \qquad T_1 = 2.0785T_2$$

This equation should now be substituted into Eq. (a) to give

$$T_1 = 601.5 \text{ lb}; \qquad T_2 = 289.4 \text{ lb}$$

$$\text{hp} = \frac{Tn}{63,025} = \frac{(601.5 - 289.4) \times 4.5 \times 1,150}{63,025} = 25.62$$

6. Length of Belt

The length of belt l can be readily found when the pulley diameters
d_1 and d_2 and the center distance c are known. Thus, in Fig. 6-8,

$$\cos \psi = \frac{r_2 - r_1}{c} \tag{9}$$

$$\frac{1}{2}l = r_2(\pi - \psi) + (r_2 - r_1)\tan \psi + r_1\psi$$

or $l = \pi d_2 + (d_2 - d_1)(\tan \psi - \psi)$ (10)

The expression $\tan \psi - \psi$ is called the involute function[8] of ψ written inv ψ. Values are given in Table 6-6. These are useful where pulley diameters and belt length are known and the center distance must be

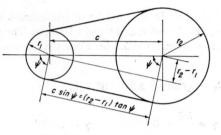

Fig. 6-8. Geometry of belt.

found. Substitution can be made in Eq. (10) after rearranging in the following form

$$\text{inv } \psi = \frac{l - \pi d_2}{d_2 - d_1} \tag{11}$$

Example 5. A V-belt is 70.9 in. long and is to operate on sheaves of pitch diameters 10 in. and 14 in. Find the required center distance.

Solution.

In Eq. (11): $\text{inv } \psi = \dfrac{70.9 - 14\pi}{4} = 6.7294$

By Table 6-6: $\psi = 83.03°$

By Eq. (9): $c = \dfrac{2}{0.12137} = 16.48$ in.

7. V-belts

The rayon and rubber V-belt is widely used in power transmission. The typical cross section, in Fig. 6-9, shows the main tension-carrying cords which are usually placed near the mid-height of the belt. Belts are made in five sizes and two qualities: standard and premium, as indicated by Table 6-7. They are suitable for use with short center distances, and are made endless, so that difficulty with splicing devices is avoided. First

---

[8] For a more extensive table see reference 9, Bibliography of Chapter 10.

TABLE 6-6

Values of Involute Function inv ψ, (where inv $\psi = \tan \psi - \psi$)

	50°	51°	52°	53°	54°	55°	56°	57°	58°	59°
0.0	0.319089	0.344779	0.372370	0.402020	0.433904	0.468217	0.505177	0.545027	0.588044	0.634535
0.1	0.321577	0.347450	0.375240	0.405105	0.437223	0.471790	0.509027	0.549182	0.592531	0.639389
0.2	0.324082	0.350141	0.378130	0.408212	0.440566	0.475390	0.512907	0.553368	0.597053	0.644281
0.3	0.326605	0.352850	0.381042	0.411342	0.443934	0.479016	0.516816	0.557586	0.601611	0.649212
0.4	0.329146	0.355579	0.383974	0.414495	0.447326	0.482670	0.520755	0.561837	0.606205	0.654182
0.5	0.331706	0.358328	0.386928	0.417671	0.450744	0.486351	0.524724	0.566121	0.610834	0.659192
0.6	0.334283	0.361096	0.389902	0.420870	0.454187	0.490060	0.528723	0.570438	0.615500	0.664243
0.7	0.336879	0.363884	0.392899	0.424093	0.457656	0.493797	0.532753	0.574789	0.620203	0.669333
0.8	0.339494	0.366693	0.395918	0.427340	0.461150	0.497562	0.536813	0.579173	0.624943	0.674465
0.9	0.342127	0.369521	0.398958	0.430610	0.464670	0.501355	0.540905	0.583591	0.629720	0.679638

	60°	61°	62°	63°	64°	65°	66°	67°	68°	69°
0.0	0.684853	0.739397	0.798622	0.863053	0.933293	1.010043	1.094119	1.186482	1.288263	1.400812
0.1	0.690110	0.745101	0.804822	0.869805	0.940663	1.018106	1.102966	1.196216	1.299009	1.412719
0.2	0.695410	0.750852	0.811074	0.876615	0.948098	1.026244	1.111896	1.206045	1.309864	1.424751
0.3	0.700753	0.756651	0.817379	0.883485	0.955600	1.034456	1.120910	1.215970	1.320829	1.436910
0.4	0.706139	0.762498	0.823738	0.890415	0.963169	1.042744	1.130011	1.225994	1.331906	1.449198
0.5	0.711570	0.768393	0.830151	0.897406	0.970806	1.051109	1.139199	1.236116	1.343097	1.461618
0.6	0.717045	0.774338	0.836619	0.904458	0.978512	1.059552	1.148474	1.246339	1.354403	1.474170
0.7	0.722564	0.780333	0.843143	0.911572	0.986288	1.068073	1.157839	1.256664	1.365826	1.486857
0.8	0.728129	0.786379	0.849723	0.918748	0.994135	1.076674	1.167295	1.267092	1.377367	1.499681
0.9	0.733740	0.792475	0.856359	0.925989	1.002053	1.085356	1.176842	1.277624	1.389029	1.512643

	70°	71°	72°	73°	74°	75°	76°	77°	78°	79°
0.0	1.525747	1.665027	1.821046	1.996762	2.195871	2.423054	2.68433	2.98757	3.34327	3.76574
0.1	1.538994	1.679832	1.837677	2.015552	2.217238	2.447534	2.71262	3.02058	3.38224	3.81237
0.2	1.552386	1.694806	1.854508	2.034579	2.238891	2.472360	2.74133	3.05412	3.42188	3.85988
0.3	1.565925	1.709953	1.871541	2.053847	2.260834	2.497540	2.77048	3.08821	3.46222	3.90830
0.4	1.579614	1.725275	1.888781	2.073362	2.283073	2.523081	2.80007	3.12286	3.50328	3.95766
0.5	1.593456	1.740775	1.906231	2.093126	2.305613	2.54899	2.83012	3.15808	3.54507	4.00798
0.6	1.607451	1.756455	1.923895	2.113146	2.328461	2.57527	2.86064	3.19389	3.58762	4.05929
0.7	1.621604	1.772320	1.941776	2.133426	2.351623	2.60194	2.89163	3.23029	3.63094	4.11162
0.8	1.635916	1.788371	1.959878	2.153970	2.375105	2.62900	2.92311	3.26732	3.67505	4.16499
0.9	1.650389	1.804612	1.978206	2.174783	2.398913	2.65646	2.95509	3.30497	3.71998	4.21945

	80°	81°	82°	83°	84°	85°	86°	87°	88°	89°
0.0	4.27502	4.90003	5.68420	6.6957	8.0483	9.9465	12.7997	17.563	27.100	55.74
0.1	4.33173	4.97040	5.77370	6.8132	8.2090	10.1792	13.1658	18.220	28.607	62.10
0.2	4.38963	5.04240	5.86552	6.9341	8.3752	10.4217	13.5512	18.925	30.281	70.06
0.3	4.44874	5.11608	5.95975	7.0587	8.5474	10.6745	13.9576	19.681	32.152	80.2!
0.4	4.50911	5.19149	6.05650	7.1871	8.7257	10.9383	14.3866	20.496	34.258	93.95
0.5	4.57077	5.26871	6.15586	7.3195	8.9106	11.2139	14.8401	21.377	36.644	113.03
0.6	4.63377	5.34780	6 25793	7.4561	9.1023	11.5022	15.3205	22.330	39.371	141.67
0.7	4.69816	5.42882	6.36283	7.5970	9.3014	11.8038	15.8300	23.367	42.518	189.42
0.8	4.76396	5.51184	6.47068	7.7426	9.5081	12.1199	16.3714	24.498	46.190	284.91
0.9	4.83124	5.59694	6.58160	7.8929	9.7230	12.4515	16.9478	25.737	50.529	571.39

cost is low, and power output may be increased by operating several belts side by side. All belts in the drive should stretch at the same rate in order to keep the load equally divided between them. When one of the belts breaks, the entire group must usually be replaced. The drive may be inclined at any angle with tight side either top or bottom. Since belts can

TABLE 6-7
Sizes and Design Constants for V-Belts

Belt Section	Width b	Height h	Recommended Pitch Diameters for Pulleys, in.	K_b		K_c, Std. and Premium
				Standard	Premium	
A	$\frac{1}{2}$	$\frac{5}{16}$	3.0–18.0	157	220	0.561
B	$\frac{21}{32}$	$\frac{13}{32}$	4.6–18.4	406	576	0.965
C	$\frac{7}{8}$	$\frac{17}{32}$	9.0–64.0	1,112	1,600	1.716
D	$1\frac{1}{4}$	$\frac{3}{4}$	13.0–96.0	3,873	5,680	3.498
E	$1\frac{1}{2}$	$\frac{29}{32}$	21.6–96.0	7,332	10,850	5.041

operate on small pulleys, large reductions of speed in a single drive are possible.

The included angle for the belt is usually from 34° to 38°. The wedging action of the belt in the groove gives a large increase in the tractive force developed by the belt.

Pulleys may be made of cast iron, stamped sheet steel, or die cast. Sufficient clearance must be provided at the bottom of the groove to prevent the belt from bottoming as it becomes narrower from wear.

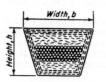

Fig. 6-9.　V-belt.

Sometimes the larger pulley is not grooved when it is possible to develop the required tractive force by running on the inner surface of the belt. The cost of cutting the grooves is thereby eliminated. Pulleys are on the market which permit an adjustment in the width of the groove. The effective pitch diameter of the pulley is thus varied, and moderate changes in the speed ratio can be secured.

During a circuit around the pulleys, the force on the belt varies over a considerable range, as is illustrated by Fig. 6-10. Here T_c is the centrifugal force, and T_1 and T_2 are the tensions in the tight and slack sides respectively. Forces T_{b1} and T_{b2} are additional forces arising from bending around the pulleys.

In general, failure of a V-belt occurs from fatigue in some portion of the structure as affected by the force peaks at C and D in Fig. 6-10. Based on long experience from laboratory and field testing, fatigue curves[9]

[9] These may be plotted to larger scale, if desired, from the data given in Table 6-8. Data, courtesy Gates Rubber Co., Denver, Colo.

TABLE 6-8

Peak Force, Pounds, vs Number of Peaks to Failure

Section	Standard		Premium	
A	93 at 10^8	75 at 10^9	128 at 10^8	104 at 10^9
B	160	130	221	179
C	284	231	392	319
D	580	472	801	651
E	836	679	1,153	937

showing the number of stress cycles to failure for the different sizes and qualities of belts are given in Fig. 6-11.

The tension ratio T_1/T_2 depends on the adjustment of the center distance of the pulleys, and thus varies with the particular installation being considered. For equal diameter pulleys, a suitable average value is

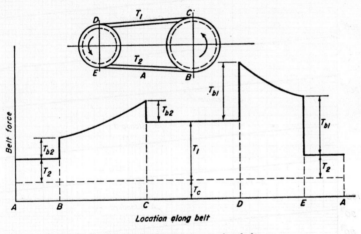

Fig. 6-10.   Forces in moving belt.

to take T_1/T_2 equal to 5 and to base the design calculations accordingly. Bending force T_b and centrifugal force T_c can be obtained from the equations[10]

$$T_b = \frac{K_b}{d} \tag{12}$$

$$T_c = K_c \left(\frac{V}{1,000}\right)^2 \tag{13}$$

where d is the pitch diameter of the sheave in inches, and constants K_b and K_c are given in Table 6-7.

[10] See reference 26, Bibliography.

A service factor must usually be applied to the net horsepower requirement to take care of starting conditions and load fluctuations. A recommended set of such values[11] is given in Table 6-9.

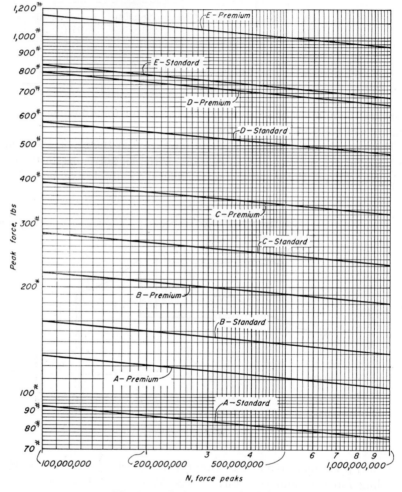

Fig. 6-11.   Fatigue curves for V-belts.

Use of the fatigue curves is illustrated by the following example.

Example 6. A premium quality C-section belt is 70.9 in. long, and is to transmit 9 hp. Service factor is 1.6. Both pulleys have a pitch diameter of 10 in. and turn 1,160 rpm. Find the expected life of the belt in hours.

[11] A more complete table is given in *Engineering Standards*, published by Multiple V-Belt Drive and Mechanical Power Transmission Assn., Chicago 3, Ill.

TABLE 6-9
Service Factors to Correct for Motor Type, Starting Method, and Kind of Load

Applications	Squirrel cage — Normal torque line start	Squirrel cage — Normal torque compensator start	Squirrel cage — High torque	Synchronous — Wound rotor (slip ring)	Synchronous — Normal torque	Synchronous — High torque	Single phase — Repulsion and split phase	Single phase — Capacitor	D.C. Motors — Shunt wound	D.C. Motors — Compound wound	Engines — Four or more cyl. gas and diesel above 700 rpm	Lineshafts and clutch starting
Agitators, paddle propelled	1.2	1.0	1.4	1.2	—	—	—	—	—	—	—	2.0
Brick and clay machinery	1.5	1.3	1.8	1.5	—	—	—	—	1.4	—	—	—
Bakery machinery	1.2	—	—	—	—	—	1.2	1.0	—	—	—	—
Compressors	1.4	1.4	—	1.5	1.5	—	1.2	1.2	1.2	—	1.2	—
Conveyors, screw	—	1.6	1.8	—	—	—	—	—	1.6	—	—	1.8
Crushing machinery	—	1.4	1.6	1.4	1.4	1.6	—	—	—	1.6	1.6	1.6
Fans and blowers	1.6	1.6	2.0	2.0	2.0	2.0	—	—	1.4	—	1.6	1.5
Flour-feed-cereal-mill machinery	1.4	1.4	1.6	1.4	1.4	—	—	—	—	—	1.8	—
Generators, exciters	1.2	—	—	—	—	—	—	—	1.2	—	2.0	1.4
Laundry machinery	1.2	—	—	—	—	—	—	—	—	1.2	1.2	—
Lineshafts	1.4	1.4	—	1.4	1.4	2.0	1.4	1.4	1.4	1.4	1.6	1.6
Machine tools	1.2	—	—	1.4	—	—	1.2	1.2	1.2	1.2	—	—
Mills	—	1.6	1.6	1.4	—	—	—	—	—	1.4	—	1.6
Oil-field machinery	1.2	1.2	1.4	—	—	—	—	—	1.4	1.4	1.4	1.6
Paper machinery	1.5	1.4	1.8	1.5	1.6	1.8	—	—	1.5	1.5	—	1.8
Printing machinery	1.2	1.2	—	1.2	—	—	—	—	1.2	1.2	—	—
Pumps	1.4	1.4	1.4	1.6	1.6	1.8	1.2	1.2	1.2	—	2.0	—
Rubber-plant machinery	1.4	1.4	1.4	1.4	—	1.8	—	—	—	—	—	—
Screens, vibrating	1.2	1.2	1.4	—	—	—	—	—	—	—	—	—
Textile machinery	1.6	—	1.8	—	—	—	—	—	—	—	—	—

Solution. $T_2 = 0.2T_1$.

Design hp: hp = 9 × 1.6 = 14.4

$$V = \frac{\pi\, dn}{12} = \frac{\pi 10 \times 1{,}160}{12} = 3{,}037 \text{ fpm}$$

By Eq. (4): $T_1 = \dfrac{33{,}000 \times 14.4}{0.8 \times 3{,}037} = 195.6 \text{ lb}$

By Eq. (12): $T_b = \dfrac{1{,}600}{10} = 160.0 \text{ lb}$

By Eq. (13): $T_c = 1.716 \times 3.037^2 = \underline{15.8} \text{ lb}$

Peak force $= \overline{371.4} \text{ lb}$

By Fig. 6-11: $N = 190,000,000$ force peaks

$$\frac{\text{Belt passes}}{\text{min}} = \frac{3,037 \times 12}{70.9} = 514$$

There are two equal force peaks in each passage of the belt.

$$\text{Expected life} = \frac{190,000,000}{514 \times 2 \times 60} = 3,100 \text{ hrs}$$

8. Designing When Pulleys Are of Unequal Diameters

When the driving pulley is smaller than the driven pulley, the arc of contact between belt and pulley becomes less than a semicircle, and the T_1/T_2 ratio of 5 cannot be maintained. Adjustment for this condition can be made by use of the factors of Table 6-10.

TABLE 6-10

Ratio T_1/T_2 for V-Belts for Various Values of Angle of Contact

Angle of Contact	$\dfrac{T_1}{T_2}$	Angle of Contact	$\dfrac{T_1}{T_2}$	Angle of Contact	$\dfrac{T_1}{T_2}$	Angle of Contact	$\dfrac{T_1}{T_2}$
180°	5.00	155°	4.00	130°	3.20	105°	2.56
175	4.78	150	3.82	125	3.06	100	2.44
170	4.57	145	3.66	120	2.92	95	2.34
165	4.37	140	3.50	115	2.80	90	2.24
160	4.18	135	3.34	110	2.67		

When the two pulleys of a drive are of unequal diameter, the combined fatigue effects must be taken into account. If the fatigue life at the small pulley is N_1 cycles, then one passage of the belt consumes $1/N_1$ of the belt life. Similarly, if N_2 is the life at the larger pulley, one passage of the belt consumes $1/N_2$ of the belt life. The proportion of belt life consumed in one passage of the belt on account of both pulleys is

$$\frac{1}{N'} = \frac{1}{N_1} + \frac{1}{N_2} \tag{14}$$

where N' is the number of belt passes determined by the combined effects of both pulleys.

Example 7. A premium C-section belt is 70.9 in. long. Driving pulley is 10 in. in diameter, and the driven pulley is 14 in. in diameter. Driver rpm is 1,160; hp is 9 with service factor equal to 1.6. Find the expected life in hours.

Solution. Small pulley.

From Example 5:　　$\psi = 83.03°$ Angle of contact $= 166.06°$

By Table 6-10:　　$\dfrac{T_1}{T_2} = 4.41$ or $T_2 = 0.227 T_1$

In Eq. (4):　　$T_1 = \dfrac{33,000 \times 14.4}{0.773 \times 3,037} = 202.4$ lb

From Example 6:　T_{b1}　　　　　　　　　$= 160.0$ lb

From Example 6:　T_c　　　　　　　　　$= \underline{15.8}$ lb

　　　　　　　　　Peak force $= \overline{378.2}$ lb

By Fig. 6-11:　　　　　　　　　$N_1 = 155,000,000$ peaks

Large pulley.　　$T_1 =$　　　　　　202.4 lb

　　　　　　$T_{b2} = \dfrac{1,600}{14} = 114.3$ lb

　　　　　　$T_c =$　　　　　15.8 lb

　　　　　Peak force $= \overline{332.5}$ lb

By Fig. 6-11:　　$N_2 = 630,000,000$ peaks

By Eq. (14):　　$\dfrac{1}{N'} = \left(\dfrac{1}{155} + \dfrac{1}{630}\right)\dfrac{1}{1,000,000} = \dfrac{0.00804}{1,000,000}$

　　　　　$N' = 124,000,000$ belt passes

From Example 6:　$\dfrac{\text{Belt passes}}{\text{min.}} = 514$

　　　　Expected life $= \dfrac{124,000,000}{514 \times 60} = 4,000$ hrs

Reference to the result for Example 6, indicates that increasing the size of one of the pulleys reduces the fatigue effects and gives a corresponding increase in the expected life.

An additional series of high capacity industrial belts is also available. The power range is covered by three sizes known as 3V, 5V, and 8V. These belts are narrower and have the tension-carrying cords located near the upper surface. Space savings can be made since the diameter and width of the sheaves are less than for the conventional type of V-belt.

When designing a V-belt drive, it is advisable to determine the cost for two or three different layouts of belts and sheaves to determine which has the lowest total cost.

9. Disk Clutch

The plate clutch, shown diagrammatically in Fig. 6-12, is used in both automotive and industrial service. Let it be assumed that the parts are sufficiently rigid to give uniform wear over the lining, and that the wear is proportional to the product of velocity and the pressure. Since the

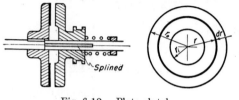

Fig. 6-12.   Plate clutch.

velocity is proportional to the radius r to the element, the following equation can be written:

$$\delta = Kpr \tag{a}$$

where δ is the wear, and K is a constant. Since δ is constant for the entire face, the maximum pressure will occur at the smallest or inner radius r_i. Hence,

$$\delta = Kp_{max}r_i \tag{b}$$

Elimination of δ and K from the equations above gives

$$p = \frac{p_{max}r_i}{r} \tag{c}$$

The total normal force F_n which must be exerted by the actuating spring is found by multiplying the element of area $2\pi r\,dr$ by the pressure and integrating over the surface.

$$F_n = \int_{r_i}^{r_o} p\,dA = \int_{r_i}^{r_o} \frac{p_{max}r_i}{r} \times 2\pi r\,dr = 2\pi p_{max}r_i(r_o - r_i) \tag{15}$$

The torque is found by multiplying the force on the element by the coefficient of friction and the radius, and integrating over the area.

$$T = \int_{r_i}^{r_o} \mu pr\,dA = \int_{r_i}^{r_o} \mu \frac{p_{max}r_i}{r} \times 2\pi r^2\,dr$$

$$= \pi\mu p_{max}r_i(r_o{}^2 - r_i{}^2) = \frac{1}{2}\mu(r_o + r_i)F_n \tag{16}$$

Equations (15) and (16) are applicable when the assumption of uniform wear can be made.

Multiple-disk clutches have friction lining on both sides of alternate plates. Since Eq. (16) gives the torque for a single face, this quantity must be multiplied by the number of faces to find the torque for the entire clutch.

Equations (15) and (16) are applicable only when the parts of the clutch are very rigid so that the wear is uniform over the lining. Suppose an alternate type of construction is used in which the clutch lining is attached to flexible plates so that the pressure p is uniform over the entire surface. The total axial force F_n required for operation is

$$F_n = \pi p(r_o^2 - r_i^2) \tag{17}$$

The torque exerted by the clutch is

$$T = \mu p \int r \, dA = 2\pi\mu p \int r^2 \, dr = 2\pi\mu p \left(\frac{r^3}{3}\right)_{r_i}^{r_o}$$

$$= \frac{2}{3} \pi\mu p (r_o^3 - r_i^3) = \frac{2\mu(r_o^3 - r_i^3)F_n}{3(r_o^2 - r_i^2)} \tag{18}$$

Equations (17) and (18) are applicable when the assumption of uniform pressure can be made.

Example 8. A plate clutch with a single friction surface is 10 in. outside diameter and 4 in. inside diameter. $\mu = 0.2$.

(a) If the uniform wear theory is valid, find the required axial force for $p_{max} = 100$ psi. Find the torque for the clutch.

(b) Do the same for a similar clutch where the uniform pressure theory is valid for $p = 100$ psi.

(c) If the uniform wear theory is valid, find the torque the clutch will carry for $F_n = 5,000$ lb, and the value of p_{max}.

(d) Do the same for a clutch where the uniform pressure theory is valid.

Solution. (a)

By Eq. (15):　　$F_n = 2\pi 100 \times 2 \times 3 = 3,770$ lb

By Eq. (16):　　$T = \pi 0.2 \times 100 \times 2(25 - 4) = 2,639$ in-lb

(b)

By Eq. (17):　　$F_n = \pi 100(25 - 4) = 6,597$ lb

By Eq. (18):　　$T = \frac{2}{3} \pi 0.2 \times 100(125 - 8) = 4,900$ in-lb

(c)

By Eq. (15):　　$p_{max} = \dfrac{5,000}{2\pi 2 \times 3} = 132.6$ psi

By Eq. (16):　　$T = \dfrac{0.2 \times 7 \times 5,000}{2} = 3,500$ in-lb

(d)

By Eq. (17): $p = \dfrac{5,000}{\pi(25 - 4)} = 75.8$ psi

By Eq. (18): $T = \dfrac{2 \times 0.2(125 - 8) \times 5,000}{3(25 - 4)} = 3,714$ in-lb

10. Cone Clutch

The cone clutch utilizes the wedging action of the parts for increasing the normal force on the lining; thus an increase in the tangential friction force and the torque results. The assumption is again made that the normal wear is proportional to the product of the normal pressure and the radius.

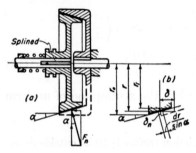

Fig. 6-13.   Cone clutch.

$$\delta_n = K p_n r \tag{a}$$

As shown in Fig. 6-13(b), the normal wear is uniform for all points on the cone. The maximum pressure thus occurs for the smallest value of r. Hence,

$$\delta_n = K p_{max} r_i \tag{b}$$

Elimination of δ_n and K in the foregoing equations gives

$$p_n = \frac{p_{max} r_i}{r} \tag{c}$$

Let the radius r in Fig. 6-13(b) locate the elemental strip running around the cone. The differential area is then equal to $2\pi r\, dr/\sin \alpha$. The total normal force F_n is equal to the product of the normal pressure and the element of area integrated over the conical surface. Hence,

$$F_n = \int_{r_i}^{r_o} p_n \, dA = \int \frac{p_{max} r_i}{r} \cdot \frac{2\pi r\, dr}{\sin \alpha} = \frac{2\pi p_{max} r_i (r_o - r_i)}{\sin \alpha} \tag{19}$$

As shown by Fig. 6-13(a), the reaction R which the actuating spring must be capable of exerting is equal to

$$R = F_n \sin \alpha = 2\pi p_{max} r_i (r_o - r_i) \tag{20}$$

This value of R is required for steady operation after the load has been put in motion. For engaging the clutch while picking up the load, a greater spring force than indicated by Eq. (20) is required.

The torque is given by

$$T = \int_{r_i}^{r_o} \mu p_n r \, dA = \int \frac{\mu p_{max} r_i}{r} \cdot \frac{2\pi r^2 \, dr}{\sin \alpha}$$

$$= \frac{\pi \mu p_{max} r_i (r_o^2 - r_i^2)}{\sin \alpha} = \frac{\mu (r_o + r_i)}{2 \sin \alpha} R \qquad (21)$$

Values of the angle α range from a minimum of about 8° to larger values. Normal pressure on the lining may reach a value of 100 psi or more.

11. Band Brakes

For the simple band brake shown in Fig. 6-14, the equation for a flat belt applies, but the terms for the centrifugal effects should be omitted.

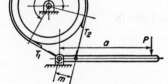

Fig. 6-14. Simple band brake.   Fig. 6-15. Differential band brake.

From Eq. (5), the relationship between the tensions in the bands is seen to be

$$\frac{T_1}{T_2} = e^{\mu \alpha} \qquad (22)$$

A smaller force P is needed for operation when the tight side of the band is attached to the stationary support, and the slack side is attached to the lever.

In the differential band brake, the friction force assists in applying the band. For the brake shown in Fig. 6-15 the following equation can be written:

$$Pa = T_2 m_2 - T_1 m_1 = T_2 (m_2 - m_1 e^{\mu \alpha}) \qquad (23)$$

Should the product $m_1 e^{\mu \alpha}$ be greater than m_2, the brake will grab or be self-locking. Sometimes this feature is desirable, and is utilized in back stop devices for preventing rotation in the reverse direction. For counterclockwise rotation, shown in Fig. 6-15, the friction tends to loosen the band, and the drum revolves freely. Should the rotation reverse and become clockwise, the friction will apply the brake, and if it is self-locking, the rotation will be stopped.

Let the analysis of Fig. 6-3(b) be applied to the band at the point of tangency for T_1. Force F_c is absent, and reaction R is equal to $brp_{max}\,d\theta$ where p_{max} is the pressure between drum and lining. The inward components of the band forces are equal to $T_1\,d\theta$. These two forces are equal to each other, and give the following useful equation.

$$T_1 = brp_{max} \tag{24}$$

A similar equation can be written for the slack side.

Example 9. A band brake similar to Fig. 6-14 has a 16 in. diameter drum and a width of lining equal to 3 in. Speed is 200 rpm, $a = 10$ in., $m = 3$ in., $\alpha = 270°$, and $\mu = 0.2$. Find the torque and horsepower if the maximum lining pressure is 70 psi.

Solution.

By Eq. (24): $T_1 = brp_{max} = 3 \times 8 \times 70 = 1,680$ lb

$\mu\alpha = 0.2 \times 1.5\pi = 0.9425$

By Table 6-1: $e^{\mu\alpha} = 2.566$

By Eq. (22): $T_2 = \dfrac{T_1}{e^{\mu\alpha}} = \dfrac{1.680}{2.566} = 655$ lb

Force: $P = \dfrac{T_2 m}{a} = \dfrac{655 \times 3}{10} = 196$ lb

Torque: $T = r(T_1 - T_2) = 8(1,680 - 655) = 8,200$ in-lb

Horsepower: $\text{hp} = \dfrac{Tn}{63,025} = \dfrac{8,200 \times 200}{63,025} = 26.0$

Band brakes are capable of exerting large torques. Careful attention must be paid to details so that the band seats properly on the drum when absorbing energy, and remains free and clear when not in use.

12. Block Brake with Short Shoe

The brake shown in Fig. 6-16 consists of a short block which is pressed against the revolving drum by means of a lever. When the block is relatively short, it may be assumed that the normal force F_n between drum and shoe is concentrated at point B. If the lever is taken as the free body, a moment equation can be written about A as the center, and forces F_n and μF_n can be determined. It should be noted that if the direction of rotation of the drum is reversed, the direction of friction force μF_n is reversed also.

When the rotation is as shown in Fig. 6-16, the moment of the friction force aids in applying the shoe to the drum. Care must be taken that the friction moment is not so large that the brake is applied without the assistance of force P. The brake will then seize or grab, and unsatisfactory or dangerous operation results. When the pivot is located on the other side of the line of action of μF_n, as shown by the dotted outline in Fig. 6-16, the friction force tends to unseat the shoe.

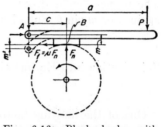

Fig. 6-16. Block brake with short shoe.

When the shoe is long, equations that take account of the variation in the pressure along the shoe must be used.

13. Pivoted Block Brake with Long Shoe

When the shoe is relatively long,[12] as shown in Fig. 6-17(a), the normal pressure p_n varies with different values of the angle φ. Frictional wear in engineering equipment is usually assumed to be proportional to the product of the velocity and the pressure. Since the velocity is the same

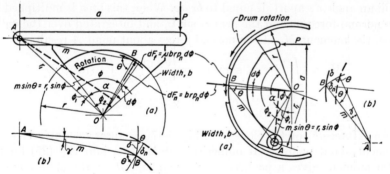

Fig. 6-17.   Block brake with long shoe.   Fig. 6-18.   Automotive type brake.

for all points of the shoe, the wear of the lining is proportional to the pressure. Hence,

$$\delta_n = K p_n \tag{a}$$

where δ_n is the wear in the direction perpendicular to the lining, and K is a constant.

Figure 6-17(b) shows the motion δ of a point on the shoe as the lining wears and as the shoe rotates about point A through angle γ. Hence,

$$\delta = \gamma m \tag{b}$$

[12] See reference 25, Bibliography.

The wear δ_n in the direction normal to the drum is then equal to

$$\delta_n = \delta \sin \theta = \gamma m \sin \theta \qquad \text{(c)}$$

The perpendicular dropped from A to radius OB has a length equal to $r_1 \sin \varphi$ or $m \sin \theta$. Substitution in Eq. (c) gives

$$\delta_n = \gamma r_1 \sin \varphi \qquad \text{(d)}$$

Substitution into Eq. (a) gives

$$K p_n = \gamma r_1 \sin \varphi \qquad \text{(e)}$$

One of the limiting factors in the design of a brake is the maximum pressure p_{max} between lining and drum. This occurs at the location having the maximum value of $\sin \varphi$ in Eq. (e). Hence,

$$K p_{max} = \gamma r_1 (\sin \varphi)_{max} \qquad \text{(f)}$$

Elimination of $\gamma r_1 / K$ between Eqs. (e) and (f) gives

$$p_n = \frac{p_{max}}{(\sin \varphi)_{max}} \sin \varphi \qquad \text{(g)}$$

Should φ_2 in Fig. 6-17 be greater than 90°, then $(\sin \varphi)_{max}$ is equal to unity. For smaller values of φ_2 use the value of $\sin \varphi_2$ for the denominator.

If b is the width of the lining, the area of a small element, cut by two radii an angle $d\varphi$ apart, is equal to $br\,d\varphi$. When this area is multiplied by the normal force p_n and the arm $r_1 \sin \varphi$, and integrated over the entire shoe, the moment M_n of the normal forces about point A results.

$$M_n = \int_{\varphi_1}^{\varphi_2} b r r_1 p_n \sin \varphi \, d\varphi = \frac{b r r_1 p_{max}}{(\sin \varphi)_{max}} \int_{\varphi_1}^{\varphi_2} \sin^2 \varphi \, d\varphi$$

$$= \frac{b r r_1 p_{max}}{4(\sin \varphi)_{max}} (2\alpha - \sin 2\varphi_2 + \sin 2\varphi_1) \qquad (25)$$

Normal force dF_n on the element of Fig. 6-17(a) causes a counterclockwise moment about point A. If numerical substitution into Eq. (25) for the total moment gives a positive result, moment M_n is therefore counterclockwise. A negative result means that M_n is clockwise about A.

The moment of the friction forces M_f about A is equal to

$$M_f = \int_{\varphi_1}^{\varphi_2} \mu p_n (r - r_1 \cos \varphi) br \, d\varphi$$

$$= \frac{\mu b r p_{max}}{(\sin \varphi)_{max}} \int \left[r \sin \varphi - \frac{1}{2} r_1 \sin 2\varphi \right] d\varphi$$

$$= \frac{\mu b r p_{max}}{4(\sin \varphi)_{max}} [r_1(\cos 2\varphi_2 - \cos 2\varphi_1) - 4r(\cos \varphi_2 - \cos \varphi_1)] \qquad (26)$$

A positive value for M_f in Eq. (26) indicates a counterclockwise moment about A for the friction forces of Fig. 6-17, and a negative result indicates a clockwise moment. If the direction of rotation is reversed, these statements have the converse meanings for M_f.

In Fig. 6-17(a) the moment of the external force is equal to Pa. The shoe and lever are in equilibrium under the action of moments Pa, M_n, and M_f. A moment equation should be written for these terms with the proper signs. These signs depend on the location of the pivot with respect to the shoe and on the direction of rotation of the drum. When the friction moment assists in applying the shoe, the brake will be self locking if M_f exceeds M_n. In practice, the ratio M_f/M_n should not be greater than about 0.7.

The torque exerted by the brake is found by taking the moment of the friction forces about the center of the drum O. Hence,

$$T = \int_{\varphi_1}^{\varphi_2} \mu p_n b r^2 \, d\varphi$$

$$= \frac{\mu b r^2 p_{max}}{(\sin \varphi)_{max}} \int \sin \varphi \, d\varphi$$

$$= \frac{\mu b r^2 p_{max}}{(\sin \varphi)_{max}} (\cos \varphi_1 - \cos \varphi_2) \qquad (27)$$

Example 10. (a) Calculate the value of p_{max}, the torque, and the horsepower for the brake of Fig. 6-19. Coefficient of friction is equal to 0.2.

(b) Make the same calculations on the assumption that the total normal and friction forces are concentrated at point B and compare results with the more exact results of part (a).

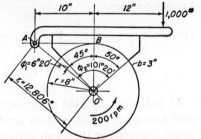

Fig. 6-19.   Brake for Example 10.

Solution. (a)

$$\tan \text{ angle } AOB = \frac{10}{8} = 1.25$$

$$\text{angle } AOB = 51°20'$$

Hence,

$$\varphi_1 = 51°20' - 45°0' = 6°20' \qquad 2\varphi_1 = 12°40'$$

$$\varphi_2 = 6°20' + 95°0' = 101°20' \qquad 2\varphi_2 = 202°40'$$

$$\alpha = 95° = 1.65806 \text{ radians}$$

$$r_1 = \sqrt{8^2 + 10^2} = 12.806 \text{ in.}$$

In Eq. (25): $M_n = \frac{1}{4} \times 3 \times 8 \times 12.806 p_{max}(3.31612 + 0.38559 + 0.21950)$

$$= 301.3 p_{max}$$

This moment is counterclockwise about point A.

In Eq. (26), $M_f = \dfrac{1}{4} \times 0.2 \times 3 \times 8p_{max}$

$$[12.806(-0.92267 - 0.97561) - 32(-0.19663 - 0.99388)]$$

$$= 1.2p_{max}(-24.309 + 38.096) = 16.5p_{max}$$

This moment is counterclockwise about point A.

Externally applied moment, $Pa = 1,000 \times 22 = 22,000$ in-lb clockwise

The equation for the equilibrium of moments for the shoe is

$$301.3p_{max} + 16.5p_{max} = 22,000$$

Solving: $p_{max} = \dfrac{22,000}{317.8} = 69.2$ psi

In Eq. (27): $T = 0.2 \times 3 \times 64 \times 69.2(0.99388 + 0.19663)$

$$= 3,164 \text{ in-lb}$$

$$\text{hp} = \frac{Tn}{63,000} = \frac{3,164 \times 200}{63,000} = 10.04$$

(b)

Moments about A: $F_n = \dfrac{1,000 \times 22}{10} = 2,200$ lb

Projected area of shoe: $A = 3(8 \sin 45° + 8 \sin 50°) = 35.36$ in.^{2}

Average pressure: $p_{av} = \dfrac{2,200}{35.36} = 62.2$ psi

Torque: $T = \mu F_n r = 0.2 \times 2,200 \times 8 = 3,520$ in-lb

$$\text{hp} = \frac{Tn}{63,000} = \frac{3,520 \times 200}{63,000} = 11.17$$

As indicated by this example, the approximate equations frequently give a smaller pressure than actually occurs on the lining as well as a larger horsepower than can actually be developed.

Figure 6-18 shows an internal brake of a type widely used in automotive service. The equation for the moment M_n of the normal forces on the shoe is the same as Eq. (25), but a positive result indicates a clockwise moment about A. The equations for friction moment M_f and torque T are the same as for the brake of Fig. 6-17. A positive or negative result for M_f should be interpreted in the same way as for a brake with an external shoe.

14. Brake with Pivoted Symmetrical Shoe

In Fig. 6-20 the brake shoe is supported by a symmetrically located pin at A. Let it be assumed that distance r_1 is of such magnitude that the friction forces dF_f have no resultant moment about A. The normal forces must then be symmetrical with respect to the vertical center line, and also have zero moment about A. Thus, no rotation of the shoe on the pin can occur, and the vertical component of the wear is uniform for the entire

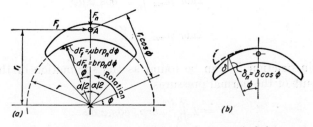

Fig. 6-20.   Block brake with pivoted symmetrical shoe.

shoe. Assume as before that normal wear is proportional to normal pressure.

$$\delta_n = Kp_n \tag{a}$$

As shown in Fig. 6-20(b) the normal wear is equal to $\delta \cos \varphi$. Hence,

$$\delta \cos \varphi = Kp_n \tag{b}$$

The maximum normal pressure occurs at the location for the maximum value of $\cos \varphi$, that is, for $\varphi = 0$, giving

$$\delta = Kp_{max}$$

Substitution into Eq. (b) gives $p_n = p_{max} \cos \varphi$ $\hspace{2em}$ (c)

The equation for the moment of the friction forces about A is found by multiplying the tangential force on an element of area by the arm $(r_1 \cos \varphi - r)$ and integrating over the entire shoe. By the foregoing assumption the result is equal to zero.

$$M_f = 2 \int_0^{\alpha/2} \mu b r p_n (r_1 \cos \varphi - r) d\varphi = 0$$

Substitution of the value for p_n from Eq. (c) gives

$$2\mu b r p_{max} \int_0^{\alpha/2} (r_1 \cos^2 \varphi - r \cos \varphi) d\varphi = 0$$

Integrating and solving for r_1,

$$\left[r_1 \left(\frac{1}{2} \varphi + \frac{1}{4} \sin 2\varphi \right) - r \sin \varphi \right]_0^{\alpha/2} = 0$$

$$r_1 = \frac{4r \sin (\alpha/2)}{\alpha + \sin \alpha} \tag{28}$$

The torque of the friction forces about O as a center is given by the following equation:

$$T = 2 \int_0^{\alpha/2} \mu b r^2 p_n \, d\varphi$$

$$= 2\mu b r^2 p_{max} \int_0^{\alpha/2} \cos \varphi \, d\varphi$$

$$= 2\mu b r^2 p_{max} \sin \frac{\alpha}{2} \tag{29}$$

The pin reaction F_n can be found as the summation of the vertical components of the normal pressures.

$$F_n = 2 \int_0^{\alpha/2} b r p_n \cos \varphi \, d\varphi$$

$$= 2 b r p_{max} \int_0^{\alpha/2} \cos^2 \varphi \, d\varphi$$

$$= \frac{1}{2} b r p_{max}(\alpha + \sin \alpha) \tag{30}$$

The pin reaction F_t is found by summing the horizontal components of the frictional forces.

$$F_t = 2 \int_0^{\alpha/2} \mu b r p_n \cos \varphi \, d\varphi = \mu F_n \tag{31}$$

15. Lining Pressures

Wooden blocks are sometimes used as the friction elements for industrial brakes. Cast iron shoes bearing on cast iron or steel wheels are in wide use for brakes in railroad service. However, most brake linings depend upon asbestos as the basic friction material because of its ability to resist the effects of heat. Asbestos may be spun into yarn, woven and infused with a binder, and then consolidated by heat and pressure. Molded blocks and linings are also made directly from asbestos and binder without weaving.

For average conditions of service, the following working pressures for asbestos materials are recommended.[13]

Molded compressed friction blocks..............	100 psi
Molded band friction lining....................	75 psi
Woven and compressed friction lining...........	50 psi
Folded and compressed friction lining..........	50 psi

When space conditions are limited, the foregoing values may be exceeded somewhat, but the rate of wear will then be more rapid.

The coefficient of friction for asbestos clutch and brake linings varies from 0.2 to 0.4, depending on the formula for the material and the condi-

[13] See reference 20, Bibliography.

tions of service for the particular application. The proper value should be obtained from the manufacturer's catalog for the particular type of lining considered. The coefficient of friction for brake materials may not remain constant in service but will vary because of conditions of temperature, or the presence of moisture and grease.

16. Heating of Brakes

The capacity of a brake or clutch to absorb power is largely determined by its ability to dispose of the frictional heat. The heat-dissipating quality is determined by factors such as the size, shape, and condition of the surface of the various parts. If the clutch or brake is not enclosed in a housing, or if the surrounding air is in motion, the brake can be more readily cooled. For service in excavating machinery, the following values for power absorption have been found to be satisfactory:

For open, exposed band and cone clutches:

Power absorption = 0.25 to 0.40 hp/in.^{2} of contact surface.

For open, exposed band brakes:

Power absorption = 0.20 to 0.30 hp/in.^{2} of contact surface.

Although clutches and brakes in this type of service operate intermittently, they generally do not have sufficient time for cooling between applications, and the operating temperature may therefore be rather high. Excessive temperatures may be damaging to the lining.[14] The coefficient of friction will usually decrease with increase in temperature. However, certain compositions of lining show an increase in the coefficient for moderate rises of temperature. Wear of the lining is an important factor in the maintenance cost of a brake. If the drum is ground to a high degree of smoothness, the wear will be less than if it is merely turned.

Experience has shown that the product of the pressure p in psi and the velocity V in fpm must be kept within certain limits. On this basis, the following values can be considered as an additional criterion for the design of brakes.

$pV \leq 55,000$ for intermittent applications of the load, comparatively long periods of rest, and poor dissipation of heat.

$pV \leq 28,000$ for continuous application of the load, as in lowering operations, and poor dissipation of heat.

$pV \leq 83,000$ for continuous application of the load and good dissipation of heat, into an oil bath for instance.

[14] See reference 20, Bibliography.

Equations for the torque T and the number of revolutions per minute n are as follows:

$$T = \mu F_n r = \mu p A r \tag{a}$$

$$n = \frac{6V}{\pi r} \tag{b}$$

Substitution in the horsepower equation gives

$$\text{hp} = \frac{Tn}{63,000} = \frac{\mu A\, pV}{33,000} \tag{32}$$

Example 11. Find the horsepower per square inch absorbed by a brake if $\mu = 0.2$ and $pV = 55,000$.

Solution.

In Eq. (32): $\dfrac{\text{hp}}{A} = \dfrac{\mu pV}{33,000} = \dfrac{0.2 \times 55,000}{33,000} = 0.33 \dfrac{\text{hp}}{\text{in.}^2}$

BIBLIOGRAPHY

Volume number shown in **bold face** type. The number immediately following is the page on which the article begins.

1. Barth, C. G., "Transmission of Power by Leather Belting," *Trans. ASME,* **31,** 29 (1909).

2. Swift, H. W., "Power Transmission by Belts," *Proc. Inst. Mech. Engs.,* **115**(2), 659 (1928).

3. Swift, H. W., "Cambers for Belt Pulleys," *Proc. Inst. Mech. Engrs.,* **122,** 627 (1932).

4. Swift, H. W., "Short-Centre Belt Drives," *Proc. Inst. Mech. Engrs.,* **135,** 485 (1937).

5. Norman, C. A., "Tension Ratio and Transmissive Power of Belts," *Mech. Eng.,* **47,** 1,111 (1925); **48,** 240 (1926).

6. Norman, C. A., "High Speed Belt Drives," *Bulletin* 83, Engineering Experiment Station, Ohio State University, 1934.

7. *How to Get the Most from Your Leather Belting,* American Leather Belting Association. (Booklet.)

8. Anett, F. A., "Power Transmission, Belts," *Power,* **91,** Feb., 79 (1947).

9. Jagger, J. G., "Power Transmission by Belting," *Proc. Inst. Mech. Engrs.,* **143,** 318 (1940).

10. Tatnall, R. R., "The Pivoted Motor Drive," *Mech. Eng.,* **57,** 287 (1935).

11. Bariffi, H. F., "Pivoted Centrifugal Friction Clutches," *Product Eng.,* **19,** Feb., 140 (1948).

12. von Mehren, O., "Internal Shoe Clutches and Brakes," *Trans. ASME,* **69,** 913 (1947).

13. Wiebusch, C. F., "The Spring Clutch," *Trans. ASME*, **61**, A-103 (1939).

14. Hagenbook, L. D., "Design of Brakes and Clutches of the Wrapping-Band Type," *Product Eng.*, **16**, 321 (1945).

15. Tack, C. E., "Development and Testing of Brakes for High-Speed Railroad Equipment," *Trans. ASME*, **73**, 167 (1951).

16. Eksergian, C. L., "High-Speed Braking," *Trans. ASME* **73**, 935 (1951).

17. Waller, I. M., "Internal Expanding Shoe Brakes for Road Vehicles," *Proc. Inst. Mech. Engrs., Automobile Div.*, Part 1, 41 (1949–1950).

18. Loewenberg, F., "Automotive Brakes With Servo Action," *Trans. ASME*, **52**(1), APM52-16, 185 (1930).

19. Rasmussen, A. C., "Internal Friction Blocks and Shoes, Analyses and Applications," *Product Eng.*, **18**, Mar., 133; May, 152; July, 106; Oct., 119; Dec., 135 (1947).

20. Rasmussen, A. C., "Heat-Radiating Capacity of Clutches and Brakes," *Product Eng.*, **2**, 529 (1931); **3**, 282 (1932).

21. Nutt, Harold, "Woven and Molded Friction Materials for Disk-Type Clutches," *Product Eng.*, **17**, 273 (1946). See also **17**, 39 (1946); **12**, 2 (1941).

22. Lowey, F. J., "Powdered-Metal Friction Material," *Mech. Eng.*, **70**, 869 (1948).

23. Parker, R. C., "The Frictional Behavior of Engineering Materials," *Engineering*, **167**, 193, 217 (1949).

24. Williams, W. A., "Design and Construction of Wide Face Steel Pulleys," *Product Eng.*, **21**, Aug., 122 (1950).

25. Fazekas, G. A. G., "Graphical Shoe Brake Analysis," *Trans. ASME*, **79**, 1322 (1957). See also, *Jour. of Applied Mech.*, **80**, 7 (1958).

26. Worley, W. S., "Design of V-Belt Drives for Mass Produced Machines," *Product Engineering*, **24**, Sept., 154 (1953).

27. Marco, S. M., Starkey, W. L., and Hornung, K. G., "A Quantitative Investigation of the Factors Which Influence the Fatigue Life of a V-Belt," *Trans. ASME*, **82**; *Jour. of Engrg. for Industry*, Feb., 47 (1960).

28. Tordion, G. V., "Creep of an Elastic Belt on a Pulley," *Trans. ASME*, **81**; *Jour. of Applied Mech.*, 451.

29. Jania, Z. J., "Friction-Clutch Transmissions," *Machine Design*, **30**, Nov. 13, Nov. 27, Dec. 11, and Dec. 25 (1958).

PROBLEMS

1. A flat belt is to transmit 25 hp with a maximum tensile stress of 250 psi, and an active arc equal to 120°. Both pulleys are 4 ft in diameter, and rpm is 300; $\mu = 0.30$. The weight of the belt material is 0.035 lb/in.^{3} Find the required cross-sectional area of the belt. *Ans.* $A = 2.36$ in.^{2}

2. An oak-tanned leather belt $\frac{18}{64}$ by 12 in. operates on cast iron pulleys 30 in. in diameter at 450 rpm. If the active arc is 120° and stress in the tight side is 250 psi, find the hp transmitted. The weight of the material is 0.035 lb/in.[3]

Ans. $hp = 30.2$.

3. An oak-tanned leather belt $\frac{13}{64}$ by 10 in. operates on wood pulleys 24 in. in diameter at 600 rpm. The belt is tightened until the active arc is 120° and the stress in the tight side is 250 psi. Find the stress in the tight side after the belt has stretched and the active arc has become 180°. The power transmitted remains constant. The material weighs 0.035 lb/in.[3]   *Ans.* $s_1 = 203$ psi.

4. An oak-tanned leather belt $\frac{20}{64}$ by 8 in. operates on 36 in. diameter cast iron pulleys at 12 ft centers. Let the center distance be increased 3 in. beyond the point of no slack and zero stress. Find the horsepower transmitted at 360 rpm. The weight of the belting 0.035 lb/in.[3]   *Ans.* hp = 22.1.

5. A $\frac{20}{64}$ by 10 in. mineral-tanned leather belt operates on 30 in. diameter wood pulleys at 300 rpm. The center distance is 12 ft. Initial tension is obtained by lengthening the center distance $2\frac{1}{2}$ in. from the condition of no slack and zero stress. If 20 hp is transmitted find the stress in the tight side. Find the minimum value of the coefficient of friction. The weight of the leather 0.035 lb/in.[3]

Ans. $s_1 = 167$ psi; $\mu = 0.31$.

6. A 7.5 by $\frac{5}{16}$ in. belt weighing 1 lb per ft is operating on two 20 in. diameter pulleys. The coefficient of friction is 0.3. Find the horsepower which this belt can transmit at a maximum stress of 300 psi and 600 rpm if the entire arc of contact is active.   *Ans.* hp = 35.9.

7. (a) A heavy double belt $\frac{23}{64}$ in. thick on 30 in. pulleys at 25 ft centers transmits 40 hp at 360 rpm. If the belt has stretched until the entire arc of contact is active, find the width of the belt required for a stress of 250 psi. The coefficient of friction is 0.3, and the weight of the belt material 0.035 lb/in.[3]

(b) What must be the lengthening of the center distance from the condition of no slack in order to secure sufficient initial tension to carry the load? $C_1 = 830$.

(c) In order to provide a period of operation without adjustment, suppose the center distance is made 1 in. greater than the minimum requirement as given in part (b). Find the stress in the tight side of the belt, and the size of the active arc.

(d) Find the width by use of the belting tables for normal atmosphere and continuous operation. Assume the driving pulley has received its power from a jerky source.

Ans.　(a) $b = 9.63$ in.; (b) $\delta_o = 5.55$ in.; (c) $s_1 = 317$ psi, $\beta = 120.5°$;
(d) $b = 6.67$ in.

8. (a) A medium double belt, $\frac{20}{64}$ by 10 in., has two 24 in. pulleys at a center distance of 18 ft. The rpm is 400. Suppose a shop mechanic thoughtlessly lengthens the center distance between shafts 6 in. from the position of no slack by means of the take-up screws. If the belt is to transmit 50 hp, what is the value of the stress in the tight strand?

(b) Find the value of the correct amount of initial lengthening for a coefficient of friction of 0.35 with the entire arc of contact active. Find the stress in the tight strand of the belt. The weight of the belt is 0.035 lb/in.[3]

     Ans. (a) $s_1 = 498$ psi; (b) $\delta_o = 4.54$ in.; $s_1 = 338$ psi.

9. The belt shown in Fig. 6-21 carries 30 hp. Find the size of the active arc for each pulley. Find the length of the belt. Material weighs 0.035 lb/in.[3] Max. $s = 250$ psi.   *Ans.* Small, $\beta_1 = 114.4°$; large, $\beta_2 = 137.3°$; length $= 286.6$ in.

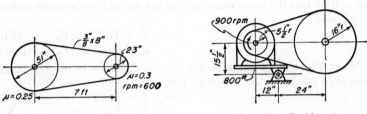

<table>
<tr><td>Fig. 6-21. Problem 9.</td><td>Fig. 6-22. Problem 11.</td></tr>
</table>

10. Find the belt forces and the size of the active arc if the drive described in Example 4 is operating at one-half capacity.

     Ans. $\beta = 75.9°$, $T_1 = 476$ lb, $T_2 = 320$ lb.

11. Find the tight and slack tensions and horsepower carried by the pivoted motor drive discussed in Fig. 6-22. Neglect centrifugal effects. The coefficient of friction is 0.25 and motor rpm is 900.   *Ans.* hp $= 19.3$

12. In Fig. 6-7 the following dimensions apply: $m = 14$ in., $f = 13\frac{1}{2}$ in., $q = 6\frac{1}{2}$ in., $l = 48$ in., $r_1 = 6$ in., $r_2 = 21$ in., $n = 1{,}200$ rpm CW, $\mu = 0.3$, $W = 1{,}200$ lb. Find the hp capacity of the drive.   *Ans.* hp $= 62.8$.

13. A pivoted motor drive has forces of 300 lb when running under no load conditions. The small pulley is of wood, 9 in. in diameter at the same elevation as the large pulley of 34 in. in diameter. The center distance is $32\frac{1}{2}$ in. The belt is oak-tanned leather; $m = 12$ in., $f = 14$ in. Find the hp capacity for dry conditions. Motor turns 1,150 rpm.   *Ans.* hp $= 22$.

14. A pivoted motor drive has a small pulley 20 in. in diameter and large pulley 48 in. in diameter. Pulley centers are at the same elevation and 60 in. apart. $m = 15$ in., $f = 22$ in., $W = 550$ lb, $\mu = 0.3$, and $n = 900$ rpm. Find the horsepower transmitted.   *Ans.* hp $= 27.6$.

15. A premium quality C-section V-belt carries a net hp of 11, but a service factor of 1.4 must be used. Both pulleys are 12 in. in pitch diameter and turn at 1,160 rpm. The belt length is 197.9 in. Find the expected life in hours for this belt.   *Ans.* 26,000 hrs.

16. A standard quality B-section V-belt carries a net hp of 4, but a service factor of 1.4 must be used. The driving pulley is 7 in. in pitch diameter and turns at 2,350 rpm. The driven pulley is 30 in. in diameter. The belt length is 106.8 in. long. Find the center distance and expected life in hours.   *Ans.* 11,900 hrs.

                                                          $c = 21.12$ in.

17. A motor driven blower turns at 420 rpm and requires 8 hp, but a service factor of 1.5 must be used. The motor sheave has a pitch diameter of 7.5 in. and turns at 1,760 rpm. B-standard belts, 121.8 in. long, are to be used. For an expected life of 8,000 hrs, find the required number of belts.

Ans. hp = 6.26 for each belt.

18. A 24 in.-OD plate clutch has a maximum lining pressure of 50 psi. One hundred and eighty horsepower are to be carried at 400 rpm. If the coefficient of friction is 0.30, find the inside diameter and the spring force required to keep the clutch engaged.

Ans. d_i = 17.22 in.; F_n = 9,170 lb and
d_i = 10.20 in.; F_n = 11,060 lb.

19. Work Problem 18 but with the outside diameter 18 in. The maximum pressure is 75 psi, hp = 150, μ = 0.25, and rpm = 600.

Ans. d_i = 12.18 in.; F_n = 8,351 lb and
d_i = 8.50 in.; F_n = 9,513 lb.

20. Find the torque that a cone clutch of mean radius 6 in. and angle α of 8° can carry if the force R for steady running is 500 lb; μ = 0.2. *Ans.* T = 4,311 in-lb.

21. A cone clutch of inclination 10° is to carry 40 hp at 600 rpm. The width of the lining along an element of the cone is 2 in. Maximum lining pressure is to be 50 psi. The coefficient of friction is 0.2. Find suitable values for r_o and r_i.

Ans. r_o = 6.04 in.; r_i = 5.70 in.

22. A cone clutch has a mean radius of 8 in. and a cone angle of 8°. Maximum lining pressure is 100 psi and the coefficient of friction is 0.2. Find the torque the clutch can exert and the engaging force required for steady operation. The lining measures 3 in. along an element of the cone. What is the hp for a speed of 600 rpm?

Ans. R = 2,046 lb; hp = 227.

23. Work Problem 22 but with the cone angle of 12°.

Ans. R = 3,014 lb; hp = 221.

24. Find the value of dimension c in Fig. 6-23 which will cause the friction forces neither to help nor resist the application of the shoe to the drum.

Ans. c = 1.414r.

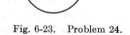

Fig. 6-23. Problem 24.

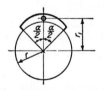

Fig. 6-24. Problem 25.

25. (a) For $\alpha/2$ = 45°, find the value of r_1 in Fig. 6-24 which will cause the shoe to be free from moment about its pivot.

(b) Work (a) using $\alpha/2$ = 60°. *Ans.* (a) r_1 = 1.10r; (b) r_1 = 1.17r.

26. If the permissible value for p_{max} in Fig. 6-25 is 100 psi, find (a) the corresponding value of P, and (b) the hp which the brake will absorb; $\mu = 0.25$.

Ans. (a) $P = 777$ lb; (b) hp $= 28.6$.

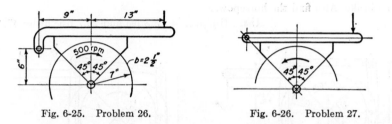

Fig. 6-25. Problem 26.   Fig. 6-26. Problem 27.

27. (a) Find the resultant vertical component of the normal and friction forces for the brake of Fig. 6-26.

(b) Find the resultant horizontal component of the normal and friction forces.

Ans. (a) $F_v = \dfrac{\sqrt{2}}{8} b r p_{max}[2(1 - \mu) + \pi(1 + \mu)];$

(b) $F_h = \dfrac{\sqrt{2}}{8} b r p_{max}[2(1 + \mu) - \pi(1 - \mu)].$

28. Find the force P required if the maximum pressure of the lining in Fig. 6-27 is equal to 100 psi; $\mu = 0.25$. The width of the lining is 2 in. Find the torque about center O.   Ans. $P = 723$ lb; $T = 1,531$ in-lb.

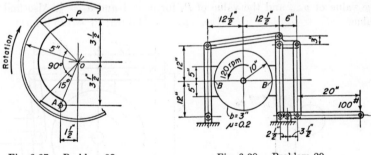

Fig. 6-27. Problem 28.   Fig. 6-28. Problem 29.

29. (a) Make an exploded view of the double-block brake in Fig. 6-28. Draw each part, including the drum separately, and show all forces and moments necessary for equilibrium. Assume that the normal and friction forces for the shoes are concentrated at points B.

(b) Compute the value of the maximum shoe pressure and the hp absorbed by the brake. Find the hp absorbed per unit area, and the pV value.

Ans. $p_{max} = 93.4$ psi; hp $= 20.5$; hp/in.$^2 = 0.34$; $pV = 58,700$.

30. (a) Make an exploded view of the double-block brake of Fig. 6-29 and show all forces and moments required for equilibrium of each part. $\mu = 0.2$; width $b = 4$ in.

(b) Find the value of p_{max} for each shoe and the value of the torque exerted by the brake. Also find the horsepower.

Ans. (b) $p_{max} = 23.3$ psi and 20.7 psi; hp $= 47.4$.

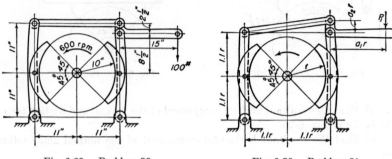

Fig. 6-29.   Problem 30.   Fig. 6-30.   Problem 31.

31. Make an exploded view of the brake in Fig. 6-30 showing the forces required for the equilibrium of each part. Write the expression for the torque in terms of μ, P_1, r, a_1, and a_2.   *Ans.* $T = 4.4\mu P_1 r a_1 / a_2$.

32. A crane brake is lowering the load shown in Fig. 6-31 at a speed of 18 fpm. The motor shaft is connected to the cable drum shaft by a gear train with a 130-to-1 ratio. Assume that the gears and bearings are frictionless. The brake drum rotates at one-half motor speed and is 16 in. in diameter; the lining is 3 in. wide; μ is equal to 0.2. The shoes and levers are arranged as in Problem 31. Find the value of p_{max} and the value of P_1 for $a_1 = 1$ and $a_2 = \frac{1}{3}$. Also find the pV value.   *Ans.* $p_{max} = 24.3$ psi; $P_1 = 125$ lb; $pV = 39,600$.

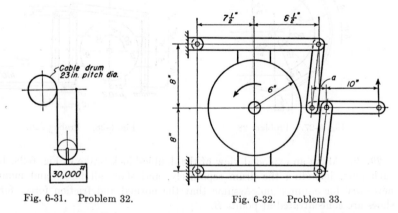

Fig. 6-31.   Problem 32.   Fig. 6-32.   Problem 33.

33. Assume the brake in Fig. 6-32 has short shoes. The coefficient of friction is 0.3. Find the value of distance a that will cause the wear to be the same for both shoes.   *Ans.* $a = 1.74$ in.

34. A block brake with a short shoe is to be designed for a pV value of 55,000; μ is equal to 0.2; the area of the shoe is 18 in.[2]; and the diameter of the brake drum is 16 in. A cable drum 12 in. in diameter is connected to the brake drum by means of gearing. The brake drum revolves three times as fast as cable drum. See Fig. 6-33. Find the uniform velocity at which a 1,000 lb weight at the end of the cable is being lowered. Find the value of the pressure of the shoe.

Ans. $V = 791$ fpm; $p = 69.5$ psi.

35. Find the hp which the brake of Fig. 6-34 can absorb, and the length of arm a. *Ans.* hp $= 5.82$; $a = 4.85$ in.

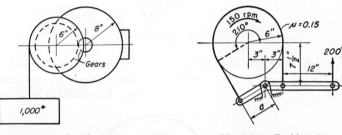

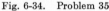

Fig. 6-33.   Problem 34.   Fig. 6-34.   Problem 35

36. The band brake in Fig. 6-35 is to absorb 6 hp at 150 rpm. The maximum pressure between lining and drum is 100 psi. The width of the band is 2 in. and $\mu = 0.12$. Find the angle of wrap α and the distance a.

Ans. $\alpha = 205.7°$; $a = 7.94$ in.

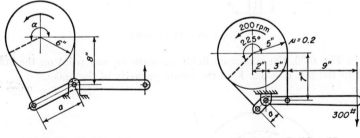

Fig. 6-35.   Problem 36.   Fig. 6-36.   Problem 37.

37. Find the hp which the brake of Fig. 6-36 can absorb, and the length of arm a. *Ans.* hp $= 13.33$; $a = 1.46$ in.

38. Find the value of the torque that the backstop in Fig. 6-37 can resist if the maximum pressure between lining and drum is 200 psi. What must be the minimum value of the coefficient of friction to insure the brake holding the load?

Ans. $T = 9,310$ in-lb, $\mu = 0.174$.

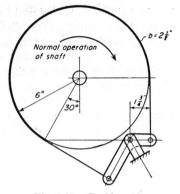

Fig. 6-37.   Problem 38.

39. In Fig. 6-38 the maximum lining pressure for any point on the brake is to be limited to 100 psi; $\mu = 0.2$. Find the torque capacity of the brake and the value of force P. *Ans.* $T = 9,080$ in-lb, $P = 487$ lb.

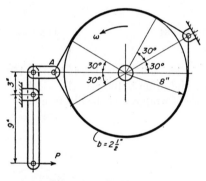

Fig. 6-38.   Problem 39.

40. In Fig. 6-39, the maximum lining pressure for any point on the brake is limited to 100 psi; $\mu = 0.2$. Find the torque capacity of the brake.
Ans. $T = 9,820$ in-lb.

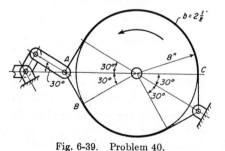

Fig. 6-39.   Problem 40.

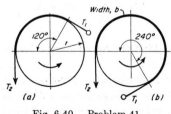

Fig. 6-40.   Problem 41.

41. (a) Write the expression for torque and the maximum lining pressure in terms of T_2 for the brake shown in Fig. 6-40 (a); $\mu = 0.3$.

(b) Do the same for the brake in sketch (b). Note that for the same value of the actuating force T_2, the brake in (b) can exert approximately three times the torque as the brake in (a), but that the lining pressure is almost twice as great.

$$Ans. \quad (a) \quad T = 0.87T_2r; \; p = 1.874T_2/br.$$
$$(b) \quad T = 2.51T_2r; \; p = 3.51T_2/br.$$

42. A band brake exerts a torque of 15,000 in-lb. The drum is 2 in. wide and 10 in. in radius. If the maximum pressure between the lining and drum is 100 psi and the coefficient of friction is 0.3, find the angle of contact between lining and drum. $Ans. \quad \alpha = 264°46'.$

The following problems are presented without answers.

43. If the maximum permissible tensile stress in Problem 1 is increased to 300 psi, find the required cross-sectional area of the belt.

44. Work Problem 6 except that the coefficient of friction is 0.25.

45. The data and dimensions are the same as those in Fig. 6-22 except that the $15\frac{1}{2}$ in. height is unknown. Find this height for $T_1 = 550$ lb and $T_2 = 350$ lb.

46. A V-belt catalog gives the hp of a standard quality D-belt, operating at 4,000 fpm, on two 17 in. diameter pulleys, as 22.8. If the belt length is 176.3 in., what would be the expected life for this belt?

47. Work Problem 15 but with the horsepower increased to 12.7. Find the expected life in hours.

48. In Problem 15 let both pulley diameters become 10 in., but let the rpm be increased so that the belt speed is the same as before. Find the expected life in hours.

49. Using the same data as that in Problem 15, except that the shaft speed has been increased to 2,650 rpm, find the expected life of the belt in hours.

50. A line shaft requires a net hp of 20, but a service factor of 1.6 must be used. The shaft turns at 250 rpm. Motor speed is 860 rpm, with a 10 in. diameter sheave. The belt length is 197.9 in. For an expected life of 14,000 hours, find the number of standard quality C-belts required for the drive.

51. A standard quality D-belt is 123.3 in. long. Sheave diameters are 15 in. and 21 in. The smaller sheave turns at 860 rpm. The hp is 12, but a service factor of 1.8 must be used. Find the center distance and the expected life in hours.

52. The weight in Fig. 6-41 must be raised at the rate of 10 fps. The motor pulley is 14 in. in diameter and turns at 850 rpm. Ignore friction, but use a service factor of 1.4. Find the diameter of the large pulley and the number of standard D-section belts required for an expected life of 10,000 hrs.

53. Work Problem 18 but with hp of 195.

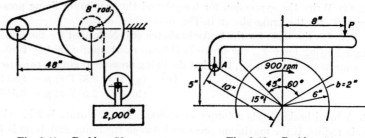

Fig. 6-41.   Problem 52.   Fig. 6-42.   Problem 54.

54. Find the hp absorbed and force P in Fig. 6-42 if the maximum lining pressure is 100 psi. $\mu = 0.2$.

55. In Fig. 6-43 the hp absorbed is 15; $\mu = 0.3$. Find the value of the actuating force P.

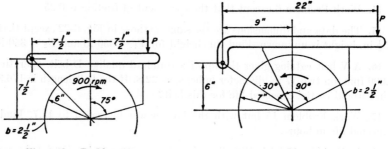

Fig. 6-43.   Problem 55.   Fig. 6-44.   Problem 56.

56. Find the value of force P for the brake in Fig. 6-44. $p_{max} = 100$ psi. $\mu = 0.25$.

57. Work Problem 33 but with the dimensions of $7\frac{1}{2}$, 8, and $8\frac{1}{2}$ in. in Fig. 6-32 each increased by $\frac{1}{2}$ in.

58. Work Problem 30 but with short shoes rigidly attached to the two uprights.

59. Work Problem 42 but with the width made equal to $2\frac{1}{2}$ in.

60. Work Problem 42 with a torque of 13,000 in-lb and μ equal to 0.25.

7

Welded and Riveted Connections

A WELD is a union between metal surfaces brought about by the localized application of heat. Welding has assemed an important place in speeding the manufacture of component parts and in the assembly of these parts into engineering structures. Forge or pressure welding of wrought iron has been practiced for centuries; methods such as torch, arc, or resistance welding have appeared only in recent years. The field of usefulness of these latter methods is being rapidly expanded.

Rivets, also, can be used for forming the joints and connections between the parts of a structure. Although welding has replaced riveting to a considerable extent, rivets are customarily employed for certain types of joints. Long experience with this method of fastening has given confidence in the reliability of riveted joints.

A, throat area
h, size of weld
l, length of weld
J, polar moment of inertia
K, stress concentration factor, constant of
    proportionality
N, number

P, load
r, radius
r_1, distance from c.g. of joint to center
    of weld or rivet
s, stress
T, torque

1. Fabrication by Welding

Because of lower initial cost, many structural parts of machinery, formerly made by casting, are now fabricated by welding. The components can be sheared or flame cut from hot-rolled steel plate and then welded together. Figure 7-1 shows a number of typical welded assemblies

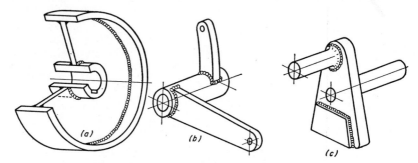

Fig. 7-1. Machine parts fabricated by fusion welding.

Sometimes the intricate portion of the body can be cast or stamped. The flat areas, made of plates, then can be attached by welding.

Welded assemblies usually provide greater strength at a reduction in weight—an important advantage for moving parts of machines and transport equipment. In a welded design it is usually necessary to do a smaller amount of machining than for an equivalent casting. In addition, the stress calculations for welded steel assemblies are sometimes more reliable than for iron castings. The design must provide accessibility to the welds so they can be properly made and inspected.

2. Fusion Welding

In the fusion process, heat is obtained from an oxyacetylene flame or from an electric arc passing between an electrode and the work. The edges of the parts are heated to the fusion temperature and joined together with the addition of molten filler material from a welding rod.

In the carbon arc process, a flux is used with some metals to envelop the molten weld in a noncontaminating atmosphere and protect it from the oxygen and nitrogen of the air. Impurities are scavenged from the weld, and a covering of slag is formed to reduce the cooling rate. In metallic arc welding, the electrode is composed of suitable filler material which is melted and fed into the joint as the weld is progressively formed. Shielded arc welding uses an electrode with a heavy coating of fluxing materials. These are consumed as the rod is melted, and perform the usual functions of a flux, as shown in Fig. 7-2. When the oxyacetylene torch is used, the molten metal is protected from the atmosphere by the outer envelope of the flame. The flame is generally adjusted until it is neutral or slightly reducing. A flux is used in the gas welding of some metals to float out any impurities that may be present and thus aid in forming a sound weld.[1]

Direct current is used with the carbon arc method, but either direct or alternating current can be used with the metallic arc process. When the weld is larger than about $\frac{3}{8}$ in. minimum thickness, it is usually made in successive layers. Deposited weld metal frequently has the coarse structure characteristic of cast metals.

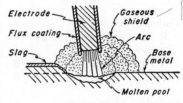

prevents oxidation

Fig. 7-2.   Arc welding with coated electrode.

Residual stresses of considerable magnitude can result from contraction of the weld metal upon cooling. Such stresses are usually greatest in the transverse direction and are thus more harmful when the weld is subjected to tensile loads. The presence of residual stress is particularly dangerous if the weld is subjected to repeated loading or impact. Removal of residual stresses can be accomplished by annealing, or by application of an overload which stresses the entire weld to the yield-point value.[2]

It is important that both the weld metal and adjacent parent metal be ductile and free from brittleness. The properties of the weld metal depend on the composition of the welding rod. However, for steel parent metal with a carbon content higher than about 0.15 per cent, there is danger of air hardening upon rapid cooling from the welding temperature. The quenching effect of the cold metal surrounding a weld can be reduced if the parts are preheated to 600 F–1500 F before the welding is done. An annealing treatment after welding may be required to restore the original ductility of the parent metal. The fusion welding characteristics[3] of some commonly used metals and alloys are given in Table 7-1.

Residual welding stresses in gray and alloy cast iron can be eliminated by preheating before welding, followed by slow cooling after welding. Plain carbon and alloy steel castings are ordinarily welded by the same procedure used for rolled steel of similar composition. Air hardening occurs if the carbon or alloy content is sufficiently high.

For the copper and aluminum alloys, strips of the parent metal are frequently used as filler material where an exact color match is required.

Fluxes are necessary in welding aluminum to remove the oxide coating

---

[1] See references 1 and 2, Bibliography.
[2] See reference 3, Bibliography.
[3] See also p. 372 of reference 1, Bibliography.

from both the parent metal and filler rods. When the welding is completed, the parts must be thoroughly cleaned of the flux to avoid corrosion. Since the welding temperature of aluminum and magnesium is below the visible light range, it is difficult for the operator to determine

TABLE 7-1

Weldability of Various Metals and Alloys

Metal or Alloy	Gas	Arc	Metal or Alloy	Gas	Arc
Carbon steels			Magnesium alloys	A	No
1. Low- and medium-carbon	A	A			
			Copper and copper alloys		
2. High-carbon	B	A	1. Deoxidized copper	A	B
3. Tool steel	B	B	2. Pitch, electrolytic, and lake	B	A
Cast steel, plain-carbon	A	A	3. Commercial bronze, red brass, low brass, and ounce metal	A	B
Gray and alloy cast iron	A	B			
			4. Spring, admiralty, yellow, and commercial brass	A	B
Malleable iron	B	B			
Low-alloy, high-tensile steels			5. Muntz metal, tobin bronze, naval brass, manganese bronze	A	B
1. Ni-Cr-Mo and Ni-Mo	B	B			
2. All other usual compositions	A	A	6. Nickel silver	A	B
			7. Phosphor bronze, bell metal, bearing bronze	A	A
Stainless steels			8. Aluminum bronze	B	A
1. Chromium	B	A	9. Beryllium copper	—	A
2. Chromium-Nickel	A	A			
			Nickel and nickel alloys	A	A
Aluminum					
1. Commercially pure Al	A	A	Lead	A	No
2. Al-Mn alloy	A	A			
3. Al-Mg-Mn and Al-Si-Mg alloy	B	A			
4. Al-Cu-Mg-Mn alloys	No	B			

A—commonly used. B—occasionally used under favorable conditions.

when the welding temperature is being approached. At high temperatures these alloys are very weak, and there is a tendency for the member to collapse unless positive support is provided during the welding operation.

Arc-weld surfacing is a convenient method for building up worn parts and wear-resisting surfaces in all kinds of machinery.

Other methods of welding, such as the flash, atomic hydrogen, thermit, unionmelt, and heliarc, are in use, particularly for specialized applications.

3. Strength of Fusion Welds

Several different types of welds with the equations for the stresses arising from the given loadings are shown in Fig. 7-3. The height h for a butt weld does not include the bulge or reinforcement a.

The fillet weld in tension of Fig. 7-4 is an important type of weld that is widely used. The size of a fillet weld is equal to the leg h of the largest inscribed isosceles right triangle. The stress situation in the weld is

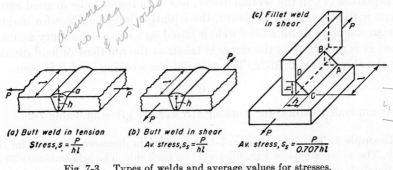

(a) Butt weld in tension
Stress, $s = \dfrac{P}{hl}$

(b) Butt weld in shear
Av. stress, $s_s = \dfrac{P}{hl}$

(c) Fillet weld in shear
Av. stress, $S_s = \dfrac{P}{0.707hl}$

Fig. 7-3.   Types of welds and average values for stresses.

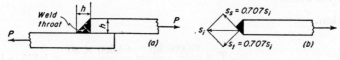

Fig. 7-4.   Fillet weld in tension.

complicated, and there is lack of agreement among engineers with respect to the simplifying assumptions which should be made in order to secure design equations. It is obvious that the number of different equations will be as great as the number of different initial assumptions. One method of analysis[4] assumes the weld to be cut through the throat or narrowest portion, as shown in Fig. 7-4(b). Bending effects are ignored and it is assumed that the only stress is s_i, which is found by dividing load P by the throat area $0.707hl$, where h is the length of the leg, and l is the length of weld perpendicular to the paper. Thus,

$$s_i = \frac{P}{0.707hl} \qquad (a)$$

This stress is divided into the shear and normal components shown in the figure. These have values of

$$s_s = \frac{P}{hl} \quad \text{and} \quad s_t = \frac{P}{hl} \qquad (b)$$

[4] See reference 7, Bibliography, and p. 843 of reference 4.

For material loaded by normal and shear stress, as in Fig. 7-4(b), the resultant normal stress is found by Eq. (38), Chapter 1. The values from Eq. (b) are substituted, to give

$$s_1 = 0.5s_t + \sqrt{(0.5s_t)^2 + s_s{}^2} = 1.618s_t = 1.618\frac{P}{hl} \tag{1}$$

4. Design Equation for Fillet Weld

Equation (1), in the section above, has been found to be in good agreement with test results. However, the equation in general use for making design calculations for a fillet weld is based on a more elementary assumption. It is merely this: the stress is taken as the quotient of load divided by the throat area $0.707hl$. The value of the working load P is then

$$P = 0.707hls \tag{2}$$

Recommended values[5] for working stresses are given in Table 7-2.

Example 1. The pulley in Fig. 7-1(a) is 15 in. in diameter with a $3\frac{1}{2}$ in. OD hub. The web plate has a $\frac{1}{4}$ in. fillet weld on each side. The belt transmits 30 hp to the shaft which turns at 1,200 rpm. What is the value of the torsional shearing stress in the welds?

Solution.

Torque:
$$T = \frac{63{,}000 \text{ hp}}{n} = \frac{63{,}000 \times 30}{1200} = 1{,}575 \text{ in-lb}$$

Radius to center of throat: $r_1 = \dfrac{3.5}{2} + \dfrac{0.25}{4} = 1.81$ in.

Force carried by welds: $P = \dfrac{1{,}575}{1.81} = 870$ lb

Length of both welds: $l = 2 \times 2\pi r_1 = 4\pi \times 1.81 = 22.8$ in.

By Eq. (2):
$$s = \frac{P}{0.707hl} = \frac{870}{0.707 \times 0.25 \times 22.8} = 216 \text{ psi}$$

A well-known rule-of-thumb for the working loads of fillet welds in tension is found from Eq. (2) and the working-stress value of 11,300 psi from Table 7-2.

Thus, for $h = \frac{1}{8}$ in., $l = 1$ in., $P = 1{,}000$ lb

for $h = \frac{1}{4}$ in., $l = 1$ in., $P = 2{,}000$ lb

for $h = \frac{3}{8}$ in., $l = 1$ in., $P = 3{,}000$ lb

etc.

[5] See reference 7, Bibliography.

TABLE 7-2

Recommended Working Stresses for Welds on Low-Carbon Steel

Type of Weld	Bare Electrodes		Coated Electrodes	
	Static Loads psi	Dynamic Loads psi	Static Loads psi	Dynamic Loads psi
Butt welds				
Tension	13,000	5,000	16,000	8,000
Compression	15,000	5,000	18,000	8,000
Shear	8,000	3,000	10,000	5,000
Fillet welds				
Transverse and				
parallel welds	11,300	3,000	14,000	5,000

TABLE 7-3

Minimum Tensile Strength and Ductility Requirements for Stress-Relieved All-Weld-Metal Tension Test Specimen

Electrode Classification No.	Tensile Strength min. psi	Yield Point min. psi	Elong. in 2 in. min. per cent
E4510	45,000	—	5
E6010	62,000	52,000	22
E7010	70,000	57,000	22
E8010	80,000	67,000	19
E9010	90,000	77,000	17
E10010	100,000	87,000	16

E4510 and E6010 for carbon and low alloy steels of weldable quality. ASTM Spec. A233-48T. AWS Spec. A5.1-48T. Other electrodes are for low-alloy steels of weldable quality. ASTM Spec. A316-48T. AWS Spec. A5.5-48T.

Hence the permissible load is equal to 1,000 lb for each $\frac{1}{8}$ in. of width of leg and each inch of length. For welds made with coated electrodes this value may be increased 25 per cent, to 1,250 lb. Strength properties for a number of arc-welding electrodes are given in Table 7-3.

5. Stress Concentration in Welds

Since abrupt changes in form occur in welds, stress concentrations are present as the force passes from one portion of the assembly to the other. Stress concentration effects are usually ignored for static or steady loads, and are applied only to the variable or range component in accordance with general design practice for fluctuating loads.

Care must be exercised that the weld metal and the plates at the base of a butt weld be thoroughly fused together. With insufficient fusion, sharp-cornered notches extend inward, as at A in Fig. 7-5(a), and a serious stress concentration results. Stress concentration also occurs at points B, where the force spreads into the reinforcement. A fillet weld has concentrations at the toe and heel, points A and B in Fig. 7-5(b), where the force is passing from one plate to the other through the weld. Values of stress concentration factors are given in Table 7-4.[6]

A fillet weld loaded by parallel forces as in Fig. 7-3(c) has stress concentrations at each end caused by the unequal elongations of the plates.

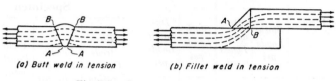

(a) Butt weld in tension   (b) Fillet weld in tension

Fig. 7-5.   Stress concentration in welds.

The upper plate at point B has the maximum elongation, because here it is carrying the entire load P. The lower plate at A has a small elongation, because it is carrying very little load at this point. Since the weld joins the two plates together, it is subjected to a greater deformation than the average for the weld as a whole, and an increase or concentration of stress

TABLE 7-4

**Stress Concentration Factors
K for Welds**

Location	K
Reinforced butt weld	1.2
Toe of transverse fillet weld	1.5
End of parallel fillet weld	2.7
T-butt joint with sharp corners	2.0

occurs at the end of the weld. Similar reasoning applies to the other end, where the lower plate at C has a large elongation and the upper plate at D has a small elongation. Similar stress concentration effects are present at the ends of the butt weld in shear, shown in Fig. 7-3(b).

6. Eccentrically Loaded Welds

When the load on a welded joint is applied eccentrically, the effect of the torque or moment must be taken into account as well as the direct load. The state of stress in such a joint is complicated, and it is necessary to make simplifying assumptions.

When a joint consists of a number of welds, it is customary to assume that the moment stress at any point is proportional to the distance from

[6] See reference 7, Bibliography, also p. 703, Vol. 2 of reference 4.

the center of gravity of the group of welds. Let the weld shown in Fig. 7-6 be one of a group forming a joint with the center of gravity of all the weld areas at O. The moment stress s acts perpendicularly to radius r on element dA of the weld. The external moment or torque T is equal to the moment from stress s integrated over all the welds of the joint.

$$T = \int sr\, dA = \int \frac{s}{r} r^2\, dA = \frac{s}{r} \int r^2\, dA = \frac{sJ}{r}$$

$$s = \frac{Tr}{J} \tag{3}$$

Ratio s/r is a constant since the stress is assumed to vary directly with r. The integral $\int r^2\, dA$ in Eq. (3) has been replaced by J, the polar moment of inertia about O for the group of welds. For the maximum torsional stress, the value of r to the point furthest removed from the center of gravity O must be used. The stress from the direct load must be added vectorially to the moment stress in order to obtain the resultant stress. For static loads, it is usual practice to assume that the direct stress in a weld is uniformly distributed throughout its area.

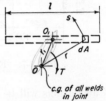

Fig. 7-6. Stress on element of eccentrically loaded welded joint.

The parallel axis equation can be used for finding the value for J for a weld about the center O. For the weld in Fig. 7-6 this equation would be written

$$J = J_o + A r_1^2 \tag{4}$$

The area A in this equation refers to the throat area of the weld. The fact that the throat for a fillet weld is inclined at 45° to the plane of the joint is disregarded. Radius r_1 extends from the center O_1 of the weld to the center of gravity O for the group. Symbol J_o represents the moment of inertia of the single-weld area about its own center O_1. This value can be found from the following equation.

$$J_o = \frac{A l^2}{12} \tag{5}$$

where A is again the throat area and l is the length of the weld.

When Eq. (5) is substituted into Eq. (4), the result is

$$J = A \left(\frac{l^2}{12} + r_1^2 \right) \tag{6}$$

The value of J for each weld about O should be computed by Eq. (6); the results are added to obtain the moment of inertia of the entire joint.

Example 2. An eccentrically loaded bracket is welded to its support as shown in Fig. 7-7. If the load is steady, find the value of the maximum stress in the weld.

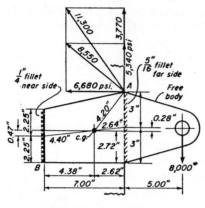

Fig. 7-7.   Example 2.

Solution. The plate is considered the free body.

$\frac{1}{4}$ in. weld, throat area:

$$A_1 = 0.707hl = 0.707$$
$$\times \frac{1}{4} \times 4.5 = 0.795 \text{ in.}^2$$

$\frac{5}{16}$ in. weld, throat area:

$$A_2 = 0.707$$
$$\times \frac{5}{16} \times 6 = 1.326 \text{ in.}^2$$

Total area $= 0.795 + 1.326$
$$= 2.121 \text{ in.}^2$$

Calculations will be made to the base of the weld and not to the center of the throat.

Take moments about the left side:

$$\bar{x} = \frac{1.326 \times 7}{2.121} = 4.38 \text{ in.}$$

Take moments about the bottom of the plate:

$$\bar{y} = \frac{0.795 \times 2.25 + 1.326 \times 3}{2.121} = 2.72 \text{ in.}$$

By Eq. (6) for left weld:

$$J = 0.795 \left(\frac{4.5^2}{12} + 4.40^2 \right) = 16.74 \text{ in.}^4$$

By Eq. (6) for right weld:

$$J = 1.326 \left(\frac{6^2}{12} + 2.64^2 \right) = 13.21 \text{ in.}^4$$

Total: $J = 16.74 + 13.21 = 29.95 \text{ in.}^4$

Uniform stress: $s = \dfrac{8,000}{2.121} = 3,770 \text{ psi}$

The maximum resultant stress occurs at A.

Torsional stress: $s = \dfrac{8,000 \times 7.62 \times 4.20}{29.95} = 8,550 \text{ psi}$

This stress is directed perpendicularly to the radius from the center of gravity to A. It has the components shown on the figure.

Resultant stress: $s = \sqrt{9,120^2 + 6,680^2} = 11,300$ psi

Although point B is further from the center of gravity than A, the directions of the moment stresses are such that the greatest resultant stress occurs at A.

Example 3. Find the value of Force P in Fig. 7-8 for a working stress of 11,300 psi.

(a) All welds are $\frac{1}{4}$ in. fillets.
(b) Welds on the left side are $\frac{1}{4}$ in. and on the right side are $\frac{1}{2}$ in.

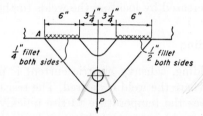

Fig. 7-8.   Example 3.

Solution. (a)

Throat area of all welds: $A = 4 \times \dfrac{1}{4} \times 6 \times 0.707 = 4.242$ in.^{2}

Then: $P = sA = 11,300 \times 4.242 = 47,900$ lb.

(b) Left, throat area: $A = 2 \times \dfrac{1}{4} \times 6 \times 0.707 = 2.121$ in.^{2}

Right, throat area: $A = 2 \times \dfrac{1}{2} \times 6 \times 0.707 = 4.242$ in.^{2}

Total area: $A = 6.363$ in.^{2}.

Take moments at left end: $\bar{x} = \dfrac{2.121 \times 3 + 4.242 \times 15.5}{6.363} = 11.33$ in.

For left welds: $J = 2.121 \left(\dfrac{6^2}{12} + 8.33^2 \right) = 153.65$ in.^{4}

For right welds: $J = 4.242 \left(\dfrac{6^2}{12} + 4.17^2 \right) = 86.37$ in.^{4}

Total: $J = 153.65 + 86.37 = 240.02$ in.^{4}

Direct stress: $s = \dfrac{P}{6.363} = 0.1572P$

Moment stress at A: $s = \dfrac{P2.08 \times 11.33}{240.02} = 0.0984P$

Total stress: $0.1572P + 0.0984P = 0.2556P = 11,300$

$$P = 44,200 \text{ lb}$$

It should be noted, that although the welds of part (b) are much larger, because of the eccentricity the carrying capacity of the joint has been actually reduced.

The method explained in this section cannot be considered an exact analysis of weld stresses, but should be looked upon simply as a reasonable effort to take into account the fact that the capacity of a joint to resist moment loads is increased by locating the welds further from the center.

7. Resistance Welding

In resistance welding, a heavy electric current is passed through the parts at the place where the weld is desired. The resistance of the metals to the current causes the temperature to rise quickly and the metal to become plastic. The weld is completed by mechanical pressure from the electrodes. This pressure brings the parts into complete union. Alternating current is used from a suitable transformer which must be capable of supplying a large current at low voltage. The copper electrodes are faced with harder alloys at the contact end. To confine the heat in the proper region, the resistance between electrode and part must be less than the resistance between the surfaces to be joined.

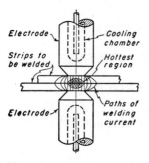

Fig. 7-9. Schematic diagram of spot welding.

Spot welding is a type of resistance welding in which cylindrical electrodes are used which have a contact area approximately equal to the size of the desired weld. As shown in Fig. 7-9, a chamber is provided for cooling water which prevents overheating and prolongs the life of the electrode. The squeezing pressure must be properly adjusted to the thickness and strength of the parts being welded. A chart[7] showing the spot welding possibilities of various combinations of metals and alloys is given in Fig. 7-10. The metal surfaces to be welded must be clean if sound welds are expected. It is especially necessary that the oxide coating on aluminum be removed by mechanical or chemical means before spot welding.

Seam welding is similar to spot welding except that copper alloy disks

[7] See reference 16, Bibliography.

about 6 by 9 in. in diameter are used. The work is rolled between the electrodes, and evenly spaced spot welds are obtained by periodic application of the current. It is possible to overlap the welds by close spacing and thus form a fluid-tight joint.

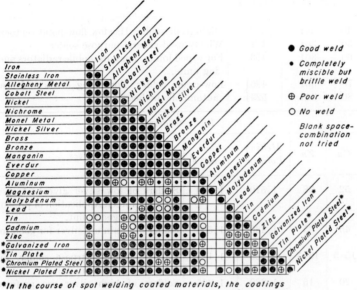

*In the course of spot welding coated materials, the coatings frequently dissolve in the other metals present or burn away.

Fig. 7-10.   Spot welding chart for various combinations of metals.

8. Soldering and Brazing

Many cast and wrought metals can be united by soldering and brazing. Soft solders are tin-lead alloys of low melting points; hard solders comprise the silver solders and brazing alloys of different compositions and melting points. In any soldering or brazing process, the parts are heated above the melting point of the solder but below that of the parts. The wetting action of the solder brings it into intimate contact with the surfaces to be joined. The solder, after cooling, serves as an adhesive to bind the two parts together, even though in some cases the solder forms an alloy with the metal of the part. In general, the strength of the joint is improved as the wetting action becomes more perfect.

The surfaces must be clean and covered with a flux which is liquid at the soldering temperature. The flux dissolves any oxides present as well as preventing oxidation while the parts are being heated. The flux is drawn into the joint by capillary attraction. When the soldering tem-

TABLE 7-5
Compositions and Uses for Solders and Brazing Alloys

Soft Solders

Sn	Pb	Melting Point, F	Flow Point, F	Uses
60	40	361	372	High-grade solder. Has low flow-point temperature.
50	50	361	421	Widely used general-purpose solder.
40	60	361	453	For wiped joints. For automobile radiators and heating units.
30	70	361	486⎫	Low-grade solder. For filling dents and seams in
20	80	361	523⎭	automobile bodies.

Silver Solders

Ag	Cu	Zn	Melting Point, F	Flow Point, F	Uses
10	52	38	1,510	1,600	Solders of low silver give best results in stainless steel. Application of pressure aids in forming good joint.
20	45	35	1,430	1,500	Solder of minimum silver for good joints in brass.
50	15.5	16.5	1,160	1,175	Cd. 18, general-purpose solder. Suitable for joining unlike metals.*
65	20	15	1,280	1,325	Solders of high silver are preferred for copper, especially for thin sections.

Miscellaneous Brazing Alloys

Alloy	Zn	Sn	Cu	Melting Point, F	Uses
Brazing alloy	Rem.		50–53	1,595–1,620	General-purpose brazing alloy.
Tobin bronze	38–43	0.50–1.50	Rem.	1,625	Strong oxyacetylene welds on steel, cast iron, copper, and nickel alloys.
Manganese bronze	38–43	0–1.5	Rem.	1,600	Mn. 0.50–0.75. Hard and wear-resistant.
Cu-Ni-Zn alloy	43		47	1,700	Ni. 10. Strong, general-purpose alloy.

* Proprietary Alloy, "Easy-Flo," Handy and Harman.

perature is reached, the solder is also drawn in by capillarity and displaces the flux. For this action, the surfaces must be closely spaced with respect to each other. The capillarity is greater for a tightly fitted joint, but higher temperatures are required to secure sufficient fluidity of the solder. In practice, clearances of 0.003 or 0.004 in. have been found satisfactory.

The strength of a soldered joint depends on many factors such as the quality of the solder, thickness of the joint, smoothness of the surfaces, kind of materials soldered, soldering temperature, and duration of contact between solder and part at the soldering temperature. Optimum stress values in shear for soft-soldered joints can be taken as 6,000 psi for copper, 5,000 psi for mild steel, and 4,000 psi for brass.[8] These are ultimate values.

The properties of soft solder metals are given in Table 7-5. Melting of the alloy begins at the melting point shown, and is completed at the temperature of the flow point.

The silver solders have higher melting temperatures, and the soldering operation is carried on while the parts are at a red heat. Cast iron, wrought iron, and carbon steels can be joined to each other or to brass, copper, nickel, silver, monel, and other nonferrous alloys. Silver solders are malleable and ductile and are suitable for vibration and impact loads. They are also resistant to corrosion. The tensile strength of cast silver solder varies from 40,000 psi to 60,000 psi.[9] Joint preparation and clearances are the same as for soft solder. Heating can be done with a torch or with a high-frequency induction heating coil.

Brazing is a form of soldering at high temperatures that uses alloys of copper and zinc. The properties of several brazing alloys are given in Table 7-5. Tobin bronze is in wide use as a welding rod for general repair service and for building up defects in iron castings. The tensile strength is approximately 50,000 psi. Manganese bronze is similarly used, especially where the deposited metal is called upon to resist abrasion. Brazing alloys for aluminum are available with a melting point below that of the aluminum parts. In fusion welding, the high temperature permits impurities to be floated away by the flux. However, for brazing, the oxides must be removed and the joint cleaned by mechanical means.

9. Furnace Brazing

Furnace or copper brazing[10] is a very satisfactory method for joining parts with pure copper. The component parts are assembled together, a ring of pure copper wire is placed adjacent to the joint as shown in Fig. 7-11, and the assembly is passed through a furnace. The copper melts at 1980 F and is drawn into the joint by capillary attraction. The strength of the assembly increases with the tightness of the fit. For steel, the clearance should run from about 0.001 in. loose to a light press fit.

Castings, forgings, and parts machined from solid stock can sometimes

[8] See reference 20, Bibliography.
[9] See reference 19, Bibliography.
[10] See references 17 and 18, Bibliography.

be redesigned and fabricated from stampings, screw machine parts, and pieces of tubing brazed together. Machining operations can be minimized and substantial economies effected. Parts must be held in their proper relationship with each other in their trip through the furnace. It is

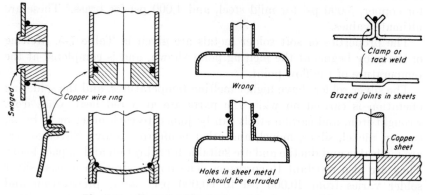

Fig. 7-11. Typical joints fabricated by furnace welding.

advantageous to have self-locking joints and thus avoid the use of holding fixtures. When the heating is done in an electric furnace with a reducing atmosphere, no flux is required, and the parts are delivered with smooth bright surfaces.

10. Riveted Joint with Central Load

Rivets are in wide use as fastenings for joints in buildings, bridges, boilers, tanks, ships, and miscellaneous frameworks. For centrally applied loads, it is customary to assume that all the rivets in a joint are equally stressed.[11] This assumption, however, is only approximately valid. As a

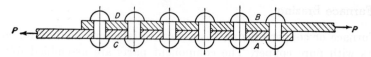

Fig. 7-12. Bars carrying tensile forces joined by single row of rivets.

simple example, consider the two bars in Fig. 7-12, which are held together by a single row of rivets. The material at B and C has large elongations, because it is carrying almost the entire load P. The material at A and D has small elongations because the bars at these points are carrying only small loads. Because of these unequal elongations, the end rivets carry

[11] See references 23 and 24, Bibliography.

excessive loads. The loads are smaller for the next rivets toward the center, until at the middle of the joint the rivets will be carrying less than the average load. For ductile materials, a more uniform distribution of the loading among the rivets occurs if the joint is first subjected to an overload which causes the material in the highly stressed regions to yield in plastic flow.

In structural steel work, it is standard practice to use punched holes which are $\frac{1}{16}$ in. larger than the diameter of the rivet. Although the rivet after driving may completely fill the hole, computations are made on the basis of the original rivet diameter. Since punching injures the metal around the circumference of the hole, work of higher quality is secured by subpunching the hole to a smaller diameter and then reaming it until it is large enough to admit the rivet. Boiler codes require the holes to be either drilled or subpunched and reamed. In boiler work, computations are made on the basis of the hole diameter, since the rivets must be tightly driven and must completely fill the holes.

Rivets must be spaced neither too close nor too far apart. The minimum rivet spacing, center to center, for structural steel work is usually taken as three rivet diameters. A somewhat closer spacing is often used in boilers. Rivets should not be spaced too far apart or buckling of the plates will take place. The maximum spacing is usually taken as 16 times the thickness of the outside plate. The edge distance, or distance from the rivet center to the edge of the plate, must not be less than a specified amount or there is danger of failure, as shown in Fig. 7-13(d) and (e).

11. Stresses in Rivets

Power-driven hot rivets contract upon cooling and draw the plates tightly together so that the friction between the parts assist in the transfer of the load. Under certain conditions, the entire load might be carried in this way. The friction in a joint breaks down as the loading increases, and the joint can then fail in a number of different ways, as shown in Fig. 7-13. For fluctuating loads, it is especially desirable to prevent slip

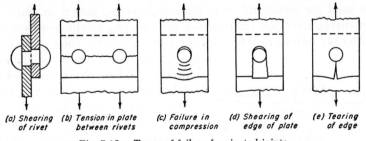

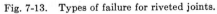

(a) Shearing   (b) Tension in plate   (c) Failure in   (d) Shearing of   (e) Tearing
of rivet   between rivets   compression   edge of plate   of edge

Fig. 7-13.   Types of failure for riveted joints.

TABLE 7-6

Working Stresses for Rivets Used in Structural Steel for Buildings*

Type of Rivet or Bolt	Bearing, psi		Shear, psi
	Double Shear	Single Shear	
Power-driven rivets or turned bolts in reamed holes	40,000	32,000	15,000
Hand-driven rivets or unfinished bolts	25,000	20,000	10,000

* See reference 21, Bibliography.

TABLE 7-7

Physical Properties of Rivet Steel

Property	ASTM A141-49T (For Buildings and Bridges)	ASTM A31-49T or ASME S-5 (For Boilers)	
		Grade A	Grade B
Tensile strength, psi	52,000–62,000	45,000–55,000	58,000–68,000
Yield point, minimum, psi, but in no case less than	28,000	0.5 tens. str.	0.5 tens. str. 32,000
Elongation in 8 in. minimum per cent	$\dfrac{1,500,000}{\text{tens. str.}}$	$\dfrac{1,500,000}{\text{tens. str.}}$ but need not exceed 30	$\dfrac{1,500,000}{\text{tens. str.}}$ but in no case less than 23

in the joint. The loading should therefore be conservative and the rivets tightly driven.

Despite the assistance given by the friction, it is customary to compute the strength of a riveted joint from the strength of the rivets in shear, the tension in the plates between the rivet holes, or the strength in compression or bearing for the rivets on the plates. Working stress values for rivets used for structural steel for buildings are shown in Table 7-6. Power-driven rivets are rivets driven by a riveting machine or by a hand-operated air hammer. When turned bolts are used, they must fit the holes with not over $\frac{1}{50}$ in. diametral clearance. When rivets are loaded in single shear, as shown in Fig. 7-14, the stress situation is complicated by the effects of the eccentricity. For loading in single shear, Table 7-6 indicates

Fig. 7-14. Eccentric load on rivet of single lap joint.

that the value of the working stress for bearing or compression is lower than when the rivet is loaded in double shear. Physical properties for rivet steels are given in Table 7-7.

Lower working stresses are used for bridges and boilers, as indicated by Tables 7-8 and 7-9. The physical properties of rivet steel for such

TABLE 7-8 Working Stress, psi, for Rivets Used in Railway Bridges*		TABLE 7-9 Ultimate Strength of Boiler Materials*	
Shear in power-driven rivets	13,500	Rivets in shear	
Shear in turned bolts and hand-driven rivets	11,000	Iron rivets	38,000
		Steel, Spec. SA-31, Grade A	44,000
Bearing on power-driven rivets	27,000	Alloy Steel, SA-202, Grade A	60,000
		Carbon steel plates in tension	55,000
Bearing on turned bolts and hand-driven rivets	20,000	C-Si or Mo steel plates in crushing	95,000

* See reference 22, Bibliography.   * See reference 25, Bibliography.

services are also given in Table 7-7. Recognized codes are available for buildings, bridges, and boilers and should be consulted for additional information on specifications of materials, working stresses, and construction details. Higher values for the working stresses can sometimes be permitted for certain kinds of machinery or equipment where failure would not endanger human life. Proper provision must be made in riveted joints for the effects of fluctuating loads, impact, and extremes of temperature.

12. Stresses in a Cylindrical Shell

The stresses in the walls of a thin cylindrical shell are generally computed on the assumption that the stress is uniform throughout the wall thickness. Let the shell of Fig. 7-15 be loaded by the internal pressure p. If the length of the section perpendicular to the paper be taken as l, an element of area on the drum surface is equal to $rl\, d\theta$. The horizontal component of

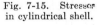

(a) Hoop forces in shell

(b) Longitudinal forces

Fig. 7-15.   Stresses in cylindrical shell.

the force on the element is $prl \cos \theta\, d\theta$. When this force is integrated over a quarter-circle, the result is equal to the hoop force F. Thus,

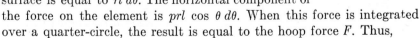

$$F = \int_0^{\pi/2} prl \cos \theta\, d\theta = prl \sin \theta \Big|_0^{\pi/2} = prl \qquad (7)$$

The hoop or tangential stress s_1 is found by dividing force F by the area

of the cross section tl, giving

$$s_1 = \frac{F}{tl} = \frac{pr}{t} \tag{8}$$

In the longitudinal direction, the stress s_2 in the material must resist the force of the internal pressure acting on the end surface of the drum. Hence,

$$2\pi r t s_2 = \pi r^2 p$$

$$s_2 = \frac{pr}{2t} \tag{9}$$

The hoop stress is seen to be twice as great as the longitudinal stress. Equations (8) and (9) are valid only when thickness t is much less than radius r. From Eq. (7) the conclusion can be drawn that the bearing or compressive force on a rivet, Fig. 7-13(c), is equal to the stress in the bearing times the projected area, or the diameter times the thickness of the plate.

A boiler joint is weaker than the plate composing the shell because of the area lost in the rivet holes. Computations can be made for various assumed types of failure that will free the main plate of the joint in order to make a comparison with the strength of the unpunched plate and thus arrive at a value for the efficiency of the joint. The process is illustrated by the following example.

Example 4. Find the working force carried by an $8\frac{1}{4}$ in. width of the triple riveted butt joint in Fig. 7-16. Make computations for the assumed types of failure shown in Table 7-10, and compute the efficiency of the joint. If this joint

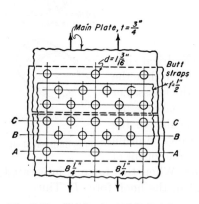

Fig. 7-16.   Triple riveted butt joint.
Example 4.

TABLE 7-10
Loads for Joint of Figure 7-16

No.	Type of Failure	Working Force, lb
(a)	Tension at A-A	58,270
(b)	Shear in rivets	87,710
(c)	Bearing on rivets	78,970
(d)	Tension at B-B } Shear at A-A	58,220
(e)	Tension at B-B } Bearing at A-A	59,750
(f)	Bearing at B-B and C-C } Shear at A-A	77,430
(g)	Tension in gross plate	68,060
(h)	Efficiency	85.5%
(i)	Permissible pressure	235 psi

is used on a 60 in. diameter cylindrical tank, find the permissible internal pressure. Use the following stress values from Table 7-9:

Tension, $s_t = 55,000$ psi ult. for steel plate

Compression, $s_c = 95,000$ psi ult. for steel plate

Shear, $s_s = 44,000$ psi ult. for steel rivets

Factor of safety, $FS = 5$

Solution.

(a) Tension in main plate at section *A-A*.

$$F = \frac{55,000}{5} (8.25 - 1.1875) \times 0.75 = 58,270 \text{ lb}$$

(b) Shear in rivets. There are 9 surfaces in shear: 4 on *B-B*, 4 on *C-C*, and 1 on *A-A*.

Area of rivet in shear: $A = \dfrac{\pi}{4} \times 1.1875^2 = 1.108 \text{ in.}^2$

$$F = \frac{44,000}{5} \times 9 \times 1.108 = 87,710 \text{ lb}$$

(c) Bearing on rivets. On *B-B* and *C-C*, failure occurs in the main plate. On *A-A*, failure occurs in the butt plate.

Area in bearing: $A = 4 \times 1.1875 \times 0.75 + 1.1875 \times 0.5 = 4.156 \text{ in.}^2$

$$F = \frac{95,000}{5} \times 4.156 = 78,970 \text{ lb}$$

(d) Tension at section *B-B*, and shear at section *A-A*.

Area in tension: $A = (8.25 - 2 \times 1.1875) \times 0.75 = 4.406 \text{ in.}^2$

$$F = \frac{55,000}{5} \times 4.406 + \frac{44,000}{5} \times 1.108$$

$$= 48,470 + 9,750 = 58,220 \text{ lb}$$

(e) Tension at section *B-B* and bearing at *A-A*.

$$F = 48,470 + \frac{95,000}{5} \times 1.1875 \times 0.5 = 59,750 \text{ lb}$$

(f) Bearing at sections *B-B* and *C-C*, and shear at section *A-A*.

$$F = \frac{95,000}{5} \times 4 \times 1.1875 \times 0.75 + 9,750 = 77,430 \text{ lb}$$

(g) Tension in unpunched plate.

$$F = \frac{55,000}{5} \times 8.25 \times 0.75 = 68,060 \text{ lb}$$

(h) Efficiency $= \dfrac{58,220}{68,060} \times 100 = 85.5\%$

(i) By Eq. (7), $p = \dfrac{F}{rl} = \dfrac{58,220}{30 \times 8.25}$

$= 235$ psi maximum permissible internal pressure

13. Riveted Joint with Eccentric Load

When the load is applied eccentrically to a group of rivets forming a joint, the effect of the torque or moment must be taken into account, as

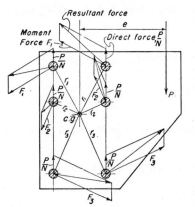

well as the direct load. A typical example is shown in Fig. 7-17, where the joint of N rivets is subjected to a moment equal to Pe. Let it be assumed that the moment load on a rivet varies directly with the distance from the center of gravity O of the group of rivets, and is directed perpendicular to the radius to the center of gravity. Equations for moment forces F_1, F_2, and F_3 in Fig. 7-17 may then be written

$$F_1 = Kr_1; \quad F_2 = Kr_2; \quad F_3 = Kr_3 \quad \text{(a)}$$

Fig. 7-17.   Riveted joint with eccentric load.

where K is the constant of proportionality.

The externally applied moment is equal to the summation of the products of these forces and their arms to the center of gravity O. Hence,

$$T = Pe = N_1 F_1 r_1 + N_2 F_2 r_2 + N_3 F_3 r_3 + \cdots$$

$$= K(N_1 r_1^2 + N_2 r_2^2 + N_3 r_3^2 + \cdots) \quad \text{(10)}$$

where N_1 is the number of rivets with radius r_1, N_2 is the number with radius r_2, and so on until the entire joint has been taken care of. When the value of K has been determined from Eq. (10), the moment force for each rivet can be computed by multiplying by the appropriate r. It is customary to assume that the direct load P/N is the same for all rivets of the joint. The vectorial sum of moment force and direct force is the resultant force on the rivet.

Example 5. Find the value of the force carried by the most heavily loaded rivet for the joint of Fig. 7-18. Find the value of the shear stress for $\frac{3}{4}$ in. rivets. and the value of the bearing stress if the plate is $\frac{5}{16}$ in. thick.

Solution. The plate is considered the free body.

Direct force on rivets: $F = \dfrac{10,000}{6} = 1,667$ lb

Take moments about the bottom row of rivets: $\hat{y} = \dfrac{2 \times 6 + 2 \times 9}{6} = 5$ in,

In Eq. (10): $10,000 \times 5 = K(2 \times 20 + 2 \times 5 + 2 \times 29)$

$$K = 463$$

Rivet at A has the maximum force.

Moment force: $F_3 = 463 \times 5.385 = 2,493$ lb

This force has the horizontal and vertical components shown in Fig. 7-18.

Resultant force: $F_r = \sqrt{(926 + 1,667)^2 + 2,315^2} = 3,476$ lb

Area in shear: $A = \dfrac{\pi}{4} \times 0.75^2 = 0.4418$ in.²

Shear stress in rivet: $s_s = \dfrac{3,476}{0.4418} = 7,870$ psi

Area in bearing: $A = \dfrac{5}{16} \times \dfrac{3}{4} = 0.2344$ in.²

Bearing stress on rivet: $s = \dfrac{3,476}{0.2344} = 14,830$ psi

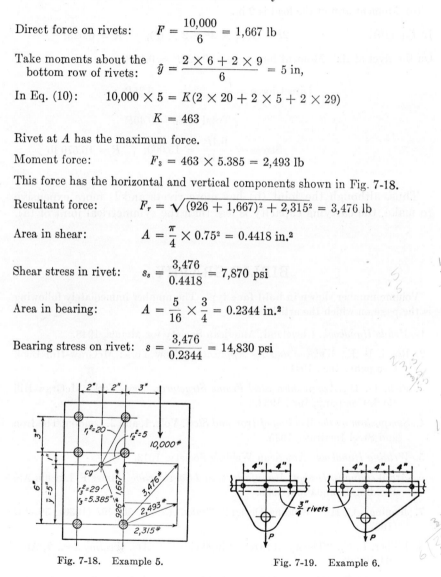

Fig. 7-18.   Example 5.   Fig. 7-19.   Example 6.

Example 6. Find the value of P for the two joints shown in Fig. 7-19 based on a working stress of 15,000 psi in shear.

Solution. Area in shear $= \dfrac{\pi}{4}\left(\dfrac{3}{4}\right)^2 = 0.4418$ in.^{2}, each rivet.

(a) $\qquad\qquad\qquad P = 3 \times 0.4418 \times 15,000 = 19,880$ lb

(b) Moment arm of the load is 2 in.

In Eq. (10): $\qquad\qquad 2P = K(2 \times 2^2 + 2 \times 6^2), \qquad K = 0.025P$

On the rivet at A: Moment force $= 6 \times 0.025P = 0.15P$

$$\text{Direct force} = \frac{P}{4} \qquad\quad = 0.25P$$

$$\text{Total force} = 0.40P$$

$$\text{Stress} = \frac{0.4P}{0.4418} = 15,000; \qquad P = 16,570 \text{ lb}$$

Thus, although the joint (b) has more rivets and is more expensive to make, the carrying capacity is less than the symmetrical joint of (a).

BIBLIOGRAPHY

Volume number shown in **bold face** type. The number immediately following is the page on which the article begins.

1. *Metals Handbook*. Cleveland: American Society for Metals, 1948.

2. Rossi, B. E., *Welding and Its Application*. New York: McGraw-Hill Book Company, Inc., 1941.

3. Fish, G. D., *Arc Welded Steel Frame Structures*. New York: McGraw-Hill Book Company, Inc., 1933.

4. *Symposium on the Welding of Iron and Steel*, Vols. 1, and 2. London: The Iron and Steel Institute, 1935.

5. *Welding Handbook*, American Welding Society, 1942.

6. *Arc Welding in Design, Manufacture, and Construction*. James F. Lincoln Arc Welding Foundation, 1939.

7. Jennings, C. H., "Welding Design," *Trans. ASME*, **58**, 497 (1936); **59**, 462 (1937).

8. Bibber, L. C., "Theory of Stresses in Welds," *J. Am. Welding Soc.*, **9**, Apr., 104 (1930).

9. Jensen, C. D., "Combined Stresses in Fillet Welds," *J. Am. Welding Soc.*, **13**, Feb., 17 (1934).

10. Solakian, A. A., "Stresses in Transverse Fillet Welds by Photoelastic Methods," *J. Am. Welding Soc.*, **13**, Feb., 22 (1934).

11. Weiskopf, W. H. and Male, M., "Stress Distribution in Side-Welded Joints," *J. Am. Welding Soc.*, **9**, Sept., 23 (1930).

12. Norris, C. H., "Photoelastic Investigation of Stress Distribution in Transverse Fillet Welds," *Welding J.* **24**, 557s (1945).

13. Stitt, J. R., "Stress Relief of Weldments for Machining Stability," *Bulletin 121*, Ohio State University, Engineering Experiment Station, Nov. (1944); also *Bulletin 123*, Sept. (1945).

14. Charlton, E. J., "Trends in the Use of Welded Machinery Parts," *Mech. Eng.*, **67**, 109 (1945).

15. "How to Weld Aluminum," *Iron Age*, **157**, June 20, 27 (1946); **158**, July 4, 11 (1946).

16. Ferguson, L., "Spot Welding Various Metals," *Welding Engr.*, **18**, July, 14; Aug., 20 (1933).

17. Webber, H. M., "Furnace Brazing of Machine Parts," *Mech. Eng.*, **72**, 863, 969 (1950). See also *Iron Age*, **142**, Sept. 8, 15, 22; Nov. 3, 10, 24; Dec. 8, 29, (1938); **143**, Feb. 2, Mar. 16, Apr. 6 (1939).

18. Wilkes, G. B., Jr., "Properties of Copper Brazed Joints," *Iron Age*, **162**, Sept. 30, 44 (1948).

19. Leach, R. H., "Silver Solders," *Proc. ASTM*, **30**(2), 493 (1930).

20. Nightingale, S. J., *Tin Solders*, London: British Non-Ferrous Metals Research Association, 1942.

21. *Steel Construction*, New York: American Institute of Steel Construction, 1948.

22. *Specifications for Steel Railway Bridges*, American Railway Engineering Association, 1950, p. 15–11.

23. Mitchell, W. D., and Rosenthal, D., "Influence of the Elastic Constants on the Partition of Load Between Rivets," *Proc. Soc. Exptl. Stress Anal.*, **7**, No. 2, 17 (1949).

24. Aleck, B. J., Goland, M., and Morris, L. D., "Load Distribution in Riveted and Spotwelded Joints," *Proc. Soc. Exptl. Stress Anal.*, **2**, No. 2, 28 (1944).

25. *Boiler Codes of the American Society of Mechanical Engineers*, 1956, "Power Boilers," "Specifications for Materials," "Unfired Pressure Vessels."

26. Grassi, R. C., Cornet, I., and Berger, R. S., "Investigating the Strength of Copper-Brazed Joints," *Mech. Eng.*, **78**, 630 (1956).

27. Diehl, C., Blumberg, H. S., and Benz, W. G., Jr., "Controlled Internal-Contour Shielded-Root Welds Without Backing Rings," *Trans. ASME*, **75**, 1103 (1953).

28. Goland, M., and Reissner, E., "The Stresses in Cemented Joints," *Trans. ASME*, **66**, A-17 (1944).

PROBLEMS

1. Find the value of the maximum stress in the weld of Fig. 7-20. Assume the direct stress to be uniformly distributed over the throat area.

Ans. s = 14,340 psi.

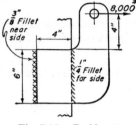

Fig. 7-20.   Problem 1.

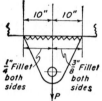

Fig. 7-21.   Problem 2.

2. Find the permissible static load P if the value of the maximum stress in the weld throat is 11,300 psi for the joint in Fig. 7-21.   *Ans.* P = 74,500 lb.

3. Work Problem 2 for the joint in Fig. 7-22.   *Ans.* P = 26,800 lb.

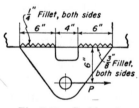

Fig. 7-22.   Problem 3.

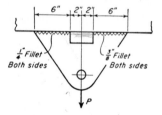

Fig. 7-23.   Problem 4.

4. Work Problem 2 for the joint in Fig. 7-23.   *Ans.* P = 44,900 lb.

5. The ends of the channel of Fig. 7-24 lie on immovable supports. If all welds are of the same size, find the length of leg h of the fillet welds required to carry the given load. Working stress for welds is 11,300 psi. The beam is to be fixed at the ends by the welds.   *Ans.* h = 0.28 in.

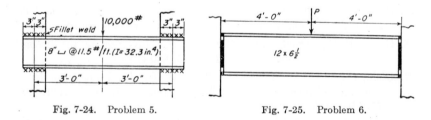

Fig. 7-24.   Problem 5.   Fig. 7-25.   Problem 6.

6. The I-beam in Fig. 7-25 is 11.87 in. deep with flanges $6\frac{1}{2}$ in. wide and of a uniform thickness of 0.355 in. The beam is welded to immovable supports by butt welds. Assume the bending moment is carried by the flange welds, and the shear forces are carried by the web welds. Flange welds are of same size as the flange of the beam. Find the value of force P for a bending stress of 12,000 psi in the flange welds.   *Ans.* $P = 25,860$ lb.

7. Find the required length l of the weld required in Fig. 7-26 if the maximum stress is 11,300 psi.   *Ans.* $l = 10.65$ in.

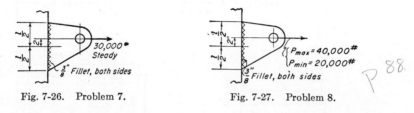

Fig. 7-26.   Problem 7.   Fig. 7-27.   Problem 8.

8. Find the length l of the weld required for the fluctuating load of the joint in Fig. 7-27. Let the weld metal have a yield point value of 25,000 psi and an endurance limit of 10,000 psi. Let the *FS* based on the yield point be 2, and the stress concentration factor be 1.5. Solve by use of working-stress triangle.
                      Ans. $l = 17.3$ in.

9. Find the value of P_{max} for the joint of Fig. 7-28 if P_{min} is equal to zero. Other data is same as that in the preceeding problem.   *Ans.* $P_{max} = 8,930$ lb.

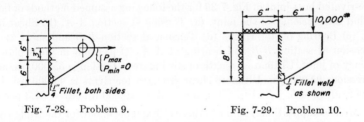

Fig. 7-28.   Problem 9.   Fig. 7-29.   Problem 10.

10. Find the value of the maximum stress for the joint in Fig. 7-29. The weld extends on the two vertical edges and across the top.   *Ans.* $s = 11,000$ psi.

11. Find the value of the maximum stress for the joint in Fig. 7-30. The weld extends on the vertical edge and across the top.   *Ans.* $s = 10,680$ psi.

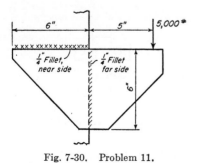

Fig. 7-30.   Problem 11.   Fig. 7-31.   Problem 12.

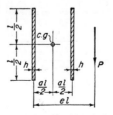

12. Derive an equation for the value of the maximum load for the weld in Fig. 7-31 if the stress is limited to 11,300 psi.

$$Ans. \quad P = \frac{16{,}000hl}{\sqrt{K^2 + (1 + aK)^2}}, \text{ where } K = \frac{3(2e - a)}{1 + 3a^2}.$$

13. Repeat Problem 12 for the joint in Fig. 7-32.

$$Ans. \quad P = \frac{16{,}000hl}{\sqrt{a^2K_1^2 + (1 + K_1)^2}}, \text{ where } K_1 = \frac{3(2e - 1)}{1 + 3a^2}.$$

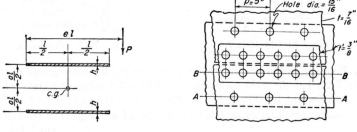

Fig. 7-32.   Problem 13.   Fig. 7-33.   Problem 14.

14. Compute and tabulate the working forces for a pitch length of 5 in. for the double-riveted butt joint of Fig. 7-33 for the following assumed methods of failure. Also find the efficiency of the joint. (a) Tension at section A-A. (b) Shear in the rivets. (c) Bearing on the rivets. (d) Tension at section B-B and shear at A-A. (e) Tension at section B-B and bearing at A-A. (f) Tension in gross plate. (g) Efficiency of joint. Ultimate strength of steel plate in tension is 55,000 psi, and in compression, 95,000 psi. Ultimate shear strength for rivets is 44,000 psi. Use a factor of safety of 5.   *Ans.*   Tension at A-A, 19,550 lb; eff. = 81.3 per cent.

15. Make computations similar to those of Example 4, but for the triple-riveted butt joint in Fig. 7-34. Tank dia. = 60 in. Use stresses from Table 7-9.

Ans.   Tension at B-B and shear at A-A, 70,860 lb; eff. = 84.1%.

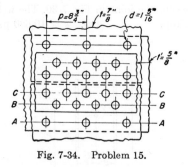

Fig. 7-34.   Problem 15.   Fig. 7-35.   Problem 16.

16. Find the resultant force on each rivet of the joint in Fig. 7-35.

17. Repeat Problem 16 for the joint of Fig. 7-36.

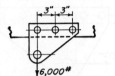

Fig. 7-36. Problem 17.

Fig. 7-37. Problem 18.

18. Find the permissible load P for the riveted joint in Fig. 7-37 if the resultant shearing stress for the most highly stressed rivet is 15,000 psi. Rivets are 1 in. in diameter. *Ans.* $P = 40,600$ lb.

19. Find the shearing stress in the most heavily loaded rivet in the group shown in Fig. 7-38. Rivets are $\frac{3}{4}$ in. in diameter. *Ans.* $s_s = 12,680$ psi.

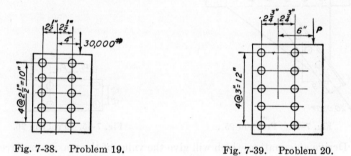

Fig. 7-38. Problem 19.

Fig. 7-39. Problem 20.

20. Find the permissible load P for the joint in Fig. 7-39 if the maximum value of the shearing stress is 15,000 psi. Rivets are $\frac{3}{4}$ in. in diameter.
Ans. $P = 30,600$ lb.

21. Find the distance b in Fig. 7-40 if the maximum shearing stress on the most heavily loaded rivet is to be 13,500 psi. *Ans.* $b = 5.04$ in.

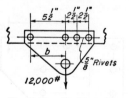

Fig. 7-40. Problem 21.

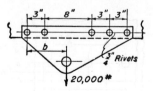

Fig. 7-41. Problem 22.

22. Repeat Problem 21 for Fig. 7-41. *Ans.* $b = 6.71$ in.

23. Find the value of the force on the most heavily loaded rivet in Fig. 7-42.

Ans.   1,270 lb.

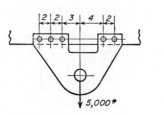

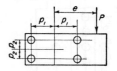

Fig. 7-42.   Problem 23.   Fig. 7-43.   Problem 24.

24. Find the value of the force on the most heavily loaded rivet in Fig. 7-43.

Ans.   4,080 lb.

25. Find the value of the force on the most heavily loaded rivet in Fig. 7-44.

Ans.   4,300 lb.

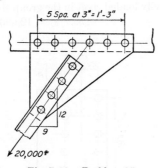

Fig. 7-44.   Problem 25.   Fig. 7-45.   Problem 26.

26. Derive an equation which will give the value of the maximum force on the right-hand rivets in Fig. 7-45.

$$Ans. \quad F = \frac{P}{4}\sqrt{\frac{(e + p_1)^2 + p_2^2}{p_1^2 + p_2^2}}.$$

The following problems are presented without answers.

27. The lap joint of Fig. 7-46 is made of carbon steel plates and rivets. Find the efficiency of the joint based on shear in the rivets on *A-A* and tension in the plate on *B-B*. Use stress values from Table 7-9.

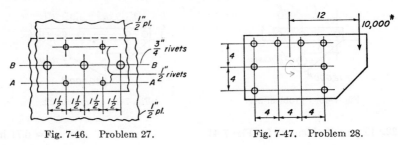

Fig. 7-46.   Problem 27.   Fig. 7-47.   Problem 28.

28. Find the resultant force on the most heavily loaded rivet in Fig. 7-47.

29. Find the value of P in Fig. 7-48 if the shearing stress on the most heavily loaded rivet is 12,000 psi.

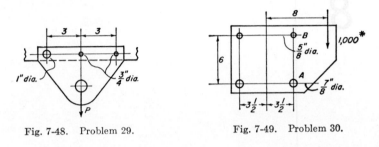

Fig. 7-48.   Problem 29.   Fig. 7-49.   Problem 30.

30. Compute the value of the shearing stress at the center of rivets A and B in Fig. 7-49.

8

Lubrication

A LUBRICANT is used to reduce the friction of bearings and sliding surfaces in machines and thus diminish the wear, heat, and possibility of seizure of the parts. Although a layer of oil will eliminate the excessive friction of metal-to-metal contact, the friction within the oil film must be taken into account. The study of lubrication and the design of bearings is therefore concerned mainly with phenomena related to the oil film between the moving parts. The literature on lubrication is very extensive, and a mathematical treatment of the subject is beyond the scope of this book. Fortunately it is possible to make design calculations from the graphs obtained by mathematical analysis.

A, area
A_c, cooling area of bearing housing
c, radial clearance of journal bearing
d, diameter of journal bearing
f, coefficient of friction
fpm, feet per minute
F, total friction force
F_1, tangential friction force per axial inch
h, film thickness
h_0, minimum film thickness
hp, horsepower
l, length in axial direction
n, rpm
p, load per unit of projected area
psi, pounds per square inch
r, radius of journal

s_s, shearing stress, psi
SUV, viscosity, Saybolt Universal Seconds
t, temperature, Fahrenheit
ΔT, rise in temperature of bearing housing
U, tangential velocity, in./sec
VI, viscosity index
W, total load, lb
W_1, load per axial inch
Z, viscosity, centipoises
$sp.gr_{60}$, specific gravity at 60 F
$sp.gr_t$, specific gravity at $t°$ F
ϵ, (epsilon) eccentricity ratio
μ, (mu) viscosity, lb sec/in.^{2}
ρ, (rho) density, mass per unit volume

1. Viscosity and Newton's Law

The plate in Fig. 8-1 is resting on top of an oil film of thickness h, and is being moved with velocity U under the action of the force F. When the plate moves, it does not slide along on top of the film. The oil adheres tightly to the plate, and motion is accompanied by slip or shear between the oil particles throughout the entire height of the film. Thus, if the plate and contacting layer of oil move with velocity U, the velocity at intermediate heights is directly pro-

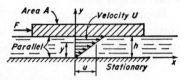

Fig. 8-1. Flat plate moving on oil film.

portional to the distance from the fixed or bottom plate, as shown in Fig. 8-1.

According to Newton, the shearing stress in the oil film varies directly with the velocity U and inversely with the film thickness h. Hence

$$s_s = \frac{F}{A} = \mu \frac{U}{h} \tag{1}$$

The factor of proportionality μ is called the coefficient of viscosity, or simply the viscosity. This equation assumes that the area A is very large as compared to h, in order that disturbances around the edges may be neglected.

Viscosity is the measure of the ability of the lubricant to resist shearing stress. It is a molecular phenomenon, and the work done by force F is turned into heat which raises the temperature of the oil and the surrounding parts.

2. Measurement of Viscosity

The unit of viscosity in the metric system is called the *poise*. Equation (1) indicates that its dimensions are dyne sec/cm². Thus, in Fig. 8-1, if a force F of one dyne is required to maintain a plate of one-square-centimeter area and one-centimeter film thickness at a velocity of 1 centimeter per second, the oil would have a viscosity of 1 poise. The viscosity of most lubricating oils is less than one poise, and the centipoise, cp, or $\frac{1}{100}$ of a poise, represented by Z, is used in lubrication calculations. The viscosity of water at 68.4 F is equal to 1 centipoise. It can be easily shown[1] that the following equations transfer viscosity from dyne sec/cm² to the English system of lb sec/in.²

$$\text{viscosity } \mu, \quad \frac{\text{lb sec}}{\text{in.}^2} = \frac{\text{viscosity, } Z \text{ centipoises}}{6,895,000} \tag{2}$$

$$= \text{viscosity, } Z \text{ centipoises} \times 0.000000145 \tag{3}$$

[1] Dyne sec/cm² can be had from lb sec/in.² by replacing pounds by 980.7 × 1,000/2.205 dynes and inches by 2.54 cm.

Another unit in use is the kinematic viscosity, ν, (nu). It is called, in the metric system, the stoke, and is found by dividing the viscosity in poises by ρ, the density in mass per cubic centimeter. Since the dimensions of ρ are dyne sec^2/cm^4, the dimensions of ν are cm^2/sec. A centistoke is equal to 0.01 stoke.

Because of experimental difficulties, these absolute units are not used commercially in designating the viscosity of lubricating oils. Terms are used which pertain to the type of viscosimeter used in making the test.

TABLE 8-1

Viscosity Range for Oils, Saybolt Universal Seconds

SAE Viscosity No.	at 0 F		at 210 F	
	Minimum	*Maximum*	*Minimum*	*Maximum*
5W	—	4,000	—	—
10W	6,000*	less than 12,000	—	—
20W	12,000†	48,000	—	—
20	—	—	45	less than 58
30	—	—	58	less than 70
40	—	—	70	less than 85
50	—	—	85	110

* Minimum viscosity at 0 F can be waived, provided viscosity at 210 F is not below 40 sec Saybolt Universal.

† Minimum viscosity at 0 F can be waived provided viscosity at 210 F is not below 45 sec Saybolt Universal.

One method in wide use is to specify viscosity by Saybolt Universal Seconds, SUV, at a given temperature. The Saybolt viscosity is the time in seconds required for 60 cc of the oil to flow through a standardized capillary tube. The change to absolute units can be made with sufficient accuracy for most purposes by means of the empirical equation

$$Z = sp.gr_t \left(0.22 \text{SUV} - \frac{180}{\text{SUV}} \right) \text{centipoises} \qquad (4)$$

where Z is viscosity in centipoises at temperature $t°$ F, $sp.gr_t$ is the specific gravity of the oil at $t°$ F, and SUV is the viscosity, Saybolt Universal Seconds, also at $t°$ F.

The specific gravity of the oil changes with the temperature, becoming smaller as the temperature rises. This property can be determined by means of the empirical equation

$$sp.gr_t = sp.gr_{60} - 0.00035(t - 60) \qquad (5)$$

where $sp.gr_{60}$ is the specific gravity at 60 F, and t is the temperature in degrees F.

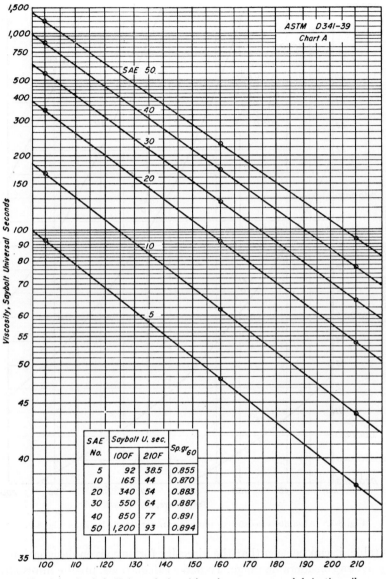

Fig. 8-2.   Saybolt Universal viscosities of some common lubricating oils.

Viscosity is only one of the many properties of a satisfactory lubricating oil. It is, however, the only variable directly related to the lubricant that appears in the design equations. The SAE classification, is widely used for specifying the viscosity of lubricating oils (see Table 8-1).[2] From

---

[2] See SAE *Handbook*.

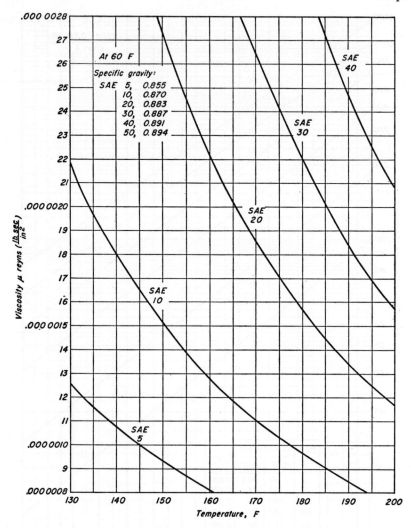

Fig. 8-3. Absolute viscosity vs temperature for the SAE oils of Fig. 8-2.

this table, it can be seen that the viscosity for any given designation can vary over a considerable range. To make calculations, precise information is needed concerning the viscosity of the oil that is to be used. Fair average values[3] for the viscosities of SAE oils are shown by the curves[4] of Fig. 8-2 plotted on ASTM Chart D341-39. It is unique that when the viscosities for two temperatures, usually 100 F and 210 F, are plotted on this chart,

[3] These are from the booklet *Physical Properties of Lubricants*, published by the Am. Soc. of Lubrication Engineers.
[4] American Society for Testing Materials, Philadelphia, Pa.

a straight line between them will give the viscosity at other desired temperatures. Since the designer requires the viscosity in absolute units, the viscosities of the oils of Fig. 8-2 are shown in lb sec/in.² units in Fig. 8-3. These curves are easily drawn by reading the SUV values from Fig. 8-2 and then by transforming to the absolute units of Fig. 8-3 by application of Eqs. (5), (4), and (3).

Example 1. An oil has a viscosity of 400 sec SUV at 100 F and 55 sec SUV at 210 F. Specific gravity at 60 F is equal to 0.93. Find the viscosity in absolute units at 170 F.

Solution. When the given viscosities are plotted on Fig. 8-2, the Saybolt viscosity at 170 F is found to be 84 sec.

The specific gravity at 170 F is found by substituting, in Eq. (5),

In Eq. (5): $sp.gr_t = 0.93 - 0.00035(170 - 60) = 0.892$

In Eq. (4): $Z = 0.892 \left(0.22 \times 84 - \dfrac{180}{84} \right) = 14.57$ centipoises

In Eq. (3): $\mu = 14.57 \times 0.000000145 = 0.00000211$ lb sec/in.²

Example 2. An oil has a SUV value of 50.5 sec at 210 F. Find the kinematic viscosity for this temperature.

Solution.

In Eq. (4): $Z = sp.gr_t \left(0.22 \times 50.5 - \dfrac{180}{50.5} \right) = 7.55 sp.gr_t$ centipoises

In the metric system, the density ρ, grams per cubic centimeters, has the same numerical value as the specific gravity $sp.gr_t$. Hence,

$$\nu = \frac{Z}{\rho} = \frac{7.55 sp.gr_t}{sp.gr_t} = 7.55 \text{ centistokes}$$

3. Viscosity Index

A widely used method for specifying the rate of change of viscosity with temperature is known as the *viscosity index*. The method was originally devised by testing samples of oils made from two extreme types of crudes. The series of oils having a small change of viscosity with temperature were given a viscosity index of 100, and the oils with a large change of viscosity with temperature were given a viscosity index of zero.

To find the viscosity index, VI, of a sample of oil, its SUV values are first determined for 210 F and 100 F and plotted on the ASTM chart as x

and y, respectively, as shown in Fig. 8-4. Among the $VI = 100$ oils, there will be one whose SUV value at 210 F will be x, the same value as that of the sample. Let the SUV at 100 F for this oil be designated by H, as shown in the figure. Similarly, the viscosity at 100 F for the $VI = 0$ oil which has the same SUV at 210 F as the sample is represented by L.

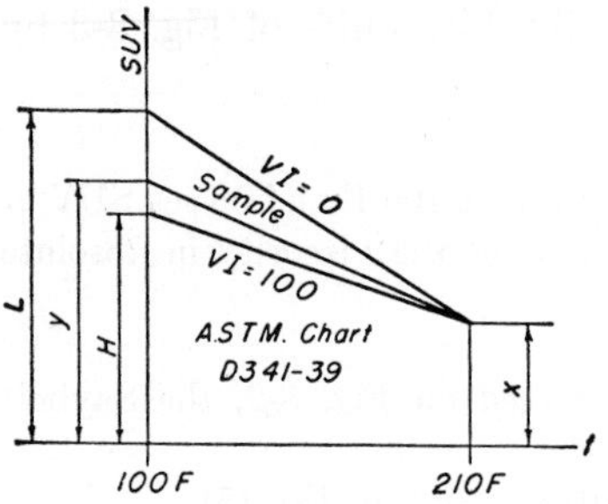

By definition, the viscosity index is found by means of the following equation:

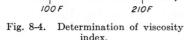

$$VI = \frac{L - y}{L - H} \times 100\% \qquad (6)$$

Fig. 8-4. Determination of viscosity index.

The viscosity index thus designates the rate of change of viscosity of an oil as compared to oils with very small and very large rates of change of viscosity. It should be noted that the VI tells nothing about the value of the viscosity at any given temperature. Values of VI below zero and above 100 are recognized.

When the SUV value at 210 F for the sample lies between 50 and 350 sec, the values of H and L can be determined from the following equations.[5]

$$H = 0.0408x^2 + 12.568x - 475.4 \qquad (7)$$

$$L = 0.2160x^2 + 12.070x - 721.2 \qquad (8)$$

Example 3. Find the viscosity index for SAE 20 oil in Fig. 8-2.

Solution. $x = 54$, and $y = 340$.

By Eq. (7): $H = 0.0408 \times 54^2 + 12.568 \times 54 - 475.4 = 322.2$

By Eq. (8): $L = 0.216 \times 54^2 + 12.07 \times 54 - 721.2 = 560.4$

By Eq. (6): $VI = \dfrac{L - y}{L - H} \times 100 = \dfrac{560.4 - 340}{560.4 - 322.2} \times 100 = 92.5$ per cent

4. Types of Plain Sleeve Bearings

A separate insert or bushing is usually provided to form the bearing surface for supporting the shaft in a sleeve bearing. It is made of a material that is known to have desirable qualities of high load capacity and low friction. The types and details of construction for sleeve bearings can vary over a considerable range.

[5] See references 9, Bibliography.

Figure 8-5(a) shows a solid bronze bushing, a type of bushing that is in wide use. It can be cast, machined from bar stock, or formed from tubing or sheets. It is usually held in place by a light press fit. The bearings shown in sketches (b) and (c) consist of a steel or bronze back with a thin lining of babbitt or one of the numerous other bearing alloys. Such

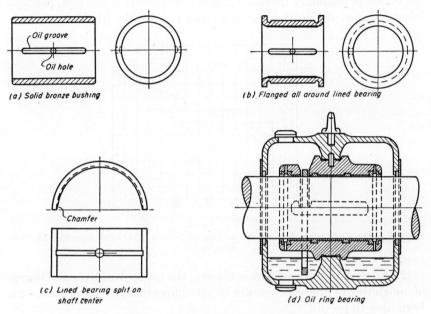

(a) Solid bronze bushing

(b) Flanged all around lined bearing

(c) Lined bearing split on shaft center

(d) Oil ring bearing

Fig. 8-5. Types of plain sleeve bearings.

bearings can be made either all around or split on the center line of the shaft. The oil ring bearing of Fig. 8-5(d) has a cast iron back with a babbitt liner cast in place.

5. The Zn/p Curve

The phenomenon which takes place when a shaft is rotating in a bearing in the presence of a lubricant can be represented by the experimentally determined curve shown in Fig. 8-6. Here the abscissa is taken as the non-dimensional group Zn/p, where Z is the viscosity in centipoises, n is the speed in rpm, and p is the load in psi of the projected journal area. The ordinate is taken as the coefficient of friction f where f is the ratio of the tangential friction force to the load carried by the bearing.

Nondimensional coordinates such as these are very convenient for engineering problems where many variables are present. Experiments can be made by changing the value of the nondimensional group without the necessity for changing the value of each individual quantity. Much labor can thereby be saved. The curve in Fig. 8-6, representing the performance of a particular bearing, can be divided into 3 more or less distinct parts.

(1) In portion AB the film is very thin, and the bearing operates in the region of boundary friction where intermolecular forces and, perhaps, interlocking of the bearing surfaces cause most of the friction.

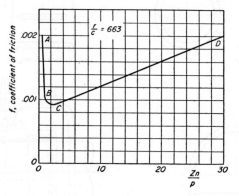

Fig. 8–6. The Zn/p curve for copper-lead bearing 2 in. $\times$ $1\frac{1}{4}$ in. (See reference 14, bibliography.)

(2) From B to C the oil film is thicker; the molecular forces and degree of roughness of the surfaces are of less importance; viscous forces are beginning to prevail.

(3) From C to D the value of the friction is largely independent of the smoothness of the surfaces or the kinds of metals used for the bearing. It depends almost entirely on the viscosity of the oil. Here the film is relatively thick and a copious supply of lubricant is required. It is only in this region that the hydrodynamic theories, as discussed in the following sections, are valid. To avoid danger of seizure, the operating value of Zn/p should be at least 5 or 6 times that of the minimum point of the curve. It can be noted from the CD portion of the curve that the coefficient of friction for lubricated surfaces increases with increase of velocity. This is in contrast with dry surfaces where the coefficient of friction is relatively independent of the velocity.

Example 4. Let the curve for Zn/p and f for a 3 in. diameter by 6 in. long bearing be a straight line passing through points $Zn/p = 75$, $f = 0.002$, and $Zn/p = 375$, $f = 0.0065$. SAE 10 oil like that in Fig. 8-2 is used. The total load on the bearing is 1,350 lb, and the rpm is 1,200. What is the hp friction loss for this bearing if the oil film has a temperature of 170 F?

Solution.

In Eq. (5): $sp.gr_t = 0.870 - 0.00035(170 - 60) = 0.832$ at 170 F.

By Fig. 8-2, at 170 F: SUV = 56.3 sec

In Eq. (4): $Z = 0.832 \left(0.22 \times 56.3 - \dfrac{180}{56.3}\right) = 7.64$ centipoises at 170 F

$$p = \frac{1350}{18} = 75 \text{ psi of projected journal area}$$

$$\frac{Zn}{p} = \frac{7.64 \times 1,200}{75} = 122$$

Draw the given Zn/p and f curve, and read $f = 0.0027$ for $Zn/p = 122$.

$$F = fW = 0.0027 \times 1,350$$

$$= 3.645 \text{ lb tangential friction force}$$

$$\text{Friction hp} = \frac{Tn}{63,000} = \frac{3.645 \times 1.5 \times 1,200}{63,000} = 0.104$$

6. Petroff's Bearing Equation

Equation (1) for the flat plate can be easily adapted to the cylindrical or journal bearing, provided that the speed and viscosity are high and that the load is very light so that the journal is in a central position in the bearing. Thus the plate in Fig. 8-1 is assumed to be wrapped into the cylindrical shaft in Fig. 8-7. If $2r$ or d is the diameter of the journal, and l its length in the axial direction, the developed journal area A is $2\pi rl$.

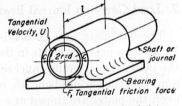

Fig. 8-7.   Very lightly loaded journal centered in bearing.

The thickness h becomes the radial clearance c, or the difference between the radius of the bearing, and the radius of the shaft. Substitution for A and h in Eq. (1) gives $F = 2\pi\mu Url/c$. However, if F_1 is taken as the tangential friction force per inch of axial length, then $F = F_1 l$, and the foregoing equation becomes

$$\frac{F_1}{\mu U}\left(\frac{c}{r}\right) = 2\pi \tag{9}$$

This is known as Petroff's equation. It is valid only for the hypothetical case of zero load and centrally located journal.

The tangential velocity of the journal is given by

$$U = \frac{\pi dn}{60} \text{ in./sec} \tag{10}$$

The friction horsepower is given by

$$\text{hp} = \frac{F_1 l U}{12 \times 550} \tag{11}$$

Example 5. Find the friction hp of a very lightly loaded 360° journal bearing. The bearing is 3 in. in diameter and 5 in. long. Radial clearance is 0.0025 in. Use SAE 20 oil of Fig. 8-2. Rpm is 1,800. Oil film temperature is 150 F.

Solution.

From Fig. 8-3, at 150 F: $\mu = 0.00000273 \dfrac{\text{lb sec}}{\text{in.}^2}$

In Eq. (10): $U = \dfrac{3\pi \times 1,800}{60} = 282.7 \dfrac{\text{in.}}{\text{sec}}$

In Eq. (9): $F_1 = \dfrac{2\pi \times 0.00000273 \times 282.7 \times 1.5}{0.0025} = 2.91 \dfrac{\text{lb}}{\text{in.}}$

In Eq. (11):   Friction hp $= \dfrac{2.91 \times 5 \times 282.7}{12 \times 550} = 0.62$

7. Load Carrying Journal Bearing

The flat plate in Fig. 8-1 is incapable of supporting a vertical load because no pressure exists in the oil film. If a vertical load were placed on the plate, the oil would squeeze out around the edges, and the plate would approach the surface beneath, resulting in metal-to-metal contact. If, however, the plates are tipped at a small angle to each other, as shown in Fig. 8-8, the oil will be drawn into the wedge-shaped opening, and sufficient pressure will be generated in the film to support the load W. This fact is utilized in the thrust bearings for hydraulic turbines and propeller shafts of ships, as well as in the conventional journal bearing with flooded-oil lubrication.

Since the same quantity of oil is drawn past each cross section, the velocity distribution throughout the height of the film is no longer linear as it is for parallel plates. The velocity curve will be concave at the wider cross sections and convex at the narrower, as indicated in Fig. 8-8.

If the shaft in Fig. 8-7 carried a downward load, the journal would no longer remain central with the bearing. For the classical case of the infinitely long bearing, the shift of the journal center is not downward, but is theoretically to one side as shown in Fig. 8-9. The shift of the journal center is usually expressed as a proportion of the radial clearance, c. Thus in Fig. 8-9 the shaft has shifted ϵc inches, where the relative eccentricity ϵ is a pure number less than unity. A copious supply of oil is assumed, which fills the entire clearance space. The oil clings to the journal and is drawn around into the region of decreasing film thickness, and thereby builds up suffi-

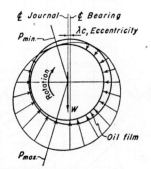

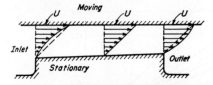

Fig. 8-8. Load on moving plate supported by wedge-shaped film.

Fig. 8-9. Oil-film pressure in full journal bearing.

cient pressure to support the load W. The bearing automatically adjusts itself to the imposed load. Thus, should W be increased, the shift to the left would become greater, and the resulting decrease of the film thickness would cause higher oil pressures which would take care of the larger load.

8. Load and Friction Curves for Journal Bearings

In actual bearings, the full continuous film of Fig. 8-9 does not exist. The film ruptures and the load is carried by a partial film located beneath the journal. Even in partial bearings, as in Fig. 8-10, the ruptured film leaves a portion of the arc at the trailing edge with zero pressure.

A computer solution for journal bearings for different bearing arcs and length-diameter ratios has been made[6] and is given by the curves in Figs. 8-11, 12, and 13. The ordinates are the nondimensional load variable

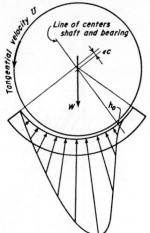

Fig. 8-10. Pressure distribution in partial bearing.

$(W_1/\mu U)/(c/r)^2$ and friction variable $(F_1/\mu U)/(c/r)$, where W_1 is the load per axial inch of bearing, and F_1 is the tangential friction force per axial inch. The abscissa is taken as the eccentricity ratio ϵ.

[6] Based on data from reference 7, Bibliography.

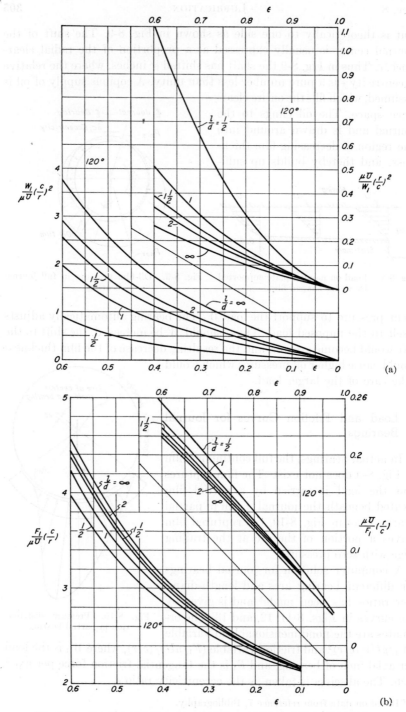

Fig. 8-11. Load and friction characteristics of 120° central partial bearing.

306

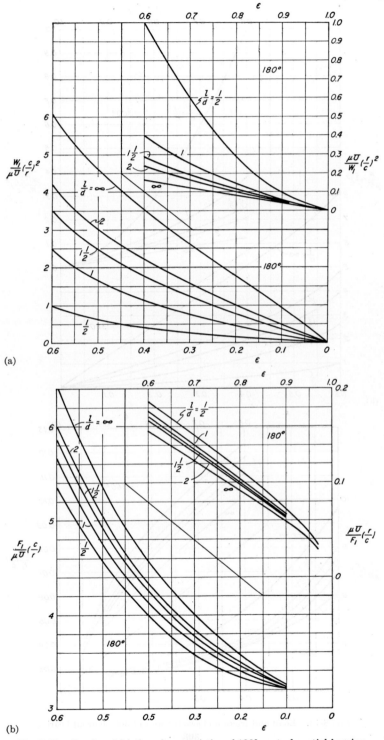

(a)

(b)

Fig. 8-12. Load and friction characteristics of 180° central partial bearing.

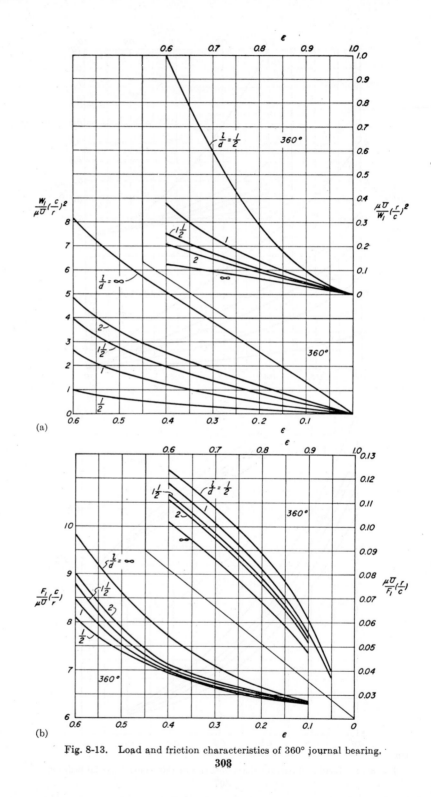

(a)

(b)

Fig. 8-13.   Load and friction characteristics of 360° journal bearing.

It is seen from Fig. 8-10 that the minimum film thickness h_0 is

$$h_o = c(1 - \epsilon) \tag{12}$$

Example 6. A 4 in. diameter by 6 in. long 120° central partial bearing has a minimum film thickness of 0.001 in. Radial clearance is 0.002 in. SAE 10 oil like that in Fig. 8-3 is used. The bearing carries a load of 82 psi of projected journal area at 900 rpm. Find the temperature of the film and the friction horsepower.

Solution.
$$U = \frac{2\pi r n}{60} = \frac{2\pi 2 \times 900}{60} = 188.5 \text{ in./sec}$$

By Eq. (12):
$$\epsilon = 1 - \frac{h_0}{c} = 1 - \frac{0.001}{0.002} = 0.5$$

$$\frac{c}{r} = \frac{0.002}{2} = \frac{1}{1,000}$$

From Fig. 8-11(a):
$$\frac{W_1}{\mu U}\left(\frac{c}{r}\right)^2 = 1.69$$

From Fig. 8-11(b):
$$\frac{F_1}{\mu U}\left(\frac{c}{r}\right) = 3.60$$

$$\mu = \frac{W_1}{1.69 U}\left(\frac{c}{r}\right)^2 = \frac{82 \times 4}{1.69 \times 188.5 \times 1,000^2}$$
$$= 0.000001028 \text{ lb sec/in.}^2$$

From Fig. 8-3. The oil film temperature is 175 F.

$$F_1 = 3.60\mu U\left(\frac{r}{c}\right)$$
$$= 3.60 \times 0.000001028 \times 188.5 \times 1,000$$
$$= 0.697 \text{ lb/in.}$$

By Eq. (11): Friction hp $= \dfrac{0.697 \times 6 \times 188.5}{12 \times 550} = 0.120$

Other variables are in use for presenting lubrication data. Thus, $W_1 = pd$ where p is the pressure, psi, on the projected area of the bearing, and $U = \pi d N'$ where N' is the speed of rotation, rps. Then

$$\frac{W_1}{\mu U}\left(\frac{c}{r}\right)^2 = \frac{p}{\pi\mu N'}\left(\frac{c}{r}\right)^2 = \frac{1}{\pi S} \tag{13}$$

where
$$S = \frac{\mu N'}{p}\left(\frac{r}{c}\right)^2 \tag{14}$$

Here S is the so-called "Sommerfeld number."

For journal bearings, the coefficient of friction, f, is defined in the usual way as the ratio of the tangential force to the normal force. Then

$$f = \frac{F}{W} = \frac{F_1}{W_1} \qquad (15)$$

9. Heat Balance of Bearings

The frictional loss of energy in a bearing is turned into heat which raises the temperature of the lubricant and the adjacent parts.[7] The rate at which such heat is produced will now be determined. Let p be the load on the bearing in pounds per square inch of projected journal area ld. Since the total load on the bearing is pld, the tangential friction force is $fpld$, where f is the coefficient of friction. The friction moment is $\frac{1}{2}fpld^2$. The number of radians turned by the shaft per minute is $2\pi n$, where n is the rpm. The work of friction per minute, or power, then is $\pi fpld^2n$ in-lb/min. Since 1 Btu is equal to 778×12 in. lb of mechanical work, the heat produced is

$$H = \frac{\pi fpld^2n}{778 \times 12} \text{ Btu/min} \qquad (16)$$

Under steady operating conditions, the heat is removed from a bearing at the same rate that it is produced. The heat, however, must be dissipated at a sufficiently rapid rate to maintain an operating temperature low enough so that no harm will come to the oil. Sometimes cooling coils are provided for large and important bearings. In forced-feed systems the excess heat is carried away by the lubricant, which is cooled before being returned to the bearing.

However, the majority of bearings in use depend upon the surrounding air as the cooling medium. Many bearings are constructed in the form of a self-contained unit with an oil reservoir in the base or pedestal,[8] as shown in Fig. 8-5(d) or Fig. 8-14. An oil ring or chain, rotating with the shaft, dips into the lubricant and carries a supply of oil to the top of the shaft where it spreads over the surface.

For self-cooled bearings of moderate rises in temperature, Newton's law of cooling is found to be sufficiently accurate. This law states that

$$H = \frac{C_1}{144 \times 60} A_c \, \Delta T \text{ Btu/min} \qquad (17)$$

where H is the heat lost, Btu/min; C_1 is the heat lost per square foot of heated surface per hour, per degree F; A_c is the area of the surface in

---

[7] See Chapter 5, of reference 5, Bibliography.
[8] See p. 99 of reference 8, Bibliography.

square inches which is losing heat; and ΔT is the difference between the temperature of the surface and the surrounding air.

The constant C_1 depends upon the shape and the condition of the surface of the bearing housing, and also on whether or not the surrounding air is in motion. Thus it is difficult to estimate C_1 accurately. A commonly used value for the rate of losing heat in still air is to take C_1 as 2 Btu/hr/ft²/deg F.

Since the area of the housing A_c is more or less under the control of the designer, fairly accurate estimates may be made for this quantity. It is usually convenient to express A_c in terms of the developed journal area πdl. Thus,

$$A_c = C_2 \pi dl \qquad (18)$$

where C_2 is a constant.

Since the heat produced under steady operating conditions is equal to the heat lost, Eqs. (16) and (17) can be set equal to each other. When this is done, and Eq. (18) substituted, the following result will be obtained.

$$fpdn = 1.0805 C_1 C_2 \, \Delta T \qquad (19)$$

By substituting $f = F_1/W_1$ and $p = W_1/d$, Eq. (19) becomes

$$F_1 n = 1.0805 C_1 C_2 \, \Delta T \qquad (20)$$

The oil film itself is at a considerably higher temperature than the exterior surface of the housing. Just how much higher, it may be difficult to say; the designer is again confronted with a situation of considerable uncertainty. However, on the basis of experiments it can be assumed that the housing rises in temperature one-half as much as the oil film.[9] Hence,

$$\text{oil-film temp.} = \text{air temp.} + 2\Delta T \qquad (21)$$

Example 7. Let the shaft diameter of a 120° central partial bearing be 3.5 in., the axial length $5\frac{1}{4}$ in., and the rpm 900. The oil film temperature is not to exceed 80 deg F above room temperature of 100 F. The r/c ratio is 1,000, and the minimum film thickness is 0.00075 in. The housing area is 8 times the developed journal area, $(C_2 = 8)$. Assume that the rate of cooling C_1 is 2 Btu/hr/ft²/deg F and that the housing rises in temperature one-half as much as the oil film.

Find the load p psi of the projected journal area which the bearing will carry.

Solution. $\qquad\qquad c = 0.00175$ in. radial clearance

$$\text{Eccentricity} = 0.00175 - 0.00075 = 0.001 \text{ in.}$$

$$\text{Eccentricity ratio } \epsilon = \frac{0.00100}{0.00175} = 0.571$$

[9] See reference 12, Bibliography.

From Fig. 8-11(a): $\qquad \dfrac{W_1}{\mu U}\left(\dfrac{c}{r}\right)^2 = 2.27$ (a)

From Fig. 8-11(b): $\qquad \dfrac{F_1}{\mu U}\left(\dfrac{c}{r}\right) = 4.13$ (b)

Divide Eq. (b) by Eq. (a): $\; f\left(\dfrac{r}{c}\right) = \dfrac{4.13}{2.27} = 1.82 \text{ or } f = 0.00182$

In Eq. (21): $\qquad\qquad\qquad \Delta T = \dfrac{1}{2}(180 - 100) = 40 \text{ deg F}$

In Eq. (19): $\qquad\qquad\qquad p = \dfrac{1.0805 \times 2 \times 8 \times 40}{0.00182 \times 3.5 \times 900} = 120.7$ psi projected journal area

The maximum temperature at which a bearing should operate depends upon the physical properties of the lubricant used. For usual industrial applications, an average film temperature in the range 160 F to 180 F is considered satisfactory.

10. Designing for Film Temperature and Minimum Film Thickness

The temperature of the oil film and the minimum film thickness at which the bearing operates are usually the important factors that the designer attempts to predict when he makes the computations for a new design. The curves of Figs. 8-11, 8-12, and 8-13 permit these quantities to be found, although not by direct calculation. The load and film thickness for a number of assumed values of the film temperature can be found and curves plotted. From such curves, the temperature and film thickness can be read for any given load that the bearing might be carrying. The procedure can be carried out conveniently in tabular form as shown by the following example.

Example 8. A 3 in. diameter by 3 in. long 120° central partial bearing operates at 1,200 rpm with SAE 10 oil of Fig. 8-3. Room temperature is 80 F; assume that housing temperature rises one-half as much as the film temperature. Assume the cooling rate to be 2 Btu/hr/ft²/deg F, and that the cooling area is 16 times the developed journal area. The r/c ratio is 1,000. Plot the curves for p vs. temperature and p vs. h_0 for the range 155 F to 165 F at 2.5 deg. intervals.

Solution.

$$U = \frac{\pi dn}{60} = \frac{\pi 3 \times 1,200}{60} = 188.5 \text{ in./sec}$$

In Eq. (20): $\quad F_1 = \dfrac{1.0805 C_1 C_2 \Delta T}{n} = \dfrac{1.0805 \times 2 \times 16 \Delta T}{1,200} = 0.0288 \Delta T$

The following table should be constructed. The values in columns 2 to 5 can be found by computation. Column 6 is determined from Fig. 8-11(b), and column 7 from Fig. 8-11(a). The values in the remaining columns can then be computed.

1	2	3	4	5	6	7	8	9	10
Film t_{av}	ΔT	$F_1 = 0.0288\Delta T$	μ	$\dfrac{\mu U}{F_1}\left(\dfrac{r}{c}\right)$	ϵ	$\dfrac{\mu U}{W_1}\left(\dfrac{r}{c}\right)^2$	W_1	p	h_o
155	37.5	1.0805	0.000 001390	4.124*	0.585	1.85*	485	161.6	0.00062
157.5	38.75	1.1165	1332	0.225	0.622	0.460	546	182.0	0.00057
160	40	1.1525	1278	0.209	0.653	0.397	607	202.3	0.00052
162.5	41.25	1.1885	1228	0.195	0.680	0.347	667	222.4	0.00048
165	42.5	1.2246	1184	0.182	0.704	0.305	733	244.2	0.00044

* Indicates inverse of quantity at column heading.

The desired curves are plotted in Fig. 8-15.

Now suppose the probable film temperature and minimum film thickness are desired when the bearing is carrying a load of 200 psi of projected journal area. Reference to Fig. 8-15 shows that the film temperature,

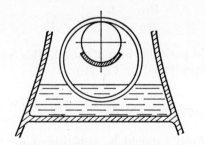

Fig. 8-14. Ring-oiled partial journal bearing.

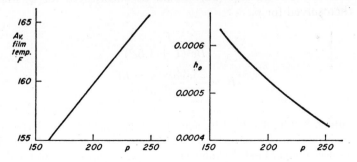

Fig. 8-15. Film temperature and minimum film thickness vs load for Example 8.

for the assumed conditions, is 160 F, and minimum film thickness is 0.00053 in.

11. Pressure Lubricated Bearing

Sometimes a 360° bearing is lubricated by a pressurized inlet line feeding the oil to a circumferential groove at the center of the bearing, Fig. 8-16. The oil flows both ways from the central groove and is extruded

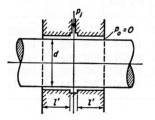

at the sides of the bearing. The clearance space can be adjusted to provide sufficient oil flow for the proper cooling of the bearing.

The quantity Q of oil flowing through one side of the bearing is given by the equation

$$Q = \frac{\pi r c^3 p_i}{6\mu l'} (1 + 1.5\epsilon^2) \frac{\text{in.}^3}{\text{sec}} \qquad (22)$$

Fig. 8-16. Pressure lubricated journal bearing.

where p_i is the inlet pressure in the central groove, and l' is the axial length for one side.

The heat removed by the flow Q for an inlet temperature of t_i and an outlet temperature of t_o is equal to the following equation when the specific heat of the lubricant is taken as $\frac{1}{2}$ Btu per lb per deg. F.

$$\frac{\text{Btu}}{\text{sec}} = \frac{1}{2} Q\gamma(t_o - t_i) \qquad (23)$$

where γ is the weight per cubic inch of the oil. This can be equated to the heat produced as represented by Eq. (16).

$$\frac{\pi f p l' d^2 n}{778 \times 12 \times 60} = \frac{1}{2} Q\gamma(t_o - t_i)$$

In this equation, F_1/W_1 should be substituted for f, W_1/d should be substituted for p, and Eq. (22) should be substituted for Q, and the result then solved for p_i.

$$p_i = \frac{F_1}{Bc^3(1 + 1.5\epsilon^2)} \qquad (24)$$

where

$$B = \frac{23,340\gamma(t_o - t_i)}{\mu l'^2 n} \qquad (25)$$

Example 9. A 2 in. dia. by 4 in. long ($l' = 2$ in.), 360° bearing has a central groove. It is lubricated with SAE 20 oil. Speed is 900 rpm, $r/c = 500$, and $p = 200$ psi projected area. Find the value of the inlet pressure if the inlet and outlet temperatures of the oil are 160 F and 175 F respectively.

Solution.

Average oil temperature is 167.5 F.

By Fig. 8-3: $\mu_{av} = 0.00000194$ lb sec/in.^{2}

By Eq. (5): $sp.gr_{167.5} = 0.883 - 0.00035 \times 107.5 = 0.8454$

Let the weight of water be taken as 62.4 lb/ft^3.

$$\gamma = \frac{62.4}{1,728} \times 0.8454 = 0.03053 \text{ lb/in.}^3$$

In Eq. (25): $B = \dfrac{23,340 \times 0.03053 \times 15}{0.00000194 \times 2^2 \times 900} = 1,530,000$

$$U = \frac{\pi d n}{60} = \frac{\pi 2 \times 900}{60} = 94.25 \text{ in./sec}$$

$$W_1 = 2 \times 200 = 400 \text{ lb/in.}$$

$$\frac{\mu U}{W_1}\left(\frac{r}{c}\right)^2 = \frac{0.00000194 \times 94.25 \times 500^2}{400} = 0.114$$

By Fig. 8-13(a): $\epsilon = 0.83$

By Fig. 8-13(b): $\dfrac{\mu U}{F_1}\left(\dfrac{r}{c}\right) = 0.076$

Then $F_1 = \dfrac{0.00000194 \times 94.25 \times 500}{0.076} = 1.20$

$$c = \frac{1}{500} = 0.002 \text{ in.}$$

In Eq. (24): $p_i = \dfrac{1.20}{1,530,000 \times 0.002^3(1 + 1.5 \times 0.83^2)}$

$$= 48.3 \text{ psi}$$

12. Thin Film or Boundary Lubrication. Oiliness

As mentioned in Section 5, thin film or boundary lubrication occurs when the value of the variable Zn/p is small or when the quantity of the lubricant is insufficient. Such operation is liable to occur for low values for the viscosity or speed, or for high values of the load. As shown by the AB portion of the curve of Fig. 8-6, a small decrease in the value of Zn/p can cause a large increase in the coefficient of friction.

The film may be only a few molecules in thickness, and hydrodynamic action, as previously discussed in this chapter, will be absent. Research has not as yet completely explained the manner in which the load is supported by this type of lubrication. It is believed that certain components of the lubricant react chemically with the bearing metal to form compounds on the surfaces which reduce the amount of metallic contact between the high spots of the journal and bearing. However, some of the peaks break through the surface film, and metal to metal contact occurs at very high pressures. These points are welded together but are immediately broken by the relative motion of journal and bearing. Frictional resistance is caused by the shearing of these metallic junctions and the plowing of the softer surface by the irregularities of the harder surface.[10] Progressive disintegration by shearing and plowing can result in appreciable wear and seizure of the surfaces. Sometimes operation in the boundary region causes an improvement in the surface of the softer metal. When this occurs, the bearing is said to be *run in*.

General design equations are not available for sleeve bearings in the region of boundary lubrication. In fact, information on this subject is specific and fragmentary. Bearings that operate in the hydrodynamic region frequently pass through a partial film condition in starting and stopping. In this connection it is beneficial to make the journal and bearing of dissimilar metals, since it has been shown experimentally that the amount of welding decreases with a decrease of solid solubility between the two members.

In boundary lubrication, one type of oil may have less friction than another of the same viscosity. This property of a lubricant has been given the name *oiliness*. Certain animal and vegetable oils and compounds are superior to mineral oils with respect to friction. They are therefore added in small quantities to mineral oils as oiliness agents. Just how they perform their function is not as yet clearly understood. It is believed that active oxygen atoms cause one end of the molecule to be firmly attached to the metal of the bearing. A plane of low slip-resistance is formed at the other end of the molecule, and the friction is thereby reduced.

The compounding of lubricating oils to achieve desirable characteristics is becoming an important field of investigation. The high temperatures of internal combustion engines cause oxidation of the lubricant. Since some of the products of oxidation are acidic, bearing corrosion results. Sludges which clog the oil lines and filters are also formed. Antioxidants and anticorrosives must therefore be added to the lubricant.

Detergents are additives which cause soluble rather than insoluble oxidation products to be produced, and thus prevent the build up of deposits. Dispersants will cause soot and oil decomposition products to be held in suspension in the oil. Additives are also used for depressing the pour point of an oil for low-temperature starting. The viscosity index of an oil can also be improved by suitable additives.

[10] See p. 460 of reference 1, Bibliography.

Solid film lubricants with a very low coefficient of friction can sometimes be advantageously employed under conditions of extreme pressure, high or low temperature, or inaccessibility. These are chemical compounds of which molykote, or molybdenum disulfide, is the best known. They can be used as dry powders or mixed with oil or a resinous binder, depending on the conditions of the application.

13. Bearing Materials

Some of the qualities required in a material for a sleeve bearing are load-carrying capacity, thermal conductivity, low coefficient of friction, smoothness of surface, and resistance to wear, fatigue, and corrosion. No one material can possess all the desired characteristics to a sufficient

TABLE 8-2

Per Cent Composition of Typical Bearing Alloys*

	Babbitt		Copper Base		Copper-Lead
	Tin Base SAE 11	Lead Base SAE 13	SAE 791	SAE 794	SAE 48
Copper (Cu)	5.75		rem	73.5	70
Tin (Sn)	87.5	6	4	3.5	30
Lead (Pb)		rem	4	23	30
Antimony (Sb)	6.75	10			
Zinc (Zn)			4		

* See SAE Handbook.

degree,[11] and it is necessary to compromise in most designs. The chemical compositions of a number of typical bearing materials are given in Tables 8-2 and 8-3.

Babbitt bearings are in very wide use and are of two general types: tin base and lead base. They are quickly run in and assume very smooth surfaces. Application is usually made to a steel back as shown in Fig. 8-5(b) and (c). Thickness of the lining is usually about 0.015 in. Thin babbitt bearings with linings 0.002–0.005 in. thick are also used and can carry somewhat heavier loads. Babbitt bearings have good *conformability*, or the property of adjusting themselves to small misalignments or shaft deflections. They also make excellent bearings from the standpoint of *imbedability* because a reasonable amount of dirt or foreign matter in the lubricant can be absorbed by the soft bearing material and the shaft is thus protected against scoring.[12]

[11] See reference 10, Bibliography.
[12] See reference 14, Bibliography.

Bronze bearings are suitable for high loads and slow speeds, but the alignment between shaft and bearing must be good. They are made in a great number of alloy compositions to obtain various physical properties.

TABLE 8-3

Maximum Design Pressures for Engine Bearings*

Bearing Material	Per Cent Composition of Material	Maximum Mean Bearing Pressure, psi
Lead-base babbitt	Pb (75–85), Sn (4–10), Sb (9–15)	600–800
Tin-base babbitt	Pb (0.35–0.6), Sn (86–90), Sb (4–9), Cu (4–6)	800–1,000
Cadmium-base alloy	Cu (0.4–0.75), Cd (97), Ni (1–1.5), Ag (0.5–1.0)	1,200–1,500
Copper-lead alloy	Pb (45), Cu (55)	2,000–3,000
Copper-lead alloy	Pb (25), Sn (3), Cu (72)	3,000–4,000
Silver	Ag (99), 0.5 to 1.0 lead on surface	5,000 up

* Pressures are based on fatigue life of 500 hr at a bearing temperature of 300 F. Bearing metal thicknesses range from 0.01 to 0.015 in. for lead, tin, and cadmium-base metals, and 0.025 in. for copper, lead, and silver, all on steel backs. At lower temperatures, the fatigue life will be greatly extended. Data from reference 11, Bibliography. See also p. 221 of reference 2.

Standardized bushings as shown in Fig. 8-5(a) can be purchased ready for use. Copper-lead bearings also have many desirable properties.

Cast iron and cast iron run well together after being properly run in. Steel and cast iron also run together if not too heavily loaded and if the finish and alignment are good. Combinations of brass and soft steel or soft steel and soft steel should not be used.

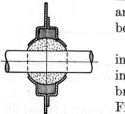

The so-called "self-lubricating" or "porous bearing" is made by sintering powdered metal and then impregnating it with oil. Various compositions of bronze are in wide use. Iron is used to a less extent. Figure 8-17 shows a self-aligning, porous-metal bearing applied to a small electric motor. The felt washer can frequently be omitted.

Fig. 8-17. Self-aligning porous bearing with oil saturated felt washer.

Plastic bearings, either plain or reinforced with woven fabric, of which Teflon is an outstanding example, are useful special applications. Soft rubber, lubricated with water, has been used for many years in pumps and general marine service. Lignum vitae and wood are also used for bearings to a limited extent.

14. Bearing Loads

Bearing loads are determined mainly from experience with similar applications that have proved successful. The permissible loading is not a direct function of the particular material under consideration, but depends rather on the type of service. Table 8-4 gives a survey of current practice and can be used as a general guide when more specific information is lacking. Careful attention should be paid to the reliability of the

TABLE 8-4

Current Practices in Bearing Design Pressures*

Type of Bearing	Design Pressure, psi
Diesel engines, main bearings,	800–1,500
Connecting rod bearings,	1,000–2,000
Wrist pins,	1,800–2,000
Electric motor bearings,	100–200
Marine line-shaft bearings,	25–35
Steam turbines and reduction gears,	100–250
Automotive gasoline engine, main bearings,	500–700
Connecting rod bearings,	1,500–2,500
Aircraft engine connecting rod bearings,	700–2,000
Centrifugal pumps,	80–100
Roll Neck bearings,	1,500–2,500
Railway axle bearings,	300–350
Light line-shaft bearings,	15–25
Heavy line-shaft bearings,	100–150

* See reference 11, Bibliography; also p. 221 of reference 2.

oil supply for small values of Zn/p which occur when the speed is slow and the load is large.

15. Construction of Bearings

In addition to choosing the material, the designer must specify the shaft clearance and the oil grooving for the bearing.

The clearance depends to some extent on the desired quality. Small clearances can be maintained with high-grade workmanship, but when costs must be reduced, the clearances usually are made larger. Table 8-5 gives a summary of clearances used in industrial applications.

For small clearances, the surface roughness of the shaft and bearing must be considered. These surfaces, when examined by a microscope, are usually far from being geometrically smooth. In many cases, the roughness consists of two orders of irregularities. Over most of the surface there are relatively small, low irregularities at close intervals. In addition, at relatively large intervals, there are high peaks and deep valleys. Roughness is usually measured from the tops of the high peaks, as shown in Fig. 8-18. To accentuate the roughness, it is customary to prepare samples with a vertical scale that is 25 times as great as the horizontal scale. Profilometers give readings for either the root-mean-square or the numerical average of the roughness. The predominant peak roughness can then be had by multiplying by a suitable factor. For example, for

TABLE 8-5

Bearing Clearances in Industrial Applications*

	Running Clearance, Thousandths of an Inch, for Shaft Dia. under				
	$\frac{1}{2}''$	$1''$	$2''$	$3\frac{1}{2}''$	$5\frac{1}{2}''$
Precision spindle practice—hardened and ground spindle lapped into the bronze bushing. Below 500 fpm and 500 psi	0.00025 to 0.00075	0.00075 to 0.0015	0.0015 to 0.0025	0.0025 to 0.0035	0.0035 to 0.005
Precision spindle practice—hardened and ground spindle lapped into bronze bushing. Above 500 fpm and 500 psi	0.0005 to 0.001	0.001 to 0.002	0.002 to 0.003	0.003 to 0.0045	0.0045 to 0.0065
Electric motor and generator practice— ground journal in broached or reamed bronze bushing or reamed babbitt bushing	0.0005 to 0.0015	0.001 to 0.002	0.0015 to 0.0035	0.002 to 0.004	0.003 to 0.006
General machine practice (continuous rotating motion)—turned steel or cold-rolled steel journals in bored and reamed bronze or poured and reamed babbitt bushings	0.002 to 0.004	0.0025 to 0.0045	0.003 to 0.005	0.004 to 0.007	0.005 to 0.008
General machine practice (oscillating motion)—journal and bearing material as above	0.0025 to 0.0045	0.0025 to 0.0045	0.003 to 0.005	0.004 to 0.007	0.005 to 0.008
Rough machine practice—turned steel or cold-rolled steel journals in poured babbitt bearings	0.003 to 0.006	0.005 to 0.009	0.008 to 0.012	0.011 to 0.016	0.014 to 0.020

* Data by Johnson Bronze Co.

ground surfaces, the rms roughness should be multiplied by 4.5 to obtain the predominant peak roughness.[13]

Figure 8-18 shows the surfaces for journal and bearing located so that the high peaks are just in contact. It has been proposed[14] that the condition illustrated be taken as the limit at which hydrodynamic lubrication can be assumed to exist. Thus if each surface has a rms roughness of

[13] See reference 11 of Bibliography of Chapter 13.
[14] See reference 25, Bibliography.

11 microinches, the minimum film thickness in Fig. 8-18 would be $2 \times 11 \times 4.5$, or 0.0001 in. Surface finish should thus be specified and closely controlled if the design calculations indicate that the bearing will operate with a very thin film. Experience has indicated, however, that other factors such as misalignment, deformation, foreign matter in the oil, and fatigue due to dynamic loads are the cause of most bearing failures.

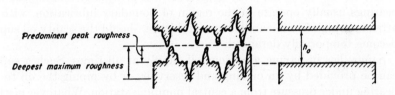

Fig. 8-18.   Lower limit at which hydrodynamic lubrication is assumed to be possible.

Oil grooves with carefully rounded edges should be provided to distribute the oil over the entire surface. It is very important, however that no grooves be placed in the load-carrying portion of the lining. When so placed, such grooves merely provide an easy exit for the oil and prevent the formation of the film and the high pressures necessary to support the load. A good rule is to use the least possible amount of grooving. Sometimes the chamfer between the bearing and cap provides a channel for the lateral flow of the lubricant. Figure 8-19 shows the reduction in load

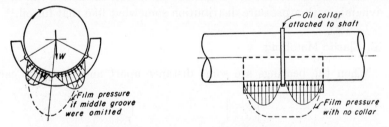

Fig. 8-19.   Loss of capacity from incorrect   Fig. 8-20.   Loss of capacity caused by oil
grooving.   collar.

capacity (for equal minimum film thickness) due to an incorrectly located oil groove. If the load on the bearing with the middle groove is not reduced, operation may take place with a dangerously thin oil film. If a belt pulley is adjacent to a bearing, care should be taken that the forces from the belt do not pull the shaft toward the side where oil grooves may be located and where a satisfactory oil film cannot be formed.

In a similar manner, a circumferential groove reduces the load-carrying qualities, as shown in Fig. 8-20. An oil collar is a very effective means of distributing the lubricant. However, an oil collar practically cuts the bearing in two, and the sum of the loads carried by each part is less than that carried by a single bearing of the total width. Forced-feed-lubricated bearings frequently are constructed without oil grooves.

The most important point to be considered when choosing the method of lubricating a bearing is the reliability of the oil supply. Because of low first cost, many bearings are lubricated by hand oil cans, drip or wick oilers, oil-soaked waste, or by grease. As was previously mentioned, such bearings usually operate in the region of boundary lubrication, with its attendant high friction and danger of seizure, should the scanty oil supply become temporarily deranged.

Safety lies in having a copious oil supply at all times. Such a supply can be provided by an oil ring and reservoir, or by piping the oil to the bearing under pressure from a central pumping station. Whatever method is used, close attention to the mechanical details is required if satisfactory operation is to be expected.

Means for preventing leakage and loss of oil at the ends of the bearing must often be provided. Felt gaskets or patented oil seals are in wide use. Sometimes the outer housing is enlarged to accommodate a small disk fastened to the shaft. The oil which has leaked past the side of the bearing is thrown off the disk by centrifugal force and caught by the housing. Often a circumferential groove at the end of the bearing is provided with drain holes to return the oil to the reservoir.

Grease is widely used for exposed locations because it is easier to retain in the bearing. Recent investigations show that the action can be hydrodynamic with a pressure distribution somewhat like that for oil.[15]

16. Elastic Matching

When the bearings are some distance apart and the shaft carries a

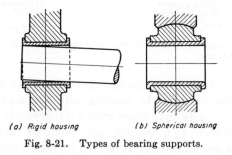

(a) Rigid housing   (b) Spherical housing

Fig. 8-21.   Types of bearing supports.

lateral load, the inclination of the shaft at the ends may be great enough to give rise to the misalignment shown in Fig. 8-21(a). Obviously such a

[15] See reference 16, Bibliography.

bearing is subjected to rapid wear and is not able to form a satisfactory load-carrying film. The difficulty can be reduced by setting the bearings closer together and using a larger diameter shaft or a smaller value for the l/d ratio. The spherical seat shown in sketch (b) gives self-alignment from all causes, but is expensive, and increases the size of the bearing. The tilting arrangement shown in Fig. 8-5(d) is free from both these drawbacks, but the bearing is less effective from the standpoint of heat transfer.

Sometimes the bearing can be located eccentrically on an elastic support in such a way that it tilts slightly under load and assumes the same inclination as the shaft. The oil film then has a uniform thickness throughout the axial length of the bearing, and the difficulty shown in Fig. 8-21(a) is overcome.

17. Dry Friction

Dry friction or the friction between nonlubricated surfaces is a very complex phenomenon.[16] Despite more than a century of study, a satisfactory explanation of the mechanism of dry friction does not as yet exist. The so-called "classical rules of dry friction" are usually stated as follows.

(1) The friction force is directly proportional to the force pressing the bodies together.

(2) The friction force is independent of the area of the contacting surfaces.

(3) The friction force is largely independent of the velocity of sliding.

(4) The friction force depends on the nature of the sliding surfaces.

The coefficient of static friction for bodies at rest, or with motion impending, is somewhat greater than for kinetic friction which prevails after the sliding member is set in motion.

According to Coulomb, 1785, the friction force is due to the interlocking of the asperities of the two surfaces and the necessity of deforming the irregularities as the two bodies pass by each other. Within rather wide limits, the magnitude of the friction force is independent of the degree of roughness of the surfaces. The asperities which are deformed are very minute so that it apparently makes no difference whether they are located on a smooth surface or consist of protuberances located upon larger irregularities.

For very rough surfaces, the protuberances may interlock to the extent that parts of them are torn off as the bodies move with respect to each other. This is a wear phenomenon and is usually not considered to be friction in the usual meaning of the term. Such action is especially likely to occur when one of the bodies is much harder than the other.

Although the nature of the sliding surfaces determines the friction

[16] See Chapter 10 of reference 2, Bibliography.

force, surfaces of naked metal do not exist in everyday life. Exposure to the atmosphere will contaminate the surface with oxide films, moisture, absorbed gases, grease, dirt, and so on. These films cling very tightly to a surface and can be removed only with difficulty. Ordinary cleaning does not suffice.[17] Even in the laboratory, unless the body is kept in an inert atmosphere, an oxide film quickly forms. Thus when two ordinary bodies are sliding together, it is the surface films which are touching each other and not the metals themselves.

Reference handbooks usually make no attempt to give exact specifications for the surfaces under consideration, and this may partially account for the wide variations in the published values for the coefficient of friction.

When bodies with very smooth surfaces are brought into intimate contact, adhesive or cohesive forces come into action and hold the bodies tightly together. Thus when gage blocks or optical flats are wrung together, a relatively large force may be required for tangential motion even though the normal force pressing them together is very small. The classical rules of friction do not apply under such conditions.

A surface of naked metal can be obtained by removal of the oxide and surface film and degassing in the laboratory. When two metallic surfaces of this kind are brought together in a vacuum or inert atmosphere, the metals weld together at the high spots where contact occurs between them. When one body is drawn along the other the welds will be made and broken continuously. The resulting motion is somewhat jerky or discontinuous and has been given the name of *stick slip*. The force required to produce motion under such conditions is relatively very large and may be as much as 20 times the value for corresponding contaminated surfaces. The force also depends upon the velocity of sliding and is thus not in accord with the classical rules of friction.

When two bodies with contaminated surfaces are brought together, actual contact occurs only at the high spots of the two surfaces. The actual area of touching may be only a very small fraction of the nominal area. The contact stress at the isolated points where the bodies touch reaches very high values. Such stresses are required to deform the asperities sufficiently to permit motion to take place. Under such conditions of extreme stress, the surface film may rupture and the welding phenomenon described above take place. Such welding, together with any adhesive forces which may be present, serves to further complicate the situation.

The wide scatter in the published values for the coefficient of friction is undoubtedly due to the lack of precise information on the conditions

[17] Washing in alcohol and drying in an oven has been known to more than double the usual value for the coefficient of friction.

of the actual surfaces being tested. "···in view of the extremely high friction found with really clean metals it is fortunate, for engineering, that metals are not found with perfectly clean surfaces in practise."[18]

BIBLIOGRAPHY

1. Shaw, M. C., and Macks, E. F., *Analysis and Lubrication of Bearings*. New York: McGraw-Hill Book Co., Inc., 1949.

2. Fuller, D. D., *Theory and Practice of Lubrication*. New York: John Wiley & Sons, Inc., 1956.

3. Norton, A. E., *Lubrication*. New York: McGraw-Hill Book Co. Inc., 1942.

4. Radzimovsky, E. I., *Lubrication of Bearings*. New York: Ronald Press Co., 1959.

5. Hersey, M. D., *Theory of Lubrication*. New York: John Wiley & Sons, Inc., 1938.

6. Slaymaker, R. R., *Bearing Lubrication Analysis*. New York: John Wiley & Sons, Inc., 1955.

7. Raimondi, A. A., and Boyd, J., "A Solution for the Finite Journal Bearing and Its Application to Analysis and Design," *Report III*, **1**, No. 1, 194, Am. Soc. of Lubrication Engineers, The Pergamon Press.

8. *General Discussion on Lubrication*. London: Institution of Mechanical Engineers, 1938.

9. *ASTM Standards*, Part 5. American Society for Testing Materials, 1955.

10. Bassett, H. N., *Bearing Metals and Alloys*. New York: Longmans, Green & Co. Inc., 1937.

11. Fuller, D. D., "Design Analysis of Journal Bearings," *Machine Design*, **28**, Feb. 9, 119 (1956).

12. Lemmon, D. C., and Booser, E. R., "Bearing Oil-Ring Performance," *Trans. ASME*, **82**, 327 (1960).

13. Tichvinsky, L. M., "Diesel-Engine Bearings," *Mech. Eng.*, **67**, 297 (1945).

14. Roach, A. E., "Performance of Oil-Film Bearings with Abrasive Containing Lubricant," *Trans. ASME*, **73**, 677 (1951).

15. McKee, S. A., and White, H. S., "Oil Holes and Grooves in Plain Journal Bearings," *Trans. ASME*, **72**, 1025 (1950).

16. Lawrence, K. B., "A Mathematical Evaluation of Pressures in a Grease-Lubricated Bearing," *Trans. ASME*, **72**, 409 (1950).

17. DuBois, G. B., and Ocvirk, F. W., "The Short Bearing Approximation for Plain Journal Bearings," *Trans. ASME*, **77**, 1173 (1955).

18. Tichvinsky, L. M., and Fischer, E. G., "Boundary Friction in Bearings at Low Loads," *Trans. ASME*, **61**, A-109. (1939).

[18] See Adam, N. K., *Physics and Chemistry of Surfaces*, 3rd ed. (New York: Oxford University Press, 1941), p. 222.

19. Koenigsberg, E., and Johnson, V. R., "Metallic Friction and Lubrication by Laminar Solids," *Mech. Eng.*, **77**, 141 (1955).

20. Burwell, J. T., *Mechanical Wear*. American Society for Metals, 1950.

21. Steijn, R. P., "An Investigation of Dry Adhesive Wear," *Trans. ASME*, **81**, 56 (1959). See also p. 67.

22. Bowden, F. P., and Tabor, D., *Friction and Lubrication of Solids*. New York: Oxford University Press, 1950.

23. Baker, J. G., "Elastic Matching Improves Bearing Life and Performance," *Machine Design*, **20**, May, 106 (1948).

24. Hori, Y., "A Theory of Oil Whip," *Trans. ASME*, **81**, 189 (1959).

25. Ocvirk, F. W., and Dubois, G. B., "Surface Finish and Clearance Effects on Journal-Bearing Load Capacity and Friction," *Trans. ASME*, **81**, 245 (1959).

PROBLEMS

1. Plot the curve for SAE 10 oil in Fig. 8-3. For this type of problem it is convenient to carry out the work in tabular form. A separate column heading should be used for each successive step in passing from the SUV values of Fig. 8-2 to μ in lb sec/in.^{2} units.

2. An oil has a VI of 60 per cent and a Saybolt viscosity at 100 F of 400 sec. Find the Saybolt viscosity for this oil at 180 F. *Ans.* SUV = 70.5 sec.

3. An oil has a VI of 90 per cent and a Saybolt viscosity at 100 F of 300 sec. Find the Saybolt viscosity of this oil at 160 F. *Ans.* SUV = 84 sec.

4. A very lightly loaded, 360° bearing, 6 in. in diameter and 9 in. long, consumes 2 hp in friction when running at 1,200 rpm. Radial clearance is 0.003 in. Find the temperature of the oil film using SAE 10 oil in Fig. 8-3.
Ans. t = 145 F.

5. A 2.5 in. diameter by 3.75 in. long 360° bearing turns at 1,200 rpm and consumes 0.1 hp in friction. SAE 10 oil in Fig. 8-3 is used; r/c = 1,000. Find the total load for the bearing if the film is at a temperature of 175 F.
Ans. W = 1,030 lb.

6. A 3 in. diameter by 3 in. long 360° bearing turns at 1,200 rpm; c/r = 0.001; h_0 = 0.001 in. SAE 20 oil is used. The film temperature is 180 F. Find the total load W. *Ans.* W = 830 lb.

7. A 3 in. diameter by 6 in. long, 120° central partial bearing is operating at a value for ϵ equal to 0.6. Coefficient of friction is equal to 0.0025. Find the value of the minimum film thickness. *Ans.* h_o = 0.00098 in.

8. A bearing 10 in. in diameter and 10 in. long operates at 1,500 rpm, carrying 25,000 lb. The c/r ratio is 0.0015. Let the viscosity of the lubricant be taken as 30 centipoises. Find the friction hp loss in accordance with Petroff's equation, 360° bearing and for the 120° central partial bearing.
Ans. 17.03; 20.17; and 10.16 hp.

9. Use data as for Example 7, except that the oil-film temperature and cooling area are not known. For this bearing, p is 125 psi of projected journal area, and SAE 10 oil in Fig. 8-3 is used. Find the required cooling area of the housing.

Ans. 4.0 ft.^{2}

10. A 120° central partial bearing 3.5 in. in diameter and 5.25 in. long carries 125 psi projected journal area at 600 rpm. Room temperature is 100 F and housing is at 140 F. $C_1 = 2$, $C_2 = 8$. $\epsilon = 0.52$. What is the minimum film thickness?

Ans. $h_o = 0.0011$ in.

11. A 120° central partial bearing 4 in. in diameter and 5 in. long carries 90 psi of projected journal area. The r/c ratio is 1,000; h_o is equal to 0.001 in. SAE 20 oil, in Fig. 8-3 is used. Room temperature is 100 F. Rpm equals 600. Assume the rate of cooling is 2.5 Btu/hr/ft²/deg F. Assume housing temperature rises one-half as much as oil film. Find the oil-film temperature and the required area of housing.

Ans. $t = 168$ F; $A_c = 2.44$ ft.^{2}

12. A 120° central partial bearing 2.5 in. in diameter and 4.0 in. long has a minimum film thickness of 0.0006 in. SAE 20 oil in Fig. 8-3 is used; $n = 860$ rpm and $r/c = 1,000$. If the oil film is at 165 F, find the load the bearing is carrying.

Ans. $W = 1,740$ lb.

13. Find the required area of housing in order to maintain the film temperature of a 3 in. diameter by 4.5 in. long, 120° central partial bearing at 165 F; rpm = 900 and $r/c = 1,000$. Room temperature is 100 F. Assume housing temperature rises one-half as much as the oil film. Cooling rate is 2 Btu/hr/ft²/deg F. SAE 10 oil is used. Load is 100 psi of projected journal area.

Ans. $A_h = 2.33$ ft².

14. A 2 in. diameter by 4 in. long, 120° central partial bearing turns 1,350 rpm. SAE 10 oil is used. Film temperature is 175 F and room temperature is 100 F. Assume housing rises one-half as much as the film, and that the cooling rate is

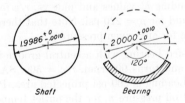

Shaft   Bearing

Fig. 8-22. Problem 14.

2 Btu/hr/ft²/deg F. Let the area of the housing be 8 times the developed journal area.

If the shaft and bearing are dimensioned as shown in Fig. 8-22, determine the load and minimum film thickness for an assembly at the loosest permissible fit, and also for an assembly at the tightest permissible fit.

Ans. Loosest, $W = 880$ lb; tightest, $W = 500$ lb.

15. A 120° central partial bearing is 2 in. in diameter and 3 in. long. $r/c = 1,000$, $n = 900$ rpm. SAE 10 oil is used. Bearing is self-cooled with $C_1 = 2$ Btu/hr/ft²/

deg F and $C_2 = 8$. Room temperature is 100 F. Assume the housing surface temperature rises one-half as much as the average film temperature.

(a) Plot the curve for average film temperature vs. p.

(b) Plot the curve for h_o vs. p.

Use temperature range from 145 F to 170 F inclusive at 5 degree intervals.

16. A 360° pressure-lubricated bearing with a central groove is 4 in. diameter by 4 in. long, ($l' = 2$ in.). $r/c = 1,000$, $p = 300$ psi projected area. $n = 900$ rpm. SAE 20 oil is used.

For an inlet temperature of 100 F and an outlet temperature of 220 F, find the value of the inlet pressure p_i if all the frictional heat is carried away by the oil.

Ans. $p_i = 27.2$ psi.

17. A 120° central partial bearing is 2 in. in diameter by 3 in. long with a radial clearance of 0.001 in. The shaft turns at 900 rpm. Loading is 150 psi of projected area. Room temperature is 100 F. SAE 10 oil is used. Heat transfer coefficient C_1 equals 2 Btu/hr/ft²/deg F. For a minimum film thickness of 0.0004 in. find the average temperature in the film and the required value for constant C_2.

Ans. $t_{av} = 162$ F, $C_2 = 6.86$.

18. (a) Use the data in Example 8 and calculate the values of p for the given temperature range for values of r/c of 600, 800, 1,200, and 1,400. Calculations for r/c of 1,000 have already been made in Example 8. Plot the curves for p vs. film temperature.

(b) From the curves read and tabulate the temperature values for pressures of 180, 200, and 220 psi for each of the values above of r/c. Plot the curve for film temperature vs. r/c for $p = 180$ psi. Do the same for $p = 200$ psi and for $p = 220$ psi. Note that there is an optimum value for r/c at which the film temperature is a minimum.

(c) Plot the ϵ values vs p for the above r/c ratios. From the curves read and tabulate the ϵ values for pressures of 180, 200, and 220 psi for each r/c curve. Calculate the corresponding h_o values and plot vs. r/c for $p = 180$ psi. Do the same for $p = 200$ psi and for $p = 220$ psi. Note that there is an optimum r/c at which h_o is a maximum for any given pressure p.

19. A 360° pressure-fed bearing with a central groove is 2 in. in diameter by 4 in. long ($l' = 2$ in.) and turns 900 rpm. $r/c = 500$. SAE 20 oil is used. Inlet temperature is 160 F. Loading is 200 psi projected area. Plot curve for outlet oil temperature t_o vs. inlet oil pressure p_i for the outlet temperature range 175 F to 190 F inclusive at 5 deg. intervals.

20. A journal bearing 3 in. in diameter and 6 in. long has the same Zn/p vs. f curve as for Example 4. Assume the specific gravity at the film temperature to be 0.84. Total load is 1,800 lb, and rpm is 1,500. Find the SUV value at the operating temperature if the power loss for the bearing is 0.15 hp.

Ans. SUV = 51 sec.

21. A journal bearing 3 in. in diameter and 6 in. long has the same Zn/p vs. f curve as that in Example 4. The oil film is at 180 F. The oil has a SUV value of 52 sec at 210 F, a VI of 80 per cent, and a $sp.gr_{60}$ of 0.9. Total load is 1,500 lb and rpm is 1,200. Find the hp loss for this bearing. *Ans.* hp = 0.133.

22. A 120° central partial bearing is 2.5 in. in diameter and 4.0 in. long. Rpm is 860; SAE 20 oil is used, and the r/c ratio is 1,000. For an oil temperature of 165 F and minimum film thickness of 0.0006 in., find the load on the bearing.

Ans. $W = 1,940$ lb.

23. Three bearings have respective film arcs of 120°, 180°, and 360°. The diameter is 2.5 in. and length is 4 in. Rpm is 1,200 r/c ratio is 1,000, and load is 200 psi of projected journal area. SAE 10 oil. Find the film temperature for each bearing if the minimum film thickness is 0.0006 in.

This problem illustrates the fact that, when the angle is reduced, the bearing must be operated at a lower temperature if the film thickness is to be maintained.

Ans. 144 F, 167 F, 175 F.

24. Let the film arcs for a series of bearings be 120°, 180°, and 360°. The diameter is 2.5 in. and the length is 4.0 in. Rpm is 1,200, r/c ratio is 1,000, and film temperature is 170 F. SAE 10 oil is used and minimum film thickness is 0.0006 in. Find the load p on the projected journal area that each bearing is carrying.

This problem illustrates the fact that the load must be reduced for smaller values of the bearing arc in order to maintain a given film thickness and oil temperature.

Ans. 132, 191, and 213 psi.

25. Let the film arcs for three bearings be 120°, 180°, and 360° respectively. Diameter is 3.5 in. and length is 4.5 in. The load on the bearings is 1,800 lb. Rpm is 900 and film temperature is 165 F. SAE 10 oil is used; r/c ratio is 800. Find the minimum film thickness and the friction horsepower.

This problem shows that a reduction in film arc will give a reduction in the friction horsepower, but that the film thickness will also be reduced.

Ans. Friction hp, 0.090, 0.106, 0.149.

9

Ball and Roller Bearings

BALL and roller bearings have been brought to their present state of perfection only after a long period of research and development. The benefits of such specialized research can be obtained when it is possible to use a standardized bearing of the proper size and type. Ball bearings are used in almost every kind of machine and device with rotating parts. However, such bearings cannot be used indiscriminately without a careful study of the loads and operating conditions. In addition, the bearing must be provided with adequate mounting, lubrication, and sealing.

1. Construction and Types of Ball Bearings

A ball bearing usually consists of four parts: an inner ring, an outer ring, the balls, and the cage or separator. To increase the contact area and permit larger loads to be carried, the balls run in curvilinear grooves in the rings. The radius of the groove is slightly larger than the radius of the ball and a very slight amount of radial play must be provided. The bearing is thus permitted to adjust itself to small amounts of angular misalignment in the assembled shaft and mounting. The separator keeps the balls evenly spaced and prevents them from touching each other on the sides where their relative velocities are the greatest.

Ball bearings are made in a wide variety of types and sizes. Single-row radial bearings are made in three series, light, medium, and heavy, for each bore, as illustrated in Figs. 9-1(a), (b), and (c). Most manufacturers use a numbering system so devised that if the last two digits are multiplied by 5, the result will be the bore in millimeters. The digit in the third place from the right indicates the series number. Thus, bearing 307

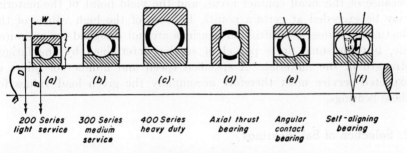

| 200 Series | 300 Series | 400 Series | Axial thrust | Angular | Self-aligning |
| light service | medium service | heavy duty | bearing | contact bearing | bearing |

Fig. 9-1.   Types of ball bearings.

signifies a medium-series bearing of 35-mm bore. Additional digits, which may be present in the catalog number of a bearing, refer to manufacturer's details. The extra light 100 series is also in wide use. Some makers list deep groove bearings and bearings with two rows of balls.

The radial bearing is able to carry a considerable amount of axial thrust. However, when the load is directed entirely along the axis, the thrust type of bearing should be used. The angular contact bearing will take care of both radial and axial loads. The self-aligning ball bearing will take care of large amounts of angular misalignment. An increase in radial capacity may be secured by using rings with deep grooves, or by employing a double-row radial bearing.

Radial bearings are divided into two general classes, depending on the method of assembly. These are the Conrad, or nonfilling-notch type,

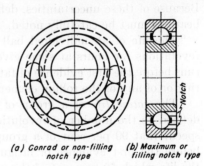

(a) Conrad or non-filling notch type   (b) Maximum or filling notch type

Fig. 9-2.   Methods of assembly for ball bearings.

and the maximum, or filling-notch type. In the Conrad bearing, the balls are placed between the rings as shown in Fig. 9-2(a). Then they are evenly spaced and the separator is riveted in place. In the maximum-type bearing, the balls are inserted through a filling notch ground into each ring, as shown in Fig. 9-2(b). Because more balls can be placed in such bearings, their load capacity is greater than that of the Conrad type.

However, the presence of the notches limits the load-carrying ability of these bearings in the axial direction.

High-carbon chromium steel, 52100, is used for balls and rings. It is heat treated to high strength and hardness, and the surfaces are smoothly ground and polished. The dimensional tolerances are very small; the balls must be very uniform in size. The stresses are extremely high because of the small contact areas, and the yield point of the material may be exceeded at certain points. Because of the high values of the fluctuating stresses, antifriction bearings are not designed for unlimited life, but for some finite period of service determined by the fatigue strength of the materials. A specified speed and number of hours of expected service must therefore accompany the given load values for these bearings.

2. Selection of Ball Bearings

Ball bearings were formerly rated on the basis of the compressive stress in the most heavily loaded ball. Except for static loads, experience has shown that the actual cause of failure is fatigue. Fatigue characteristics are thus used for load rating and are dependent to a large extent on experimental results.

Experience has indicated that the life of an individual bearing cannot be predicted. It is also impossible to predict the minimum life which any one of a group of apparently identical bearings under test will exceed. Because of these uncertainties, definitions of terms relating to the life of bearings must be carefully noted.

"The life of an individual ball bearing is defined as the number of revolutions (or hours at some given constant speed) which the bearing runs before the first evidence of fatigue develops in the material of either ring or of any of the rolling elements." [1]

"The *rating life* of a group of apparently identical ball bearings is defined as the number of revolutions (or hours at some given constant speed) that 90 per cent of a group of bearings will complete or exceed before the first evidence of fatigue develops. As presently determined, the life which 50 per cent of the group of ball bearings will complete or exceed is approximately *five times* this rating life."

"The *basic load rating* is that constant stationary radial load which a group of apparently identical ball bearings with stationary outer ring can endure for a rating life of one million revolutions of the inner ring."

The basic load rating C for a rating life of one million revolutions for

---

[1] See *Methods of Evaluating Load Ratings of Ball Bearings*, Sec. 9. Anti-Friction Bearing Mfg. Assn. Inc., 60 East 42nd St., New York 17, N. Y., 1957. For bearings with static loads, see reference 19, Bibliography.

TABLE 9-1
Constants for Single-Row Radial Contact Groove Ball Bearings

$\dfrac{D \cos \alpha}{d_m}$	f_c	$\dfrac{D \cos \alpha}{d_m}$	f_c	$\dfrac{F_a}{iZD^2}$	X	Y
0.05	3,550	0.22	4,530	25	0.56	2.30
0.06	3,730	0.24	4,480	50		1.99
0.07	3,880	0.26	4,420	100		1.71
0.08	4,020	0.28	4,340	150		1.55
0.09	4,130	0.30	4,250	200		1.45
0.10	4,220	0.32	4,160	300		1.31
0.12	4,370	0.34	4,050	500		1.15
0.14	4,470	0.36	3,930	750		1.04
0.16	4,530	0.38	3,800	1,000		1.00
0.18	4,550	0.40	3,660			
0.20	4,550					

f_c is also valid for single- and double-row angular contact groove ball bearings
X and Y are also valid for double-row radial contact groove ball bearings.

radial and angular contact ball bearings, except filling slot bearings, with balls not larger than one inch diameter is[2] given by the equation

$$C = f_c(i \cos \alpha)^{0.7}Z^{2/3}D^{1.8} \tag{1}$$

where f_c = a constant from Table 9-1, as determined by value of $(D \cos \alpha)/d_m$

i = number of rows of balls in the bearing

α = nominal angle of contact (angle between line of action of ball load and plane perpendicular to bearing axis)

Z = number of balls per row

D = ball diameter

d_m = pitch diameter of ball races

Table 9-2 shows dimensions for typical ball bearings, and the basic load rating C.

Example 1. Find the value of C for a 207 radial bearing.

Solution.

By Table 9-2: $\qquad d_m = \dfrac{1}{2}(2.8346 + 1.3780) = 2.1063$ in.

$$\frac{D \cos \alpha}{d_m} = \frac{0.4375}{2.1063} = 0.208, \quad \text{By Table 9-1:} f_c = 4,550$$

[2] For balls larger than one inch diameter, the exponent for D is 1.4.

TABLE 9-2

Dimensions for Typical Single-Row Radial Ball Bearings and Basic Load Rating C for a Rating Life of One Million Revolutions

Brg. No.	Bore		Outside Dia.		Width		Balls		C
	mm	inch	mm	inch	mm	inch	dia.	no.	
102	15	0.5906	32	1.2598	9	0.3543	$\frac{3}{16}$	9	970
202			35	1.3780	11	0.4331	$\frac{1}{4}$	7	1,340
302			42	1.6535	13	0.5118	$\frac{11}{32}$	6	2,040
103	17	0.6693	35	1.3780	10	0.3937	$\frac{3}{16}$	10	1,040
203			40	1.5748	12	0.4724	$\frac{9}{32}$	8	1,860
303			47	1.8504	14	0.5512	$\frac{11}{32}$	7	2,340
104	20	0.7874	42	1.6535	12	0.4724	$\frac{1}{4}$	8	1,500
204			47	1.8504	14	0.5512	$\frac{5}{16}$	8	2,210
304			52	2.0472	15	0.5906	$\frac{3}{8}$	7	2,760
105	25	0.9843	47	1.8504	12	0.4724	$\frac{1}{4}$	10	1,740
205			52	2.0472	15	0.5906	$\frac{5}{16}$	9	2,420
305			62	2.4409	17	0.6693	$\frac{7}{16}$	7	3,660
106	30	1.1811	55	2.1654	13	0.5118	$\frac{9}{32}$	11	2,290
206			62	2.4409	16	0.6299	$\frac{3}{8}$	9	3,360
306			72	2.8346	19	0.7480	$\frac{31}{64}$	8	4,850
107	35	1.3780	62	2.4409	14	0.5512	$\frac{5}{16}$	11	2,760
207			72	2.8346	17	0.6693	$\frac{7}{16}$	9	4,440
307			80	3.1496	21	0.8268	$\frac{17}{32}$	8	5,750
108	40	1.5748	68	2.6772	15	0.5906	$\frac{5}{16}$	13	2,990
208			80	3.1496	18	0.7087	$\frac{15}{32}$	9	5,040
308			90	3.5433	23	0.9055	$\frac{19}{32}$	8	7,040
109	45	1.7717	75	2.9528	16	0.6299	$\frac{11}{32}$	13	3,630
209			85	3.3465	19	0.7480	$\frac{1}{2}$	9	5,660
309			100	3.9370	25	0.9843	$\frac{11}{16}$	8	9,120
110	50	1.9685	80	3.1496	16	0.6299	$\frac{11}{32}$	14	3,770
210			90	3.5433	20	0.7874	$\frac{1}{2}$	10	6,070
310			110	4.3307	27	1.0630	$\frac{3}{4}$	8	10,680
111	55	2.1654	90	3.5433	18	0.7087	$\frac{13}{32}$	13	4,890
211			100	3.9370	21	0.8268	$\frac{9}{16}$	10	7,500
311			120	4.7244	29	1.1417	$\frac{13}{16}$	8	12,350
112	60	2.3622	95	3.7402	18	0.7087	$\frac{13}{32}$	14	5,090
212			110	4.3307	22	0.8661	$\frac{5}{8}$	10	9,070
312			130	5.1181	31	1.2205	$\frac{7}{8}$	8	14,130
113	65	2.5591	100	3.9370	18	0.7087	$\frac{13}{32}$	15	5,280
213			120	4.7244	23	0.9055	$\frac{21}{32}$	10	9,900
313			140	5.5118	33	1.2992	$\frac{15}{16}$	8	16,010
114	70	2.7559	110	4.3307	20	0.7874	$\frac{15}{32}$	14	6,580
214			125	4.9213	24	0.9449	$\frac{11}{16}$	10	10,760
314			150	5.9055	35	1.3780	1	8	18,000

By Table 9-2: $D = \dfrac{7}{16} = 0.4375$ in.

$$\log D = 9.64098 - 10$$
$$1.8 \log D = 9.35376 - 10$$
$$D^{1.8} = 0.2258$$
$$Z = 9, \quad Z^{2/3} = \sqrt[3]{9^2} = 4.327$$

By Eq. (1): $C = 4{,}550 \times 4.327 \times 0.2258 = 4{,}440$ lb, load for one million revolutions.

If two groups of identical bearings are run under different loads P_e and P_r, then their lives N_e and N_r are found to be inversely proportional to the cubes of the loads.

$$\frac{N_e}{N_r} = \left(\frac{P_r}{P_e}\right)^3 \tag{2}$$

In this equation for a rating life N_r of one million cycles, the corresponding load P_r is called C. Then

$$\frac{N_e}{1{,}000{,}000} = \left(\frac{C}{P_e}\right)^3 \tag{3}$$

If the equivalent radial load P_e for a bearing is known, the (rating) life N_e can be found from Eq. (3) by use of the appropriate value of C as given by the table.

Example 2. For the bearing of Example 1, find the radial load for a life of 500 hrs, or an expected average life of 2,500 hrs, at 1,500 rpm.

Solution. $N_e = 60n$ hrs $= 60 \times 1{,}500 \times 500 = 45{,}000{,}000$ cycles

In Eq. (3): $P_e = \dfrac{100C}{N_e^{1/3}} = \dfrac{100 \times 4{,}440}{45{,}000{,}000^{1/3}} = \dfrac{444{,}000}{355.7} = 1{,}250$ lb

When an axial component of load is present in addition to the radial, the *equivalent radial load* P_e is the larger of the values given by the two following equations.

$$P_e = V_1 F_r \tag{4}$$

$$P_e = X V_1 F_r + Y F_a \tag{5}$$

where F_r = radial component of load

F_a = axial component of load

X = radial factor from Table 9-1

Y = axial or thrust factor from Table 9-1 as determined from value of F_a / iZD^2

V_1 = race rotation factor, equal to unity for inner ring rotation, and 1.2 for outer ring rotation

Equations (4) and (5) apply to radial and angular contact bearings, but not to filling-slot bearings.

A service factor C_1 can be inserted into Eqs. (4) and (5) to care for any shock and impact conditions to which the bearing may be subjected.

$$P_e = C_1 V_1 F_r \tag{6}$$

$$P_e = C_1(X V_1 F_r + Y F_a) \tag{7}$$

Values to be used for C_1 depend on the judgment and experience of the designer, but Table 9-3 may serve as a guide.

TABLE 9-3
Shock and Impact Factors

Type of Load	C_1
Constant or steady	1.0
Light shocks	1.5
Moderate shocks	2.0
Heavy shocks	2.5
Ex. heavy or extreme shocks	3.0

Example 3. Suppose the bearing in Example 1 carries a combined load of 400 lb radially and 300 lb axially at 1,200 rpm. The outer ring rotates, and the bearing is subjected to moderate shock. Find the average expected life of this bearing in hours.

Solution.

$$\frac{F_a}{i Z D^2} = \frac{300}{9 \times 0.4375^2} = 174, \quad \text{By Table 9-1, } Y = 1.50$$

By Table 9-3: $C_1 = 2,$

By Eq. (7): $P_e = 2(0.56 \times 1.2 \times 400 + 1.5 \times 300)$

$\qquad\qquad = 1,440$ lb equivalent radial load.

By Eq. (3): $N_e = \left(\dfrac{100 \times 4,440}{1,440}\right)^3 = 29,500,000$ rev expected rating life

$$\text{Expected rating life} = \frac{29,500,000}{1,200 \times 60} = 410 \text{ hrs.}$$

Expected average life = $410 \times 5 = 2,050$ hrs.

Example 4. What change in the loading of a ball bearing will cause the expected life to be doubled?

Solution. Let P'_e and N'_e be the new load and new life of the bearing, where $N'_e = 2N_e$.

By Eq. (3),
$$100^3 C^3 = N_e P_e{}^3 = N'_e P'_e{}^3$$

$$N_e P_e{}^3 = 2N_e P'_e{}^3$$

$$P'_e = \frac{1}{\sqrt[3]{2}} P_e = 0.794 P_e$$

Hence a reduction of the load to 79 per cent of its former value will cause a doubling of the expected life.

3. Design for Variable Loading

Ball bearings frequently operate under conditions of variable load and speed. Design calculations should take into account all portions of the work cycle and should not be based solely on the most severe operating conditions.

The work cycle should be divided into a number of portions in each of which the operating conditions can be taken as constant. Suppose P_{e1} is the loading for the first portion of the work cycle. Equation (3) gives the expected rating life N_{e1} as $100^3 C^3 / P_{e1}{}^3$. One revolution then consumes $1/N_{e1}$ or $P_{e1}{}^3 / 100^3 C^3$ of the total life. If there are N_1 revolutions turned in the first portion, then $N_1 P_{e1}{}^3 / 100^3 C^3$ of the life is consumed in this portion.

Similarly if P_{e2} is the load for the second portion, the expected life N_{e2} is $100^3 C^3 / P_{e2}{}^3$. If there are N_2 revolutions in the second portion, this portion consumes $N_2 P_{e2}{}^3 / 100^3 C^3$ of the total life.

Similar expressions can be written for each of the separate portions. The sum of them represents the life consumed in one full cycle. This can be set equal to $N_e P_e{}^3 / 100^3 C^3$ where N_e is the equivalent life at the constant load P_e. The resulting equation is

$$N_1 P_{e1}{}^3 + N_2 P_{e2}{}^3 + \cdots = N_e P_e{}^3 \tag{8}$$

If desired, N_1, N_2, ... , in Eq. (8), can be taken as the revolutions in the 1st, 2nd, ... portions of the work cycle respectively. In this case N_e is the total number of revolutions in the cycle.

Example 5. A 207 bearing is to operate on the following work cycle.

Radial load of 1,400 lb at 200 rpm for 25 per cent of the time.
Radial load of 2,000 lb at 500 rpm for 20 per cent of the time.
Radial load of   800 lb at 400 rpm for 55 per cent of the time.

The inner ring rotates. The loads are steady. Find the expected average life of this bearing in hours.

Solution. Equation (8) will be applied on the basis of a work cycle of one minute.

P_e	Assumed interval min.	rpm	Rev. in assumed interval
1,400 lb	0.25	200	50
2,000	0.20	500	100
800	0.55	400	220
	1.00 min		370 Average rpm

In Eq. (8): $50 \times 1,400^3 + 100 \times 2,000^3 + 220 \times 800^3 = 370P_e{}^3$

$370P_e{}^3 = 1,049,840,000,000$ $P_e = 1,420$ lb equivalent constant radial load

In Eq. (3): $N_e = \dfrac{100^3 \times 4,440^3}{1,420^3} = 30,848,000$ rev rating

Rating life $= \dfrac{30,848,000}{370 \times 60} = 1,390$ hours

Average life $= 5 \times 1,390 = 6,950$ hours

Example 6. A 306 radial ball bearing with inner ring rotation has a 10 sec work cycle as follows.

For 2 sec	For 8 sec
$F_r = 800$ lb	$F_r = 600$ lb
$F_a = 400$ lb	$F_a = 0$
$n = 900$ rpm	$n = 1,200$ rpm
Light shock	*Steady load*

Find the expected average life of this bearing.

Solution.

For 2 sec:

Data from Table 9-2: $\dfrac{F_a}{iZD^2} = \dfrac{400}{8 \times 0.4844^2} = 213$

By Table 9-1: $Y = 1.43$

In Eq. (7): $P_e = 1.5(0.56 \times 1 \times 800 + 1.43 \times 400)$

$= 1,530$ lb equivalent radial load

No. of revolutions $= 2 \times \dfrac{900}{60} = 30$

For 8 sec: $P_e = F_r = 600$ lb

No. of revolutions $= 8 \times \dfrac{1,200}{60} = 160,$

Average rpm for the whole cycle is $\dfrac{30 + 160}{10} \times 60 = 1{,}140$

By Eq. (8): $30 \times 1{,}530^3 + 160 \times 600^3 = 190P_e{}^3$

$$P_e{}^3 = 747{,}400{,}000 \quad P_e = 910 \text{ lb equivalent radial load}$$

In Eq. (3): $N_e = \dfrac{100^3 \times 4{,}850^3}{910^3} = 152{,}600{,}000 \text{ rev rating life}$

$$= 152{,}600{,}000 \times 5 = 763{,}000{,}000 \text{ rev average life}$$

$$\text{Expected average life} = \frac{763{,}000{,}000}{1{,}140 \times 60} = 11{,}200 \text{ hrs}$$

4. Friction and Lubrication of Ball Bearings

Rolling friction prevails to a large extent in ball bearings. However, some sliding is always present since geometrically pure rolling contact cannot be secured. Because of the relatively large loads on the small areas

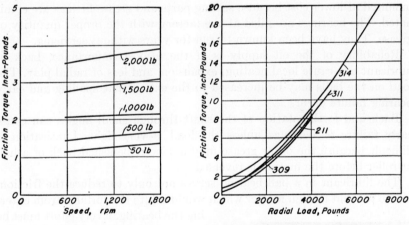

Fig. 9-3. Friction of single-row, deep-groove ball bearing number 314.

Fig. 9-4. Friction of single-row, deep-groove ball bearings of various sizes at 1,800 rpm.

in contact, the deformation of the metal accounts for a considerable proportion of the resistance in a ball bearing. Ball bearings, in general, have slightly less frictional resistance than high-grade partial journal bearings operating with flooded lubrication. Ball bearings have definitely less friction than journal bearings operating with scanty oil supply.

Test results on a 314 deep-groove bearing are shown in Fig. 9-3. The friction torque increases only slightly with increase in the speed of the shaft but varies almost directly with the radial load.[3] For constant load, the friction torque is not affected to any great extent by the size of the

[3] See reference 5, Bibliography.

bearing, as indicated by the curves of Fig. 9-4. However, the friction is affected by the type of bearing used.

The amount and viscosity of the lubricating oil used determine to a large extent the friction of a ball bearing. Tests have shown that drip feed which supplies a drop of oil every 2 to 4 hours gives much lower friction values than a more copious oil supply. In fact, for flooded lubrication, the power lost in churning the oil may be greater than the friction of the bearing alone. A very light or thin oil will give lower friction than one whose viscosity is high.

A light coating of oil or grease is all that is required to maintain an oil film between balls and races. When oil lubrication is used, more or less elaborate seals are needed to retain the lubricant. Lubrication by oil mist has proven successful for very high-speed applications.

Grease tends to remain in the bearing and protect the surfaces. Therefore it does not require such elaborate retainers. At low temperatures, the balls cut a channel through the grease, but enough oil usually sweats off to provide lubricant. Prelubricated sealed bearings can frequently be mounted at lower cost because sealing parts and grease fittings are eliminated. The bearings are filled at the factory with the proper quantity of grease. They have been known to run for years without servicing.

Reliability of the oil supply is of the utmost importance. Lack of lubricant can cause local heating, expansion, and loss of radial play. The load on the balls may be increased to the extent that spalling and early bearing failure occur.

Back and forth rotation of the shaft through small angles can cause early failure of bearings unless the load is very light. Lubrication is difficult because the oil or grease may not be replenished back of a ball or roller before the motion is reversed.

The lubricant in a ball bearing serves not only to reduce the friction, but to prevent foreign matter which would injure the surfaces from entering the bearing. Every effort must be made to protect the highly polished surfaces from grit, water, acids, or anything which will cause scratches or corrosion. Corrosion fatigue is particularly injurious in causing early fatigue failure of the bearing. Fatigue failures are caused by the bearing surface breaking down; small particles of the metal come out and leave pits or spalls, as illustrated in Fig. 9-5. This breakdown is preceded by minute surface cracks which are de-

Fig. 9-5. Failure of bearing race by pitting or spalling. (*Courtesy of New Departure, Division of General Motors.*)

veloped by repeated stress applications until they become sufficiently large to form zones of local weakness.

5. Mounting of Ball Bearings

For a rotating shaft, relative rotation between shaft and bearing is usually prevented by mounting the inner ring with a press fit and securing it with a nut threaded on the shaft. Excessive interference of metal must

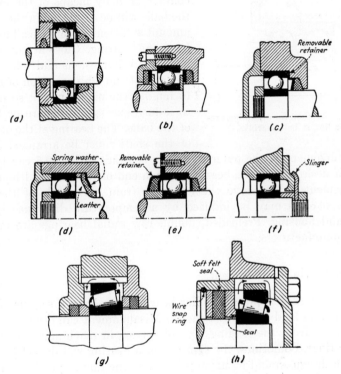

Fig. 9-6. Details of typical anti-friction bearing mountings.

be avoided in press fits, or the stretching of the inner ring may decrease the small but requisite internal looseness of the bearing.

Although the outer ring, when the shaft rotates, is mounted more loosely than the inner ring, rotational creep between the ring and housing should be prevented. When 2 bearings are mounted on the same shaft, the outer ring of one of them should be permitted to shift axially to care for any differential expansion between shaft and housing. Several examples of typical mounting details with oil retainers are shown in Fig. 9-6.

The catalogs of the various manufacturers contain useful illustrations of this kind, as well as other practical information.[4]

Shafts or spindles in machine tools and precision equipment which must rotate without play or clearance in either the radial or axial directions can be mounted on preloaded ball bearings.[5] The preloading, which removes all play from the bearing, can be secured in a number of different ways. For example, suppose the outer rings of the bearings at A in Fig. 9-7 project a small but controlled amount beyond the inner rings.

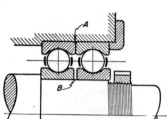

Fig. 9-7.   Method for obtaining pre-loading in ball bearings.

When the inner rings are brought into contact at B by means of the lock-nut, the balls will be displaced in the rings an amount sufficient to remove all looseness from the bearing. Close attention must be paid to dimensions and tolerances to secure just enough projection of the ring to remove the play, but not so much as to induce excessive pressure or binding of the balls. The bearing at the other end of the shaft must be arranged for free axial movement of the outer ring. The bearings in Fig. 9-7 can be separated if desired with one bearing at each end of the shaft. Although this arrangement will remove the looseness from both ends of the shaft, serious stresses may be induced by a temperature difference between shaft and housing. Preloaded, double-row radial bearings are made by some manufacturers.

6. Permissible Misalignment

Misalignment of ball and roller bearings can have a serious effect on their life and load carrying capacity. Misalignment can occur from shaft deflections, from the loading, or from errors in machining the supports for the rings. Sometimes the support for a bearing will deflect elastically and the design should be arranged so that the housing deflection offsets the shaft deflection rather than opposing it.

Anti-friction bearings are manufactured with various amounts of internal clearance. If the misalignment does no more than remove the internal clearance of a ball bearing, in general no shortening of the life will occur. Pressing a ring on a shaft may remove a portion of the original clearance. Permissible misalignment is also influenced by such factors as types of loading, race curvature and depth, diameter and number of balls, method of lubrication, retainer geometry, and minor dimensional details of the various makes.

[4] See also reference 6, Bibliography.
[5] See reference 4, Bibliography.

Roller bearings are more sensitive to the effects of misalignment so that any slope of the shaft has a bad effect on the life and load capacity. A slight crown on the rolls has proved to be beneficial in overcoming the effects of misalignment. In needle bearings the rollers depend on each other for guidance so that some resultant clearance is necessary for satisfactory operation.

Recommended misalignment limits are given in Table 9-4. In this

TABLE 9-4
Permissible Angular Misalignment Between Bearing and Shaft

Single row radial ball bearing:	
Slow speed and loose fit	0.0020 to 0.0040 in./in.
High speed	0.0010 in./in.
Cylindrical roller bearing	0.0003 to 0.0015 in./in.
Needle bearing	0.0003 to 0.0010 in./in.
Tapered roller bearing	0.0005 in./in.

table some makers recommend the lower ranges, while others permit the higher values. In case of doubt, the safest plan is to obtain the assistance of the maker of the particular bearing that is under consideration.

7. Other Types of Ball Bearings

The foregoing discussion has referred to ball bearings of the highest quality of materials and workmanship. Other bearings of lower quality can be purchased for installations requiring less accuracy, or where cost is the controlling factor. The retainer is usually omitted, and the outer ring is split by a plane through the ball centers perpendicular to the shaft. They are assembled on automatic machinery by spinning the edges of the bushing to retain the rings, as shown in Fig. 9-8. Other types of such bearings are made with a split inner ring.[6] The grooves for the balls are machined but not ground. The rings, however, should be hardened. A ball bearing of this type is sometimes cheaper than an equivalent plain bushing.

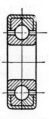

Fig. 9-8. Ball bearing of non-precision type.

For very light loads, ball bearings can often be improvised at low cost, as shown in Fig. 9-9. Separators are not used, and the rings are made on automatic screw machines. When the mounting is rigid, as in castings, both rings may be sections of a torus. However, for use in stampings, where there is danger of misalignment, one of the rings should be a section of a sphere. The manner in which such a bearing will accommodate itself to a ring not located at 90° to the shaft is shown

[6] See reference 8, Bibliography.

in Fig. 9-9(a). The sphere and torus may be interchanged if desired, as shown in Fig. 9-9(b). If some form of localized hardening is applied to the bearing surfaces, larger loads can be carried.

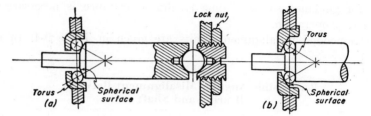

Fig. 9-9. Self-aligning light-weight ball bearings.

8. Relative Advantages of Ball and Plain Bearings

Some of the advantages of ball bearings are:

(1) Starting friction is low; a desirable feature for intermittent service or for starting at low temperatures.

(2) Loads can be inclined at any angle in the transverse plane.

(3) Thrust components can be carried.

(4) Maintenance costs are low.

(5) Bearings are easily replaced when worn out.

(6) Less axial space is required than for journal bearings. Shafts are thus shorter, and may even be smaller in diameter.

Some of the advantages of plain bearings are:

(1) First cost is usually lower.

(2) Less radial space is required than for ball bearings.

(3) Are better suited to overload and shock conditions.

(4) Operation quieter than with ball bearings, especially after wear has taken place.

(5) Less difficulty with fatigue.

(6) Less easily injured by foreign matter.

9. Roller Bearings

When shock and impact loads are present, or when a large bearing is needed, cylindrical and tapered roller bearings are usually used. A roller bearing in general consists of the same 4 elements as a ball bearing: the 2 rings, the cage, and the rollers. Some typical examples of roller bearings are shown in Fig. 9-10.

In the cylindrical roller bearing, the flanges on the rings serve to guide the rollers in the proper direction. When the flanges are omitted from one of the rings, as shown in Fig. 9-10, the rings can then be displaced axially with respect to each other, and no thrust component can be carried.

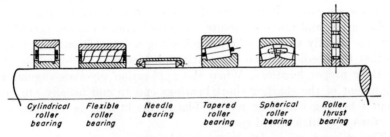

Cylindrical   Flexible   Needle   Tapered   Spherical   Roller
roller   roller   bearing   roller   roller   thrust
bearing   bearing   bearing   bearing   bearing

Fig. 9-10.   Types of roller bearings.

In addition to the radial load, the tapered roller bearing can carry a large axial component whose magnitude depends on the angularity of the rollers. The radial load will also produce a thrust component. The outer ring is separable from the remainder of the bearing. In this type of bearing, it is possible to make adjustment for the radial clearance. Two bearings are usually mounted opposed to each other, and the clearance is controlled by adjusting one bearing against the other. Double-row tapered roller bearings are also available.

Roller bearings in general can be applied only where the angular misalignment caused by shaft deflection is very slight. This deficiency is not present in the spherical roller bearing. It has excellent load capacity and can carry a thrust component in either direction.

In the flexible roller bearing, the rollers are wound from strips of spring steel, and afterwards are hardened and ground to size. If desired, the rollers can bear directly

Fig. 9-11. Full roller type bearing. Skewing of the rolls is prevented by the center guide. The shaft seals retain the lubricant and prevent entrance of foreign matter. (*Courtesy McGill Mfg. Co.*)

on the shaft without an inner ring, particularly if the shaft surface has been locally hardened.

The needle bearing has rollers that are very long as compared to their diameter. Cages are not used, and the inner ring may or may not be present. The outer ring may consist of hardened thin-walled metal as shown in Fig. 9-10, the housing in which the bearing is mounted must have sufficient thickness to give adequate support. The friction of needle bearings is several times as great as for ordinary cylindrical roller bearings. Because of the tendency of the unguided rollers to skew, needle bearings are particularly adapted to oscillating loads as in wrist pins, rocker arms, and universal joints. For continuous rotation, needle bearings are usually suitable where the loading is intermittent and variable so that the needles will be frequently unloaded and thus tend to return to their proper locations. When the application involves angular misalignment of the shaft, 2 short bearings end to end usually are better than 1 bearing with long rollers. The needle bearing is low priced and requires very little radial space.

Thrust bearings can be constructed by the use of straight or tapered rollers.

Roller bearings are selected by a process similar to that used for ball bearings. They must be chosen, however, in accordance with the recommendations given in the catalog of the manufacturer of the particular type of bearing under consideration.

10. Contact Stress Between Cylinders

Contact stress between bodies frequently reaches a very high value. The case of two cylinders with parallel axes pressed together is shown in

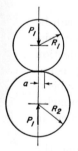

Fig. 9-12. Cylinders with parallel axes in contact.

Fig. 9-12. The small contact area has a half width a of

$$a = 2 \sqrt{\frac{P_1(1 - \mu^2) \left(\dfrac{1}{E_1} + \dfrac{1}{E_2} \right)}{\pi \left(\dfrac{1}{R_1} + \dfrac{1}{R_2} \right)}} \qquad (9)$$

where P_1 is the load per axial inch

μ is Poisson's ratio

E_1, E_2 are the moduli of elasticity

R_1, R_2 are the radii of the two bodies

The maximum value of the compressive contact stress occurs at the center of the contact zone and is given by

$$p_o = \sqrt{\frac{P_1\left(\dfrac{1}{R_1} + \dfrac{1}{R_2}\right)}{\pi(1 - \mu^2)\left(\dfrac{1}{E_1} + \dfrac{1}{E_2}\right)}} \qquad (10)$$

These equations can be easily adjusted to the case of a roller pressed against a plane. To do this, the value of one of the R's must be taken as infinity.

BIBLIOGRAPHY

Volume number shown in **bold face** type. The number immediately following is the page on which the article begins.

1. Barish, Thomas "Ball Bearing Machine Tool Spindles," *Trans. ASME*, **49–50**(2), MSP-50-10 (1927–1928).

2. Koon, S. G., "Heavy-Duty Anti-Friction Bearings," *Trans. ASME*, **51**(2), IS-5 (1929).

3. Almen, J. O., "Lubricants and False Brinelling of Ball and Roller Bearings," *Mech. Eng.*, **59**, 415 (1937).

4. Brunner, H. E., "Preloaded Ball Bearings as Applied to Machine-Tool Spindles," *Trans. ASME*, **54**, MSP-39 (1932).

5. Styri, Haakon, "Friction Torque in Ball and Roller Bearings," *Mech. Eng.*, **62**, 886 (1940).

6. Palmgren, Arvid, *Ball and Roller Bearing Engineering*, 3rd ed. Philadelphia: S. H. Burbank & Company, 1959.

7. Smith, R. J., "Rules for Application of Needle Bearings," *Machine Design*, **30**, Jan. 9, 116 (1958).

8. Recknagel, F. W., "Construction and Characteristics of Low-Cost Ball Bearings." *Product Eng.*, **21**, Jan., 106 (1950).

9. Barish, Thomas, "Antifriction-Bearing Developments for Aviation Engines," *Trans. ASME*, **65**, 261 (1943).

10. Allan, R. K., *Rolling Bearings*. London: Sir Isaac Pitman & Sons, Ltd., 1945.

11. Moore, C. C., and Jones, F. C., "Operating Characteristics of High-Speed Ball Bearings at High Oil-Flow Rates," *Trans. ASME*, **78**, 997 (1956).

12. Blood, H. L., "Housings and Spindles for Antifriction Bearings," *Mech. Eng.*, **72**, 131 (1950). Additional articles on various topics are given on pp. 134, 137, 142.

13. Korff, Walter H., "Twelve General Considerations for Needle Bearing Applications," *Product Eng.*, **15**, 389 (1944).

14. Macks, E. F., Nemeth, Z. M., and Anderson, W. J., "Operating Characteristics of Cylindrical Roller Bearings at High Speeds," *Trans. ASME*, **74**, 705 (1952).

15. Patterson, F. G., "Factors When Considering Anti-Friction Bearings for Oscillating Service," *Product Eng.*, **21**, Oct., 141 (1950).

16. Jones, F. C., and Wilcock, D. F., "Mechanism of Lubrication Failure in High-Speed Ball Bearings," *Mech. Eng.*, **72**, 817 (1950).

17. Kendall, G. H., "Noise and Vibration in Ball Bearings," *Product Eng.*, **22**, Dec., 150 (1951).

18. Kalikow, Irving, "Creep of Ball Bearing Races," *Product Eng.*, **20**, Apr., 129 (1949).

19. Shaw, M. C., and Macks, E. F., *Analysis and Lubrication of Bearings*, Chapter 10. New York: McGraw-Hill Book Co. Inc., 1949.

20. Buckwalter, T. V., "Roller-Bearing Service in Locomotive, Passenger, and Freight Equipment," *Trans. ASME*, **56**, 23 (1934).

21. Jones, A. B., "The Life of High-Speed Ball Bearings," *Trans. ASME*, **74**, 695 (1952).

22. Hetenyi, M., and McDonald, P. H., Jr., "Contact Stresses under Combined Pressure and Twist," *Trans. ASME*, **80** (1958); *Jour. of App. Mech.*, 396.

PROBLEMS

In the following problems, it is assumed that the bearing has but one row of balls.

1. If a 308 bearing is installed at the left reaction in Fig. 9-13, find the expected average life in hours. Speed is 1,800 rpm and the bearing is subjected to light shock. Inner rings are pressed on the shaft; outer rings have free fits.

Ans. 8,770 hrs.

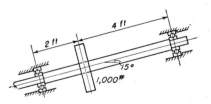

Fig. 9-13. Problem 1.

2. Use Fig. 9-13 but the rise is 5 in. vertically for 12 in. horizontally. A 208 bearing is installed at left end. The shaft rotates 1,800 rpm for 60 per cent of the time and 750 rpm for the remainder of the time. Loads are steady. Make a diagram and show the reaction at each end. Compute the expected life of the left bearing.   *Ans.*   10,400 hrs.

3. A cross section through an industrial car, and the loading for one axle, are shown schematically in Fig. 9-14. The inner rings of the bearings are fixed on the shaft; the outer rings have free fits. Wheels are press-fitted on the axle.

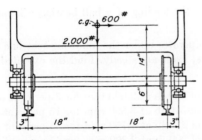

Fig. 9-14.   Problem 3.

Separate the framework from the axle and wheels and place on each portion all forces necessary for equilibrium. Draw and dimension the bending moment diagram for the axle. Consider the forces from bearings and wheels to be concentrated at their respective centers.

Based on the loading conditions of the left bearing, find the expected average life of a 310 bearing at a speed of 300 rpm. Assume the bearing is subjected to moderate shock.   *Ans.*   15,150 hrs.

4. Work Problem 3, except the downward load is 2,400 lb and sidewise load is 450 lb.   *Ans.*   16,910 hrs.

5. In Fig. 3-14, let the loads be steady and the rpm equal to 900. Find the expected average life for a 312 bearing installed at the left reaction.
Ans.   17,940 hrs.

6. A 205 bearing carries a 1,000 lb radial and a 250 lb axial load for one-sixth of the work cycle, and 500 lb radial for the remainder of the cycle. Speed is uniform at 1,200 rpm. The inner ring rotates and loads are steady. Find the expected average life for this bearing.   *Ans.*   3,630 hrs.

7. A 310 bearing has a work cycle with 1,000 rpm for one-third of the time, 2,000 rpm for one-third of the time, and 4,000 rpm for one-third of the time. The outer ring rotates. Assume light shock conditions. The radial load is 800 lb and axial load is 300 lb. Find the expected average life for this bearing.
Ans.   9,490 hrs.

8. A 307 bearing carries a radial load of 2,000 lb at 500 rpm for half the time, and 600 lb radial at 3,600 rpm for the remaining half of the time. The inner ring rotates, and the loads are steady. Find the expected average life.
Ans.   6,630 hrs.

9. A 206 bearing is subjected to the following work cycle.

Radial load of 1,000 lb at 150 rpm for 30 per cent of the time
Radial load of 1,500 lb at 600 rpm for 10 per cent of the time
Radial load of 500 lb at 300 rpm for 60 per cent of the time

The inner ring rotates; loads are steady. What is the expected average life of this bearing?   *Ans.* 11,700 hrs.

The following problems are presented without answers.

10. What change in the loading of a ball bearing will cause the expected life to be halved?

11. A 205 bearing operates under the following schedule of loads and speeds. The inner ring rotates; loads are steady. Find the expected average life for this bearing.

Radial load of 740 lb at 2,000 rpm for 5 per cent of the time
Radial load of 510 lb at 3,300 rpm for 15 per cent of the time
Radial load of 250 lb at 1,750 rpm for 35 per cent of the time
Radial load of 200 lb at 2,200 rpm for 45 per cent of the time

12. A ball bearing maker lists the capacity of a 205 bearing at 985 lbs at 500 rpm for an expected average life of 2,500 hrs.
Another maker lists the capacity of this bearing as 881 lbs at 500 rpm for an expected average life of 3,400 hrs.
Show by means of Eq. (2) that these two bearings should give almost exactly the same length of service.

13. The work cycle for a 304 ball bearing is as follows.

1,000 lb radial and 250 lb axial at 300 rpm for one-half the cycle.
1,200 lb radial at 500 rpm for one-quarter of the cycle.
700 lb radial at 1,000 rpm for one-quarter of the cycle.

Loads are steady; the outer ring rotates. Find the expected average life of this bearing.

14. Find the expected rating life of a 309 bearing that is subjected to a steady radial load of 615 lb, and an axial load of 350 lb. The inner ring rotates. The speed is 3,600 rpm.

15. An electric motor for a drill press has 204 bearings mounted as in Fig. 9-13 except that the shaft is vertical. Bearings are 10 in. center to center. The center of V-belt pulley is located 2.5 in. from the lower motor bearing. During two-thirds of the work cycle the steady belt forces equal 128 lb at 900 rpm. During the remainder of the cycle the steady belt forces equal 88 lb at 1770 rpm. The motor armature weighs 70 lbs. Find the expected rating life of the most heavily loaded bearing in hours.

10

Spur Gears

THE designer is frequently confronted with the problem of transferring power from one shaft to another while maintaining a definite ratio between the velocities of rotation of the shafts. Various types of gearing have been developed for this purpose which will operate quietly and with very low friction losses. Smooth and vibrationless action is secured by giving the proper geometric shape to the outline of the teeth. The proportions of the gear tooth, as well as the sizes of the teeth, have been standardized. This procedure has simplified design calculations and has reduced the required number of cutting tools to a minimum. The proper material must be selected to obtain satisfactory strength, fatigue, and wear properties. Ease of manufacture and ease of inspection are necessary if production costs are to be kept at their lowest level. All these problems must be taken into account by the designer.

a, addendum
b, face width
BHN, Brinell Hardness Number
c, center distance
d, pitch diameter
e, shift in position of generating rack
f, clearance
F_b, strength of tooth in bending, lb
F_d, dynamic load

F_t, transmitted load
F_w, strength of tooth in wear, lb
hp, horsepower
K, constant from Table 10-3
n, revolutions per minute, rpm
N, number of teeth
p, circular pitch
P, diametral pitch
p_b, base pitch
r, pitch radius

351

rpm, revolutions per minute

   s, bending stress

   s_{ec}, surface endurance limit in com-
      pression

   t, circular thickness of tooth

   T, torque

   V, pitch line velocity in feet per
      minute, fpm

y, form factor for circular pitch

Y, form factor for diametral pitch

z, length of contact for meshing
   teeth

φ, (phi) pressure angle

ω, (omega) angular velocity, radians
   per second

1. Introduction

In the friction cylinders of Fig. 10-1, the tangential velocities of the surfaces are equal if it is assumed that no slip occurs at the point of contact O. Hence,

$$r_1\omega_1 = r_2\omega_2 \tag{1}$$

where r_1 and r_2 refer to the radii, and ω_1 and ω_2 are the angular velocities in radians per second. These cylinders can be transformed into spur

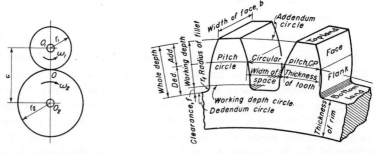

Fig. 10-1.   Friction cylinders.   Fig. 10-2.   Principal parts of gear teeth.

gears by placing teeth on them that run parallel to the axes of the cylinders. The circles in Fig. 10-1 are then called the pitch circles; their diameters are called the pitch diameters of the gears. The teeth are arranged to extend both outside and inside the pitch circles. The names of some of the more important parts of spur gear teeth are shown in Fig. 10-2. When operating together, the teeth of one gear extend to the working-depth circle of the other. Clearance f is required to prevent the end of the tooth of one gear from riding on the bottom land of the mating gear.

For positive transmission of motion, the teeth need not be of any particular shape. However, for quiet and vibrationless operation, the velocities of the pitch circles of the 2 gears must be the same at all times. This statement refers especially to the short interval of time during which 2 particular teeth are in contact. If the pitch circle of

the driver is moving with constant velocity, the shape of the teeth must
be such that the velocity of the pitch circle of the driven gear is neither
increased nor decreased at any instant while the two teeth are touching.
When this condition is satisfied, the gears are
said to fulfill the fundamental law of toothed
gearing.

2. Fundamental Law of Toothed Gearing

Portions of two gears having centers at O_1
and O_2 are shown in Fig. 10-3. The gears have
angular velocities of ω_1 and ω_2, respectively.
The teeth are in contact at point K_1, but no
particular shape has as yet been specified for
the outline of the teeth. Lines NN and TT
represent respectively the normal and tangent
drawn to the tooth surfaces at K_1. Normal
NN intersects the line of centers at point O.
The vector K_1M_1 represents the velocity of
K_1 considered as a point of gear 1. The vector
is perpendicular to radius O_1K_1. Similarly,
K_1M_2 represents the velocity of K_1 when K_1
is considered as a point on gear 2. Since the
teeth remain in contact, the projection K_1N_1
on the common normal of the velocity vectors must be the same for both
gears.

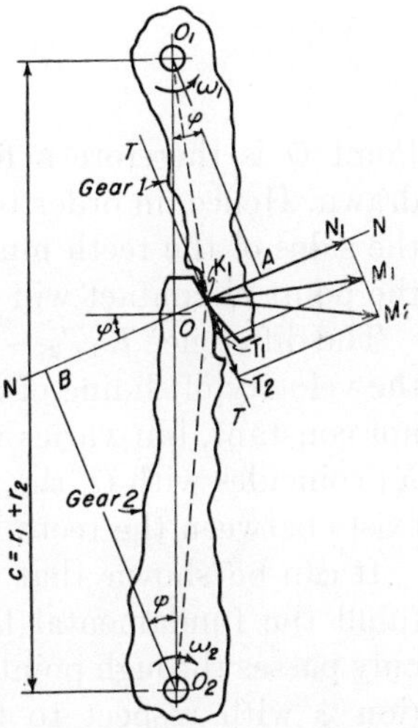

Fig. 10-3.　Normal compo-
nents of velocities at point of
contact are same for both
gears.

From the figure, $K_1M_1 = \omega_1 \times O_1K_1$, and $K_1M_2 = \omega_2 \times O_2K_1$, so that

$$\frac{\omega_2}{\omega_1} = \frac{O_1K_1}{K_1M_1} \times \frac{K_1M_2}{O_2K_1} \tag{a}$$

From sides of similar triangles, the following relationships are secured
from the figure.

$$\frac{O_1K_1}{K_1M_1} = \frac{O_1A}{K_1N_1} \quad \text{and} \quad \frac{K_1M_2}{O_2K_1} = \frac{K_1N_1}{O_2B} \tag{b}$$

Substitution in Eq. (a) gives $\qquad \dfrac{\omega_2}{\omega_1} = \dfrac{O_1A}{O_2B}$ $\hfill$ (c)

Also, from similar triangles, $\qquad \dfrac{O_1A}{O_2B} = \dfrac{O_1O}{O_2O}$ $\hfill$ (d)

Substitution in Eq. (c) gives $\quad \omega_1 \times O_1O = \omega_2 \times O_2O$ $\hfill$ (2)

The ratio ω_1/ω_2 from Eq. (2) must remain constant at all times if there
is to be no change in the velocity ratio of the two gears. Equations (1) and

(2) should be solved simultaneously, making use of the relationship

$$r_1 + r_2 = O_1O + O_2O$$

The result is

$$O_1O = r_1$$

$$O_2O = r_2 \qquad\qquad\qquad (e)$$

Point O is therefore a fixed point through which the pitch circles are drawn. Hence, in order to fulfill the fundamental law of toothed gearing, the sides of the teeth must be so shaped that the normal drawn through the point of contact will at all times pass through the pitch point O.

The difference $K_1T_2 - K_1T_1$ between the tangential vectors is equal to the velocity of sliding of one tooth on the other. The velocity of sliding is not constant, but varies with the location of the contact point K_1. When K_1 coincides with O, the sliding velocity is zero, and pure rolling contact exists between the teeth for this point.

It can be shown that gear teeth composed of involutes or cycloids fulfill the fundamental law. For involute gearing, the normal NN not only passes through point O at all times, but maintains a constant inclination φ with respect to the common tangent to the pitch circles. For cycloidal gearing, point O remains fixed, but angle φ varies as the location of the point of contact K_1 changes.

3. Kinematics of Involute Gear Teeth

Assume that the required velocity ratio for a pair of gears is secured by pitch circles of radii O_1O and O_2O, respectively, in Fig. 10-4(a). Draw the line AB at an angle φ to the common tangent to the circles. In practice, φ is usually made either $14\frac{1}{2}°$ or $20°$. Circles are drawn tangent to AB and are called the base circles of the gears. Let cylinders be made equal to the base circles, and let a string be passed around the base circle of gear 1, then from A to B, and then around the base circle of gear 2 somewhat in the manner of one strand of a crossed belt.

In Fig. 10-4(a), let a smooth plate S_1 be attached to gear 1, and let a scribing point be fastened to the cord at location O. Keeping the string taut, give the cylinders a small rotation in both directions, thus drawing the curve CD shown in Fig. 10-4(b). For all locations of the gear, the distance K_1A is equal to the arc AC. The curve CD is therefore an involute and is at all times normal to the string. A similar procedure should be followed on gear 2 after first removing S_1 and attaching surface S_2 to gear 2. A corresponding curve EF will be obtained as shown in Fig. 10-4(c).

If certain portions of S_1 and S_2 are now removed, both plates may be attached to the gear simultaneously, as in Fig. 10-4(d). The tooth outlines are in contact at K_1, and one gear may be turned by a pressure supplied by the other at this point. The string is therefore not required for producing motion and may be removed. The common normal to the tooth outlines coincided with the string and therefore will always cross

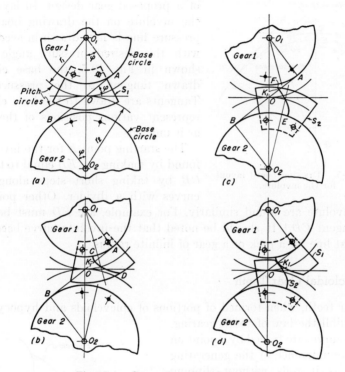

Fig. 10-4.   Generation of involute teeth.

the line of centers at the fixed point O. The rule of gearing is accordingly fulfilled. The resulting velocity ratio for the gears will be the same as the velocity ratio of the given pitch circles.

In the similar triangles O_1AO and O_2BO

$$\frac{O_2B}{O_1A} = \frac{O_2O}{O_1O} \tag{3}$$

Substitution in Eq. (2) gives

$$\omega_1 \times O_1A = \omega_2 \times O_2B \tag{4}$$

Thus the linear velocities of the base circles of the 2 gears are also equal to each other.

In involute gearing, at least 1 pair of teeth must always be in contact with each other along the line AB. This line is accordingly called the line of action, or the pressure line, and the angle φ is usually referred to as the pressure angle.

A large-scale drawing of gear teeth is frequently helpful or necessary in studying the form or kinematic action of a proposed gear design. In laying out the involute on the drawing board, the pressure line is first drawn in accordance with the desired pressure angle φ. As shown in Fig. 10-5, the base circle is drawn tangent to the pressure line. Tangents are drawn to the base circle to represent various positions of the string as it unwinds.

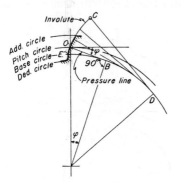
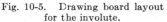

Fig. 10-5. Drawing board layout for the involute.

The starting point E for the involute is found by making arc EB equal to tangent OB by taking short steps along these curves with a divider. Other points on the involute are found similarly. For example, arc ED must be equal to tangent CD.[1] It should be noted that the involute curve becomes a straight line for a rack or a gear of infinite radius.

4. Cycloidal Gear Teeth

Gear teeth, when formed of portions of epicycloids and hypocycloids, also fulfill the law of tooth gearing. These curves are traced by a point on the circumference of the generating circle as it rolls without slipping along the inside and outside of the pitch circle of the gear as shown in Fig. 10-6.

Cycloidal gearing was formerly in extensive use for cast iron gears with cast teeth. Cycloidal gearing has been superseded by the involute tooth form, principally because the cutting tools required for manufacturing the latter are simpler in form. Variations in center distance have no effect on

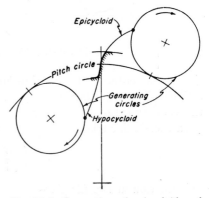

Fig. 10-6. Generation of epicycloid and hypocycloid.

involute teeth, whereas for cycloidal gearing, tooth action is not correct unless the center distance is accurately maintained. The chief interest at the present time in cycloidal gearing lies in the fact that the outline for

[1] See also reference 11, Bibliography.

the $14\frac{1}{2}°$ composite system is partially composed of cycloids. The rotors of the Root positive blower are also cycloidal in shape.

5. Pitches of Gear Teeth

For gear calculations, the following different pitches are in use.

(a) *Circular pitch* is defined as the distance in inches from a point on the pitch circle of one tooth to the corresponding point on the adjacent

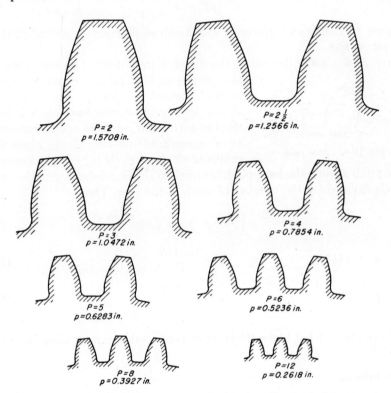

Fig. 10-7.   Actual sizes of gear teeth of various diametral pitches.

tooth measured along the pitch circle. If circular pitch is represented by p, pitch diameter by d, and the number of teeth in the gear by N, then

$$p = \frac{\pi d}{N} \tag{5}$$

(b) *Diametral pitch* is defined as the number of teeth in the gear per inch of pitch diameter. If diametral pitch is represented by P, then

$$P = \frac{N}{d} = \frac{N}{2r} \tag{6}$$

From Eq. (6), the following equation can be easily derived for center distance c.

$$c = r_1 + r_2 = \frac{N_1 + N_2}{2P} \tag{7}$$

The smaller of two meshing gears is usually called the *pinion*. Combination of Eqs. (5) and (6) gives the useful relationship

$$pP = \pi \tag{8}$$

Figure 10-7 shows a number of gear teeth of different diametral pitches in actual size.

(c) *Base pitch* is defined as the distance from a point on one tooth to the corresponding point on the adjacent tooth measured around the base circle. As shown in Fig. 10-8, the base pitch is also the distance from tooth to tooth measured on a tangent to the base circle. Since the radius of the base circle is $r \cos \varphi$, where r is the pitch radius, the base pitch is equal to the circumference of the base circle divided by the number of teeth in the gear. Thus,

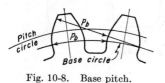

Fig. 10-8. Base pitch.

$$p_b = \frac{2\pi r \cos \varphi}{N} = p \cos \varphi = \frac{\pi \cos \varphi}{P} \tag{9}$$

For $\varphi = 14\frac{1}{2}°$, $$p_b = \frac{3.0415}{P} \tag{10}$$

For $\varphi = 20°$, $$p_b = \frac{2.9521}{P} \tag{11}$$

Example 1. What is the thickness of a $4P$ tooth measured along the pitch circle?

Solution.

By Eq. (8): $$p = \frac{\pi}{P} = \frac{\pi}{4} = 0.7854 \text{ in.}$$

The thickness of the tooth along the pitch circle can be taken as one-half the value of the p if clearance or backlash is neglected. Hence

$$\text{tooth thickness} = \frac{1}{2} \times 0.7854 = 0.3927 \text{ in.}$$

Example 2. A 20 tooth $5P$ gear meshes with a 63 tooth gear. Find the value of the standard center distance.

Solution.

By Eq. (6):   Pitch radius: $r_1 = \dfrac{N_1}{2P} = \dfrac{20}{2 \times 5} = 2.0$ in.

             Pitch radius: $r_2 = \dfrac{N_2}{2P} = \dfrac{63}{2 \times 5} = 6.3$ in.

             Center distance: $c = r_1 + r_2 = 2.0 + 6.3 = 8.3$ in.

Example 3. Two 8-P gears are to be mounted on a center distance of 16 in. The speed ratio is to be 7:9. Find the number of teeth in each gear.

Solution.

By the given conditions: $\dfrac{N_1}{N_2} = \dfrac{7}{9}$ or $N_1 = \dfrac{7}{9} N_2$

In Eq. (7): $2Pc = N_1 + N_2 = \dfrac{7}{9} N_2 + N_2 = \dfrac{16}{9} N_2$

$$N_2 = \frac{9}{16} \times 2Pc = \frac{9}{16} \times 2 \times 8 \times 16 = 144 \text{ teeth}$$

$$N_1 = \frac{7}{9} \times 144 = 112 \text{ teeth}$$

6. Standard Systems of Gearing

The American Gear Manufacturers Association has recommended[2] that the basic pressure angle φ be either 20° or 25° with full-depth addendums equal to $1/P$. Standards are retained for the $14\frac{1}{2}°$ full-depth involute system, the $14\frac{1}{2}°$ composite system, and the 20° involute stub-tooth system. These latter systems are required mainly for the replacement of gears already in service.

As the number of teeth in a gear is increased, the involute tooth outline becomes straighter until at the limit, when the radius is infinite, the gear becomes a rack with straight-sided teeth. Such racks have been standardized by the AGMA as follows.

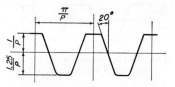

Fig. 10-9. Basic rack for 20° full-depth involute system. 25° system is similar except for change in angle.

(a) 20° *Full-Depth Involute.* These gears have a 20° pressure angle and basic rack illustrated in Fig. 10-9. This is a widely used system of

[2] See reference 10, Bibliography.

gearing. The rack for φ equal to 25° is similar except for the change in the angle.

(b) $14\frac{1}{2}°$ *Full-Depth Involute.* This is an involute tooth form whose basic rack has straight-sided teeth, as shown in Fig. 10-10. This system of gearing is very satisfactory, provided there is a considerable number of teeth in the gears. As will be explained, when the number of teeth is small, these gears, if made by one of the generating processes, are subject to

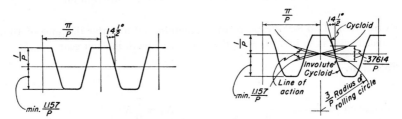

Fig. 10-10.   Basic rack for $14\frac{1}{2}°$ full-depth   Fig. 10-11.   Basic rack for $14\frac{1}{2}°$ composite
involute system.   system.

undercutting which may reduce the duration of contact between the teeth. They cannot be operated interchangeably with gears of the $14\frac{1}{2}°$ composite system. The tooth outlines are different, and true gear action cannot take place.

(c) $14\frac{1}{2}°$ *Composite System.* In this system, the tooth curve is an involute for a short distance each side of the pitch line, but is a cycloid for the inner and outer portions of the outline. Such gears are usually cut with the formed milling cutter shown in Fig. 10-13. The proportions for the basic rack for the system are given in Fig. 10-11. The least number of teeth for satisfactory action is 12. This system is sometimes erroneously called the "standard $14\frac{1}{2}°$ involute system." However, as mentioned above, only a portion of the tooth is of involute form.

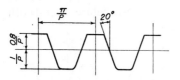

Fig. 10-12.   Basic rack for 20° stub-tooth involute system.

(d) 20° *Stub-Tooth Involute.* Gears in this system operate on a pressure angle of 20°, and have shorter addenda and dedenda than the full-depth systems. The basic rack is shown in Fig. 10-12. Although undercutting has been lessened, the short addendum reduces the duration of contact. Vibration may occur, especially in gears of few teeth, because of insufficient overlap in the gear action, as is explained in Section 14.

(e) *Fellows Gear Shaper System.* This system uses a pressure angle of 20° and two diametral pitches, such as $\frac{4}{5}$, $\frac{6}{8}$, and so forth. The numerator indicates the pitch which determines the thickness of the tooth and the pitch diameter. The denominator is used for determining the addendum in the usual manner. A gear having stub teeth is thus produced.

Figures 10-9 to 10-12, inclusive, illustrate the basic racks for the designated systems of gearing. The actual cutting tools, however, must have the tip of the teeth extended in order to cut the clearance f on the mating gear. This clearance is usually made equal to $0.25/P$ for $20°$ involute gears.

7. Methods of Manufacture

Gear teeth are formed by the following milling or generating processes.

(a) *Milling Cutter.* Spur gears may be made from a blank by removing the material between the teeth on a milling machine that uses the formed cutter shown in Fig. 10-13.

Gears of the $14\frac{1}{2}°$ composite system are usually made by this method. Since the geometric curves forming the sides of the teeth vary with the number of teeth in the gear, 8 cutters are required for each pitch if gears of all sizes are to be cut. The 8 cutters and the range of each are as follows:

No. 1: 135 to rack
No. 2: 55 to 134 teeth
No. 3: 35 to 54 teeth
No. 4: 26 to 34 teeth
No. 5: 21 to 25 teeth
No. 6: 17 to 20 teeth
No. 7: 14 to 16 teeth
No. 8: 12 and 13 teeth

Fig. 10-13. Formed circular cutter for gear teeth. (*Courtesy Illinois Tool Works.*)

Cutters are theoretically correct only for the lowest number of teeth in each range. If, when gears are being cut near the higher end of the range, a more accurate tooth form is desired, cutters in half numbers suitable for gears with such numbers of teeth are also available.

The following pitches are considered standard:

P 1 to P 2 varying by $\frac{1}{4}$ diametral pitch
P 2 to P 3 varying by $\frac{1}{2}$ diametral pitch
P 3 to P 12 varying by 1 diametral pitch
P 12 to P 32 varying by 2 diametral pitch

Gears with large-size teeth are frequently made by formed cutters because of the lack of suitable generating machines and tools.

Example 4. Two spur gears have a 3:1 ratio. The center distance is to be 11.600 in. Determine if it is possible to use standard gears of $P = 4$ for this train.

Solution.
$$N_2 = 3N_1$$

In Eq. (7):
$$N_1 + N_2 = N_1 + 3N_1 = 2Pc$$

$$4N_1 = 2 \times 11.6P$$

$$N_1 = 5.8P$$

When $P = 4$ is substituted in this equation, the right side will not be an integer. Gears with $P = 4$ therefore cannot be used for this train.

(b) *Rack Generation.* Gear tooth forms may be produced by another method, known as generating. Since a rack may be considered a gear

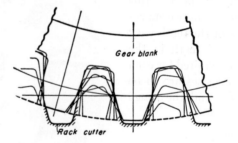

Fig. 10-14.   Rack generation of involute teeth.

of infinite radius, a tool of this shape may be constructed of hardened steel with cutting edges around the boundaries of the teeth. The tool is given a reciprocating motion parallel to the gear axis. At the same time, the gear blank is slowly rotated, and the rack is given a lateral motion equal to the pitch-line velocity of the gear. The material between the gear teeth is cut away and involute teeth are generated, as shown in Fig. 10-14. Only 1 tool for each pitch will be required to cut gears of any number of teeth.

(c) *Hobbing.* The hobbing process generates teeth from a straight-sided tool as shown in Fig. 10-15. The hob may be considered a cylinder around which a thread of the same cross section as a rack tooth has been helically wound. The resulting worm is gashed, the edges are relieved, and are then hardened and ground. The hob is located to give the proper depth of cut and is then rotated. Kinematically, the action of the hob on the blank is equivalent to that of a rack cutter. The lead of the helix of the hob as it rotates simulates the lateral motion of the rack. As the cutting progresses, the hob is fed axially along the blank until the teeth extend across the entire width of face. The hobbing process accounts for the major portion of gears made in quantity production.

(d) *Fellows Gear Shaper Method.* This is a generating process using a cutter that resembles a hardened gear with properly relieved edges. Cutter and blank are mounted on parallel axes and are slowly rotated; the cutter is given an additional reciprocating motion on its axis. Teeth are generated in the blank as shown in Fig. 10-16. At the beginning, the cutter is fed radially into the blank a distance equal to the depth of the tooth. The Fellows method must be used

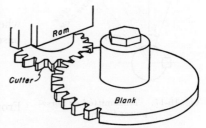

Fig. 10-15. Hob with partially cut gear blank.　　Fig. 10-16. Fellows gear shaper method of forming gear teeth.

for cutting internal gears. The method is also suitable for shoulder gears where space is restricted at one end of the teeth, as in the cluster gears of automobile transmissions. Fellows cutters are made to cut gears of all systems.

Hobbed and shaped teeth are usually provided with a small amount of tip relief. The cutting tools are modified to cut the tooth slightly narrower in the outer portion. The oncoming pair of teeth pick up the load more gradually, and errors in tooth form and spacing have less effect in producing noise and vibration. When the gear tooth surfaces are finished by shaving or grinding, the cutting tools must be arranged to leave sufficient stock for these operations.

8. Transmitted or Horsepower Load

With a pair of gears, power is transmitted by the force which the tooth of one gear exerts on the tooth of the other. This force is directed along the pressure line, as shown in Fig. 10-4. If the gears are transmitting power at a constant rate and are turning at a constant rpm, the force along the pressure line must be a constant also. The velocity along the pressure line is equal to the tangential velocity of the base circles.

The tangential velocity of the pitch circle is given by

$$V = \frac{\pi dn}{12} \text{ fpm} \tag{12}$$

where d is the pitch diameter in inches, and n is the rpm.

A principle of mechanics states that a force can be considered as acting at any point along its line of action. In Fig. 10-17 let the force F_n between the teeth be considered as acting at the pitch point O. This force has the value

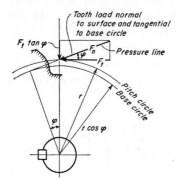

$$F_n = \frac{33{,}000 \text{ hp}}{V_b} \tag{a}$$

where V_b is the tangential velocity of the base circle in fpm. It is equal to

$$V_b = \frac{\pi dn \cos \varphi}{12} = V \cos \varphi$$

Fig. 10-17. Transmitted or horse-power force.

From Fig. 10-17: $F_n = \dfrac{F_t}{\cos \varphi}$

When these are substituted into Eq. (a), the result is

$$F_t = \frac{33{,}000 \text{ hp}}{V} \tag{13}$$

The radial component F_r of force F_n is equal to $F_t \tan \varphi$.

9. Bending Capacity of Spur Gear Teeth

It is possible, when two meshing gears have large numbers of teeth, for several pairs to be in contact simultaneously. It is customary, however, to assume that the entire load is carried by a single pair and that the load is acting through the corner or most unfavorable point on the tooth as shown in Fig. 10-18. This tooth load causes bending stresses in the material.

The force along the pressure line in Fig. 10-18 is considered as being applied at the center line of the tooth where it is divided into radial and tangential components. The radial component causes a uniform compressive stress over the cross section, but it is customary to neglect this force when making stress computations. The tangential component F_t

produces a bending moment $F_b l$ at the base or narrowest portion of the tooth.

It is customary to compute the bending stress on the assumption that the tooth is a cantilever beam. If the elementary equation, $s = 6M/bh^2$, for bending stress is used, the result at best is only approximate. Accuracy cannot be secured because the tooth is short and thick and non-uniform in cross section. It must be remembered that the derivation of the equation for bending stress assumed a long thin beam of constant cross section. In addition, for concentrated loads, the equation is valid only at points a considerable distance away from the point of application of the force. Nevertheless it is customary to use the equation, and to make application in the following manner.

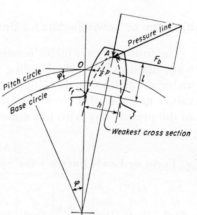

$$s = \frac{6M}{bh^2} = \frac{F_b}{b} \times \frac{6l}{h^2} \qquad (14)$$

Here b is the width of the tooth in the axial direction, and l and h are the height and thickness, as shown in Fig. 10-18.

Fig. 10-18.   Beam strength of gear teeth.

The factor $h^2/6l$ is a purely geometrical property of the size and shape of the tooth and may be written as a function of the circular pitch. Therefore let

$$py = \frac{h^2}{6l} \quad \text{or} \quad y = \frac{h^2}{6lp} \qquad (15)$$

The term y is a pure number and is called the form or Lewis factor. It depends on the number of teeth in the gear and the system of gearing used. Dimensions h and l must be for the cross section which makes $h^2/6l$ a minimum.

Substitution of Eq. (15) into Eq. (14) gives

$$F_b = sbyp \qquad (16)$$

Lewis

Equation (16) gives the tangential load which the tooth can carry in beam action. Values of y for gears of different numbers of teeth are given in Table 10-1. Sometimes the form factor is expressed as Y, which includes the factor π. Thus,

$$Y = \pi y \qquad (17)$$

Since $p = \pi/P$, Eq. (16) may be written

$$F_b = sb\,\frac{Y}{P} \qquad (18)$$

The distinction between Eqs. (13) and (16) should be noted. Equation (13) gives the value of the tangential force the gears are carrying. Equation (16) gives merely the capacity of the tooth to resist a bending load and makes no reference to the actual load the teeth may be carrying.

10. Form or Lewis Factors for Spur Teeth

The form or Lewis factor is named for the American engineer who first made application of the bending equation to gear teeth.[3] Although gear materials and methods of manufacture have changed greatly since the values in Table 10-1 were published in 1893, they have remained in use to the present day with but minor changes.

TABLE 10-1

Form or Lewis Factor y for Spur Gears with Load at Tip of Tooth

No. of Teeth	$14\frac{1}{2}°$ Full Depth	$20°$ Full Depth	$20°$ Stub	No. of Teeth	$14\frac{1}{2}°$ Full Depth	$20°$ Full Depth	$20°$ Stub	No. of Teeth	$14\frac{1}{2}°$ Full Depth	$20°$ Full Depth	$20°$ Stub
10	0.056	0.064	0.083	19	0.088	0.100	0.123	43	0.108	0.126	0.147
11	0.061	0.072	0.092	20	0.090	0.102	0.125	50	0.110	0.130	0.151
12	0.067	0.078	0.099	21	0.092	0.104	0.127	60	0.113	0.134	0.154
13	0.071	0.083	0.103	23	0.094	0.106	0.130	75	0.115	0.138	0.158
14	0.075	0.088	0.108	25	0.097	0.108	0.133	100	0.117	0.142	0.161
15	0.078	0.092	0.111	27	0.099	0.111	0.136	150	0.119	0.146	0.165
16	0.081	0.094	0.115	30	0.101	0.114	0.139	300	0.122	0.150	0.170
17	0.084	0.096	0.117	34	0.104	0.118	0.142				
18	0.086	0.098	0.120	38	0.106	0.122	0.145	Rack	0.124	0.154	0.175

Values of l and h, from which y could be computed by Eq. (14), are somewhat uncertain since they are influenced to a large extent by the size of the fillet radius r_f. For teeth made by milling cutters, the radius may sometimes be as small as $0.05p$. For radii of this size, the actual values of y are smaller than those shown in the table, and the teeth are then not as strong as Eq. (16), using tabular values, would indicate. In fact, fillets of rather generous size are required to give the y values of Table 10-1.

[3] See reference 15, Bibliography.

. For teeth which increase in thickness all the way to the base, the length of the moment arm l may be found by inscribing a parabola within the tooth outline. It should be tangent to the fillets on either side, and the vertex should be at A, as in Fig. 10-18. The bending stresses are then computed for the cross section passing through the points of tangency.

Example 5. Two 20° full-depth involute steel gears have 40 teeth each. The width of the face is 3 in. and diametral pitch is 3. Find the bending capacity of the tooth for a working stress of 28,000 psi.

Solution.

By Eq. (8): $\qquad p = \dfrac{\pi}{P} = \dfrac{\pi}{3}$

By Eq. (16): $\qquad F_b = sbyp = 28{,}000 \times 3 \times 0.124 \times \dfrac{\pi}{3}$

$\qquad\qquad\qquad = 10{,}900 \text{ lb.}$

Mechanical properties and working stresses for gears with different types of heat treatment[4] are given in Table 10-2.

TABLE 10-2

Mechanical Properties of Steel Gears Made by Different Processes

	Soft	Heat Treated	Induction or Flame-hardened	Carburized or Nitrided
Core hardness, BHN	190	250	280	330
Rockwell C	14	26	30	35
Case hardness, Rockwell C	14	26	55	60
Tensile strength at outer fiber, psi	90,000	125,000	250,000	300,000
Typical allowable bending stress, psi	15,000	20,000	28,000	40,000
Typical allowable surface compression stress, psi	75,000	90,000	135,000	160,000
Reliable maximum operating pitch-line velocity, fpm	5,000	20,000	30,000	40,000

11. Dynamic Load

The tangential pitch-line force F_t transmitted from one gear to another, may be easily determined from the horsepower by Eq. (13). However, this is not the entire force that acts between the teeth. Inaccuracies of tooth form and spacing, as well as misalignments in mounting, together

[4] See reference 8, Bibliography.

with the inertia of the rotating masses, produce dynamic forces which also act upon the teeth. Unevenness in the work load can also give large momentary forces between the teeth. No satisfactory solution to the problem is available, and it is here that the greatest uncertainty arises in the design of gears. The dynamic effects become less with better quality of gears and mounting. As a guide to the designer, the following equations will assist in forming an estimate for the magnitude of the dynamic load.

Class 1 Gears. These are ordinary commercial quality gears made with a form cutter or with one pass of the hob. Velocities are less than 2,000 fpm.

$$F_d = F_t \left(\frac{600 + V}{600} \right) \tag{19}$$

Note that the dimensions of V are feet per minute.[5]

Class 2 Gears. These are accurately hobbed or generated gears with a pitch line velocity of 4,000 fpm or less.

$$F_d = F_t \left(\frac{1,200 + V}{1,200} \right) \tag{20}$$

Class 3 Gears. These are precision gears as resulting from shaving, grinding, or lapping operations.

$$F_d = F_t \left(\frac{78 + \sqrt{V}}{78} \right) \tag{21}$$

Example 6. Using the same data as that of Example 5, but the horsepower is 200, and the speed is 900 rpm, find the dynamic load for the 3 classes of gears as specified above.

Solution.

By Eq. (6):
$$d = \frac{N}{P} = \frac{40}{3}$$

By Eq. (12):
$$V = \frac{\pi dn}{12} = \frac{\pi 40 \times 900}{3 \times 12} = 3,142 \text{ fpm}$$

By Eq. (13):
$$F_t = \frac{33,000 \text{ hp}}{V} = \frac{33,000 \times 200}{3,142} = 2,100 \text{ lb}$$

Class 1, Eq. (19):
$$F_d = 2,100 \times \frac{600 + 3,142}{600} = 13,100 \text{ lb}$$

Class 2, Eq. (20):
$$F_d = 2,100 \times \frac{1,200 + 3,142}{1,200} = 7,600 \text{ lb}$$

Class 3, Eq. (21):
$$F_d = 2,100 \times \frac{78 + \sqrt{3,142}}{78} = 3,600 \text{ lb}$$

[5] This is known as the Barth equation.

It is thus seen that the quality of the gears and the mounting can cause a wide range in the expected value of the dynamic load. All features pertaining to the design must therefore be given careful consideration by the designer.

The bending capacity F_b of the tooth must be equal to or greater than the dynamic load F_d.

$$F_b \geqslant F_d \tag{22}$$

12. Limit Load for Wear

In addition to tooth breakage from the bending stress, failure of a gear can be caused by compressive surface fatigue, as evidenced by pitting. It has been found that the Hertz equation for contact stress between cylinders with parallel axes is applicable. It has become customary[6] to call the limit load in surface compression by the name of wear load F_w.

In Eq. (10) of Chapter 9, let the maximum surface compressive stress p_o be replaced by the surface endurance stress s_{ec}, and let load P_1 per axial inch be replaced by F_w/b. Then

$$s_{ec}{}^2 = \frac{F_w \left(\dfrac{1}{R_1} + \dfrac{1}{R_2}\right)}{\pi(1 - \mu^2)b \left(\dfrac{1}{E_1} + \dfrac{1}{E_2}\right)} . \tag{23}$$

The contact stress, although very high, quickly diminishes for points removed from the area of contact. Radii R_1 and R_2 can be replaced by the radii of curvature for the involute curves when contact occurs at the pitch point O. Thus

$$R_1 = \frac{d_1}{2} \sin \varphi \tag{a}$$

$$R_2 = \frac{d_2}{2} \sin \varphi = \frac{N_2 d_1}{2N_1} \sin \varphi \tag{b}$$

The last form of Eq. (b) results from the relationship $d_1/N_1 = d_2/N_2$. When these are substituted into Eq. (23), the result can be reduced to

$$F_w = d_1 b Q K \tag{24}$$

where

$$Q = \frac{2N_2}{N_1 + N_2} = \frac{2d_2}{d_1 + d_2} \tag{25}$$

and

$$K = \frac{s_{ec}{}^2 \sin \varphi}{1.4} \left(\frac{1}{E_1} + \frac{1}{E_2}\right) \tag{26}$$

The values of K and s_{ec} to be used in Eqs. (24) and (26) for various combinations of materials for gear and pinion are given in Table 10-3.

[6] See reference 16, Bibliography.

Note that the value of s_{ec} for steel increases with the hardness as given by the Brinell Hardness Number BHN. The table takes into account the fact that the material in the harder gear will cold work the softer material of the other, and thus increase the compressive endurance limit

TABLE 10-3

Values of Compressive Endurance Limit s_{ec} and of K for Various Combinations of Gear Materials

Steel Pinion BHN	Gear		s_{ec} psi	K $14\frac{1}{2}°$	K $20°$	Steel Pinion BHN	Gear		s_{ec} psi	K $14\frac{1}{2}°$	K $20°$
	Material	BHN					Material	BHN			
150	Steel	150	50,000	30	41	400	Steel	400	170,000	344	470
200	Steel	150	60,000	43	58	500	Steel	400	175,000	364	497
250	Steel	150	70,000	58	79	600	Steel	400	180,000	385	526
200	Steel	200	70,000	58	79	500	Steel	500	190,000	430	588
250	Steel	200	80,000	76	103						
300	Steel	200	90,000	96	131	600	Steel	600	230,000	630	861
250	Steel	250	90,000	96	131	150	Cast iron		50,000	44	60
300	Steel	250	100,000	119	162	200	Cast iron		70,000	87	119
350	Steel	250	110,000	144	196	250 & up	Cast iron		90,000	144	196
300	Steel	300	110,000	144	196	150	Ph. bronze		50,000	46	62
350	Steel	300	120,000	171	233	200	Ph. bronze		70,000	91	124
400	Steel	300	125,000	186	254	250 & up	Ph. bronze		85,000	135	204
350	Steel	350	130,000	201	275	Cast iron	Cast iron		90,000	193	284
400	Steel	350	140,000	233	318						
500	Steel	350	145,000	250	342						

of the combination. The capacity of the gears in wear, as given by Eq. (24), must be equal to or greater than the dynamic load F_d.

$$F_w \geqslant F_d$$

Example 7. Find the limit load for wear for the gears in Example 5 if both gears are hardened to a Brinell Hardness Number of 350.

Solution.

By Eq. (25): $Q = \dfrac{2N_2}{N_1 + N_2} = 1$

By Table 10-3: $s_{ec} = 130,000$ psi

In Eq. (26): $$K = \frac{130{,}000^2 \sin 20°}{1.4} \left(\frac{2}{30{,}000{,}000}\right)$$

$$= 275$$

By Eq. (24): $$F_w = d_1 b Q K$$

$$= \frac{40}{3} \times 3 \times 1 \times 275 = 11{,}000 \text{ lb}$$

If desired, the value of K can be taken directly from the table.

Examples 5, 6, and 7 cover the same pair of gears. By Example 6 it is seen that the gears must have a quality of Class 2 or better since the tooth has a bending capacity of but 10,900 lb. Class 2 gears are also satisfactory in wear since Example 7 shows that F_w is equal to 11,000 lb.

For 20° steel gears, Eq. (24) reduces to

$$F_w = \frac{d_1 b s_{ec}^2}{61{,}400{,}000}\left(\frac{2N_2}{N_1 + N_2}\right) \tag{27}$$

13. Direct Calculation for Diametral Pitch

Calculations for an exact value of the diametral pitch must usually be modified, and a somewhat larger tooth must be used in order to employ an available cutting tool of standard pitch. It is therefore possible to introduce a small approximation for y in Eq. (16) for bending capacity F_b. For a limited range, the following equations[7] give good values for the form factor y.

For $14\frac{1}{2}°$ full-depth involute, $\quad y = \dfrac{2N}{15(N + 10)}$ for 15 to 35 teeth   (28)

For 20° full-depth involute, $\quad y = \dfrac{N}{7(N + 8)}$ for 15 to 35 teeth   (29)

Substitution of the equations above together with $p = \pi/P$ into Eq. (16) gives

For $14\frac{1}{2}°$ full-depth involute, $\quad F_b = \dfrac{2\pi s b d}{15(Pd + 10)}$ for 15 to 35 teeth   (30)

For 20° full-depth involute, $\quad F_b = \dfrac{\pi s b d}{7(Pd + 8)}$ for 15 to 35 teeth   (31)

Example 8. Two 20° full-depth Class 2 steel involute gears have a speed ratio of 3:1 on a center distance of 10 in. Horsepower is 100 at a speed of 1,800 rpm for the pinion. The width of the face is 2 in. For flame-hardened gears, find a suitable diametral pitch and the required BHN of the surface.

[7] See reference 27, Bibliography.

Solution.

For the pinion: $\qquad r_1 = \dfrac{10}{4} = 2.5$ in., $\quad d_1 = 5$ in.

In Eq. (12): $\qquad V = \dfrac{\pi 5 \times 1,800}{12} = 2,356$ fpm

In Eq. (13): $\qquad F_t = \dfrac{33,000 \times 100}{2,356} = 1,400$ lb

In Eq. (20): $\qquad F_d = 1,400 \times \dfrac{1,200 + 2,356}{1,200} = 4,150$ lb

In Eq. (31): $\qquad 4,150 = \dfrac{\pi 28,000 \times 2 \times 5}{7(5P + 8)}$

$$5P + 8 = 30.3; \quad P = 4.46, \text{ but use } P = 4,$$

$$N_1 = Pd_1 = 4 \times 5 = 20, \quad N_2 = 60$$

The bending capacity for $P = 4$ is

$$F_b = 28,000 \times 2 \times 0.102 \times \frac{\pi}{4} = 4,500 \text{ lb}$$

This can be taken as F_w in Eq. (27),

$$s_{ec} = \sqrt{\frac{61,400,000 \times 4,500}{5 \times 2} \times \frac{80}{120}} = 135,500 \text{ psi}$$

Interpolation in Table 10-3 gives BHN = 357.

Many gear problems can be handled, as in the example above, by determining the dynamic load and then proportioning so that the tooth is sufficiently strong in bending, and the surface is sufficiently hard for wear.

14. Number of Pairs of Teeth in Contact

Figures 10-19 to 10-22 inclusive show successive stages in the movement of the point of contact between two teeth, X on gear 1 and Y on gear 2. Contact between X and Y has just been made at B_1 where the addendum circle of gear 1 crosses the line of action. Contact also occurs between another pair of teeth at K_1.

In Fig. 10-20, contact between X and Y has moved to K_2 at which time the contact between the other pair is about to be broken at A_1 where the addendum circle of gear 2 crosses the line of action.

In Fig. 10-21, the contact between X and Y has passed through the pitch point O and now occurs at K_1. A new pair of teeth are coming into contact at B_1.

Fig. 10-22 shows contact between X and Y is about to be broken at A_1. Contact between the other pair has moved to K_2.

It should be noted that during the time when contact occurred in lengths B_1K_2 and K_1A_1, the load was divided between 2 pairs of teeth,

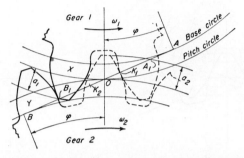

Fig. 10-19.   Teeth X and Y coming into engagement at B_1. Contact also occurs at K_1. Centers for gears are at O_1 and O_2 with pitch radii r_1 and r_2 respectively.

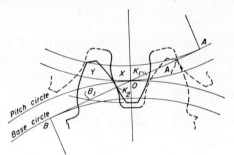

Fig. 10-20.   Position of gears with contact at K_2 for teeth X and Y. Contact at A_1 about to be broken.

but that when contact occurred in K_2OK_1, the entire load was carried by a single pair.

The Lewis equation for bending, Eq. (16), assumes that the entire load is carried at the tip of but 1 tooth. The figures above show that this assumption is overly conservative. When contact does occur at B_1 for tooth X, Fig. 10-19, the load is shared by another pair in contact at K_1. Similarly, when contact occurs at A_1, Fig. 10-22, the load is carried not only by Y, but by the other pair in contact at K_2. During normal service, the actual bending loads are thus less than that indicated by the equation. On this basis it is usually possible to neglect the effects of stress concentration in the fillet at the base of the tooth.

When the teeth in a gear are smaller and more numerous, it is found that more then 2 pairs may be in contact during part of the cycle.

It is obvious that length of contact A_1B_1 or z must be somewhat greater than a base pitch so that a new pair of teeth will come into contact before the pair that had been carrying the load separate. In fact, for smooth and vibrationless operation, there should be considerable overlap of gear action. The designer usually tries to obtain a minimum value of 1.4 for the quotient z/p_b. Distance z, or A_1B_1, can be computed as follows.

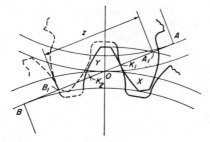

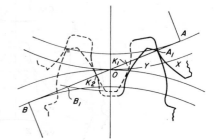

Fig. 10-21.   Position of gears with contact at K_1 for teeth X and Y. A new pair of teeth has come into contact at B_1.

Fig. 10-22.   Position of gears when contact for teeth X and Y is about to be broken at A_1. Contact between teeth also occurs at K_2.

Distance OA_1 is equal to A_1B minus OB. Length A_1B can be found as the short leg of a right triangle where $r_2 + a_2$ is the hypotenuse, and $r_2 \cos \varphi$ is the long leg. Length OB is merely $r_2 \sin \varphi$. Then

$$z = OA_1 + OB_1 \tag{32}$$

$$OA_1 = A_1B - OB = \sqrt{(r_2 + a_2)^2 - r_2^2 \cos^2 \varphi} - r_2 \sin \varphi \tag{33}$$

By similar reasoning,

$$OB_1 = AB_1 - OA = \sqrt{(r_1 + a_1)^2 - r_1^2 \cos^2 \varphi} - r_1 \sin \varphi \tag{34}$$

Example 9. Two 20° full-depth gears have a diametral pitch of 6 and operate on a center distance of 7.5 in. The speed ratio is 1.5 to 1. Find the number of base pitches in the length of contact.

Solution. $c = r_1 + r_2 = r_1 + 1.5r_1 = 2.5r_1 = 7.5$, $r_1 = 3$ in., $r_2 = 4.5$ in.

In Eq. (33): $OA_1 = \sqrt{\left(4.5 + \dfrac{1}{6}\right)^2 - 4.5^2 \times 0.93969^2} - 4.5 \times 0.34202$

$$= 1.9740 - 1.5391 = 0.4349 \text{ in.}$$

In Eq. (34): $OB_1 = \sqrt{\left(3 + \dfrac{1}{6}\right)^2 - 3^2 \times 0.93969^2} - 3 \times 0.34202$

$$= 1.4424 - 1.0261 = 0.4163 \text{ in.}$$

By Eq. (11): $p_b = \dfrac{2.9521}{P} = \dfrac{2.9521}{6} = 0.4920$ in.

$$\text{number} = \frac{0.4349 + 0.4163}{0.4920} = 1.73 \text{ tooth intervals in length of contact}$$

If the number of teeth in the gears is decreased, the radii become proportionally smaller and the addenda proportionally larger. Thus, point A_1 in Fig. 10-19 will eventually coincide with point A. Should gears be made with still fewer teeth, interference of metal will occur, unless the flanks are undercut, as will be explained later. The equations above for length of contact are applicable only to gears that are free from undercutting.

Points A and B in Fig. 10-19 are called the interference points for the gears. It is possible to have gear action all the way along the pressure line to the interference point. However, when the gears are highly stressed, it is good practice to have contact begin and end a considerable distance short of the interference points. Figure 10-5 shows how the radius of curvature of the involute curve becomes progressively smaller as the interference point, or the beginning of the involute, is approached. Contact stresses caused by the tooth load increase rapidly as the radius of curvature of the body is decreased. The stresses may become so high that pitting and surface failure will occur if the involute is too heavily loaded in the region of small radius of curvature.

15. Materials for Gears

Gears are made from a wide variety of materials, such as gray and alloy cast iron, cast and forged steel, brass and bronze, and impregnated fabric. Cast iron has good wearing properties but is weak in bending. It therefore requires the use of relatively large teeth. To secure a hard wearing surface, carbon and alloy wrought steels must, in general, be given some sort of heat treatment, as, for example, quenching and tempering. If it is desired to harden only the surface, the steel may be heated by induction using high-frequency currents. The heated region is then quickly cooled by a water spray before the temperature of the interior has risen enough to be affected by the quenching. In some cases, the heating is done with a torch or a gas flame. A hard surface can also be secured by case hardening or carburizing. Carbon is absorbed by the tooth surfaces while the gear is held at a red heat in a furnace. The core or interior of the gear will be strengthened, but it will retain its original ductility to a large extent. A number of typical heat-treating steels used for gears are shown in Table 10-4. Composition and physical properties for these steels are given in the chapter on engineering materials. Cold working the tooth surface by shot peening also gives an increase in fatigue strength.

Warping or distortion of the gear in heat treatment is a serious matter. The load is then likely to be concentrated on a corner of the tooth instead of being evenly distributed across the face. Alloy steels retain their shape after heat treatment better than do plain carbon steels. Accuracy of cutting and rigidity of mounting must also be given consideration so that a uniform load across the tooth may be obtained. Selection of a suitable material for a gear is frequently difficult and is usually based

TABLE 10-4

Typical Steels Used for Heat-Treated Gears

Quenched and Tempered		Carburized	
SAE 1045	Plain-Carbon	SAE 2315	Nickel
SAE 3140	Nickel-Chromium	SAE 3115	Nickel-Chromium
SAE 4140	Chromium-Molybdenum	SAE 4615	Nickel-Molybdenum
SAE 4640	Nickel-Molybdenum	SAE 6115	Chromium-Vanadium
SAE 5140	Chromium	AISI A8620	Chromium-Nickel-Molyb-
AISI A8640	Chromium-Nickel-Molyb-		denum
	denum		

upon such considerations as cost, freedom from warping in heat treatment, good wearing properties, ability to sustain impact loads, and lack of sensitivity to stress concentrations. The tensile strength and chemical composition are thus of secondary importance except in so far as they contribute to the foregoing desirable qualities.

Distortion can be eliminated if the teeth are first rough cut in a blank that has been suitably prepared for machining by normalizing or annealing. The gear is then hardened to the upper limit for machining, about 300 Brinell, and the teeth are brought to final size by taking a finish cut. No subsequent heat treatment will be done. A free-machining steel of suitable physical properties is sometimes employed with the foregoing process, and a reduction in the machining costs can thereby be effected. Shaving cutters are also used for the final sizing of gear teeth. The teeth of fully hardened spur gears can be brought to size, and a smooth surface can be obtained, by finish grinding. The rough cutting for all the foregoing must leave sufficient stock on the teeth for removal by the finishing operation. The designer usually specifies teeth of the smallest permissible size in order that the overlap of gear action may be as large as possible.

Another type of gearing failure is scoring. It is evidenced by a decided roughness on the flanks of the teeth looking as though the mating surfaces had seized. In fact, it is generally accepted that scoring is the result of the continual welding and tearing apart of the high spots of the 2 surfaces. Scoring results from high values of compressive stress and velocity and usually occurs in the early stages of operation. This type of failure is sometimes referred to as scuffing, seizing, or galling.

The surface resistance of gears can be improved by shot peening. Extreme pressure lubricants have proven effective under certain kinds of adverse conditions.

16. Determination of Tooth Loads

The tooth loads and bearing reactions for the various shafts of a gear train can be easily found by making suitable sketches. A typical case is

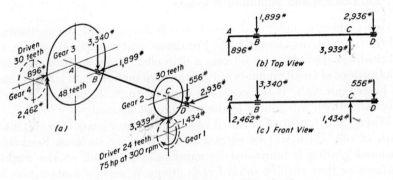

Fig. 10-23.   Shaft and gears of Example 10.

shown in Fig. 10-23, the computations for which are carried out in the following example.

Example 10. Find the tooth loads and bearing reactions for the shaft shown in Fig. 10-23(a). All gears are 20° pressure angle with diametral pitch equal to 3. Make top and front views showing the loading for the shaft. Assume frictional losses to be negligible. $AB = 6$ in., $BC = 20$ in., $CD = 5$ in.,

Solution.

For gear 1: $d = \dfrac{N}{P} = \dfrac{24}{3} = 8$ in.

For gears 1 and 2: $V = \dfrac{\pi d n}{12} = \dfrac{\pi 8 \times 300}{12} = 628.3$ fpm

By Eq. (13): $F_t = \dfrac{33,000 \text{ hp}}{V} = \dfrac{33,000 \times 75}{628.3} = 3,939$ lb tangential force on gear 2

Then $F_r = F_t \tan \varphi = 3,939 \times 0.36397 = 1,434$ lb

For gear 3: $V = \dfrac{48}{30} \times 628.3 = 1{,}005.3$ fpm

$$F_t = \frac{33{,}000 \times 75}{1{,}005.3} = 2{,}462 \text{ lb tangential force on gear 3}$$

Then $F_r = F_t \tan \varphi = 2{,}462 \times 0.36397 = 896$ lb

The tooth loads described above are shown in Fig. 10-23(a). The bearing reactions are found by simple statics. The top and front views for the shaft loads are shown in sketches (b) and (c), respectively. Bending moments and stresses for the shaft can be found in the usual manner.

17. Lubrication and Mounting of Gears

Gears operate under a diversity of conditions, and the methods of lubrication will vary accordingly. For unenclosed or exposed gearing, the lubricant is applied by an oil can, a drip oiler, or by a brush. Frequent applications of small amounts of lubricant are preferable to large volumes at longer intervals. If the gears are exposed to water or acids, a sticky lubricant which will adhere to the metal must be used.

When gears run in an enclosed casing, the larger gears may dip into a bath of oil, which will be carried to the wearing surfaces. Sometimes enclosed gearing is lubricated by spraying a jet of oil on the working surfaces as they revolve toward each other. When the contact pressure is very high, extreme-pressure E.P. lubricants must be used to prevent rupture of the oil film and the resulting metal-to-metal contact of the parts. Lubricants of the E.P. type contain additives which increase the load-carrying properties as well as prevent the squeezing out of the lubricant.

The mounting of gears is very important. Care must be exercised that shafts are parallel, or the entire load will be carried by the end of the tooth instead of across the entire width of each face. Improperly mounted gears are subjected to greater wear and danger of breakage; they are also the cause of noise and vibration.

In general, spur gears operate at high efficiencies. Good-quality commercial gears properly mounted and lubricated should not consume in friction more than 1 or 2 per cent of the power transmitted.[8]

18. Backlash

When making gearing calculations, it is standard practice to assume that the thickness of the tooth measured around the pitch circle is

[8] See references 31 and 33, Bibliography.

exactly one-half the circular pitch. Because of unavoidable inaccuracies, it is necessary to provide some clearance so that the gears will not bind but will roll together smoothly. This clearance is called *backlash*. It is illustrated in Fig. 10-24 and is defined as the amount by which a tooth space exceeds the thickness of the engaging tooth. The measurement is to be made on the pitch circle. If the measurement is made normal to the tooth profile, as by a feeler gage, the reading can be converted to a length taken along the pitch circle.

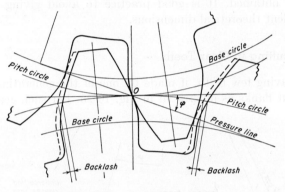

Fig. 10-24.　Backlash in gears.

Backlash is usually obtained by setting the cutting tools deeper into the blank so as to produce a thinner tooth and wider space. Tooth thickness is usually reduced for each gear, although it is possible to obtain the backlash by making the teeth thinner on but one of the gears. Backlash can also be increased or decreased by giving a small variation to the center distance at which the gears are mounted. For most applications in machinery, the backlash varies from $0.03/P$ to $0.05/P$. For gear trains in precision equipment and instruments it is frequently necessary to keep the backlash at a very low value. For involute teeth, backlash and variation in center distance have no effect on theoretically correct gear tooth action.

19. Dimensioning of Gears

The drawing for a gear should show the outside diameter and thickness of the blank with suitable tolerances. The number of teeth, diametral pitch, and pressure angle should be given. Backlash should be taken into account, and the tooth thickness, as measured around the theoretical pitch circle, should be shown. Tooth thickness should be expressed with a tolerance, but the pitch circle diameter should be given as a flat dimension. From the information above the maker can calculate any additional dimensions required by his particular system of manufacture and inspection. For standard teeth, it is usually not necessary to make a drawing of the outline of the tooth.

However, if a drawing is made it is helpful if it shows the number of teeth in the mating gear, the minimum center distance, and the backlash after assembly. If only a few sets are to be made and interchangeability is not important, the maker can mount the gears on a test stand and adjust tooth thicknesses until satisfactory operation with the specified backlash is obtained. It is good practice to avoid giving superfluous interdependent theoretical dimensions.

20. Undercutting in Gear Teeth

A gear having few teeth, if made by one of the generating processes, has undercut flanks as illustrated in Fig. 10-25. For such gears, the end

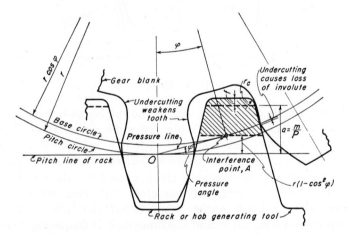

Fig. 10-25.   Undercutting in generated gear resulting from insufficient number of teeth.

of the cutting tool extends inside the interference point, or point of tangency of base circle and pressure line, and removes an excessive amount of metal. Undercutting not only weakens the tooth, but removes a small portion of the involute adjacent to the base circle; this loss of involute may cause a serious reduction in the length of contact. Gear action can take place only on the involute which ends at the base circle. The portion of the mating tooth which projects inside the interference point is therefore not needed for the operation of the gears.

Undercutting can be prevented by using more and smaller teeth in the gear. No undercutting can occur if the addendum does not extend inside the interference point A. In Fig. 10-25 the height from the interference point to the center of the gear is $r \cos^2 \varphi$. The height at which the addendum should be terminated in order that no undercutting may occur is equal to

$$\frac{m}{P} = r(1 - \cos^2 \varphi) = r \sin^2 \varphi \tag{a}$$

Since the pitch radius r is equal to $N/2P$, the equation for determining the minimum number of teeth which a gear may contain and not be undercut becomes

$$N = \frac{2m}{1 - \cos^2 \varphi} = \frac{2m}{\sin^2 \varphi} \tag{35}$$

For $14\frac{1}{2}°$ full-depth gears: $m = 1$; $N = 32$

For $20°$ full-depth gears: $m = 1$; $N = 17$

For $20°$ stub teeth: $m = 0.8$; $N = 14$

Generated gears having fewer teeth than indicated above should be used only when the resulting loss of involute will not reduce the length of contact below a satisfactory value. The superiority of $20°$ gears, when the number of teeth is small, should be noted.

Should the gear in Fig. 10-25 be made by some method which would not undercut the flanks, there would be interference of metal, and the gear would probably neither mesh nor roll with another gear. Undercutting and interference can be avoided in gears of few teeth by using a system with a larger pressure angle, or by cutting the teeth on the long and short addendum system described in the following section. Cycloidal gear teeth neither undercut nor interfere. This advantage is retained by the $14\frac{1}{2}°$ composite system.

Involutes are of course produced by all the standard generating systems. However, in order to determine what the teeth actually look like, the method of production and the particular tool that will be used must be taken into account. Such information can be secured by making a large-scale layout of the teeth of both gears. It is especially needed when the number of teeth is small, and it is necessary to determine the extent of the undercutting. A magnified cutter should be made from a piece of tracing paper and rolled over the circle representing the blank; successive positions should be traced until the tooth outline is generated. The teeth of both gears can then be meshed together, and definite information can be had regarding undercutting and loss of involute, radius of fillet, length of contact, overlap, length of addendum, and depth of cut.

21. Long and Short Addendum Gearing

A very successful method of avoiding undercutting is to use the so-called "long and short addendum gearing." The addendum on the pinion or smaller gear is made longer than standard, and the addendum of the larger gear is made shorter by an identical amount. The gears are generated by the same rack or hob as for gears with standard addenda. The pressure angle during operation is unchanged.

The outside diameter of the pinion is increased, and since the hob penetrates less deeply into the blank, undercutting is reduced or eliminated. The increase of radius for the blank at which undercutting can be just avoided is equal to the value of e, as shown in Fig. 10-26. Here the end of the rack tooth, not counting clearance f, passes through the interference point. From the figure

$$e = \frac{1}{P} - r(1 - \cos^2 \varphi) = \frac{1}{P} - r \sin^2 \varphi \qquad (36)$$

Example 11. Find the shift in the position of the rack necessary to eliminate undercutting in a $14\frac{1}{2}°$ full-depth gear of 18 teeth. $P = 1$.

Solution. $r = \dfrac{N}{2P} = \dfrac{18}{2} = 9$ in.

In Eq. (36): $e = \dfrac{1}{1} - 9(1 - 0.96815^2) = 1 - 0.5642 = 0.4358$ in.

Although the value of e can be selected at the discretion of the designer, it is frequently rounded off to a value somewhat larger than that given by Eq. (36).

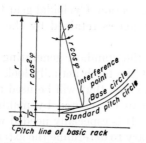

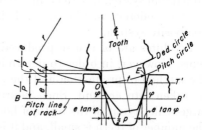

Fig. 10-26. Shift in position of generating rack to cause addendum to pass through interference point of gear. $P = 1$.

Fig. 10-27. Change in tooth thickness resulting from non-standard setting of generating rack.

The teeth in Fig. 10-26 are thicker than those of a standard gear, and the spaces are thinner. Tooth thickness can be easily determined from Fig. 10-27, which shows an oversize blank with teeth cut by a rack located a distance e from the pitch circle of the gear. The pitch circle rolls without slipping along pitch line TT' of the rack. Segment PA equals arc PE, and the tooth thickness t on the pitch circle for the chosen value of e is

$$t_1 = 2e \tan \varphi + \frac{1}{2} p \qquad (37)$$

Figure 10-27 illustrates the cutting of an oversize pinion. When the undersize gear blank is cut, the rack is located a distance e inside the pitch circle, and the tooth thickness is reduced to

$$t_2 = -2e \tan \varphi + \frac{1}{2} p \qquad (38)$$

Example 12. Find the thickness of the tooth on the pitch circle for $14\frac{1}{2}°$ gears if e is taken as 0.5 in. for $P = 1$.

Find the thickness of tooth for the gear.

Solution. $$p = \frac{\pi}{P} = 3.1416 \text{ in.}$$

In Eq. (37); for pinion: $t_1 = 2 \times 0.5 \times 0.25862 + 0.5 \times 3.1416$

$$= 0.2586 + 1.5708 = 1.8294 \text{ in.}$$

In Eq. (38); for gear: $t_2 = -2 \times 0.5 \times 0.25862 + 0.5 \times 3.1416$

$$= -0.2586 + 1.5708 = 1.3122 \text{ in.}$$

The teeth for this example, for $N_1 = 18$ and $N_2 = 62$, are illustrated in Fig. 10-28. It can be seen that the pinion tooth, which normally would be badly undercut, is not.

Because the larger gear is undersize and the hob has been shifted inwardly, undercutting can be avoided only by having a sufficiently large

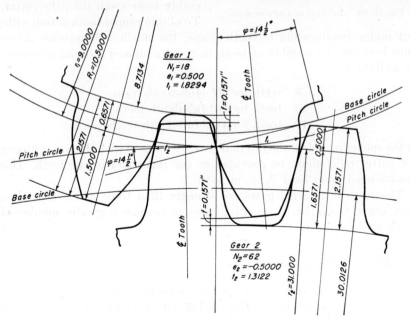

Fig. 10-28.   Long and short addendum gears.

number of teeth. The larger gear should have at least as many teeth in excess of the minimum number given in Section 20 as the smaller gear has fewer than the minimum.

Because of the change in tooth thickness, the y-factors of Table 10-1 cannot be used with long and short addendum gears.

When both mating gears have few teeth, undercutting in both can be prevented by the use of positive values for e. Assembly, when both gears have thicker teeth, can be made only at an increased center distance. The calculations become involved and are beyond the scope of this book.

22. Internal or Annular Gears

A gear can also be made as a ring, see Fig. 10-29, with teeth on the inside which are somewhat like the spaces between the teeth of an

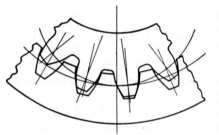

external spur gear. The assembly of an internal and external gear is very compact, with a reduced distance between the shaft centers.

Internal gears are cut on the Fellows gear shaper. In order to prevent the corners on the inner ends of the teeth from being cut away, the gear must have considerably more teeth than the cutter. To obtain proper tooth action with-

Fig. 10-29.   Internal or annular gear.

out undue modification of tooth shape, the smallest permissible difference between the number of teeth in the pinion and internal gear must be as follows.

8   teeth for 20° stub-tooth form
10   teeth for 20° full-depth teeth
12   teeth for 14½° full-depth teeth

If the spokes or web of the internal gear are integral with the rim, a groove for cutter relief must be provided at the inner end of the teeth. This groove must be at least $\frac{3}{32}$ in. in width.

The teeth of internal gears are stronger than those of corresponding spur gears. Operation is smooth and quiet because a greater number of teeth are in contact.

23. Speed Ratios of Gear Trains

The speed ratio of a gear train can be easily found if the number of teeth in each gear is known. Thus in Fig. 10-30 the ratio between n_4, the rpm of the shaft for gear 4, and n_1, the rpm of the shaft for gear 1, is given by the following equation.

$$\frac{n_4}{n_1} = \frac{N_1}{N_2} \cdot \frac{N_3}{N_4} \tag{39}$$

Additional ratios can be inserted into Eq. (39) if the train consists of a larger number of gears.

The inverse problem, that of finding the number of teeth each gear should have if the ratio of the train is to equal an arbitrarily chosen

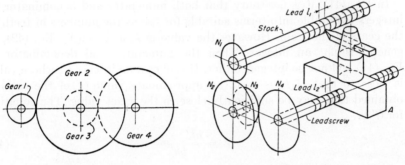

Fig. 10-30.   Gear train.   Fig. 10-31.   Thread being cut by lathe.

value, is much more difficult. Such problems arise whenever it is necessary to give a specified relative motion to two portions of a mechanism.

A typical example is shown in Fig. 10-31 where a thread of lead l_1 is being cut by an engine lathe whose lead screw has a lead of l_2. Let gear 1 make one complete revolution. Gear 4 makes N_1N_3/N_2N_4 revolutions, and carriage A moves a distance $N_1N_3l_2/N_2N_4$ inches. The distance must be equal to l_1. Hence

$$\frac{N_1N_3}{N_2N_4} = \frac{l_1}{l_2} \tag{40}$$

The problem is thus reduced to that of finding the numbers of teeth in the various gears.

In general, a given ratio cannot be exactly produced by a gear train because the individual members must necessarily contain integral numbers of teeth. It is possible, however, to approximate the desired ratio with a degree of accuracy that is sufficient for most applications. Although trial and error is involved, a systematic procedure helps reduce the labor to a minimum. A number of different methods can be used, of which the following is very effective.

Let the given ratio between the first and last shafts be represented by G, and let a/b be a common fraction, a and b integers, whose value is close to that of G. Ratio G can be exactly represented by

$$G = \frac{ah - m}{bh} \tag{41}$$

where m is an integer, and h has the value obtained by solving the equation. Thus

$$h = \frac{m}{a - bG} \tag{42}$$

In Eq. (41), it is necessary that both numerator and denominator be integers factorable into terms suitable for use as the numbers of teeth in the gears of the train. However the value of h, as given by Eq. (42), in general is not an integer. Then the numerator and denominator in Eq. (41) will not be integers either. However if an integer h', whose value is close to that of h, is used, an approximate value G' of the ratio is obtained that may be sufficiently close to the exact value. The equation for G' is

$$G' = \frac{ah' - m}{bh'} \tag{43}$$

The use of the above equations is illustrated by the following example.

Example 13. Suppose the shaft on the left in Fig. 10-30 is to make 2.54 revolutions for each revolution of the shaft on the right. Find suitable numbers of teeth for the gears.

Solution. $G = \dfrac{1}{2.54} = 0.3937008$

By trial it is found that fraction $\frac{24}{61}$ has a value close to G. Hence

$$\frac{a}{b} = \frac{24}{61}$$

Let $\qquad m = 1$

In Eq. (42): $\quad h = \dfrac{1}{24 - 61 \times 0.3937008} = -63.499$

Suppose $\qquad h' = -63$

In Eq. (43): $\quad G' = \dfrac{-24 \times 63 - 1}{-61 \times 63} = \dfrac{1{,}513}{3{,}843} = \dfrac{17 \times 89}{61 \times 63} = 0.3937028$

$\qquad\qquad$ error $= 0.3937028 - 0.3937008 = 0.0000020$

If the solution above is sufficiently accurate, the numbers of teeth in the gears can be made $N_1 = 17$, $N_2 = 61$, $N_3 = 89$, and $N_4 = 63$.

Another solution can be had by taking

$$h' = -64$$

In Eq. (43): $\quad G' = \dfrac{-24 \times 64 - 1}{-61 \times 64} = \dfrac{1{,}537}{3{,}904} = \dfrac{29 \times 53}{61 \times 64} = 0.3936988$

Another solution can be obtained as follows.

Let $\qquad\qquad m = 3$

$$h = \frac{3}{24 - 61 \times 0.3937008} = -190.498$$

Let $\qquad\qquad h' = -190$

In Eq. (43): $\quad G' = \dfrac{-24 \times 190 - 3}{-61 \times 190} = \dfrac{4{,}563}{11{,}590} = \dfrac{13 \times 13 \times 27}{10 \times 19 \times 61}$

$$= 0.3937015$$

$$\text{error} = 0.0000008$$

The accuracy has been improved, but a train of six gears is required.

If the numerator in Eq. (43) is not factorable, a different value of h' should be used. A factor table, such as that in *Machinery's Handbook*,[9] is very helpful. Because of the unavailability of large gears, it is frequently specified in change gear work that the largest gear should not exceed 100 or 120 teeth.

Suitable values for the fraction a/b can be found on the slide rule. Thus if the end of the C scale is set at the value for G on the D scale, numerous combinations for a/b can be found. Some additional values for the example above are $\frac{13}{33}$, $\frac{35}{89}$, $\frac{37}{94}$, $\frac{41}{104}$, $\frac{87}{221}$, $\frac{102}{259}$, $\frac{124}{315}$, and $\frac{137}{348}$.

Suitable values for a/b can also be found on a standard calculating machine. The given value for G should be placed on the keyboard, and successive values added until the sum is very close to an integer. Thus

$$bG \approx a \tag{44}$$

In the example above 61 times the value of G is a number very close to 24. Hence a/b can be taken as $\frac{24}{61}$.

24. Planetary Gear Trains

Planetary or epicyclic gear trains provide a compact arrangement suitable for speed reducers. In Fig. 10-32, the right-hand shaft is integral with arm 0. Gears 1 and 3 are keyed to a short length of shaft which

[9] Published by Industrial Press, New York, N. Y.

revolves in a bearing in arm 0. Gear 1 meshes with the fixed gear 2, and gear 3 meshes with gear 4, which in turn is keyed to the left-hand shaft.

Let N_1, N_2, N_3, and N_4 be the number of teeth in gears 1, 2, 3, and 4, respectively. As shown in the figure, arm 0, which was originally vertical, has been given an angular displacement α, which causes gear 1 to traverse arc AB on gear 2. Arc BC turned by gear 1 is equal to arc AB. Since

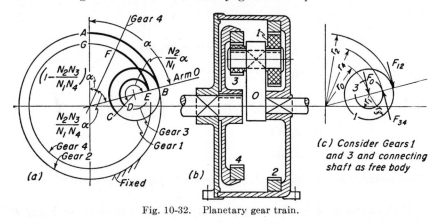

Fig. 10-32. Planetary gear train.

angles are inversely proportional to the radii, or to the number of teeth, gears 1 and 3 are turned through angle $\alpha N_2/N_1$.

While the foregoing was taking place, gears 3 and 4 were rotating on each other through the equal arcs DE and EF. Gear 4 is turned in the reverse direction through angle $\alpha N_2 N_3/N_1 N_4$.

The net effect of these 2 operations is to move the point of gear 4, which was originally vertical at G, over to location F. Gear 4 has thus been rotated clockwise through angle

$$\left[1 - \frac{N_2 N_3}{N_1 N_4}\right] \alpha$$

This latter value, when divided by α, gives the ratio of the rotations of shafts 4 and 0, respectively.

$$\frac{n_4}{n_0} = 1 - \frac{N_2 N_3}{N_1 N_4} \tag{45}$$

The equation above for the speed ratio can be derived in another way by giving consideration to the various torques. In Fig. 10-32(c) consider gears 1 and 3 and the connecting shaft as the free body. Let F_0 be the force exerted on the free body from arm 0, F_{12} be the force from gear 2 upon gear 1, and F_{34} be the force from gear 4 upon gear 3. If arm 0 is the driver, the input torque T_o is equal to $F_o r_o$. The output torque T_4 is equal to $F_{34} r_4$.

The moments of the forces about the center of the planet gears must be in equilibrium. Let r_1 be the radius of gear 1 and r_3 the radius of gear 3.

$$F_{12}r_1 = F_{34}r_3 \tag{a}$$

The moments about the main shaft centers must also be in equilibrium.

$$F_o r_o + F_{12}r_2 = F_{34}r_4 \tag{b}$$

or

$$F_o r_o = F_{34}r_4 - F_{12}r_2 \tag{c}$$

The value of F_{12} from Eq. (a) should now be substituted.

$$F_o r_o = F_{34}r_4 - \frac{F_{34}r_3r_2}{r_1} = F_{34}r_4 \left[1 - \frac{r_2 r_3}{r_1 r_4} \right]$$

or

$$T_o = T_4 \left[1 - \frac{N_2 N_3}{N_1 N_4} \right]$$

If friction is neglected, the input and output energies for the gear train are equal. Hence

$$T_4 n_4 = T_o n_o$$

or

$$\frac{n_4}{n_o} = \frac{T_o}{T_4} = 1 - \frac{N_2 N_3}{N_1 N_4} \tag{46}$$

The reaction or housing torque T_2 is equal to $F_{12}r_2$. Its value can be found by substitution for F_{34} from Eq. (a) into Eq. (c).

$$F_o r_o = \frac{F_{12}r_1 r_4}{r_3} - F_{12}r_2 = F_{12}r_2 \left[\frac{r_1 r_4}{r_2 r_3} - 1 \right]$$

$$T_o = T_2 \left[1 - \frac{N_2 N_3}{N_1 N_4} \right] \frac{N_1 N_4}{N_2 N_3}$$

or

$$T_2 = \frac{N_2 N_3 / N_1 N_4}{1 - N_2 N_3 / N_1 N_4} T_o \tag{47}$$

The foregoing methods can be applied to all types of epicyclic systems, including those containing bevel gears. Either shaft 0 or 4 can be used as the driver.

Instead of a single arm 0, an actual gear train is usually constructed with either 2 or 3 equally spaced arms each of which carries a pair of planet gears.

BIBLIOGRAPHY

Volume number shown in **bold face** type. The number immediately following is the page on which the article begins.

1. Buckingham, Earle, *Spur Gears.* New York: McGraw-Hill Book Company, Inc., 1928.

2. Buckingham, Earle, *Analytical Mechanics of Gears*. New York: McGraw-Hill Book Company, Inc., 1949.

3. Merritt, H. E., *Gears*. London: Sir Isaac Pitman & Sons, Ltd., 1946.

4. Merritt, H. E., *Gear Trains*. London: Sir Isaac Pitman & Sons, Ltd., 1947.

5. Buckingham, Earle, *Manual of Gear Design*, Sections 1 and 2, 1935, Section 3, 1937. New York: The Industrial Press.

6. Dudley, D. W., *Practical Gear Design*, New York: McGraw-Hill Book Co., Inc., 1954.

7. Colvin, F. H., and Stanley, F. A., *Gear Cutting Practice*, 2d ed. New York: McGraw-Hill Book Company, Inc., 1943.

8. Botsteiber, D. W., "Manufacturing Methods of Power-Transmission Gears and Their Influence on Design Considerations," *Mech. Eng.*, **76,** 735 (1954). Also *Machine Design*, **24,** Dec., 161 (1952).

9. Vogel, Werner F., *Involutometry and Trigonometry*. Detroit: Michigan Tool Co., 1946.

10. "Tooth Proportions for Coarse-Pitch Involute Spur Gears, AGMA 201.02." One Thomas Circle, Washington 5, D. C.: American Gear Manufacturers Assn. 1958.

11. Candee, Allan H., "Formulas for Involute Curve Layouts," *Product Eng.*, **19,** Aug., 145 (1948).

12. Bohle, Fred, "Analysis of Gear Tooth Contact by Line of Action Drawings," *Product Eng.*, **16,** 532 (1945).

13. Reswick, J. B., "Dynamic Loads on Spur and Helical Teeth," *Trans. ASME*, **77,** 635 (1955).

14. Spotts, M. F., "A Practical Method for Designing Gear Trains," *Product Eng.*, **24,** Feb., 211 (1953).

15. Lewis, Wilfred, "Investigations of the Strength of Gear Teeth," *Proc. Engineer's Club of Philadelphia*, **10,** 16 (1893).

16. Buckingham, Earle, *Dynamic Loads on Gear Teeth*. New York: American Society of Mechanical Engineers, 1931. (Research publication).

17. Timoshenko, S., and Baud, R. V., "Strength of Gear Teeth," *Mech. Eng.*, **48,** 1105 (1926).

18. Dolan, T. J., and Broghamer, E. L., "A Photoelastic Study of Stresses in Gear Tooth Fillets," *Bulletin 335*, University of Illinois Engineering Experiment Station, 1942.

19. Baud, R. V., "Contact Stresses in Gears," *Mech. Eng.*, **53,** 667 (1931).

20. Thomas, H. R., and Hoersch, V. A., "Stresses Due to the Pressure of One Elastic Solid Upon Another," *Bulletin 212*, University of Illinois Engineering Experiment Station, 1930.

21. Way, S., "Pitting Due to Rolling Contact," *Trans. ASME*, **57,** A49 (1935).

22. Schlesinger, George, "Modern Methods of Spur Gear Calculation," *Engineering*, **142,** 457, 567 (1936).

23. Tuplin, W. A., "Dynamic Loads on Gear Teeth," *Machine Design*, **25**, Oct., 203 (1953).

24. Baud, R. V., and Peterson, R. E., "Load and Stress Cycles in Gear Teeth," *Mech. Eng.*, **51**, 653 (1929).

25. Walker, H., "Gear Tooth Deflection and Profile Modification," *The Engineer*, **166**, Oct. 14, p. 409; Oct. 21, p. 434 (1938).

26. Baud, R. V., and Hall, Elmer, "Stress Cycles in Gear Teeth," *Mech. Eng.*, **53**, 207 (1931).

27. Meier, D. R., and Rhoads, J. C., "Design and Application of Rail Transportation Gearing," *Trans. ASME*, **68**, A-127 (1946).

28. McFarland, Forest R., "Tooth Deflection and Scuffing in Design of Highly Loaded Gears," *Product Eng.*, **18**, Feb., 141 (1947).

29. Worthington, W. H., and Rich, B. G., "Current Practice in Tractor Transmission Gears," *SAE Quart. Trans.*, **2**, 379 (1948).

30. Buckingham, Earle, "Surface Fatigue of Plastic Materials," *Trans. ASME*, **66**, 297 (1944).

31. Borsoff, V. N., Accinelli, J. B., and Cattaneo, A. G., "Effect of Oil Viscosity on the Power Transmitting Capacity of Spur Gears," *Trans. ASME*, **73**, 687 (1951).

32. Straub, John C., "Shotpeening as a Factor in the Design of Gears," *Mech. Eng.*, **73**, 565 (1951).

33. Gatcombe, E. K., "Lubrication Characteristics of Involute Spur Gears," *Trans. ASME*, **67**, 177 (1945).

34. Hense, V. E., Miller, H. H., and Schench, R. B., "Automotive Gear Steels," *SAE Journal*, **58**, Oct., 25 (1950).

35. Martin, Louis D., "Backlash Considerations When Designing Gears," *Product Eng.*, **19**, July, 108 (1948).

36. Scott, G., "102,336 Four Gear Ratios Among 26 Basic Gears," *Tagtow* (Mirova, Milano, 1953).

37. Miller, F. H., and Young, C. H., "Proportions of Elliptic Gears for Quick Return Mechanisms," *Product Eng.*, **16**, 462 (1945).

38. Laughlin, H. G., Holowenko, A. R., and Hall, A. S., "How to Determine Circulating Power in Controlled Epicyclic Gear Systems," *Machine Design*, **28**, 132 (March 22, 1956).

39. Rasche, William H., "Gear Train Design," *Bulletin 14*, Engineering Experiment Station, Virginia Polytechnic Institute, 1933.

40. Lancaster, F., "Calculation of Change-gear Trains," *Machinery* (London), **53**, Nov. 17, 193 (1938).

41. Lichtwitz, O., "Change Wheel Gearing," *Eng's. Digest*, **11**, Jan. to June (1950).

42. Simpson, H. W., "Planetary Transmissions," *SAE Quart. Trans.*, **3**, 69 (1949).

43. Stibitz, G. R., "An Application of Number Theory to Gear Ratios," *Am. Math. Monthly*, **45**, 22 (1938).

44. M'Ewen, E., "Theory of Gear-changing," *Proc. Inst. Mech. Engrs.*, Automobile Division, Part I, 30 (1949–1950).

45. Poppinga, R., "Efficiency of Planetary Gear Trains," *Engr's. Digest*, **11**, Dec., 421 (1950).

46. Allen, J. F., "Limitations of Epicyclic Gearing for Variable-Speed Drives," *Product Eng.*, **15**, 653 (1944).

47. "Design Factors in Highly Loaded Planetary Gear Trains," *Product Eng.*, **21**, Sept., 141 (1950).

48. Kavan, George, *Factor Table.* New York: The Macmillan Company, 1937.

49. Cowie, A., *Kinematics and Design of Mechanisms*, International Textbook Co., 1961.

PROBLEMS

1. From a piece of vellum, make a rack cutter similar to that in Fig. 10-33. $\varphi = 14\frac{1}{2}°$; $P = 1$. Use Standard clearances at top and bottom of the tooth. Use a radius of the fillet $1\frac{1}{3}$ times the clearance. The fillet is tangent to both the sloping cutting edge and the clearance line. In order to preserve the strength of the tool, only a small portion of the paper along the cutting edges should be removed, as shown. The numbered lines at right angles to the pitch line are spaced one-eighth of a p apart. Also, draw Fig. 10-34 to simulate the blank of a 12-tooth gear. The numbered radial lines are also spaced one-eighth of a p apart around the pitch circle.

Tool and blank are synchronized by placing the pitch line of the rack on the pitch circle of the gear, and having the correspondingly numbered lines coincide. A sharp drafting pencil should be drawn along the cutting edges for each position of the rack; an involute tooth is thus generated in the manner illustrated by Fig. 10-14.

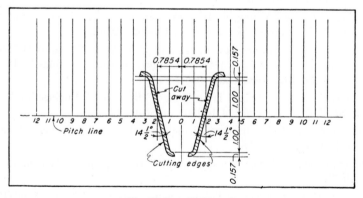

Fig. 10-33. Problem 1.

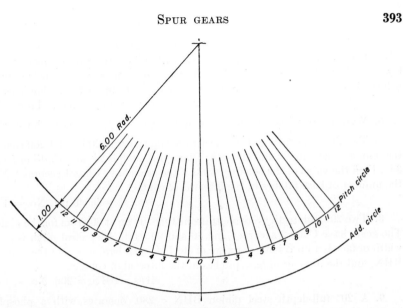

Fig. 10-34. Problem 1.

Note the large amount of undercutting when a gear of few teeth is made by this process. Draw the base circle on the gear and estimate the percentage of involute lying between the base and pitch circles which has been lost by undercutting. If greater accuracy is desired, this problem can be worked out at twice the scale mentioned above.

2. For the gears of Problem 1, assume that the undercutting, as shown in Fig. 10-25, extends one-third of the way from the base to the pitch circles. Make a full size layout and compute the number of tooth intervals in the remaining length of contact if 2 of these gears are meshed together. Note the seriousness of the loss of even a small portion of the involute curve.

Ans. No. of tooth intervals = 0.42.

3. How many teeth must there be in a $14\frac{1}{2}°$ gear of full-depth involute teeth if the base and working-depth circles coincide? Ans. $N = 62.8$.

4. Make a full-size layout of a 20° full-depth involute tooth. $N = 12; P = 1$. Make the flank of the tooth radial inside the base circle. Let the radius of the fillet be $0.05p$ on one side of the tooth and $0.15p$ on the other side. Assume that the load is located on the pressure line at the end of the tooth similar to Fig. 10-18. Length l should be measured from point A to the cross section of minimum depth h.

Measure the tooth and compute y by Eq. (15). Do the same for several nearby cross sections until the one is found which gives the smallest value for y. Two sets of measurements and computations are needed, one for the tooth of small fillet and the other for the large. Note how the size of the fillet as actually produced on the tooth will cause changes in the value of the y-factor. Can you obtain the tabulated value of 0.078 for y? If $r_f = 0.05p$, will the tooth be safe when carrying the load indicated by Eq. (16)?

5. A phosphor bronze gear of 40 teeth runs with a 20-tooth steel pinion of 175 BHN. Gears are cut on 20° involute system with full-depth teeth. Diametral pitch is 4 and width of face is 2 in. Find the hp based on wear which this pair of gears will safely carry if the gears have Class 1 accuracy. Rpm for the pinion is 900.

Ans.   hp = 14.9.

6. Work Problem 5, but with $N_2 = 120$.   *Ans.*   hp = 19.2.

7. Two 20° full-depth cast iron gears are transmitting 20 hp at 1,200 rpm for the pinion. There are 20 and 60 teeth. Diametral pitch is $2\frac{1}{2}$, and width of face is 3 in. Find the value of the bending stress if the gears have Class 1 accuracy. Find the number of base pitches in the interval of contact.

Ans. $s = 3,540$ psi, No. = 1.67.

8. Two 20° stub teeth gears are transmitting 100 hp at 600 rpm for the pinion. The gears have Class 2 accuracy and 30 and 90 teeth. Diametral pitch is 3 and width of face is 4 in. If both gears are of steel of equal hardness, find the required BHN, and the number of base pitches in the interval of contact.

Ans.   BHN = 200, No. = 1.40.

9. A 20° full-depth steel pinion BHN = 280, operates with a phosphor bronze gear. Bending stress for the gear is 20,000 psi. The pinion turns at 900 rpm. Diametral pitch is 4. Numbers of teeth are 24 and 96. Width of face is 3 in. Find the permissible hp for this reduction if the gears have Class 2 accuracy.

Ans.   hp = 116.

10. A 24-tooth 20° steel gear of $3P$ carries 50 hp at 900 rpm. The gear has Class 1 accuracy and operates with another steel gear of equal hardness of 40 teeth. Width of face is 3 in. Find required BHN for long life.

Ans.   BHN = 240.

11. Two $14\frac{1}{2}°$ full-depth heat treated steel gears have BHN = 250. Diametral pitch is 4. Width of face is 3 in. The gears have 48 and 72 teeth. Find the permissible hp at 900 rpm for the pinion if the gears have Class 1 accuracy.

Ans.   hp = 62.

12. Two $14\frac{1}{2}°$ full-depth cast iron gears transmit 25 hp at 100 rpm of the pinion. Numbers of teeth are 30 and 75. Gears have Class 1 accuracy. Width of face is 4 in. Find the required value of the diametral pitch for a working stress in bending of 12,000 psi.   *Ans.* $P = 3$.

13. Two $14\frac{1}{2}°$ full-depth flame-hardened steel gears with Class 1 accuracy are transmitting 50 hp at 1,200 rpm for the pinion. Speed ratio is 2:1 and center distance is 18 in. Width of face is 2 in. Find ˙
(a) Required BHN if both gears are of equal hardness.
(b) P of smallest tooth which will carry the load.
(c) Number of base pitches in the contact interval.

Ans.   BHN = 250; $P = 6$; No. in contact = 2.32.

14. A 20° full-depth steel pinion and cast iron gear with Class 2 accuracy are transmitting 175 hp at 1,140 rpm for the pinion. Speed ratio is 3:1 with center distance of 20 in. Width of face is 4 in. Let the working stress for cast iron be 10,000 psi. Find
(a) Required BHN for the pinion.

(b) P of the smallest tooth which will carry the load.

(c) Number of pitches in the interval of contact.

Ans. BHN = 190, P = 2.5; No. = 1.66.

15. Find the hp which two 20° cast iron gears with full-depth cast teeth with Class 1 accuracy will carry at 300 rpm for the pinion. Numbers of teeth are 20 and 100. P is 4 and width of face is 3 in. Let the working stress for the material be 10,000 psi. Ans. hp = 17.3.

16. Two 20° cast iron gears with full-depth cast teeth of Class 1 accuracy are carrying 35 hp at 50 rpm for the pinion. Numbers of teeth are 16 and 40. Let the working stress be 12,000 psi. Width of face is 5 in. Find the P of the smallest tooth which will carry the load. Ans. P = 1.5.

17. Find the minimum value of the pressure angle for a system of gearing which will generate a 12-tooth full-depth pinion without undercutting.

Ans. φ = 24°6′.

18. A 72-tooth $14\frac{1}{2}°$ gear meshes with a 144-tooth gear on a standard center distance of 18 in. The smaller gear has full-depth teeth; and the larger gear has standard stub teeth. Find the number of tooth intervals in the length of contact. P = 6. Ans. No. intervals = 2.10.

19. In Fig. 10-19, distance OA_1 is equal to three-fourths of OA. Gear 1 has 20 teeth. If gear 2 has full-depth addenda, find the (theoretical) value of r_2. Make computations for P = 1, and φ = 20°. Ans. r_2 = 22.74 in.

20. Two 20° spur gears have 17 teeth each. What must be the value of the addendum if the length of contact extends two-thirds of the way from the pitch point to the interference point? P = 1. Find the number of teeth in contact.

Ans. Add. = 0.842 in.; No. = 1.31.

21. The length of contact on a 20° full-depth gear of 18 teeth extends two-thirds of the way from the pitch point to the interference point. Find the length of the addendum of the mating gear if it has 72 teeth. P = 1. Find the number of teeth in contact. Ans. Add. = 0.752; No. = 1.46.

22. In Fig. 10-35, consider shaft B together with gears 2 and 3 as the free body. Determine the tooth forces for these gears based on the hp. Draw a top view of shaft B and show all horizontal loads and reactions. Draw an elevation of shaft B and show all vertical loads and reactions. P = 6, φ = 20°.

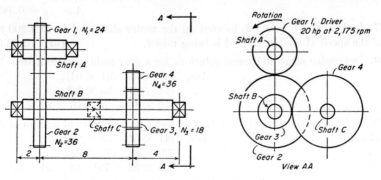

Fig. 10-35. Problem 22.

23. Work Problem 22 but with view AA as given by Fig. 10-36.

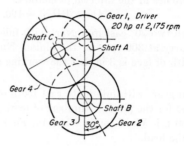

Fig. 10-36.   Problem 23.

24. In Fig. 10-37, gear 1 has 15 teeth of $P = 5$, and turns 2,150 rpm. Gear 4 has 43 teeth of $P = 4$, and turns 450 rpm. The distance between shafts A and C is 13 in. Find the number of teeth in gears 2 and 3.   *Ans.* $N_2 = 35; N_3 = 21$.

25. In Fig. 10-37, gear 1 has 24 teeth and gear 2 has 70 teeth of $P = 4$. Gear 3 has 20 teeth and gear 4 has 50 teeth of $P = 3$.

(a) Find value of center distance between shafts A and C.

(b) Find rpm of gear 4 if gear 1 turns 1,200 rpm.

(c) Find the torque at shaft C if the input hp at shaft A is 50. The efficiency of each pair of gears is 98 per cent.   *Ans.*   (a) 23.417 in.; (b) $n_4 = 164.6$ rpm; (c) $T = 18,390$ in-lb.

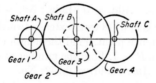

Fig. 10-37.   Problems 24 and 25.   Fig. 10-38.   Problem 26.

26. In Fig. 10-38, $N_1 = 32$, $N_2 = 75$, and $N_3 = 24$. Find the value of the p for gear 3 if the rack is to be moved 0.5 ft for each revolution of gear 1.

Ans. $p = 0.586$ in.

27. In Fig. 10-39, gear 1 is located on the motor shaft and turns 1,200 rpm. Find the speed at which the load is being raised.   *Ans.*   52.36 fpm.

28. Determine some additional solutions for a gear train of ratio 2.54 to 1.

Ans. $(29 \times 53)/(61 \times 64)$;
$(11 \times 67)/(36 \times 52)$;
$(13 \times 19 \times 71)/(16 \times 32 \times 87)$, etc.

29. Determine the suitable numbers of teeth for the gears of a train of ratio 251:93.   *Ans.* $(41 \times 61)/(75 \times 90)$;
$(29 \times 67)/(57 \times 92)$;
$(15 \times 53 \times 79)/(43 \times 54 \times 73)$, etc.

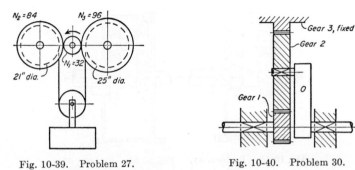

Fig. 10-39.   Problem 27.   Fig. 10-40.   Problem 30.

30. Make a front view of the reducer shown in Fig. 10-40 and show the relative displacements of all gears for a given rotation α of arm 0. Mark the values of all angles used in deriving the equation for the speed ratio.   *Ans.* $\dfrac{n_1}{n_o} = 1 + \dfrac{N_3}{N_1}$.

31. Make a front view of the epicyclic gear train shown in Fig. 10-41. By a process similar to that illustrated in Section 24, derive the equation for the speed ratio of shafts 4 and 0.   *Ans.* $\dfrac{\text{rpm}_4}{\text{rpm}_0} = -\dfrac{N_2 N_3}{N_1 N_4} + 1$.

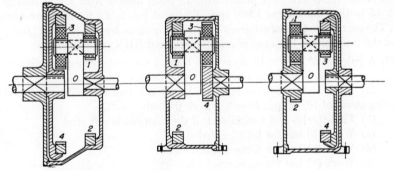

Fig. 10-41.   Problem 31.   Fig. 10-42.   Problem 32.   Fig. 10-43.   Problem 33.

32. Work Problem 31 with the epicyclic system shown in Fig. 10-42.

Ans. $\dfrac{\text{rpm}_4}{\text{rpm}_0} = 1 + \dfrac{N_2 N_2}{N_1 N_4}$.

33. Work Problem 31 for Fig. 10-43.   *Ans.* $\dfrac{\text{rpm}_4}{\text{rpm}_0} = 1 + \dfrac{N_2 N_3}{N_1 N_4}$.

34. Work Problem 31 for Fig. 10-44.   *Ans.* $\dfrac{\text{rpm}_4}{\text{rpm}_0} = -\dfrac{N_2 N_3}{N_1 N_4} + 1$.

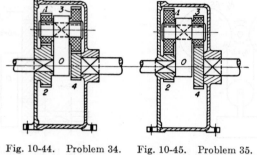

Fig. 10-44.   Problem 34.   Fig. 10-45.   Problem 35.

35. Work Problem 31 for Fig. 10-45.   *Ans.* $\dfrac{\text{rpm}_4}{\text{rpm}_0} = 1 - \dfrac{N_2 N_3}{N_1 N_4}.$

The following problems are presented without answers.

36. Two $14\frac{1}{2}°$ full-depth cast iron gears with Class 1 accuracy are transmitting 10 hp at 125 rpm of the 8 in. diameter pinion. Width of the face is 1.75 in. Find the required value of the diametral pitch for a bending stress of 10,000 psi.

37. Two 20° full-depth heat-treated steel gears with Class 2 accuracy are transmitting 100 hp for 1,800 rpm of the pinion. Center distance is 7.5 in., and the speed ratio is 1.5:1. Width of face is 2 in. Find the required BHN for gears of equal hardness and the pitch of the smallest tooth that can carry the load.

38. A 20° full-depth steel pinion with 18 teeth meshes with a cast iron gear with 75 teeth. Pinion turns 1,800 rpm. Width of face is 3.5 in. Diametral pitch is 4. The gears have Class 2 accuracy. The bending stress for cast iron is 12,000 psi. Find the transmitted horsepower and the required BHN of the pinion.

39. A pair of 20° full-depth gears with Class 2 accuracy have pitch diameters of 6 in. and 12 in. The pinion turns 900 rpm. Width of face is 2 in.

(a) Find the transmitted hp if the material is cast iron with an allowable bending stress of 10,000 psi. $P = 3$. Check the value of F_w.

(b) Find the hp and a suitable P if the material is soft steel.

(c) Work (b) but for heat treated steel.

(d) Work (b) but for flame-hardened steel.

(e) Work (b) but for carburized steel.

40. Two 20° full-depth soft steel gears with Class 2 accuracy are transmitting 75 hp at 1,200 rpm of the pinion. Center distance is 14 in. Speed ratio is $2\frac{1}{2}:1$. Width of face is 3 in. Find a suitable value for the diametral pitch. Check for safety in wear.

11

Bevel, Worm and
Helical Gears

BEVEL, worm, and helical gears are advanced forms of gearing capable of meeting special requirements of geometry or strength that cannot be obtained from spur gears. Bevel gears, with straight or spiral teeth cut on cones, can be used to connect intersecting shafts. A worm gear, consisting of a screw meshing with a gear, can be used to obtain a large speed reduction. Helical gears have teeth that lie in helical paths on the cylinders instead of teeth that are parallel to the shaft axis. The geometry of these different types of gearing is considerably more involved than for spur gears, and the problems of production and inspection are also more complicated.

A_c, cooling area of worm gear housing, ft^2

C_1, coefficient of cooling

d_i, inside pitch diameter of bevel gear

d_o, outside pitch diameter of bevel gear

F_i, input force from worm acting on tooth of wheel

F_o, output force acting on tooth of wheel

hp_i, input hp of worm drive

hp_o, output hp of worm drive

l_p, pitch cone radius of bevel gear

l_1, lead of worm

N', formative number of teeth

p_n, circular pitch normal to elements of tooth

P_n, normal diametral pitch

ΔT, rise in temperature of worm gear housing

V_s, velocity of sliding of worm on wheel tooth

α, (alpha) helix angle of worm

399

φ_n, (phi) pressure angle in plane normal
   to elements of tooth
λ, (lambda) velocity ratio N_1/N_2
μ_1, (mu) coefficient of friction

ψ, (psi) helix angle of helical gear
Other notation is the same as for spur
gears.

1. Straight Tooth Bevel Gears

When intersecting shafts must be connected by gearing, the pitch

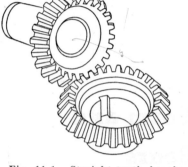

cylinders are replaced by pitch cones tangent to each other along an element, with their apexes at the intersection of the shafts. Teeth are placed on the cones, forming bevel gears, as illustrated in Fig. 11-1. The names of some of the principal parts of a bevel gear are given in Fig. 11-2. The back cone, as shown in the latter figure, has elements which are perpendicular to those of the pitch cone. The outlines of the teeth, as generated on the back cone, are shown in view A-A. Because of difficulties in securing uniform bearing along the tooth, the width of face b

Fig. 11-1. Straight-tooth bevel gears. (*From Lubrication, published by The Texas Co.*)

is generally not made longer than one-third of the pitch cone radius l_p. Undercutting occurs in bevel gears having few teeth.

2. Beam Strength of Bevel Gears

The beam strength of bevel gear teeth is computed by the Lewis equation. It is assumed that the bevel gear tooth is equivalent to a spur tooth whose cross section is the same as the cross section of the bevel tooth at the midpoint of the face b. The symbol F_b, however, designates the load carried at the outside radius $\frac{1}{2}d_o$ of the gear. The torque for this load is $\frac{1}{2}d_oF_b$. In order to carry this torque at the midpoint of the face, a greater force F'_b is required. Thus,

$$F'_b = \frac{T}{\frac{1}{4}(d_o + d_i)} = \frac{\frac{1}{2}d_o}{\frac{1}{4}(d_o + d_i)} F_b \tag{a}$$

The circular pitch p' at the midpoint of the face is

$$p' = \frac{1}{2}(d_o + d_i)\frac{\pi}{N} \tag{b}$$

where N is the number of teeth in the gear. At the outside radius, the circular pitch p is $\pi d_o/N$. Substitution for π/N in Eq. (b) gives

$$p' = \frac{p}{2d_o}(d_o + d_i) \tag{c}$$

The Lewis equation for the midpoint of the face is written

$$F'_b = sbyp' \tag{d}$$

Substitution of Eqs. (a) and (c) into (d) gives

$$F_b = sbyp\,\frac{d_o{}^2 + 2d_od_i + d_i{}^2}{4d_o{}^2} \tag{e}$$

For practical gears, the sum of $d_o{}^2$ and $d_i{}^2$ is but slightly larger than $2d_od_i$. The small approximation introduced by this substitution is on the safe side. The equation for beam strength can then be more conveniently written as

$$F_b = sbyp\,\frac{d_i}{d_o} = sbyp\,\frac{l_p - b}{l_p} \tag{1}$$

When the form factor is expressed as $Y = \pi y$, Eq. (1) can be written as

$$F_b = \frac{sbY}{P}\cdot\frac{l_p - b}{l_p} \tag{2}$$

It must be remembered that F_b and p refer to the load and circular pitch at the outside radius $\frac{1}{2}d_o$. The diametral pitch also refers to the outside diameter, that is, $P = N/d_o$.

3. Formative or Virtual Number of Teeth

Although the number of teeth in a bevel gear is N, reference to view A-A of Fig. 11-2 shows that the outline of the teeth on the back cone has the same shape as the teeth of a spur gear of radius l_b. The number of teeth in a fictitious gear of this radius is called the formative or virtual number of teeth N' for the bevel gear. The form factor y must therefore be selected for a gear of N' teeth. Now

$$N = \frac{\pi d_o}{p} \tag{a}$$

and

$$N' = \frac{2l_b\pi}{p} \tag{b}$$

Substitution of the value of π/p from Eq. (a) into Eq. (b) gives the following equation for N'.

$$N' = \frac{2l_bN}{d_o} = \frac{N}{\cos\alpha} \tag{3}$$

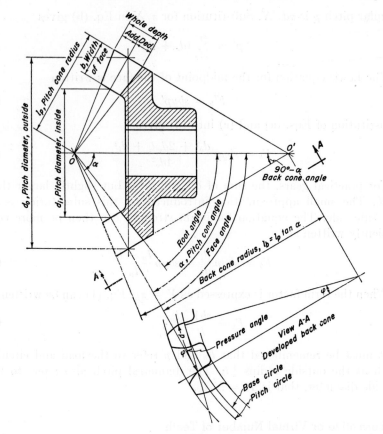

Fig. 11-2. Straight-tooth bevel gear.

The y-factors for N' teeth, as computed by Eq. (3), are given in Table 10-1.

4. Dynamic Load and Limit Load for Wear of Bevel Gears

The dynamic tooth load may be estimated from Eqs. (19), (20), or (21) of Chapter 10. The velocity V is based on the outside diameter d_o, and the tangential force F_t is computed for this velocity by Eq. (13), Chapter 10.

The limit load for wear is

$$F_w = \frac{(d_o)_1}{\cos \alpha_1} bKQ' \tag{4}$$

where

$$Q' = \frac{2N'_2}{N'_1 + N'_2} \tag{5}$$

and N'_1 and N'_2 refer to the numbers of teeth in the formative pinion and gear, respectively. Quantity K is the same as previously defined for spur gears, and $(d_o)_1$ and α_1 refer to the outside diameter and pitch cone angle, respectively, for the pinion.

As for the case of spur gears, the method of design is based on beam strength, dynamic load, and wear. It must be pointed out, however, that investigators are not in agreement with respect to the exact causes of gear tooth failure.[1] The situation is complicated by many variables which affect the problem simultaneously. There is no doubt, however, that stress concentration from sharp fillets, scratches, or tool marks at highly stressed points, and from warping during heat treatment, play an important part in reducing the life of bevel gearing. Rigidity of mounting is also important. Deflections of shafts and bearings localize the entire load at one end of the tooth, causing higher stresses and increasing the possibility of fatigue failure. When gears are to be made in quantities, the foregoing equations should be considered as giving merely the first approximation of the solution; the final design should be determined from the results of tests.

Example 1. Find the BHN required for wear, and a suitable P for a stress of 28,000 psi in bending for a pair of 20° full-depth steel bevel gears to transmit 100 hp at 600 rpm for the pinion. Speed ratio is 3:2, with outside diameters of 15 in. and 10 in. Width of face is 2.5 in. Gears have Class 2 accuracy.

Solution. Cross section through the pitch cones is shown in Fig. 11-3.

$$V = \frac{\pi (d_0)_1 n_1}{12} = \frac{\pi 10 \times 600}{12} = 1{,}571 \text{ fpm at outside diameter}$$

$$F_t = \frac{33{,}000 \text{ hp}}{V} = \frac{33{,}000 \times 100}{1{,}571} = 2{,}101 \text{ lb at outside diameter}$$

$$F_d = F_t \frac{1{,}200 + V}{1{,}200}$$

$$= 2{,}101 \frac{1{,}200 + 1{,}571}{1{,}200} = 4{,}850 \text{ lb}$$

By Fig. 11-3(a):

$$\tan \alpha_1 = \frac{10}{15}; \quad \alpha_1 = 33°41.4'$$

$$\alpha_2 = 56°18.6'$$

---

[1] See reference 14, Bibliography.

By Eq. (3):
$$N'_1 = \frac{N_1}{\cos \alpha_1} = \frac{N_1}{0.83205} = 1.2019 N_1$$

$$N'_2 = \frac{N_2}{\cos \alpha_2} = \frac{1.5 N_1}{0.55470} = 2.7042 N_1$$

By Eq. (5):
$$Q' = \frac{2 \times 2.7042}{1.2019 + 2.7042} = 1.3846$$

The tooth must carry the dynamic load in wear. Hence $F_w = F_d$.

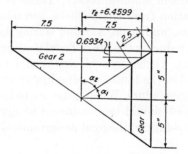

Fig. 11-3.   Pitch cones for gears of Example 1.

By Eq. (4):
$$K = \frac{F_w \cos \alpha_1}{(d_o)_1 b Q'} = \frac{4{,}850 \times 0.83205}{10 \times 2.5 \times 1.3846} = 117$$

By Table 10-3:

BHN = 236, for both teeth of same hardness

Assume $P = 4$. Then

$$p = \frac{\pi}{4} = 0.7854 \text{ in.}$$

$$N_1 = 10 \times 4 = 40$$

By Eq. (3):
$$N'_1 = \frac{40}{0.83205} = 48$$

By Table 10-1: $y = 0.129$

In Fig. 11-3: $l_p = \sqrt{7.5^2 + 5^2} = 9.0139$ in.

By Eq. (1): $F_b = sbyp \dfrac{l_p - b}{l_p}$

$$= 28{,}000 \times 2.5 \times 0.129 \times 0.7854 \frac{9.0139 - 2.5}{9.0139}$$

$$= 5{,}125$$

The strength in bending is satisfactory.

5. Tooth Loads of Bevel Gears

As for spur gears, corresponding forces F'_t, $F'_t \tan \varphi$ and F'_n at the midpoint of the tooth, are present for bevel gears. However, for a bevel gear, the plane of these forces is inclined at angle α to the plane of rotation as shown in Fig. 11-4. Force $F'_t \tan \varphi$ can be divided into components parallel and perpendicular to the axis. The forces of Fig. 11-4 are used for finding the torque, thrust, and bearing reactions for the shaft of the gear.

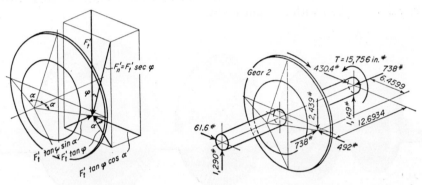

Fig. 11-4. Forces at midpoint of   Fig. 11-5. Tooth loads and shaft reactions for
bevel gear tooth.   Example 2.

Example 2. Let the base of the pitch cone of the larger gear of Example 1 be located at the midpoint of a 24 in. simply supported shaft. Make a free-body diagram of the gear and shaft for the horsepower load at the midpoint of the face. Let thrust and torque be resisted at right-hand end of shaft in Fig. 11-5.

Solution. From Example 1, F_t equals 2,101 lb.

At midpoint of face: $r_2 = 7.5 - 1.25 \sin \alpha_2 = 6.4599$ in.

At midpoint of face: $F'_t = 2{,}101 \times \dfrac{7.5}{6.460} = 2{,}439$ lb

Axial thrust: $F'_t \tan \varphi \sin \alpha_2 = 2{,}439 \times 0.36397 \times 0.83205 = 738$ lb

Separating force: $F'_t \tan \varphi \cos \alpha_2 = 2{,}439 \times 0.36397 \times 0.55470 = 492$ lb

Torque: $T = r_2 F'_t = 6.460 \times 2{,}439 = 15{,}756$ in-lb

The forces above are shown on the gear in Fig. 11-5. The reactions at the bearings are found by simple statics.

The efficiency of bevel gearing is very high, providing the gears are properly mounted and adjusted. Not more than 1 or 2 per cent of the power should be lost by accurately manufactured gears that are properly mounted.

6. Spiral Bevel Gears

Bevel gears can also be made with teeth lying in spiral paths on the pitch cones. More teeth are then in contact simultaneously, and smoother and quieter action can be obtained from such gears. Accuracy of adjustment between a pair of bevel gears can be more readily secured with spiral teeth than with straight teeth.

Fig. 11-6. Hypoid gears on non-intersecting shafts. (*Courtesy Gleason Works.*)

The Gleason Works has developed a system of bevel gearing, both straight tooth and spiral, which is in wide use. The addenda are arranged on the long and short plan to avoid undercutting and to give greater strength to pinions having few teeth. The addendum of the pinion is made longer than the usual value, and the addendum of the gear is shortened a corresponding amount. A variety of pressure angles are used in order to obtain the best operating conditions for each velocity ratio.

Hypoid gears have spiral teeth and shafts which do not intersect.[2] It is thus possible to connect continuous nonintersecting shafts by such gears, as shown in Fig. 11-6. Hypoid gears have been used in automobiles so that the drive shaft can be placed beneath the level of the floor.

In the rear axles of automobiles, the bevel gear stresses are very low under normal conditions of service. Such gears are therefore designed on the assumption that operation in low gear at full engine torque for a relatively short period, perhaps 0.1 per cent of the life of the car, would normally be sufficient to cause fatigue failure. The requirements are somewhat higher for trucks and busses. Gear steels for automotive service are selected mainly on the basis of machining characteristics, cost, and

[2] See reference 12, Bibliography.

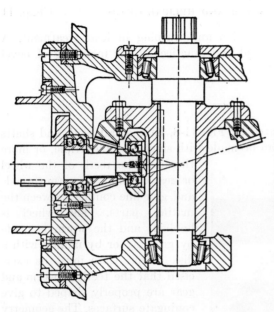

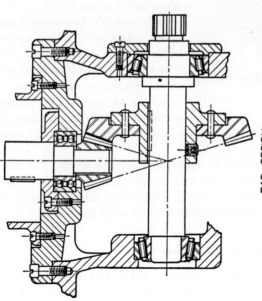

BAD DESIGN

Face width too great, more than one third of cone distance.

Metal at small end of pinion between teeth and bore too thin for proper strength. Cutter would interfere seriously with arbor in cutting operation.

Webbed section of steel ring gear adds to cost of material and machining. Use of rivets to hold gear to hub introduces danger of runout.

A setscrew is inadequate to hold gear in correct axial position, and tends to "cock" gear on shaft.

Pinion held on shaft only by fit of bore.

An overhung pinion cannot be held in line by one double-row bearing.

No means of adjustment for definitely placing gears in correct mounting position.

GOOD DESIGN

Face width reasonable, less than one third of cone distance.

Sufficient metal at small end of pinion to provide strength and avoid interference of cutter with arbor.

Section of ring gear simpler and more direct in design. Gear is supported directly on back and is centered on large bore.

Screws to hold gear to hub are preferable.

Gear is positively held in position on shaft.

Pinion locked in position by washer and screw.

Pinion rigidly supported by addition of inboard bearing.

Adjusting washers provided, to be ground to thickness required to obtain correct position of pinion and gear.

Pinion and bearings can be assembled as a complete unit.

Fig. 11-7. Design and arrangement of spiral bevel gears. Comparison of good and bad practice.

407

resistance to stress concentration and warping in heat treatment. A comparison between good and bad practice[3] in the mounting of bevel gears is shown in Fig. 11-7.

7. Worm Gears

Worm gears, as illustrated by Fig. 11-8, have spiral teeth and shafts at right angles. Worms can be made with single, double, triple, or more

threads. The teeth of the wheel or gear envelop the worm threads and give line contact between the mating parts. The wheel is hobbed, and the worm is made by grinding or by milling with a disk cutter. Care must be exercised that the teeth of worm and gear are properly shaped to give conjugate surfaces. The geometry of worm gearing is very complicated, and reference should be made to the literature for complete information.[4]

It is possible to secure a large speed reduction or a high increase of torque by means of worm gears. The velocity ratio does not depend upon diameters, but upon the numbers of teeth. The pressure angle should not be less than 20°

Fig. 11-8.　Worm and wheel. (*Courtesy D. O. James Gear Mfg. Co.*)

for single- and double-thread worms, and 25° for triple- and multi-thread worms.

Case hardened alloy steel is recommended for the worm. The worm wheel should be of bronze of approved composition. The wheel should usually contain not less than 29 teeth. The wheel should be provided with axial adjustment to obtain correct contact with the worm.

8. Geometric Relationships of Worm Gears

Figure 11-9 shows a worm of helix angle α. Let p_1 and p_2 be the circular pitches in the planes of rotation for worm and gear, respectively. Let p_n

---

[3] Taken from reference 11, Bibliography.
[4] See reference 15, Bibliography.

be the circular pitch normal to the direction of the teeth. Then

$$p_n = p_1 \sin \alpha = p_2 \cos \alpha \tag{6}$$

Let N_1 be the number of starts for the worm, and let N_2 be the number of teeth in the gear. Let d_1 and d_2 be the pitch diameters of worm and gear, respectively. Now $\pi d_1 = N_1 p_1$. The value of p_1 from Eq. (6) can be substituted to give

$$d_1 = \frac{N_1 p_1}{\pi} = \frac{N_1 p_n}{\pi \sin \alpha} \tag{7}$$

Similarly, $\pi d_2 = N_2 p_2$. Substitution for p_2 from Eq. (6) gives

$$d_2 = \frac{N_2 p_2}{\pi} = \frac{N_2 p_n}{\pi \cos \alpha} \tag{8}$$

The values given above for d_1 and d_2 can be substituted into the equation for the center distance c to give

$$c = \frac{1}{2}(d_1 + d_2) = \frac{p_n}{2\pi}\left(\frac{N_1}{\sin \alpha} + \frac{N_2}{\cos \alpha}\right) \tag{9}$$

or

$$\frac{\lambda}{\sin \alpha} + \frac{1}{\cos \alpha} = \frac{2\pi c}{N_2 p_n} \tag{10}$$

where

$$\lambda = \frac{N_1}{N_2} \tag{11}$$

Now $\sin^2 \alpha + \cos^2 \alpha = 1$. When the values for $\sin \alpha$ and $\cos \alpha$ from Eqs. (7) and (8) are substituted, the following useful equation is obtained.

$$\frac{N_1{}^2}{d_1{}^2} + \frac{N_2{}^2}{d_2{}^2} = \frac{\pi^2}{p_n{}^2} \tag{12}$$

Let l_1 be the lead of the worm, or the distance the pitch circle of the wheel is advanced for each revolution of the worm. Then

$$l_1 = N_1 p_2 \tag{13}$$

The pitch line velocities V_1 and V_2 for the worm and wheel are

for worm:

$$V_1 = \frac{\pi d_1 n_1}{12} = \frac{n_1 N_1 p_1}{12} \text{ fpm} \tag{14}$$

for wheel:

$$V_2 = \frac{\pi d_2 n_2}{12} = \frac{n_1 N_1 p_2}{12} \text{ fpm} \tag{15}$$

where n_1 and n_2 are the speeds, rpm, for the worm and wheel, respectively. The last form of Eq. (15) is obtained by observing in Fig. 11-9 that the pitch line velocity $\pi d_2 n_2$ of the wheel is equal to the speed $n_1 l_1$ or $n_1 N_1 p_2$ along the worm axis.

From Fig. 11-9 and Eqs. (14) and (15)

$$\tan \alpha = \frac{l_1}{\pi d_1} = \frac{p_2}{p_1} = \frac{V_2}{V_1} \tag{16}$$

When designing a worm gear reduction, it is a good plan, before deciding on the diameter of the worm, to ascertain if a hob of the proper size is available for cutting the wheel. The purchase of a special tool may be

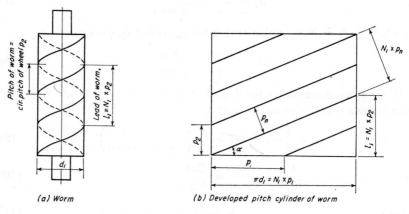

(a) Worm   *(b) Developed pitch cylinder of worm*

Fig. 11-9.   Geometry of the worm.

avoided by changing the diameter of the worm so that the wheel can be cut by a hob that is already on hand. Gear cutting firms sometimes catalog their worm gear hobs to enable their customers to take advantage of available tools.

Example 3. A triple-threaded worm gear hob has a pitch diameter of 4.7856 in. and a p_n equal to 1.5708 in. Hob is used for making the gear for a 12 to 1 reduction. Find value of d_2.

Solution. $N_2 = 36$

By Eq. (7): $\sin \alpha = \dfrac{N_1 p_n}{\pi d_1} = \dfrac{3 \times 1.5708}{\pi 4.7856} = 0.31344$

$\alpha = 18°16'$

By Eq. (8): $d_2 = \dfrac{N_2 p_n}{\pi \cos \alpha} = \dfrac{36 \times 1.5708}{\pi 0.94961} = 18.9552$ in.

Example 4. A double-threaded worm has a lead of 2.18 in. The gear has 30 teeth and is cut with a hob of $p_n = 1.0472$ in. Find pitch diameters of the worm and gear, and center distance of shafts.

Solution.

By Eq. (13): $p_2 = \dfrac{l_1}{N_1} = \dfrac{2.18}{2} = 1.09$ in.

By Eq. (6): $\cos \alpha = \dfrac{p_n}{p_2} = \dfrac{1.0472}{1.09} = 0.96073$

$\alpha = 16°6.6'$

By Eq. (7): $d_1 = \dfrac{N_1 p_n}{\pi \sin \alpha} = \dfrac{2 \times 1.0472}{\pi 0.27747} = 2.4026$ in.

By Eq. (8): $d_2 = \dfrac{N_2 p_n}{\pi \cos \alpha} = \dfrac{30 \times 1.0472}{\pi 0.96073} = 10.4087$ in.

Center distance: $c = \dfrac{1}{2}(d_1 + d_2) = \dfrac{1}{2}(2.4026 + 10.4087)$

$= 6.4056$ in.

Example 5. A worm gear drive has a center distance of 8 in., and a p_n equal to 0.7854 in. The worm is quadruple and the wheel has 48 teeth. Find the pitch diameters of the worm and wheel and the value of the helix angle.

Solution. This type of problem must be solved by trial and error using either Eq. (10) or (12). The following values satisfy these equations.

$d_1 = 3.4676$ in.; $d_2 = 12.5324$ in.; $\alpha = 16°45.7'$

In general such problems have two solutions. The other one is

$d_1 = 1.9070$ in.; $d_2 = 14.0930$ in.; $\alpha = 31°37.6'$

Figure 11-19 for helical gears can be used for worm gears if angle α is substituted for ψ_2.

9. Beam Strength, Dynamic Load, and Wear of Worm Gears

Let hp_o be the output horsepower for the two gears. The output force F_o tangential to the pitch circle of the wheel then is

$$F_o = \frac{33{,}000 hp_o}{V_2} \tag{17}$$

Beam Strength. The Lewis equation is used for the beam strength of the gear.

$$F_b = sb_2 y p_2 \tag{18}$$

The letters have the same meaning as for spur gears. When the sum of the teeth in worm and wheel exceeds 40, the following values may be used for y.

$$\varphi = 14\tfrac{1}{2}°; \quad y = 0.100$$

$$\varphi = 20°; \quad y = 0.125$$

$$\varphi = 25°; \quad y = 0.150$$

$$\varphi = 30°; \quad y = 0.175$$

Bending stress values for various materials are given in Table 10-2.

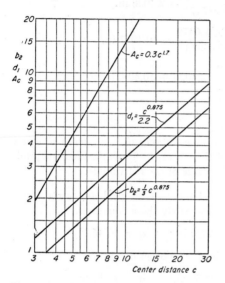

Fig. 11-10. Plots of various quantities used in design of worm gears.

Dynamic Load. The dynamic load for metal worm gearing can be estimated from

$$F_d = \frac{1200 + V_2}{1200} F_o \qquad (19)$$

where V_2 and F_o are found from Eqs. (15) and (17), respectively.

Limit Load for Wear. The tooth pressures in worm gearing are frequently very high. Worms should be hardened to at least 250 Brinell. The limit load for wear is given by the equation

$$F_w = d_2 b_2 K' \qquad (20)$$

where d_2 is the pitch diameter of the wheel, and b_2 is the face width. Constant K' depends on the kind of material used for the wheel. Values are shown in Table 11-1.

TABLE 11-1*
**Values of K' for Various Materials
for Worm Wheels**

Material of Wheel	K'
Cast iron or semi-steel	50
Manganese bronze	80
Phosphor bronze	100
Bakelite or other similar material	125

* *Kent's Mechanical Engineers' Handbook,* 12th ed., "Design and Production," p. 14–43.

The recommended face width b_2 for the wheel can be found by the following equation.

$$b_2 = \frac{1}{3} c^{0.875} \tag{21}$$

Width b_2 can also be taken from Fig. 11-10.

Example 6. A quadruple hardened steel worm and phosphor bronze gear have an output horsepower of 10. The wheel has 40 teeth; p_n is 1.0472 in. Center distance is 8.9333 in. Worm speed n_1 is 600 rpm. Find the value of the dynamic load, and check if the tooth is sufficiently strong in bending and wear. Take allowable bending stress for bronze as 20,000 psi. $\varphi = 25°$.

Solution.

By trial in Eq. (12): $d_1 = 3.1808$ in. $d_2 = 14.6859$ in.

By Eq. (14): $V_1 = \dfrac{\pi d_1 n_1}{12} = \dfrac{\pi 3.1808 \times 600}{12} = 499.6$ fpm

By Eq. (7): $\sin \alpha = \dfrac{N_1 p_n}{\pi d_1} = \dfrac{4 \times 1.0472}{\pi 3.1808} = 0.41918$

$$\alpha = 24°47.0'$$

By Eq. (16): $V_2 = V_1 \tan \alpha = 499.6 \times 0.46171 = 230.7$ fpm

By Eq. (17): $F_o = \dfrac{33,000 hp_o}{V_2} = \dfrac{33,000 \times 10}{230.7} = 1,431$ lb

By Eq. (19): $F_d = \dfrac{1200 + V_2}{1200} F_o = \dfrac{1200 + 230.7}{1200} \times 1,431 = 1,706$ lb

By Fig. 11-10 or Eq. (21): $b_2 = 2.265$ in.

$$p_2 = \frac{\pi d_2}{N_2} = \frac{14.6859\pi}{40} = 1.1534 \text{ in.}$$

By Eq. (18): $F_b = s b_2 y p_2 = 20,000 \times 2.265 \times 0.150 \times 1.1534 = 7,840$ lb

By Eq. (20): $F_w = d_2 b_2 K' = 14.6859 \times 2.265 \times 100 = 3,327$ lb

The gear tooth is thus seen to be amply strong in bending and wear.

The worm diameter at the base of the threads must be large enough to provide sufficient rigidity. When worm threads are integral with the shaft, it is recommended that the pitch diameter d_1 be not less than the value given by

$$d_1 = \frac{c^{0.875}}{2.2} \tag{22}$$

This equation should be used as a check and not for making design calculations.

10. Tooth Loads and Efficiency of Worm Gears

Figure 11-11 shows the worm wheel with the tooth inclined at an angle α to the wheel axis. A cross section normal to the tooth indicates a pressure line inclined at angle φ_n to the plane tangent to the pitch cylinder at P. Force F_n normal to the tooth surface lies along the pressure line. A section through the wheel in the plane of rotation shows a pressure angle equal to φ. The projection PC of force F_n in the tangent plane is inclined at angle α to the plane of rotation.

The relationship between φ_n and φ can be found as follows.

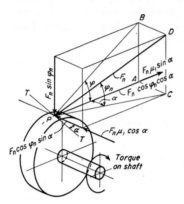

$$\tan \varphi_n = \frac{CD}{PC} = \frac{AB}{PC} \tag{a}$$

But

$$AB = AP \tan \varphi$$

and

$$PC = \frac{AP}{\cos \alpha}$$

Substitution into (a) gives

$$\tan \varphi_n = \tan \varphi \cos \alpha \tag{23}$$

Fig. 11-11. Forces acting on tooth of worm wheel.

Force F_n can be resolved into the 3 components with values shown in Fig. 11-11. When the gears are revolving, force F_n causes a friction force $F_n\mu_1$, where μ_1 is the coefficient of friction. This force lies along tangent T-T to the tooth and can be resolved into components $F_n\mu_1 \cos \alpha$ along the axis, and $F_n\mu_1 \sin \alpha$ perpendicular thereto.

The input force F_i from the worm is

$$F_i = F_n(\cos \varphi_n \sin \alpha + \mu_1 \cos \alpha) = \frac{33{,}000 \text{hp}_i}{V_1} \tag{b}$$

where hp_i is the input horsepower.

The output force F_o acting on the wheel is

$$F_o = F_n(\cos \varphi_n \cos \alpha - \mu_1 \sin \alpha) = \frac{33{,}000 \text{hp}_o}{V_2} \tag{c}$$

The efficiency of the gears is equal to hp_o/hp_i.

$$\text{Eff} = \frac{\text{hp}_o}{\text{hp}_i} = \frac{(\cos \varphi_n \cos \alpha - \mu_1 \sin \alpha) V_2}{(\cos \varphi_n \sin \alpha + \mu_1 \cos \alpha) V_1} \tag{d}$$

$$= \frac{(\cos \varphi_n \cos \alpha - \mu_1 \sin \alpha)\sin \alpha}{(\cos \varphi_n \sin \alpha + \mu_1 \cos \alpha)\cos \alpha} \tag{e}$$

$$= \frac{\cos \varphi_n - \mu_1 \tan \alpha}{\cos \varphi_n + \mu_1 \cot \alpha} \tag{24}$$

Equation (16) is substituted into Eq. (d) to give Eq. (e). It should be noted that Eq. (24) is the same as Eq. (13) of Chapter 5. In fact, the action of a worm and wheel is similar to that of a screw and nut, with the nut replaced by the continuously acting wheel.

The coefficient of friction μ_1 depends on the speed of sliding V_s between worm and gear. The value of V_s can be found from

$$V_s = \frac{V_1}{\cos \alpha} \tag{25}$$

Values of μ_1 for different values of V_s are given in Table 11-2.

TABLE 11-2*

Values of Coefficient of Friction μ_1 for Different Values of Speed of Sliding V_s

V_s, fpm	μ_1	V_s, fpm	μ_1	V_s, fpm	μ_1	V_s, fpm	μ_1
0	0.2000	80	0.0553	750	0.0375	4,000	0.0822
10	0.1209	90	0.0522	1,000	0.0420	5,000	0.0919
20	0.0993	100	0.0495	1,250	0.0465	6,000	0.1007
30	0.0859	150	0.0408	1,500	0.0506	7,000	0.1088
40	0.0764	200	0.0365	1,750	0.0545	8,000	0.1163
50	0.0693	300	0.0330	2,000	0.0582	9,000	0.1233
60	0.0637	400	0.0327	2,500	0.0650	10,000	0.1300
70	0.0591	500	0.0358	3,000	0.0712		

* By permission from *Analytical Mechanics of Gears*, by Earle Buckingham. Copyright 1950, McGraw-Hill Book Company, Inc.

11. Thermal Capacity of Worm Gear Reductions

The hp capacity of a worm gear reduction in continuous operation is usually limited by the heat dissipating capacity of the case or container. The cooling rate for rectangular or box-type casings can be estimated by the curves[5] in Fig. 11-12. The cooling rate is greater at high velocities of the wormshaft, which causes a better circulation of the oil within the box. The cooling rate can be increased by a fan that directs a stream of air on the sides of the box.

Cooling rate C_1 is expressed in Btu/hr/ft²/deg F. Values from the curve can be divided by 60 to obtain the heat lost per minute. The total heat lost depends on the area of the housing A_c in square feet, and the temperature difference ΔT between the housing surface and the surrounding air. The energy lost in Btu can be multiplied by 778 to give the equivalent energy in ft-lb. The lost energy, in terms of horsepower, is then.

$$\text{lost hp} = \frac{778 C_1 A_c \Delta T}{60 \times 33,000} \tag{26}$$

[5] See reference 7, Bibliography.

The housing should have a liberal clearance to avoid churning the oil and to provide for the dissipation of the heat. The cooling area can be estimated by the curve in Fig. 11-10 or by the following equation.

$$A_c = 0.3c^{1.7} \qquad (27)$$

The lost hp is equal to the difference between the input and output

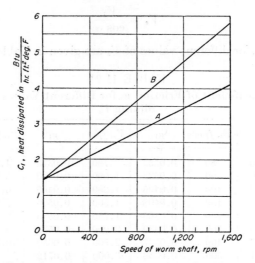

Fig. 11-12. Heat dissipating capacity of worm gear box. *A*, without fan; *B*, with fan on worm shaft.

horsepower. The output horsepower is equal to the input horsepower multiplied by the efficiency. Hence

$$\text{lost hp} = \text{hp}_i - \text{hp}_o = \text{hp}_i - \text{hp}_i \times \text{Eff} = \text{hp}_i(1 - \text{Eff})$$

or
$$\text{hp}_i = \frac{\text{lost hp}}{1 - \text{Eff}} \qquad (28)$$

The oil temperature should not exceed 180 F.

Example 7. Find the input and output hp for the worm reduction in Example 6 for continuous operation based on the cooling of the housing in still air. The housing temperature rise to be 90 deg F. The pressure angle in the normal section is $\varphi_n = 25°$.

Solution.

By Fig. 11-10
   or Eq. (27): $A_c = 12.4$ ft^2

By Fig. 11-12: $C_1 = 2.43$ Btu/hr/ft^2/deg F

By Eq. (26): lost hp $= \dfrac{778 C_1 A_c \Delta T}{60 \times 33{,}000} = \dfrac{778 \times 2.43 \times 12.4 \times 90}{60 \times 33{,}000} = 1.067$

By Eq. (25): $V_s = \dfrac{V_1}{\cos \alpha} = \dfrac{499.6}{0.90790} = 550$ fpm

By Table 11-2: $\mu_1 = 0.0361$

By Eq. (24):   Eff $= \dfrac{0.90631 - 0.0361 \times 0.46171}{0.90631 + 0.0361 \times 2.1659} = 0.904$

By Eq. (28): $\text{hp}_i = \dfrac{\text{lost hp}}{1 - \text{Eff}} = \dfrac{1.067}{1 - 0.904} = 11.069$

$\text{hp}_o = \text{hp}_i \times \text{Eff} = 11.069 \times 0.904 = 10.002$

A considerably greater output can be obtained in intermittent service if short periods of operation are followed by sufficiently long cooling periods. Artificial cooling also permits operation at larger loads.

12. Helical Gears

If a number of spur gears formed from thin plates are assembled with a small angular displacement between the teeth, the stepped gear of Fig. 11-13 results. A helical gear can be considered the limiting case of a stepped gear as the thickness of the plates and the angular displacements are made progressively smaller. A typical example of a pair of helical gears is given by Fig. 11-14(a). Because of the helix angle there will be end thrust on the shafts of helical gears which must be provided for in the design of the bearings. End

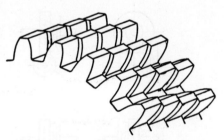

Fig. 11-13. Stepped gears. Helical gears result if the plates are made progressively thinner.

thrust can be eliminated by cutting a right-hand spiral over one-half the face, and using a left-hand spiral for the other half; herring-bone gears are thus formed, as illustrated in Fig. 11-14(b). A central groove must usually be provided around the gear for clearance for hob or cutter. Herringbone gears made on the Sykes type of generating machine do not require the central clearance groove.

The helix angle ψ, illustrated in Fig. 11-17, usually varies from 15° to 30° for helical gears, and from 23° to 30°, or even 45°, for herringbone gears. Helical gears can be cut by the same hobs used for making spur gears. When the gear shaper is used, however, a special cutter is required.

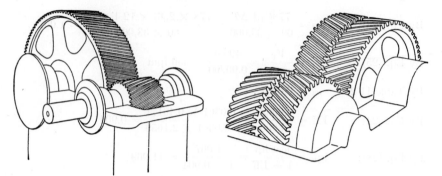

Fig. 11-14.   Types of spiral gears: left, helical gears; right herringbone gears. (*From Lubrication, published by The Texas Co.*)

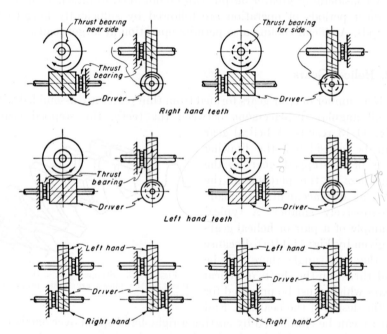

Fig. 11-15.   Directions of rotation and thrust for helical gears.

The relationship between directions of rotation and thrust for helical gears is shown in Fig. 11-15.

Gears with helical teeth possess certain inherent advantages. More teeth are in contact simultaneously, and the load is transferred gradually and uniformly as successive teeth come into engagement. Helical gears thus operate more smoothly and carry larger loads at higher speeds than spur gears. The line of contact extends diagonally across the face of mating teeth. Since more teeth are in contact, undercutting causes little trouble in helical gearing.

Helical gears can also be used for transmitting power between non-parallel shafts, as shown in Fig. 11-16. When used in this way, the teeth have only point contact, which does not shift axially along the teeth during operation. Such gears are usually used only for the transmission of relatively small loads.

13. Pitch Diameter of Helical Gear

Let the pitch diameter of a helical gear be called d, and let the helix angle ψ be measured between an element of the tooth at the pitch cylinder and the center line of the shaft, as shown in Fig. 11-17. Let the symbol p represent the circular pitch or distance from tooth to tooth measured on the pitch cylinder in the plane of rotation. The normal circular pitch p_n is measured normal to the tooth elements. It should be noted that

Fig. 11-16. Helical gears on non-parallel shafts. (*Courtesy Socony-Vacuum Oil Co.*)

$$p_n = p \cos \psi \qquad (29)$$

The pitch diameter of a helical gear is then equal to

$$d = \frac{Np}{\pi} = \frac{Np_n}{\pi \cos \psi} \qquad (30)$$

where N is the number of teeth in the gear. The pitch diameter of a

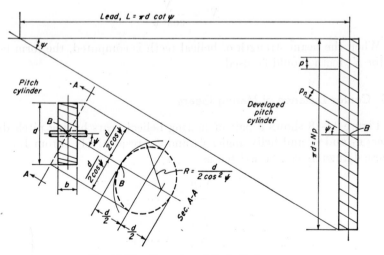

Fig. 11-17.   Geometry of the helical gear.

helical gear thus depends upon the helix angle ψ as well as upon the normal circular pitch and the number of teeth.

When a helical gear is cut with a hob, the circular pitch of the tool is equal to p_n of Fig. 11-17. However, when the gear shaper is used, the circular pitch of the cutter and p of Fig. 11-17 coincide. Angle ψ is usually made large enough to give an overlapping of tooth action, that is, $b \tan \psi$ is greater than p, where b is the width of the face.

14. Formative Number of Teeth

A plane normal to the element of the tooth at point B in Fig. 11-17 intersects the pitch cylinder (extended) in the ellipse shown by sec. A-A. The shape of the tooth at B would be that generated on a cylindrical surface having the same radius of curvature as the ellipse at B. From analytic geometry, the radius of curvature R at the end of a semiminor axis of an ellipse is known to be

$$R = \frac{d}{2 \cos^2 \psi} \qquad (a)$$

The formative number of teeth N' is defined as the number of teeth in a gear of radius R.

$$N' = \frac{2\pi R}{p_n} = \frac{\pi d}{p_n \cos^2 \psi} \qquad (b)$$

Substitution of the value for $\pi d/p_n$ from Eq. (30) gives the following equation for N'.

$$N' = \frac{N}{\cos^3 \psi} \qquad (31)$$

When the beam strength of helical teeth is computed, the form factor y for N' teeth should be used.

15. Center Distance of Mating Gears

Figure 11-18 shows a pair of mating helical gears having pitch diameters d_1 and d_2 and helix angles ψ_1 and ψ_2, respectively. From Eq. (30), these diameters can be written as

$$d_1 = \frac{N_1 p}{\pi} = \frac{N_1 p_n}{\pi \cos \psi_1} \qquad (32)$$

$$d_2 = \frac{N_2 p}{\pi} = \frac{N_2 p_n}{\pi \cos \psi_2} \qquad (33)$$

When meshed together, the center distance c for these gears is

$$c = \frac{d_1 + d_2}{2} = \frac{p_n}{2\pi}\left[\frac{N_1}{\cos \psi_1} + \frac{N_2}{\cos \psi_2}\right] \qquad (a)$$

Let the pitch-line velocities of the gears be V_1 and V_2, respectively. As illustrated by Fig. 11-18, the common velocity V_n normal to the tooth surfaces of both gears is

$$V_n = V_1 \cos \psi_1 = V_2 \cos \psi_2$$

or $\quad V_2 = \dfrac{\cos \psi_1}{\cos \psi_2} V_1 \qquad (b)$

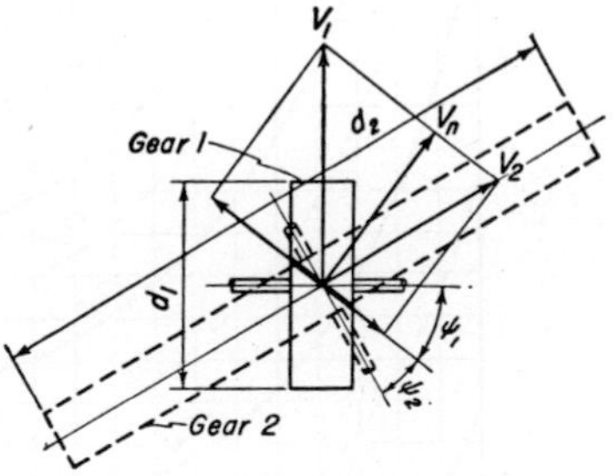

The angular velocities of the two gears are

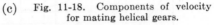

$$\omega_1 = \frac{2V_1}{d_1}$$

and $\quad \omega_2 = \dfrac{2V_2}{d_2} = \dfrac{2 \cos \psi_1}{d_2 \cos \psi_2} V_1 \qquad (c)$

Fig. 11-18. Components of velocity for mating helical gears.

The velocity ratio ω_1/ω_2 becomes

$$\frac{\omega_1}{\omega_2} = \frac{d_2 \cos \psi_2}{d_1 \cos \psi_1} \qquad (d)$$

Substitution from Eqs. (32) and (33) gives

$$\frac{\omega_1}{\omega_2} = \frac{N_2}{N_1} \qquad (34)$$

The velocity ratio of the gears thus depends on the number of teeth, and is independent of the helix angles and diameters. Substitution of Eq. (11) for velocity ratio $\lambda = N_1/N_2$ into Eq. (a) gives

$$\frac{\lambda}{\cos \psi_1} + \frac{1}{\cos \psi_2} = \frac{2\pi c}{N_2 p_n} \qquad (35)$$

Sometimes the center distance c, the angle between the shafts $\psi_1 + \psi_2$, and the velocity ratio λ are fixed. Suitable values for N_2 and p_n are chosen for the conditions of the problem, and the values of ψ_1 and ψ_2 are found by trial and error in Eq. (35).

16. Solution When Shafts Are at Right Angles

When the shafts for a pair of helical gears are at right angles, a solution to Eq. (35) can be made by the Newton-Raphson method.[6] Since ψ_1 is

[6] See reference 16, Bibliography.

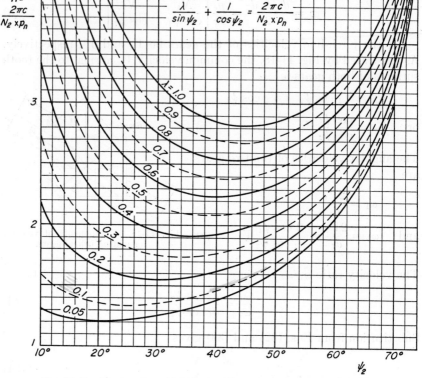

Fig. 11-19.   Design chart for helical and worm gears for 90° shaft angle.

equal to 90° minus ψ_2, $\cos \psi_1$ can be replaced by $\sin \psi_2$. Let the right-hand side in Eq. (35) be called H.

$$H = \frac{2\pi c}{N_2 p_n} \tag{36}$$

Then
$$\frac{\lambda}{\sin \psi_2} + \frac{1}{\cos \psi_2} = H \tag{37}$$

In this equation, let H be transposed, and let all terms be multiplied by $\sin \psi_2$. Call the result $f(\psi_2)$. Then

$$f(\psi_2) = \lambda + \tan \psi_2 - H \sin \psi_2 \tag{38}$$

The equation above is now differentiated with respect to ψ_2.

$$f'(\psi_2) = \frac{1}{\cos^2 \psi_2} - H \cos \psi_2 \tag{39}$$

In addition, let
$$h = -\frac{f(\psi_2)}{f'(\psi_2)} \tag{40}$$

By the Newton-Raphson method, if ψ_2 is a trial root for Eq. (37), then in general, a better value ψ'_2 for the root is

$$\psi'_2 = \psi_2 + h \tag{41}$$

If the new root ψ'_2 is not sufficiently close, the process can be repeated, using ψ'_2 as a new trial root to obtain a new increment h' to give a still better value of ψ_2.

A first trial value of ψ_2 can be had from Fig. 11-19 which represents a plot of Eq. (37) for different values of λ. The process is illustrated by the following example.

Example 8. Two helical gears with 90° shafts have a center distance of 12 in. The gears have 21 and 77 teeth. The normal diametral pitch is 6. Find the required values for the helix angles. Find the corresponding pitch diameters of the two gears.

Solution.

By Eq. 36: $$H = \frac{2\pi 12 \times 6}{77\pi} = 1.87013$$

$$\lambda = \frac{3}{11} = 0.27273$$

From Fig. 11-19, trial values: $\psi_2 = 20°$ and $48°30'$.

For $\psi_2 = 20°$:

In Eq. (38): $f(\psi_2) = 0.27273 + 0.36397 - 1.87013 \times 0.34202 = -0.00292$

In Eq. (39): $f'(\psi_2) = \dfrac{1}{0.93969^2} - 1.87013 \times 0.93969 = -0.62486$

In Eq. (40): $h = -\dfrac{-0.00292}{-0.62486} = -0.004673$ radians $= -16.1'$

New value: $\psi_2 = 20°0' - (0°16.1') = 19°43.9'$

In Eq. (38): $d_1 = \dfrac{21\pi}{6\pi 0.33761} = 10.3666$ in.

In Eq. (33): $d_2 = \dfrac{77\pi}{6\pi 0.94128} = 13.6334$ in.

For $\psi_2 = 48°30'$:

In Eq. (38): $f(\psi_2) = 0.27273 + 1.13029 - 1.87013 \times 0.74896 = 0.00237$

In Eq. (39): $f'(\psi_2) = \dfrac{1}{0.66262^2} - 1.87013 \times 0.66262 = 1.03838$

In Eq. (40): $h = -\dfrac{0.00237}{1.03838} = -0.0022824$ radians $= -7.9'$

New value: $\psi_2 = 48°30' - (0°7.9') = 48°22.1'$

In Eq. (32): $d_1 = \dfrac{21\pi}{6\pi 0.74744} = 4.6826$ in.

In Eq. (33): $d_2 = \dfrac{77\pi}{6\pi 0.66433} = 19.3174$ in.

The curves of Fig. 11-19 are frequently helpful in solving worm gear problems.

17. Tooth Loads of Helical Gears

Figure 11-20 shows the forces acting on the tooth when the axes of the mating gears are parallel to each other. Force F_t is the transmitted or horsepower load found from the usual equation

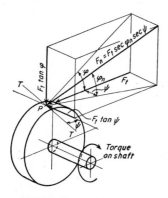

$$F_t = \frac{33,000 \text{ hp}}{V} \qquad (42)$$

where V is the pitch-line velocity in fpm.

Force F_n is normal to the tooth surface. It is inclined to the plane tangent to the pitch cylinder at the normal pressure angle φ_n. The projection of F_n in the tangent plane is inclined at helix angle ψ to the plane of rotation. The projection of F_n on the plane of rotation is inclined at angle φ to force F_t. The relationship between φ and φ_n is given by

Fig. 11-20.   Forces acting on tooth of helical gear when axes are parallel.

$$\tan \varphi_n = \tan \varphi \cos \psi \qquad (43)$$

The proof is similar to that for Eq. (23). The values of the various components of the tooth forces are shown in Fig. 11-20.

Helical gears on parallel shafts operate at high values for the efficiency.

18. Beam Strength, Dynamic Load, and Wear of Helical Gears

The equations for beam strength, dynamic load, and wear are similar to those for spur gears.[7] However, adjustments must be made to take care of the effects of the helix angle ψ.

Beam Strength. The same equation as used for spur gears is used for computing the beam strength of helical gears.

$$F_b = sbyp \qquad (44)$$

The value of y should be taken for the formative number of teeth.

[7] See p. 14–27 reference 2, Bibliography.

Dynamic Load. The dynamic load for helical gears with parallel shafts can be estimated by use of the same equations as those used for spur gears.

Limit Load for Wear. The limit load for wear for external gears on parallel shafts can be taken as

$$F_w = \frac{d_1 b K}{\cos^2 \psi} Q \tag{45}$$

where
$$Q = \frac{2N_2}{N_1 + N_2} \tag{46}$$

The symbols in the equations above have the same meanings which previously were defined for spur gears. Tabular values may also be taken from the preceding chapter.

Example 9. Two helical gears with Class 2 accuracy have parallel shafts and a p_n equal to 0.7854 in. Numbers of teeth are 32 and 44. Center distance is 10 in. Gears carry 100 hp at 600 rpm for the pinion. The width of face is 2.5 in. The pressure angle φ_n is 20°.

(a) Find required value of helix angle.
(b) Find BHN required for wear, and capacity of tooth in bending for a stress of 28,000 psi. Gears are of steel.

Solution. (a) $\dfrac{\frac{1}{2}d_1}{N_1} = \dfrac{c}{N_1 + N_2}$

or
$$d_1 = \frac{2N_1 c}{N_1 + N_2} = \frac{2 \times 32 \times 10}{76} = 8.4211 \text{ in.}$$

also
$$d_2 = \frac{2N_2 c}{N_1 + N_2} = \frac{2 \times 44 \times 10}{76} = 11.5789 \text{ in.}$$

By Eq. (32): $\cos \psi_1 = \dfrac{N_1 p_n}{\pi d_1} = \dfrac{32 \times 0.7854}{\pi 8.4211} = 0.95000 \qquad \psi_1 = 18°11.7'$

(b)
$$V = \frac{\pi d_1 n_1}{12} = \frac{\pi 8.4211 \times 600}{12} = 1{,}323 \text{ fpm}$$

By Eq. (42):
$$F_t = \frac{33{,}000 \text{ hp}}{V} = \frac{33{,}000 \times 100}{1{,}323} = 2{,}495 \text{ lb}$$

$$F_d = 2{,}495 \frac{1{,}200 + 1{,}323}{1{,}200} = 5{,}240 \text{ lb}$$

By Eq. (46):
$$Q = \frac{2N_2}{N_1 + N_2} = \frac{2 \times 44}{32 + 44} = 1.1579$$

Wear load F_w must be equal to dynamic load F_d. Hence

By Eq. (45):
$$K = \frac{F_w \cos^2 \psi}{d_1 b Q} = \frac{5{,}240 \times 0.95^2}{8.4211 \times 2.5 \times 1.1579} = 194$$

By Table 10-3, for gears of equal hardness, BHN $= 300$

By Eq. (31): $N'_1 = \dfrac{N_1}{\cos^2 \psi_1} = \dfrac{32}{0.95^3} = 37.3$

By Table 10-1: $y = 0.121$ for N'_1 teeth

By Eq. (44): $F_b = sbyp = 28{,}000 \times 2.5 \times 0.121 \times 0.7854$

$= 6{,}650$ lb, capacity of tooth in bending. This is satisfactory.

BIBLIOGRAPHY

Volume number shown in **bold face** type. The number immediately following is the page on which the article begins.

1. Dudley, D. W., *Practical Gear Design*. New York: McGraw-Hill Book Co., Inc., 1954.

2. *Kent's Mechanical Engineers' Handbook*, 12th ed., Part 3. New York: John Wiley & Sons, Inc., 1950.

3. Buckingham, Earle, *Analytical Mechanics of Gears*. New York: McGraw-Hill Book Company, Inc., 1949.

4. Buckingham, Earle, *Manual of Gear Design*, Section 3. New York: The Industrial Press, 1937.

5. Merritt, H. E., *Gears*. London: Sir Isaac Pitman & Sons, Ltd., 1946.

6. *Design and Rating of Worm Gearing for Power Transmission, Standard* 340.01. American Gear Manufacturers Association, 1947.

7. Walker, H., "Thermal Rating of Worm Gear Boxes," *Proc. Inst. Mech. Engs.*, **151**, 326 (1944).

8. Walker, H., "Heat Dissipation from Gear Boxes with Special Reference to Worm Gearing," *Machinery* (London), **49**, 159, 561 (1936); **50**, 71, 545 (1937).

9. Merritt, H. E., "Worm Gear Performance," *Proc. Inst. Mech. Engrs.*, **129**, 127 (1935).

10. Candee, A. H., "Large Spiral and Bevel Gears," *Trans. ASME*, **51**(2), MSP-51-9, 59 (1929).

11. Candee, A. H., "Industrial Applications of Spiral Bevel Gears and Hypoid Gears," *Trans. ASME*, **60**, 549 (1938).

12. Wildhaber, E., "Basic Relationship of Hypoid Gears," *Am. Machinist*, **90**, Feb. 14, 28; Mar. 14; June 6, 20; July 18; Aug. 1, 15 (1946).

13. Schmitter, W. P., "Determining Capacity of Helical and Herringbone Gearing," *Machine Design*, **6**, June, 40; July, 33 (1934).

14. Almen, J. O., and Boegehold, A. L., "Rear Axle Gears," *Proc. ASTM*, **35**, Part 2, 99 (1935).

15. Dudley, D. W., and Poritsky, H., "On Cutting and Hobbing Gears and Worms," *Trans. ASME*, **65**, A-139, A-197 (1943); **66**, A-247 (1944).

16. Saari, Oliver, "Designing Right-Angle Helical Gears," *Machine Design*, **24**, July, 145 (1953).

17. Wildhaber, E., "Surface Curvature," *Product Engineering*, **27**, May 184 (1956).

PROBLEMS

1. Two 20° full-depth bevel gears are made of cast iron with Class 1 accuracy. $P = 3$. The gears have 24 and 60 teeth. Width of face is 3 in. Speed is 300 rpm for the pinion. Find the hp these gears can carry. Bending stress $= 10,000$ psi.

Ans. hp $= 23.1$.

2. Two 20° full-depth bevel gears are made of cast iron with Class 1 accuracy. $P = 4$. The gears have 30 and 45 teeth. Width of face is 2.5 in. Find permissible rpm for the pinion if the gears carry 15 hp. Bending stress $= 10,000$ psi.

Ans. $n_1 = 382$ rpm.

3. Two 20° full depth steel bevel gears with Class 1 accuracy are carrying 50 hp at 900 rpm for the pinion. Outside pitch diameters are 6 in. and 12 in. Width of face is 2 in. Base of the pitch cone of the larger gear is located at center of a 16 in. long simply supported shaft. Torque and axial thrust are resisted at the right end of shaft as in Fig. 11-5.

(a) Find BHN required for wear if both gears have same hardness, and find a suitable value for the P for a stress of 28,000 psi in bending.

(b) Make a drawing similar to Fig. 11-5 and represent the values of all tooth loads and shaft reactions thereon.

Ans. BHN $= 290; P = 3; F'_t, = 1,372$ lb.

4. A worm has a lead of 2.1901 in. The worm is double threaded and has a pitch diameter of 2.2802 in. Find the center distance if the ratio is 16 to 1.

Ans. $c = 6.7172$ in.

5. A double-threaded worm has a pitch diameter of 3 in. The wheel has 20 teeth and a pitch diameter of 5 in. Find the value of the helix angle.

Ans. $\alpha = 9°27.7'$.

6. A worm gear reduction has a ratio of 18:1. The helix angle is 16°40'. The center distance is 8.3535 in. Find the values of pitch diameters d_1 and d_2.

Ans. $d_1 = 2.6150$ in.; $d_2 = 14.0920$ in.

7. A worm gear drive has a helix angle of 19° and a center distance of 9.084 in.; p_n is 0.7854 in. Find suitable values for N_1 and N_2.

8. A worm gear drive must be designed for a center distance of 8 in. The worm is double threaded; the gear has 30 teeth; p_n is to be $\pi/2.5$ in. Find pitch diameters of worm and wheel and the helix angle for each of the two possible solutions.

Ans. $d_1 = 3.7111$ in.; $d_2 = 12.2889$ in.; $\alpha = 12°27'$.

9. Work Problem 8 but with a center distance of 7.75 in.

10. A quadruple-threaded worm has a p_n of 1.0472 in. and a helix angle of 23°. Normal pressure angle φ_n is 25°. The gear has 40 teeth. Input hp is equal to 20 at 1,050 rpm of the worm shaft.

(a) Find the value of input force and the normal tooth force F_n in Fig. 11-11.

(b) Find the value of the output force, and from it the output hp and the efficiency of the drive.

(c) Check the value of the efficiency by Eq. (24).

Ans. $F_n = 1{,}790$ lb; $F_o = 1{,}464$ lb; Eff. $= 0.883$.

11. A triple-thread hardened-steel worm and phosphor bronze wheel have a p_n of 0.7854 in. and a normal pressure angle φ_n of 25°. Speed ratio is 20:1. The worm turns 1,150 rpm and has a pitch diameter of 3.1838 in.

(a) Compute the values of the helix angle.

(b) Compute the input hp for continuous operation based on the cooling capacity of the housing for a rise of 90 deg. F in still air.

(c) Compute the value of the dynamic load for the hp of part (b). Check the strength of the tooth in bending and wear by computing F_b and F_w. Bronze, bending stress = 24,000 psi.

Ans. $\alpha = 13°37.4'$; $\text{hp}_i = 9.32$
$F_d = 1{,}314$ lb; $F_b = 6{,}831$ lb.
$F_w = 3{,}624$ lb.

12. A double-threaded hardened steel worm and phosphor bronze wheel have a p_n of $\pi/2.5$ in., and a normal pressure angle φ_n of 30°. Speed ratio is 15:1. Center distance is 7.625 in. The worm turns at 420 rpm. Find values of diameters d_1 and d_2 and make computations similar to those of Problem 11. Make calculations for the larger diameter worm. Bronze, bending stress = 24,000 psi.

Ans. $\text{hp}_i = 6.01$, $F_d = 2{,}041$ lb.
$F_b = 10{,}908$ lb, $F_w = 2{,}480$ lb.

13. Two helical gears have parallel shafts and are cut with a hob of p_n equal to 0.5236 in. Speed ratio is 2:1 and the center distance is equal to 9 in. Find the required value of the helix angle if the smaller gear has 35 teeth.

Ans. $\psi_1 = 13°32'$.

14. Two helical gears have shafts at 90° and helix angles of 45°. Speed ratio is 3:1; p_n is equal to 0.7854 in. Find the center distance if the smaller gear has 20 teeth.   *Ans.* $c = 14.1422$ in.

15. Work Problem 14 but with the helix angle ψ_1 for the smaller gear equal to $37\frac{1}{2}°$.   *Ans.* $c = 15.4713$ in.

16. Work Problem 14 but with the helix angle ψ_1 for the smaller gear equal to $52\frac{1}{2}°$.   *Ans.* $c = 13.5603$ in.

17. Let the gears of Problem 13 transmit 50 hp at 900 rpm for the pinion. Normal pressure angle φ_n is 20°. Width of face is 2 in. Find the required BHN to which both gears must be hardened. Check the capacity of the tooth in bending for a stress of 28,000 psi. Gears have Class 2 accuracy.   *Ans.* BHN $= 265$.

18. Two helical gears have shafts at 90° and a center distance of 14 in. The speed ratio is 3:1. The smaller gear has 20 teeth; p_n is 0.7854 in. Find suitable values for the helix angles and the corresponding pitch diameters of the gears.

Ans. $\psi_1 = 63°38'$; $\psi_2 = 26°22'$;
or $\psi_1 = 46°13.8'$; $\psi_2 = 43°46.2'$.

19. Two helical gears have shafts at a 60° angle. Numbers of teeth are 35 and 105. Center distance is 8 in. p_n equals $\pi/10$. Find suitable values for angles ψ_1 and ψ_2 and the pitch diameters of the gears.

20. A pair of helical gears is cut with a 20° spur gear hob of P equal to 4. The speed ratio is 3:1; the smaller gear has 45 teeth and turns at 1,050 rpm. The center distance is 25 in. The hp is 40. Draw a view of the pinion and show values of all forces at the midpoint of tooth. Shafts are parallel.

Ans. $F_t = 384.2$ lb;

$F_t \tan \varphi = 155.4$ lb;

$F_t \tan \psi = 186.0$ lb.

21. A helical gear has 30 teeth and a pitch diameter of 11 in. The gear is cut with a 20° spur gear hob of $P = 3$. The force normal to the tooth surface is 570 lb. Find the hp transmitted at 600 rpm.   *Ans.* hp = 25.5.

22. A worm gear reducer has an input hp of 15. The worm shaft turns at 1,000 rpm. What is the efficiency of the reducer based on the cooling capacity for a 90 deg. rise in temperature for continuous operation? The center distance is 12 in.

Ans. Eff = 0.85.

12

Miscellaneous
Machine Elements

DESIGN methods are given in this chapter for a miscellaneous group of machine elements that require only brief treatment.

1. Stresses in a Thick Cylinder

The thick-walled cylinder shown in Fig. 12-1 is subjected to uniform pressures p_i and p_o on the internal and external lateral surfaces, respectively. The top and bottom surfaces, are assumed to be free from load. Since the body and the loading are symmetrical about the axis, shear stresses in the tangential and radial directions are not present, and only normal stresses s_t and s_r act on the element, as illustrated in Fig. 12-1(a).

When the wall of the cylinder is thin, the tangential or hoop stress s_t can be assumed to be uniform throughout the wall thickness, and its value can be found by the elementary equations of Chapter 7. This assumption cannot be made for a thick-walled cylinder, and the equations of the following derivation should be used for finding the stresses.

Consider the stresses acting on the semicircular element of Fig. 12-1(b). The thickness in the direction perpendicular to the paper has been taken equal to unity. The vertical component of the inward radial stresses across the diameter of the element is equal to $2s_r r$, and for the outward component of the stresses, $2(s_r + ds_r)(r + dr)$. The equilibrium equation for this element is then

$$2s_r r + 2s_t\, dr = 2(s_r + ds_r)(r + dr) \tag{a}$$

The right-hand side should be expanded and terms of higher order should be neglected. The equation can then be rewritten as

$$r\frac{ds_r}{dr} + s_r = s_t \tag{1}$$

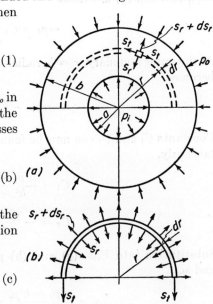

The strain or unit deformation ϵ_o in the direction perpendicular to the paper can be found from the stresses s_t and s_r as follows.

$$\epsilon_o = -\frac{\mu s_t}{E} - \frac{\mu s_r}{E} \tag{b}$$

where μ is Poisson's ratio and E is the modulus of elasticity. This equation may be rearranged as

$$s_t + s_r = -\frac{\epsilon_o E}{\mu} \tag{c}$$

The right-hand side is a constant. For convenience it will hereafter be called $2C_1$. Substitution into Eq. (1) gives

Fig. 12-1. Thick-walled cylinder subjected to internal and external pressures.

$$r\frac{ds_r}{dr} + 2s_r = 2C_1 \tag{d}$$

or

$$r^2\frac{ds_r}{dr} + 2rs_r = 2rC_1 \tag{e}$$

or

$$\frac{d}{dr}(r^2 s_r) = 2rC_1$$

Integration gives

$$r^2 s_r = C_1 r^2 + C_2 \tag{f}$$

where C_2 is the constant of integration. Equation (f) may be written as follows.

$$s_r = C_1 + \frac{C_2}{r^2} \tag{g}$$

This value for s_r should be substituted into Eq. (c), to give

$$s_t = C_1 - \frac{C_2}{r^2} \tag{h}$$

At the inner boundary, $r = a$, the radial stress s_r becomes equal to $-p_i$, and Eq. (g) is written

$$-p_i = C_1 + \frac{C_2}{a^2} \tag{i}$$

At the outer boundary, $r = b$, radial stress s_r is equal to $-p_o$, and Eq. (g) becomes

$$-p_o = C_1 + \frac{C_2}{b^2} \tag{j}$$

Constants C_1 and C_2 can now be found by solving Eqs. (i) and (j) simultaneously.

$$C_1 = \frac{a^2 p_i - b^2 p_o}{b^2 - a^2} \tag{k}$$

$$C_2 = -\frac{a^2 b^2 (p_i - p_o)}{b^2 - a^2} \tag{l}$$

Substitution into Eqs. (g) and (h) gives[1] the values of the stresses s_r and s_t.

$$s_r = \frac{a^2 p_i - b^2 p_o}{b^2 - a^2} - \frac{a^2 b^2 (p_i - p_o)}{r^2 (b^2 - a^2)} \tag{2}$$

$$s_t = \frac{a^2 p_i - b^2 p_o}{b^2 - a^2} + \frac{a^2 b^2 (p_i - p_o)}{r^2 (b^2 - a^2)} \tag{3}$$

For many applications, the outer pressure p_o is equal to zero. Equations (2) and (3) then reduce to the following forms.

$$s_r = \frac{a^2 p}{b^2 - a^2} \left(1 - \frac{b^2}{r^2} \right) \tag{4}$$

$$s_t = \frac{a^2 p}{b^2 - a^2} \left(1 + \frac{b^2}{r^2} \right) \tag{5}$$

where p_i is now called p. The stresses are a maximum at the inner edge, where $r = a$, and the value of s_r is $-p$. The tangential stress for this point is seen to be

$$s_t = p \left[\frac{1 + (a/b)^2}{1 - (a/b)^2} \right] \tag{6}$$

[1] These are known as the Lamé equations. See p. 239 of reference 1, Bibliography.

At the inner boundary, $r = a$, the tangential elongation ϵ_t is equal to

$$\epsilon_t = \frac{1}{E_h} (s_t - \mu s_r) \tag{m}$$

where E_h is the modulus of elasticity for the material. The total increase in length of the inner boundary is equal to $2\pi a \epsilon_t$, giving an increase u_h in the radius of the hole equal to $2\pi a \epsilon_t / 2\pi$, or $a\epsilon_t$. Hence,

$$u_h = \frac{a}{E_h} (s_t - \mu s_r) = \frac{ap}{E_h} \left[\frac{1 + (a/b)^2}{1 - (a/b)^2} + \mu \right] \tag{7}$$

Radial displacement u_h is, of course, outward.

2. Shrink and Press Fit Stresses

In a shrink or press fit, pressure p is caused by the interference of metal between the shaft and the hub. Because of this pressure, the radius of the hole is increased, and the radius of the shaft is decreased. The decrease u_s in the radius of the shaft is equal to

$$u_s = a\epsilon_t = \frac{a}{E_s} (s'_t - \mu s'_r) \tag{a}$$

where E_s is the modulus of elasticity for the material composing the shaft. For a solid shaft, stresses s'_r and s'_t are both equal to $-p$, and the radial deformation becomes

$$u_s = -\frac{ap}{E_s} (1 - \mu) \tag{8}$$

This displacement is inward, as indicated by the minus sign. The sum of the absolute values for u_h and u_s is the radial interference of metal for the shrink or press fit as shown by Fig. 12-2.

When hub and shaft are composed of the same material, the modulus of elasticity for both parts is the same and can be represented by E. The double sum of the absolute values of u_h and u_s is the diametral interference of metal Δ. By Eqs. (7) and (8), $\Delta = 2(|u_h| + |u_s|)$.

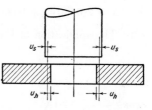
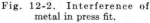

Fig. 12-2. Interference of metal in press fit.

$$\Delta = \frac{4ap}{E} \left[\frac{1}{1 - (a/b)^2} \right] \tag{9}$$

If Eq. (9) is solved for p, the value of the radial stress, corresponding to a given value for the diametral interference is obtained.

$$s_r = -p = -\frac{E\Delta}{4a} \left[1 - \frac{a^2}{b^2} \right] \tag{10}$$

When this value for p is substituted into Eq. (6), the equation for s_t for the hub is obtained.

$$s_t = \frac{E\Delta}{4a}\left[1 + \frac{a^2}{b^2}\right] \tag{11}$$

Example 1. An 8 in. diameter steel shaft is to have a press fit in a 20 in. diameter cast iron disk. The maximum tangential stress in the disk is to be 5,000 psi. The modulus of elasticity for steel is 30,000,000 psi, and for cast iron, 15,000,000 psi. Poisson's ratio is equal to 0.3.

(a) Find the required diametral interference of metal.
(b) Plot the values of s_t along a radius of the disk.
(c) If the disk is 10 in. thick in the axial direction, find the force required to press the parts together if the coefficient of friction is equal to 0.12. Also find the torque which the joint could carry because of the shrink-fit pressure.

Solution. (a) $a = 4$ in.; $b = 10$ in.; $b/a = 2.5$; $a/b = 0.4$.

From Eq. (6):

$$p = \frac{s_t[1 - (a/b)^2]}{1 + (a/b)^2} = \frac{5,000(1 - 0.16)}{1 + 0.16} = 3,620 \text{ psi}$$

By Eq. (7):

$$u_h = \frac{4 \times 3,620}{15,000,000}\left[\frac{1.16}{0.84} + 0.3\right] = 0.00162 \text{ in. increase in hole radius}$$

By Eq. (8):

$$u_s = -\frac{4 \times 3,620}{30,000,000}(1 - 0.3) = -0.00034 \text{ in. decrease in shaft radius}$$

$$\Delta = 2(0.00162 + 0.00034) = 0.0039 \text{ in. diametral interference}$$

(b) The application of Eq. (5) for various values of r gives the curve of Fig. 12-3 for stresses s_t.

(c) Force required for assembly,

$$F = 8\pi \times 10 \times 3,620$$
$$\times 0.12 = 109,200 \text{ lb}$$

Torque carried by press fit,

$$T = 109,200 \times 4 = 436,800 \text{ in-lb}$$

3. Stress Concentration Caused by Press Fit

A shaft with bending stress has a stress concentration at the edge of a

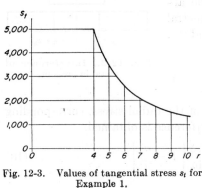

Fig. 12-3. Values of tangential stress s_t for Example 1.

press fitted member as at A in Fig. 12-4(a). When the bending stress is alternating, a rubbing or fretting corrosion occurs at this point. This effect, together with the stress concentration, has been the cause of many failures. Some improvement in fatigue strength can be obtained by grooving the disk as shown in Fig. 12-4(b). Experiments have shown that rolling the shaft between small diameter rollers under pressure high

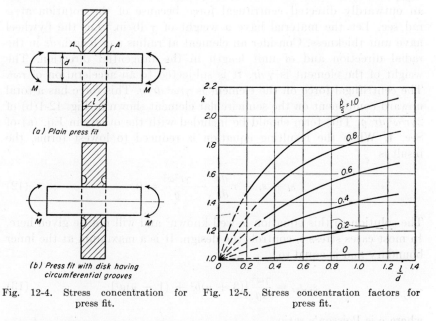

Fig. 12-4. Stress concentration for press fit.

Fig. 12-5. Stress concentration factors for press fit.

enough to deform the surface has also resulted in improved fatigue strength. Stress concentration factors K for plain press fitted assemblies[2] are given by Fig. 12-5.

Example 2. Find the stress concentration factor for the shaft of Example 1 if the shaft carries an alternating bending moment of 350,000 in-lb.

Solution.

$$I = \frac{\pi d^4}{64} = \frac{\pi 8^4}{64} = 201.06 \text{ in.}^4$$

$$s = \frac{Mc}{I} = \frac{350,000 \times 4}{201.06} = 6,963 \text{ psi}$$

$$\frac{p}{s} = \frac{3,620}{6,963} = 0.52$$

$$\frac{l}{d} = \frac{10}{8} = 1.25$$

By Fig. 12-5: $K = 1.56$

Max. bending stress: $s_{max} = 1.56 \times 6,963 = 10,860 \text{ psi}$

[2] See reference 5, Bibliography.

4. Stresses in Disk Flywheel

Flame cut disk flywheels are widely used because of the uniformity and high strength of steel plate.

Let Fig. 12-1(a) be a view of such a flywheel. Pressures p_o and p_i are not present. In addition to stresses s_r and s_t, the element is loaded by an outwardly directed centrifugal force because of the rotation at ω rad/sec. Let the material have a weight of γ lb/in.[3] Let the flywheel have unit thickness. Consider an element at radius r of length dr in the radial direction and of unit length in the tangential direction. The weight of the element is $\gamma \, dr$. It is subjected to an acceleration of $r\omega^2$. The centrifugal force on the element is $\gamma r\omega^2 \, dr/g$. This force has a total upward component on the semicircular element shown in Fig. 12-1(b) of $2\gamma r^2 \omega^2 \, dr/g$. This term should be included with the others in Eq. (a) of Sec. 1. When the resulting equation is reduced to lowest terms, the result is

$$s_t - s_r - r\frac{ds_r}{dr} - \frac{\gamma r^2 \omega^2}{g} = 0 \qquad (12)$$

The solution to this equation is well known[3] and will not be given here. In most cases stress s_t controls the design. It is a maximum at the inner boundary and is equal to

$$s_{t \, max} = \frac{\gamma \omega^2}{4g}[(3 + \mu)b^2 + (1 - \mu)a^2] \qquad (13)$$

where μ is Poisson's ratio.

Example 3. A circular steel plate flywheel is 24 in. in outside diameter and has a 6 in. hole. The flywheel rotates at 3,000 rpm. Find the value of the maximum tangential stress. $\mu = 0.3$. $\gamma = 0.283$ lb/in.[3]

Solution. $g = 12 \times 32.174 = 386$ in./sec²

$$\omega = \frac{2\pi n}{60} = \frac{2\pi 3,000}{60} = 314.16 \text{ rad/sec}$$

In Eq. (13), $s_{t \, max} = \dfrac{0.283 \times 314.16^2}{4 \times 386}[(3 + 0.3) \times 12^2 + (1 - 0.3) \times 3^2]$

$$= 18.09(475.2 + 6.3) = 8,710 \text{ psi}$$

If the plate is drilled near the inner boundary for bolting to a flange, stress concentration occurs at the bolt holes.

[3] See p. 245 of reference 1, Bibliography.

The moment of inertia I of a disk flywheel is

$$I = \frac{\gamma \pi l}{2g} (b^4 - a^4) \text{ lb in. sec}^2 \tag{13a}$$

where γ is the weight per cubic inch of the material, l is the thickness in the axial direction, and g is the gravitational constant, 386 in./sec².

The energy ΔKE delivered by a change in speed from ω_{max} to ω_{min} is given by

$$\Delta KE = \frac{1}{2} I(\omega_{max}^2 - \omega_{min}^2) \tag{13b}$$

5. Flywheel with Spokes and Rim

Figure 12-6 shows a cast flywheel with spokes and rim. When the wheel rotates, a uniformly distributed force F_c acts outwardly on the rim and

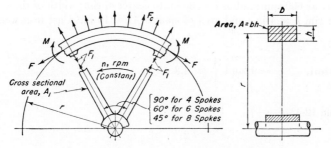

Fig. 12-6.   Forces and moments on segment of fly wheel.

produces the tensile force F. The spokes exercise a restraining influence on the expansion of the rim, and cause moments M to act as shown. Equations for F and M, as well as for the tensile force F_1 in the spoke,[4] are given in Table 12-1. Here w is the weight of the rim per inch of cir-

TABLE 12-1

Equations for Forces and Moments in Flywheel Spokes and Rim

	H	F_1, lb	F, lb	M, in-lb
4 spokes	$\dfrac{\frac{2}{3}}{(0.0730r^2/h^2) + 0.643 + (A/A_1)}$	$\dfrac{wr^2n^2}{35,200} \times H$	$\dfrac{wr^2n^2}{35,200} (1 - 0.500H)$	$0.1366F_1 r$
6 spokes	$\dfrac{\frac{2}{3}}{(0.0203r^2/h^2) + 0.957 + (A/A_1)}$	$\dfrac{wr^2n^2}{35,200} \times H$	$\dfrac{wr^2n^2}{35,200} (1 - 0.866H)$	$0.0889F_1 r$
8 spokes	$\dfrac{\frac{2}{3}}{(0.0091r^2/h^2) + 1.274 + (A/A_1)}$	$\dfrac{wr^2n^2}{35,200} \times H$	$\dfrac{wr^2n^2}{35,200} (1 - 1.207H)$	$0.0662F_1 r$

[4] See p. 98 of reference 1, Bibliography, for derivation.

cumference, and symbols r, n, h, A, and A_1 have the meanings indicated in Fig. 12-6. In these equations, the depth of section h is assumed to be small as compared to radius r.

The tensile stress in the spoke is equal to F_1/A_1. The tensile stress in the rim is equal to F/A plus the effect of the bending moment $6M/bh^2$. Stress concentration effects are present at the junction between the spoke and rim. Sudden changes in the velocity of rotation, as well as belt tensions, cause additional bending stresses in spokes and rim.

Care must be exercised to assure that dimensions and speed of rotation for cast iron flywheels have such values that the resulting tensile stresses do not exceed safe working values for this material. Tensile stress values for cast iron vary over a considerable range, depending on the composition and quality of the material.

Example 4. Find the stresses in a cast iron flywheel with 6 spokes rotating uniformly at 600 rpm; radius $r = 36$ in. to center of rim; width of rim $b = 12$ in.; depth of rim $h = 4$ in.; and area of spokes $A_1 = 10$ in.^{2} Cast iron weighs 0.256 lb/in.^{3}

Solution. $\dfrac{r}{h} = 9$, and $\dfrac{A}{A_1} = 4.8$

By Table 12-1:

$$H = \frac{\dfrac{2}{3}}{0.0203 \times 81 + 0.957 + 4.8} = 0.0901$$

$$w = 0.256 \times 12 \times 4 = 12.29 \text{ lb per in. of rim}$$

$$F_1 = \frac{12.29 \times 36^2 \times 600^2}{35{,}200} \times 0.0901$$

$$= 162{,}900 \times 0.0901 = 14{,}680 \text{ lb}$$

Tensile stress in spoke:

$$s = \frac{14{,}680}{10} = 1{,}470 \text{ psi}$$

$$F = 162{,}900(1 - 0.866 \times 0.0901) = 150{,}200 \text{ lb}$$

Tensile stress in rim:

$$s = \frac{150{,}200}{12 \times 4} = 3{,}130 \text{ psi}$$

$$M = 0.0889 \times 14{,}680 \times 36 = 46{,}980 \text{ in-lb}$$

Bending stress in rim:

$$s = \frac{6M}{bh^2} = \frac{6 \times 46,980}{12 \times 16} = 1,470 \text{ psi}$$

Resultant tensile stress in rim:

$$s = 3,130 + 1,470 = 4,600 \text{ psi}$$

Suppose the spokes in the foregoing example are not present and the rim freely expands under the influence of centrifugal force. The weight per lineal inch of rim is w, and the acceleration is $r\omega^2$. The centrifugal force F_c per inch of rim is

$$F_c = \frac{w}{g} r\omega^2 = \frac{wr}{g} \left(\frac{2\pi n}{60}\right)^2 = \frac{wrn^2}{35,200} \tag{14}$$

Force F in the rim is equal to $F_c r$.

Example 5. Find the stresses for the data of Example 4 if the spokes are not present and the flywheel consists of a freely rotating ring.

Solution.

By Eq. (14): $F_c = \dfrac{12.29 \times 36 \times 600^2}{35,200} = 4,520 \text{ lb/in.}$

Force in rim: $F = F_c r = 4,520 \times 36 = 162,900 \text{ lb}$

Stress: $s = \dfrac{F}{A} = \dfrac{162,900}{48} = 3,390 \text{ psi}$

It can be seen from this example that the elementary method which considers the flywheel as a rotating ring free to expand give stresses on the unsafe side. Also, the elementary method gives no indication of the value of the stress in the spokes.

6. Flywheel Requirements

Many kinds of machinery, such as punches, riveting machines, reciprocating pumps, and crushers, are loaded intermittently. Such machines are provided with flywheels to maintain a more uniform rotation than would otherwise occur. During the working stroke of a punch, for example, energy is removed from the flywheel, and a reduction in the speed of the machine results. This energy is replaced, and the machine is brought up to speed during the remainder of the cycle when no work is being done.

The average angular velocity ω_{av} in radians per second is

$$\omega_{av} = \frac{\omega_{max} + \omega_{min}}{2} \tag{15}$$

where ω_{max} and ω_{min} are the maximum and minimum angular velocities, respectively, for a single work cycle. A coefficient of fluctuation C_f for the flywheel speed is defined as follows.

$$C_f = \frac{\omega_{max} - \omega_{min}}{\omega_{av}} \qquad (16)$$

Values of C_f suitable for various types of machinery are given in Table 12-2.

TABLE 12-2

Coefficient of Fluctuation*

Type of Equipment	C_f
Crushing machinery	0.200
Electrical machinery	0.003
Electrical machinery, direct-driven	0.002
Engines with belt transmission	0.030
Flour-milling machinery	0.020
Gear-wheel transmission	0.020
Hammering machinery	0.200
Machine tools	0.030
Paper-making machinery	0.025
Pumping machinery	0.030–0.050
Shearing machinery	0.030–0.050
Spinning machinery	0.010–0.020
Textile machinery	0.025

* *Kent's Mechanical Engineers' Handbook*, 12th ed., "Design and Production," p. 7–40.

Before a flywheel can be designed, the energy requirements of the machine must be known as well as the permissible variation in flywheel speed.

Sometimes the load is constant and the prime mover exerts a fluctuating torque on the shaft.[5] Figure 12-7 shows the torque T for different values of the crank position θ in a single-cylinder, four-cycle gas engine. Torque tending to increase the angular velocity is plotted upward. The area of the T vs. θ diagram is equal to the work done by the engine per cycle. The useful work divided by the angle 4π over which it takes place gives the average torque T_{av}. It represents the steady load on the engine. The torque curve crosses the T_{av} line at points $\theta_1, \theta_2, \theta_3, \ldots$

Angular velocity ω is equal to $d\theta/dt$, or $\dot{\theta}$, and angular acceleration is equal to $d^2\theta/dt^2$ or $\ddot{\theta}$. Let the moment of inertia for the engine flywheel

[5] See p. 182 of reference 2, Bibliography.

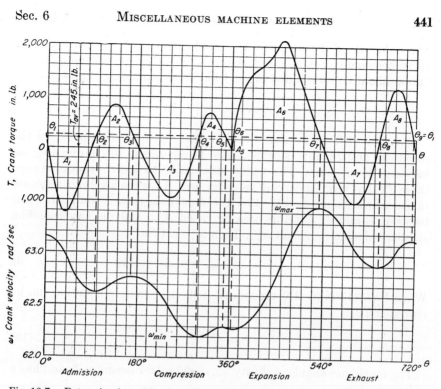

Fig. 12-7.   Determination of flywheel size for single cylinder internal combustion engine.

be called I. Then by Newton's law for rotational motion

$$I\ddot{\theta} = T - T_{av} \qquad (17)$$

Here $T - T_{av}$ is the net value of the torque on the shaft. This equation can be written

$$I\frac{d\dot{\theta}}{dt} = T - T_{av} \qquad (a)$$

Now

$$\dot{\theta}\, dt = d\theta \qquad (b)$$

Equations (a) and (b) should be multiplied together to give

$$I\frac{d\dot{\theta}}{dt}\,\theta\, dt = \frac{1}{2}\, I\, d(\dot{\theta}^2) = (T - T_{av})d\theta$$

This equation is now integrated between any 2 values of θ such as θ_a and θ_b.

$$\frac{1}{2}\, I\dot{\theta}^2 \Big|_a^b = \int_{\theta_a}^{\theta_b} (T - T_{av})d\theta \qquad (c)$$

The right side of this equation represents the net area A_{ab} of the torque curve between points θ_a and θ_b referred to the T_{av} line as the axis. The limits should be substituted in the left side remembering that $\dot\theta = \omega$.

$$\frac{1}{2} I(\omega_b{}^2 - \omega_a{}^2) = A_{ab} \tag{18}$$

Equation (18) shows that the difference between the squares of the speeds for any 2 points is proportional to the area of the torque diagram between those points. The widest fluctuation in speed occurs between those θ's that give the largest value for area A_{ab} when algebraic signs are taken into account. In Fig. 12-7 the maximum area is found to occur between θ_4 and θ_7. Let this area be called A_{max} and the corresponding angular velocities ω_{max} and ω_{min}. Then in Eq. (18)

$$\frac{1}{2} I(\omega_{max} + \omega_{min})(\omega_{max} - \omega_{min}) = A_{max} \tag{d}$$

When Eqs. (15) and (16) are substituted, the resulting equation can be rearranged as

$$I = \frac{A_{max}}{C_f \omega_{av}{}^2} \tag{19}$$

The maximum angular velocity ω_{max} in Fig. 12-7 occurs at θ_7 and has a value equal to

$$\omega_{max} = \omega_{av}\left(1 + \frac{1}{2} C_f\right) \tag{20}$$

This can be easily verified by direct substitution. The minimum angular velocity ω_{min} occurs at θ_4, and has a value

$$\omega_{min} = \omega_{av}\left(1 - \frac{1}{2} C_f\right) \tag{21}$$

The acceleration $\ddot\theta$ in Eq. (17) is zero for those points where the torque curve crosses the T_{av} line, because $T - T_{av}$ is zero at such points. The angular velocity $\dot\theta$ or ω therefore has a maximum or a minimum at all such points.

Velocity θ_8 can be found as θ_b in Eq. (18) by substituting ω_7 or ω_{max} for ω_a and area A_7 for A_{ab}. The process can be repeated until the angular velocity curve of Fig. 12-7 is found.

Example 6. Find the required I of the flywheel for the engine with the torque curve of Fig. 12-7. Speed is 600 rpm, and C_f is 0.02. Find the mean radius if the flywheel consists of a ring 3 by 3 in. in cross section. Material is cast iron; weight is 0.25 lb per in.³ Complete the value of ω for each maximum and minimum, and plot the graph for the flywheel velocity throughout the cycle.

Solution. Horizontally, each small division represents 20° or $20\pi/180$ radian. Vertically, each division represents 200 in-lb of torque. Each small square thus represents $200 \times 20\pi/180$ or 69.813 in-lb of work. The number of small squares in each area can be estimated and multiplied by the above conversion factor. Referred to the θ-axis, these are

$$A_1 = -1,120 \text{ in-lb}; \qquad A_6 = \quad 4,070 \text{ in-lb};$$

$$A_2 = \quad 810 \text{ in-lb}; \qquad A_7 = -1,140 \text{ in-lb};$$

$$A_3 = -1,100 \text{ in-lb}; \qquad A_8 = \quad 1,030 \text{ in-lb}$$

$$A_4 = \quad 530 \text{ in-lb};$$

The sum of the above gives a net work per cycle of 3,080 in-lb. This work takes place through an angle of 4π radians.

Average torque, $$T_{av} = \frac{3,080}{4\pi} = 245 \text{ in-lb}$$

The areas above should now be adjusted to the T_{a1} line as an axis. The results are

$$A_1 = -1,520 \text{ in-lb}; \qquad A_5 = \quad -30 \text{ in-lb};$$

$$A_2 = \quad 460 \text{ in-lb}; \qquad A_6 = \quad 3,330 \text{ in-lb};$$

$$A_3 = -1,610 \text{ in-lb}; \qquad A_7 = -1,610 \text{ in-lb};$$

$$A_4 = \quad 260 \text{ in-lb}; \qquad A_8 = \quad 720 \text{ in-lb}$$

The areas above must add to zero, since the work referred to the T_{av} line is equal to zero.

$$A_{max} = A_4 + A_5 + A_6 = 260 - 30 + 3,330 = 3,560 \text{ in-lb}$$

$$\omega_{av} = \frac{2\pi n}{60} = \frac{2\pi 600}{60} = 20\pi \text{ radians/sec}$$

By Eq. (19): $$I = \frac{A_{max}}{C_f \omega_{av}{}^2} = \frac{3,560}{0.02 \times 400\pi^2} = 45.1 \text{ lb in. sec}^2$$

Weight of flywheel: $$W = 2\pi r \gamma 3 \times 3 = 2\pi r 0.25 \times 9 = 14.137r$$

$$I = \frac{Wr^2}{g} = \frac{14.137r^3}{386} = 45.1 \text{ lb in. sec}^2$$

$$r^3 = 1231$$

$$r = 10.72 \text{ in. mean radius}$$

By Eq. (20): $$\omega_7 = \omega_{max} = \omega_{av}\left(1 + \frac{1}{2}C_f\right) = 20\pi\left(1 + \frac{0.02}{2}\right)$$

$$= 63.46 \text{ radians/sec}$$

By Eq. (18): $\qquad \omega_8{}^2 = \dfrac{2A_7}{I} + \omega_7{}^2 = \dfrac{-2 \times 1{,}610}{45.1} + 63.46^2$

$$= -71.416 + 4{,}027.172 = 3{,}955.756$$

$$\omega_8 = 62.89 \text{ radians/sec}$$

The process can be continued for the remaining values of ω. The results are

$\omega_1 = \omega_9 = 63.15$ radians/sec; $\qquad \omega_4 = \omega_{min} = 62.20$ radians/sec;

$\omega_2 = 62.61$ radians/sec; $\qquad\qquad \omega_5 = 62.30$ radians/sec;

$\omega_3 = 62.78$ radians/sec; $\qquad\qquad \omega_6 = 62.28$ radians/sec

The equation for the energy, ΔKE, removed from the flywheel by a change in speed from ω_{max} to ω_{min} can be written as

$$\Delta KE = \frac{1}{2} I(\omega_{max}^2 - \omega_{min}^2) \tag{21a}$$

7. Impact of Elastic Bodies

Let a uniform stress s_0 be suddenly applied to the end of a long bar as shown in Fig. 12-8. At the first instant, an infinitely thin layer of material in the bar is compressed.[6] This compression is transferred to the next layer, and so on. In other words a compression wave, moving with velocity c, travels along the bar. After time t, a length ct is compressed and the remainder of the bar is at rest in the unstressed condition.

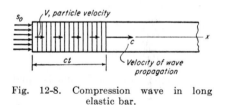

Fig. 12-8. Compression wave in long elastic bar.

The deformation δ of the compressed zone is

$$\delta = \frac{s_0 ct}{E} \tag{22}$$

The velocity V of the particles in the compressed zone is

$$V = \frac{\delta}{t} = \frac{s_0 c}{E} \qquad \text{or} \qquad c = \frac{VE}{s_0} \tag{23}$$

The velocity V of the particles should be distinguished from the velocity c of the wave front.

Let the material in the bar have a weight of γ lb per cu in. The density ρ, mass per cu in., is equal to γ/g, where g is the gravitational constant, 386 in./sec². The mass of the moving particles in the wave is equal to

---

[6] See reference 12, Bibliography.

$\rho A ct$, where A is the cross-sectional area of the bar. The force on the end of the bar is equal to $A s_o$. The momentum and impulse equation states that mass times velocity is equal to force times time. Hence

$$\rho A ct V = A s_0 t \quad \text{or} \quad s_0 = c \rho V$$

Substitution of Eq. (23) gives

$$s_0 = V \sqrt{E \rho} \tag{24}$$

The force k required to compress the bar a unit distance is equal to AE/l, where l is the length of the bar; hence $E = kl/A$. The weight W_b of the bar is equal to $Al\gamma$ or $Alg\rho$; hence $\rho = W_b/Alg$. Substitution in Eq. (24) gives

$$F = s_0 A = V \sqrt{\frac{kW_b}{g}} \tag{25}$$

where F is the force due to impact. Equations (23) and (24) can be combined to give

$$c = \sqrt{\frac{E}{\rho}} \tag{26}$$

Example 7. Find the velocity of propagation for a compression wave in steel. $\gamma = 0.283$ lb/in.³

Solution.

In Eq. (26): $\quad c = \sqrt{\dfrac{E}{\rho}} = \sqrt{\dfrac{Eg}{\gamma}} = \sqrt{\dfrac{30,000,000 \times 386}{0.283}}$

$$= 202,280 \text{ in./sec} = 3.19 \text{ miles/sec}$$

Impact stresses can be caused by a moving weight striking the end of the bar as shown in Fig. 12-9. A compression wave travels along the bar and is reflected at the wall; it returns to weight W and is again reflected; and so on. The maximum stress may thus be several times as great as that given by Eq. (24). The exact analysis of this problem is very involved. However an approximate solution, based on energy, can be obtained if simplifying assumptions are made.

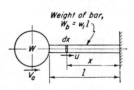

Weight of bar, $W_b = w, l$

Fig. 12-9. Free end of horizontal bar struck by moving weight.

Weight W has velocity V before striking, but after impact the velocity is reduced to V_a. If it is assumed that the weight and bar remain in contact after striking, the end of the bar also has the velocity V_a. The solution to the problem by the energy method is based on the assumption that all elements in the bar upon impact are instantly given velocities which are proportional to their distances from the wall. Thus, if u is the velocity for the element at distance x from the wall, the following proportion will hold.

$$\frac{u}{x} = \frac{V_a}{l} \qquad \text{or} \qquad u = \frac{V_a}{l}x \tag{a}$$

The kinetic energy of the system after impact is given by

$$KE = \frac{W}{2g} V_a{}^2 + \int_0^l \frac{u^2}{2g} w_1 dx$$

where w_1 is the weight per lineal inch of the bar.

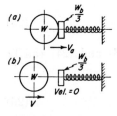

(a)

(b)

Vel. = 0

Fig. 12-10. Impact when bar of Fig. 12-9 is replaced by weight at end of spring.

Substitution of the value of u from Eq. (a) and integration gives

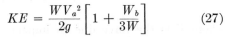

$$KE = \frac{WV_a{}^2}{2g} \left[1 + \frac{W_b}{3W} \right] \tag{27}$$

Thus, by Eq. (27), the kinetic energy after impact would be unaffected if the bar were replaced by a weight of magnitude $W_b/3$ at the end of a weightless spring having the same elastic stiffness as the bar. Such a system is shown in Fig. 12-10(a). The situation before impact has occurred, when W has its original velocity V and when $W_b/3$ is not moving, is illustrated in Fig. 12-10(b). The total momentum before and after impact remains unchanged. Hence,

$$WV = \left[W + \frac{W_b}{3} \right] V_a \qquad \text{or} \qquad V_a = \frac{1}{1 + W_b/3W} V \tag{b}$$

Substitution in Eq. (27) gives the value of the kinetic energy of the system after impact.

$$KE = \frac{WV^2}{2g} \left[\frac{1}{1 + W_b/3W} \right] \tag{28}$$

Upon impact the force in the bar increases uniformly from zero to a maximum value of F. The average value is $\frac{1}{2}F$. If δ represents the maximum shortening of the bar under impact, the strain energy of the bar at the instant of maximum compression is $\frac{1}{2}F\delta$. If k represents the force required to compress the bar a unit distance, then $\delta = F/k$ and the energy is equal to $\frac{1}{2}F^2/k$. This is equal to the KE in Eq. (28). When these values are equated, the following expression results.

$$F = V \sqrt{\frac{kW}{g} \left[\frac{1}{1 + (W_b/3W)} \right]} \tag{29}$$

The stress in the bar is found by dividing both sides of this equation by the cross-sectional area A. The equation can then be rearranged as follows.

$$s = \frac{V}{A} \sqrt{\frac{kW_b}{g}} \sqrt{\frac{W}{W_b} \left[\frac{1}{1 + (W_b/3W)} \right]}$$

or

$$\frac{s}{s_0} = \sqrt{\frac{W}{W_b} \left[\frac{1}{1 + (W_b/3W)} \right]} \tag{30}$$

where s_0 is given by Eq. (25). Equation (30), derived from the energy assumption, is plotted in Fig. 12-11.

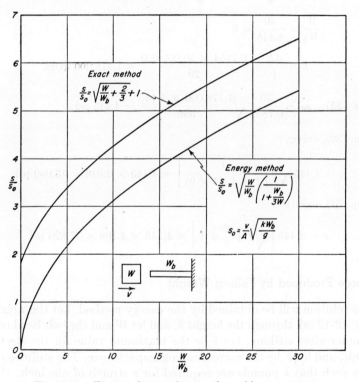

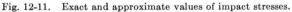

Fig. 12-11.   Exact and approximate values of impact stresses.

The exact solution to this problem is obtained by more involved methods. The results can be closely represented by the following empirical equation which is also plotted in Fig. 12-11.

$$\frac{s}{s_0} = \sqrt{\frac{W}{W_b} + \frac{2}{3}} + 1 \tag{31}$$

Examination of the curves indicates that large discrepancies are present when the energy method is used and when the ratio of striking weight to weight of bar, W/W_b, is small.

Example 8. A 1 in. diameter round steel bar 20 in. long is struck by a 40 lb weight moving at a velocity of 30 in. per sec. Find the value of the stress due to impact by the energy method and compare with the results of the exact solution.

Solution.

$$W_b = \frac{\gamma \pi d^2 l}{4} = \frac{0.283\pi 1^2 \times 20}{4} = 4.445 \text{ lb}$$

$$\frac{W}{W_b} = \frac{40}{4.445} = 9$$

$$k = \frac{AE}{l} = \frac{0.7854 \times 30,000,000}{20} = 1,178,000 \text{ lb/in.}$$

By Eq. (25): $s_0 = \frac{30}{0.7854} \sqrt{\frac{1,178,000 \times 4.445}{386}} = 4,445 \text{ psi}$

By Eq. (30), energy:

$$s = 4,445 \sqrt{9 \left[\frac{1}{1 + 1/(3 \times 9)} \right]} = 4,445 \times 2.946 = 13,080 \text{ psi}$$

By Eq. (31), exact:

$$s = 4,445 \left[\sqrt{9 + \frac{2}{3}} + 1 \right] = 4,445 \times 4.108 = 17,820 \text{ psi}$$

8. Force Produced by Falling Weight

The solution will be obtained by the energy method. Let the weight W in Fig. 12-12 fall through the height h, and let W and the bolt head remain in contact after striking. Let δ be the maximum value for the stretch of the bolt, and let F be the corresponding impact force. The stiffness of the bolt is such that k pounds are required for a stretch of one inch.

After impact, and at the lowest point of travel, the elastic energy gained by the bolt is equal to $F\delta/2$, as illustrated by the force-deformation graph in Fig. 12-12. This energy comes from the kinetic energy of the weight, as given by Eq. (28), together with the potential energy $W\delta$ given up by the additional lowering of the weight. Hence,

$$\frac{F\delta}{2} = \frac{WV^2}{2g} \cdot \frac{1}{1 + (W_b/3W)} + W\delta \tag{a}$$

When the substitutions for the impact deflection, $\delta = F/k$, and for the statical deflection, $\delta_{st} = W/k$, are made in the expression above, a quadratic equation results, which, upon solution for F/W, gives the following result.

$$\frac{F}{W} = 1 + \sqrt{1 + \frac{2h}{\delta_{st}} \cdot \frac{1}{1 + (W_b/3W)}} \qquad (32)$$

The value of the impact force F can be obtained by substitution in this equation. It can be written in terms of velocity V for the falling weight, if desired, by use of the relationship $V^2 = 2gh$, where g is the gravitational constant. Equation (32) indicates that if the weight is held just above the bolt head, $h = 0$, and then released, $F = 2W$.

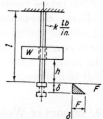

The value of k for a cylindrical bar is equal to AE/l, where A is the cross-sectional area, and E is the modulus of elasticity. This value is found by taking the equation for deformation, $\delta = Fl/AE$, and letting δ be equal to unity when the load F becomes equal to k. In all the foregoing, it is assumed, of course, that the elastic limit for the bolt material is not exceeded.

Fig. 12-12. Force and deformation caused by falling weight.

Example 9. In Fig. 12-12 let the bar be round, with a diameter of $\frac{1}{2}$ in. and length of 12 in. If weight W is 10 lb, find the maximum stress in the bolt if height h is 4 in. Material weighs 0.283 lb/in.³; $E = 30,000,000$ psi.

Solution. $A = \dfrac{\pi d^2}{4} = 0.1964$ in.², area of bolt

$$\delta_{st} = \frac{Wl}{AE} = \frac{10 \times 12}{0.1964 \times 30,000,000} = 0.00002037 \text{ in.}$$

$$W_b = 12 \times 0.1964 \times 0.283 = 0.6668 \text{ lb}$$

In Eq. (32), $\dfrac{F}{10} = 1 + \sqrt{1 + \dfrac{2 \times 4}{0.00002037} \cdot \left(\dfrac{1}{1 + 0.6668/(3 \times 10)}\right)}$

$$F = 6,200 \text{ lb}$$

$$s = \frac{6,200}{0.1964} = 31,570 \text{ psi}$$

This problem indicates that high stresses are readily produced by impact loads. It may also be noted that the weight of the bar W_b, when small, has but little effect on the force caused by impact.

If the yield point stress of the material is exceeded, a portion of the energy of the falling weight is used in giving a permanent stretch to the bar.

If the lower end of the bolt in the foregoing problem were threaded, and if the weight were stopped in its fall by the nut, the entire force of 6,200 lb would pass through the net section at the threads, and the stress would thereby be considerably increased. Thus, for $\frac{1}{2}''$–13UNC with an area at the root of thread of 0.1416 in.², the stress would be 43,790 psi. Furthermore, there would be stress concentration effects at the root of the threads.

The impact stress can be reduced by decreasing the stiffness of the stressed member. Thus, suppose it were permissible to reduce the bolt, for the entire 12 in. length above the nut, to the stress area of the thread. A further substitution in Eq. (32) shows that force F is reduced to 5,290 lb. The stress becomes 37,360 psi, as compared with 43,790 psi when the full $\frac{1}{2}$ in. body was used.

Hence, decreasing the cross section of the main body of the bolt, which must absorb the energy of the impact, to that of the minimum size through which the force must pass, has brought about a substantial reduction in the magnitude of the force. A further reduction in size, however, would cause the stress in the bolt to increase.

9. Impact of Weight on Beam

Impact between a weight and a simply supported beam is illustrated in Fig. 12-13. The energy method can also be applied to this problem; it gives the following equation for the ratio between the impact force F and the weight W.

$$\frac{F}{W} = 1 + \sqrt{1 + \frac{2h}{\delta_{st}} \cdot \frac{1}{1 + (17W_b/35W)}} \qquad (33)$$

where W_b is the weight of the beam, and h and δ_{st} have the same meanings as in the preceding section. Equation (33) is known as the Cox equation. It has been in use for almost a century. Like all energy solutions, it is of somewhat limited usefulness.

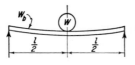

Fig. 12-13. Impact of weight on beam.

For most metals, the yield point and ultimate strength are raised when the load is very quickly applied and is of short duration. Because of the many uncertainties present, designers are rarely inclined to take advantage of these raised properties when deciding upon suitable values for the working stresses.

10. Gaskets and Seals

Gaskets and seals are divided into two main classes: static and dynamic. The static gasket is used to prevent the loss of fluid in a pressure vessel.

A dynamic seal is used to prevent loss of fluid in a sliding or rotating joint. Numerous types of materials are used such as organic and mineral fibers, leather, natural and synthetic rubber, cork, paper, and soft metals.

For static seals, a flat rigid surface and a thin gasket are preferable, and a minimum amount of packing surface should be exposed to the fluid.

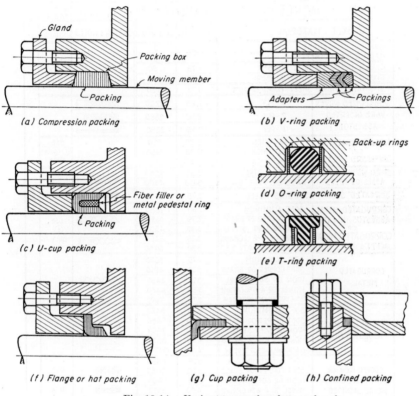

Fig. 12-14.   Various types of gaskets and seals.

Sometimes the sealing is created by friction. Sometimes the gasket is confined to a chamber and distorted to effect a seal by jamming the packing across the leakage path. Allowance must sometimes be made for a change in volume if the gasket material swells upon contact with the fluid. For a dynamic seal it is most important that the sliding member have a very smooth hard surface.

Various shapes for a number of different gaskets and seals are shown in Fig. 12-14. The stuffing box shown in (a) has the disadvantage of high friction when the pressure of the gasket is high enough to prevent loss of fluid. The V-ring or chevron packing shown in (b) has less friction and tends to seal more tightly with increase of pressure. The molded U-cup packing is widely used for low and medium pressures. The O-ring shown in (d) has the advantage of low friction and simplicity of design. The ring should be slightly compressed after assembly. This seal is popular in aeroplane hydraulic mechanisms. The plastic back-up rings prevent

TABLE A: GASKET FACTORS m AND YIELD VALUES y — REFER TO TABLE B:

GASKET MATERIAL		GASKET FACTOR m	YIELD VALUE y	SKETCH & NOTES	FACING LIMITATION	USE COL
GUM RUBBER SHEET		.50	0			
HARD RUBBER SHEET		1.00	180			
CLOTH INSERTED SOFT RUBBER		.75	50		USE ①④⑥ ONLY	
CLOTH INSERTED HARD RUBBER		1.25	400			
VEGETABLE FIBRE SHEET (HEMP OR JUTE)		1.75	1120			
RUBBERIZED WOVEN WIRE INSERTED ASBESTOS	3-PLY	2.25	2200			
	2-PLY	2.50	2880			
	1-PLY	2.75	3650			
ASBESTOS COMPOSITION OR COMPRESSED ASBESTOS	1/8" THICK	2.00	1620		USE ①④⑥ ONLY	
	1/16" THICK	2.75	3650			
	1/32" THICK	3.50	6480			
SPIRAL-WOUND METAL, ASBESTOS FILLED	CARBON STEEL	2.50	2880			
	KA25 OR TYPE 316	3.00	4500			
SERRATED STEEL, ASBESTOS FILLED		2.75	3650			**II**
CORRUGATED METAL, ASBESTOS INSERTED OR CORRUGATED METAL JACKET, ASBESTOS FILLED	SOFT ALUMINUM	2.50	2880		USE ① ONLY	
	SOFT COPPER OR BRASS	2.75	3650			
	IRON OR SOFT STEEL	3.00	4500			
	MONEL OR 4-6% CHROME	3.25	5450			
	11-13% CHROME, KA25 OR TYPE 316	3.50	6480			
CORRUGATED METAL	SOFT ALUMINUM	2.75	3650			
	SOFT COPPER OR BRASS	3.00	4500			
	IRON OR SOFT STEEL	3.25	5450			
	MONEL OR 4-6% CHROME	3.50	6480			
	11-13% CHROME, KA25 OR TYPE 316	3.75	7600			
FLAT METAL JACKET, ASBESTOS FILLED	SOFT ALUMINUM	3.25	5450			
	SOFT COPPER OR BRASS	3.50	6480			
	IRON OR SOFT STEEL	3.75	7600			
	MONEL OR 4-6% CHROME	4.00	8820			
	11-13% CHROME, KA25 OR TYPE 316	4.25	10120			
GROOVED IRON OR SOFT STEEL CORE, METAL JACKETED	SOFT ALUMINUM	3.25	5450		USE ①④⑥ ONLY	
	SOFT COPPER OR BRASS	3.50	6480			
	IRON OR SOFT STEEL	3.75	7600			
	MONEL OR 4-6% CHROME	4.00	8820			
	11-13% CHROME, KA25 OR TYPE 316	4.25	10120			
SOLID METAL, 1/8 THICKNESS OR MORE (FOR THINNER GASKETS SEE NOTE)	SOFT ALUMINUM	4.00	8820	NOTE: FOR EACH 1/32" REDUCTION IN THICKNESS BELOW 1/8" INCREASE m BY .25, COMPUTE $y = 180(2m-1)^2$		**I**
	SOFT COPPER OR BRASS	4.75	13000			
	IRON OR SOFT STEEL	5.50	18000			
	MONEL OR 4-6% CHROME	6.00	21780			
	11-13% CHROME, KA25 OR TYPE 316	6.50	25920			

(Reproduced from Mechanical Engineering, reference 18, bibliography.)

extrusion of the soft rubber into the clearance space under very high pressures. The flange or hat packing shown in (f) is used in a number of different forms. Sometimes a circumferential spring is used to press the lip of the packing against the shaft.

In piping service, rubber and other nonmetallic materials, as well as low-melting metals, are generally limited to temperature below 250 F. Materials such as asbestos, with or without metal jacketing, may be used up to 850 F. For temperatures higher than 850 F, all-metal gaskets must be used.

Various kinds of gaskets are illustrated in Table A. To maintain a fluid-tight joint it is necessary that the parts be tightly bolted together. The initial or bolting-up pressure must be enough to cause local yielding of the gasket where it is in contact with the asperities of the metal flange surfaces. This minimum contact pressure, necessary to secure a tight joint even for low values of the internal pressure, is called the "yield" value y of the gasket. Values are given in Table A.

The internal fluid pressure in the pipe or vessel reduces the gasket contact pressure. Experience has shown that the ratio between the resultant contact pressure and the fluid pressure should not be less than a certain value if the joint is to remain tight. This ratio is called the gasket factor m. As indicated by Table A, it varies for different kinds of gaskets.

The bolting-up and fluid pressures cause a distortion in the flanges and adjacent parts of the joint. The chief effect is a rotation that tends to concentrate the entire gasket force on the outer edge of the gasket. Gasket pressures are accordingly not computed for the entire width, but only for a narrow band on the outer edge, called the effective gasket yielding width b. Equations for determining this width are found in Table B. Although these equations are empirical, they are based on long experience in the design of fluid-tight joints.[7]

FACING SKETCH	BASIC GASKET YIELDING WIDTH b_0	
	COL. I	COL. II
(1a)	$\dfrac{n}{2}$	$\dfrac{n}{2}$
(1b)	$\dfrac{w+t}{2}\left(\dfrac{w+n}{4}\,max\right)$	$\dfrac{w+t}{2}\left(\dfrac{w+n}{4}\,max\right)$
(2)	$\dfrac{w+n}{4}$	$\dfrac{w+3n}{8}$
(3)	$\dfrac{w}{2};\left(\dfrac{n}{4}\,min\right)$	$\dfrac{w+n}{4}:\left(\dfrac{3n}{8}\,min\right)$
(4)	$\dfrac{3n}{8}$	$\dfrac{7n}{16}$
(5)		
(6)		
(7)	$\dfrac{n}{4}$	$\dfrac{3n}{8}$
(8)	$\dfrac{w}{8}$	

TABLE B: EFFECTIVE GASKET WIDTH b

EFFECTIVE GASKET YIELDING WIDTH b

$b = b_0$, when $b_0 \leqq \frac{1}{4}''$

$b = \dfrac{\sqrt{b_0}}{2}$, when $b_0 > \frac{1}{4}''$

LOCATION OF GASKET LOAD ATTACK

INSIDE GASKET　WITH NUBBIN　FULL FACE GASKET

O.D. CONTACT FACE　Ⴒ NUBBIN　I.D. BOLTS　Ⴒ BETWEEN O.D. BOLTS & O.D. OF FLANGE

(*Reproduced from* Mechanical Engineering, *reference 18, bibliography.*)

The area subjected to fluid pressure is assumed to extend to the edge of the effective gasket area.

Figure 12-15 shows the forces acting in a gasketed joint. Before the fluid pressure is acting, the force F_o in the bolt and on the gasket is

$$F_o = A_o q \qquad (34)$$

[7] See reference 18, Bibliography.

where A_g is the effective area of the gasket, and q is pressure on the gasket caused by tightening the bolts.

After the fluid pressure p is acting, a force $A_i p$ is produced, where A_i is the area subjected to internal pressure. The force on the gasket required

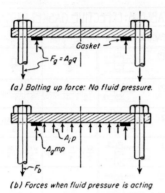

(a) Bolting up force: No fluid pressure.

(b) Forces when fluid pressure is acting

Fig. 12-15. Equilibrium of gasketed joint.

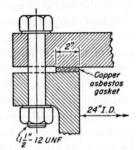

Fig. 12-16. Gasketed manhole cover, Example 10.

to prevent loss of pressure is $A_g mp$. The bolt force F_b then is

$$F_b = p(A_i + A_g m) \tag{35}$$

Forces F_g and F_b can be taken as substantially equal to each other. Then

$$A_g q = p(A_i + A_g m) \tag{36}$$

Example 10. A cross section through a gasketed manhole joint is shown in Fig. 12-16. The internal fluid pressure is 500 psi gage. If 24 bolts are used for holding the cover in place, find the tensile stress in the net area of the threads.

Solution.

From Table B: $\quad b_o = \dfrac{n}{2} = \dfrac{2}{2} = 1$ in.

$$b = \frac{\sqrt{b_o}}{2} = \frac{\sqrt{1}}{2} = 0.5 \text{ in., effective gasket width}$$

Effective gasket area: $\quad A_g = 27.5\pi \times 0.5 = 43.2$ in.^{2}

Area subjected to

internal pressure: $\quad A_i = \dfrac{\pi}{4} \times 27^2 = 572.6$ in.^{2}

By Table A: $\quad m = 3.5$

In Eq. (36):
$$q = \frac{500(572.6 + 43.2 \times 3.5)}{43.2}$$

$$= 8,380 \text{ psi}$$

This value for the gasket pressure is satisfactory, since Table A indicates that a compression of 6,480 psi is sufficient to seat the gasket properly.

For $1\frac{1}{2}''$–12 UNF: Stress area = 1.58 in.²

By Eq. (35): $F_b = 500(572.6 + 43.2 \times 3.5) = 361,900 \text{ lb}$

Tensile stress: $s = \dfrac{361,900}{24 \times 1.58} = 9,540 \text{ psi}$

For small diameters or low pressures, the initial gasket contact pressure, when computed as in the foregoing example, may be smaller than the y-value given in Table A. Additional bolt-ing-up force should be applied until the contact pressure is equal to, or slightly greater than, the tabulated value. However, for large diameters or high pressures, care must be exercised to assure that the bolting-up pressure on the effective area does not exceed the true yield point value in compression for the gasket material. The gasket must retain sufficient elasticity to maintain a tight joint after the initial compression has been reduced by the fluid pressure. Published information is lacking at the present time on the maximum permissible contact pressure for the various types of gaskets. For solid metal gaskets, the yield point value in compression would be used.

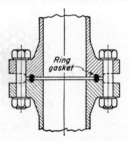

Fig. 12-17.   Ring-type flange joint for high pressure service.

Considerable experience is required to design high-pressure joints properly. The maximum internal pressure that a particular type of gasket can retain depends on a number of factors, such as flange design, type of facing, bolt location and arrangement, and relaxation of bolts at elevated temperature. Stresses and deformations at the joint arising from the thermal expansion of the connected parts must also be considered. For severe service conditions, the ring-type joint illustrated in Fig. 12-17 has proved very successful. It is easily made tight and the gasket can be used over and over again. The cross section is either oval or octagonal, and the temper should be dead soft. This type of gasket will not blow out if a leak develops in service.

It is sometimes difficult, in high pressure joints, to secure sufficient initial bolt force. Bolts with larger diameters will carry more force, but it is difficult to tighten larger bolts to the same stress that is easily secured in bolts of smaller diameter. A torque wrench must, of course, be used if a predetermined stress is to be secured in the bolt. Experience has shown that installation stresses due to torque loads for various sizes of alloy-steel studs made in accordance with the 8-pitch thread series in sizes larger than 1 inch are approximately equal to those given by the following empirical equation.

$$s = \frac{45,000}{\sqrt{d}} \tag{37}$$

where d is the nominal diameter of bolt stud.[8]

11. Wire Rope

Wire rope is used in conveying and hoisting equipment, and also in such stationary applications as guy wires and stays. A number of wires,

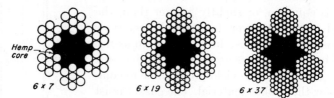

Fig. 12-18.   Cross sections of typical wire rope.

such as 7, 19, or 37, are first twisted into a strand. A number of strands, usually 6 or 8, are then twisted about a core or center to form the rope. Cores may be of hemp or of wire. Several typical cross sections for wire rope are given in Fig. 12-18. The wires are made of various grades of steel, although wrought iron is also used. For long life the core, as well as the entire rope, must be continuously saturated with lubricant.

Flexibility in wire ropes is secured by using a large number of small-diameter wires. Ropes of few wires of relatively large size, such as the 6 × 7, are used for guy wires, but are too stiff for hoisting service unless the sheaves have very large diameters. The 6 × 19 and 6 × 37 types are the most widely used ropes for hoisting service. The radius of the groove in the sheave should be just large enough to provide clearance for the rope without pinching. The circular cross section of the rope is preserved and the stresses are more evenly distributed. The condition and proper alignment of the sheaves are also important factors in affecting the useful life. When wire rope is wound on drums in two or more layers, abrasion and severe crushing stresses are induced, particularly where the rope must cross over the depressions made by the preceding layers.

[8] See reference 19, Bibliography.

Wire ropes are subjected to various kinds of stresses. There is the direct tension stress T/A, where T is the force in the rope and A is the cross-sectional area. Bending stresses also occur in the wires when the rope is passing over a sheave. From elementary mechanics, it is known that

$$\frac{M}{EI} = \frac{1}{r} = \frac{2}{d_s}$$

$$s = \frac{Mc}{I} = \frac{Md_w}{2I}$$

(a)

where d_w is the diameter of the wire, d_s is the diameter of the sheave, I is the moment of inertia of a single wire, and E is the modulus of elasticity for the material. Elimination of M/I between these equations gives the following expression for the bending stress.

$$s = \frac{d_w E}{d_s}$$

(38)

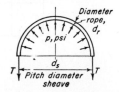

Fig. 12-19. Forces in wire rope passing around sheave.

An increase in wire size is thus seen to give an increase in stress. A decrease in sheave size also gives an increase in bending stress, and care must be exercised that wire rope is not operated on excessively small sheaves.

The pressure p between rope and sheave can be determined by consideration of Fig. 12-19. This pressure is assumed to be uniformly distributed over the curved surface of the groove which receives the rope and which runs circumferentially around the sheave. The value of the tensile force T in the rope is then equal to $\frac{1}{2}pd_rd_s$, where d_r is the diameter of the rope. Hence

$$p = \frac{2T}{d_r d_s}$$

(39)

Because of the small areas in actual contact between the wires, or between wires and groove, merely nominal values for p cause very high compressive stresses in the materials.

Failure of a wire rope occurs as a result of fatigue and wear in passing over the sheaves. Recent investigations[9] have shown that the ratio of pressure p to the ultimate strength of the material is a significant variable for determining the fatigue life. Figure 12-20 shows the results of plotting p/s_{ult} vs. bends to failure for various kinds of wire rope. A flexing and unflexing of the rope in passing over a sheave counts as a single bend. This figure indicates, for example, that if a 6 × 19 rope has a p/s_{ult} value

[9] See reference 28, Bibliography.

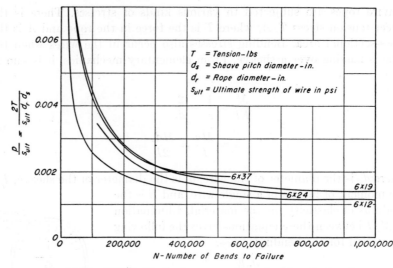

Fig. 12-20. Fatigue life of wire rope as determined by experiments.

of 0.0014, a very long life can be expected so far as fatigue failure is concerned. The product $d_r d_s$ in the denominator of the variable indicates that a decrease in the diameter of the sheave permits an increase in the size of the rope; however, a practical lower limit exists for sheave size beyond which it is not safe to go because of high bending stresses and abrasion of the wires.

Dimensional data for ropes and information on the physical properties of the materials are given in Table 12-3. The minimum diameters for

TABLE 12-3

Wire Rope Data

Metallic Cross-Sectional Area (d_r = Dia Rope)		Diameter of Outer Wire d_w	Minimum Diameter d_s for Sheaves for Steel Rope	Modulus of Elasticity of Steel Rope	Breaking Stress	
Type	in.²	in.	in.	psi	Type of Material	psi
6 × 7	$0.380d_r^2$	$\frac{1}{9}d_r$	$42d_r$	14,000,000	Improved plow steel	200,000
6 × 19	$0.404d_r^2$	$\frac{1}{16}d_r$ *	$24d_r$	12,000,000	Plow steel	175,000
6 × 37	$0.404d_r^2$	$\frac{1}{22}d_r$	$18d_r$	11,000,000	Extra-strong cast steel	160,000
8 × 19	$0.352d_r^2$	$\frac{1}{19}d_r$	$20d_r$	10,000,000	Cast steel	140,000
					Iron	65,000

* Filler wire type. For Warrington type large outer wires, $d_w = \frac{1}{14}$.

sheaves for iron rope are 50 per cent greater than the values for steel rope. Values for the minimum factor of safety for various kinds of applications are shown in Table 12-4.

TABLE 12-4

Minimum Factors of Safety

Type of Service	FS	Type of Service			FS
		Hot-ladle cranes			8
Track cables	3.2	Slings			8
Guys	3.5				
Mine shafts, 500-ft depth	8	Elevators—	Pas-	Freight	Dumb-
1,000–2,000-ft depth	6	Carspeed, fpm	senger		waiters
3,000 ft-depth and more	4				
Miscellaneous hoisting equipment	5	50	7.50	6.67	5.33
Haulage ropes	6	150	8.20	7.32	5.98
Overhead and gantry cranes	6	300	9.17	8.20	6.88
Jib and pillar cranes	6	500	10.25	9.14	8.00
Derricks	6	800	11.25	10.02	
Small electric and air hoists	7	1,100	11.67	10.43	
		1,500	11.87	10.61	

Example 11.

(a) What diameter of 6 × 19 wire rope of improved plow steel would be required for a 5-ton load supported on 8 lines? Compute for long life and continuous operation.

(b) What is the permissible static load for the rope of part (a)? Use a factor of safety of 6.

(c) If the rope is always loaded to the full static value, find the number of bends, using minimum size pulleys, which the rope can sustain before fatigue failure may be expected. On the basis of 100 bends per working day, what would be the expected life of the cable?

(d) What minimum size sheave would be required for the rope to be free from fatigue if operation takes place at the static load value?

Solution. (a)

By Table 12-3: $s_{ult} = 200,000$ psi, and $d_s = 24d_r$. $T = \dfrac{5 \times 2,000}{8} = 1,250$ lb

From Fig. 12-20: $\dfrac{2T}{s_{ult}d_r d_s} = 0.0014$

Hence: $d_r d_s = 24d_r^2 = \dfrac{2T}{0.0014 s_{ult}} = \dfrac{2 \times 1,250}{0.0014 \times 200,000} = 8.93$

Solving: $d_r = 0.61$ in. Use $\frac{5}{8}$-in. diameter rope

$d_s = 24 \times \frac{5}{8} = 15$ in. recommended minimum diameter of sheave

(b)

By Table 12-3: $A = 0.404d_r{}^2 = 0.404 \times 0.625^2$

$= 0.158$ in.² metallic cross-sectional area

Max. static load $= \dfrac{0.158 \times 200,000}{6} = 5,200$ lb

The maximum permissible static load is over 4 times as great as the working load when fatigue is considered.

(c)

$$\frac{2T}{s_{ult}d_r d_s} = \frac{2 \times 5,200}{200,000 \times 0.625 \times 15} = 0.00555$$

From Figure 12-20:

No. of bends to failure $= 65,000$

Expected life $= \dfrac{65,000}{100} = 650$ working days

(d)

$$d_s = \frac{2T}{s_{ult}d_r \times 0.0014} = \frac{2 \times 5,200}{200,000 \times 0.625 \times 0.0014} = 59.5 \text{ in.}$$

This result is the diameter of the sheave for operation at the permissible static load and for freedom from fatigue. It is obviously an impractical result. Therefore, a reduced load must be used, as was done in part (a), if sheaves of reasonable size are to be used, and if freedom from fatigue is to be achieved as well.

Catalogs of wire rope manufacturers contain a large amount of valuable information on the selection and maintenance of rope. Their knowledge of field conditions, collected over many years of experience, should be utilized by the purchaser.

12. Curved Beams

Curved beams in the form of hooks and brackets are frequently used as machine elements. When such bodies are subjected to bending moments, the stress distribution is not linear on either side of the neutral axis, but increases more rapidly on the inner side. For curved beams, the assumption can usually be made with sufficient accuracy that cross sections normal to the curved elements of the unloaded beam remain plane and perpendicular to the elements after the bending moments are acting. The deformations thus vary directly with the distance from the neutral axis.

Consider the elements of the curved beam of Fig. 12-21 lying between two axia' planes AB and DE separated by the angle φ. Let the total angular deformation of plane AB with respect to DE be represented by $d\varphi$. A shorter element on the inner side thus deforms the same amount as a longer element, symmetrically located with respect to the neutral surface, deforms on the outer side. The inner element, however, has the

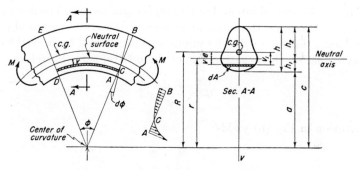

Fig. 12-21.   Curved beam in pure bending.

higher stress, since its deformation has taken place over a shorter length element.

The cross sections of the beam of Fig. 12-21 are assumed to be symmetrical with respect to the v-axis, as is indicated by view A-A. Because of the higher stresses on the inner elements, the neutral surface for a curved beam no longer passes through the center of gravity of the cross sections, but shifts inward a small amount, designated e in the figure. The total deformation for an element located a distance v below the neutral surface is $v\,d\varphi$. This deformation takes place in an element whose length is $(r - v)\varphi$. The elongation or unit deformation ϵ then is

$$\epsilon = \frac{v\,d\varphi}{(r - v)\varphi} \tag{a}$$

Multiplication by the modulus of elasticity E gives the stress at this point. Thus

$$s = \frac{Ev\,d\varphi}{(r - v)\varphi} = \frac{E\,d\varphi}{\varphi}\left[\frac{r}{r - v} - 1\right] \tag{b}$$

This equation indicates that the distribution of stress over the cross section is hyperbolic.

From the condition of static equilibrium, the sum of the stresses over a cross section must add to zero, and the moment made by the stresses must be equal to the applied moment M. Hence

$$\int s\,dA = \frac{E\,d\varphi}{\varphi}\int \frac{v\,dA}{r - v} = 0 \tag{c}$$

$$\int sv\,dA = \frac{E\,d\varphi}{\varphi}\int \frac{v^2\,dA}{r - v} = M \tag{d}$$

The integrations in the equations above are to extend over the entire cross section. By division of numerator by denominator, Eq. (d) becomes

$$M = -\frac{E\,d\varphi}{\varphi}\int v\,dA + \frac{E\,r\,d\varphi}{\varphi}\int \frac{v\,dA}{r-v} \tag{e}$$

By Eq. (c), the second integral of Eq. (e) is equal to zero. The first integral of Eq. (e) represents the moment of area of the cross section about the neutral axis, that is, $-eA$. The minus sign is required because the center of gravity lies on the negative side of the neutral axis. Therefore

$$M = \frac{E\,d\varphi}{\varphi}eA \tag{f}$$

Substitution in Eq. (b) yields

$$s = \frac{M}{eA}\frac{v}{r-v} \tag{g}$$

Substitution of the limits for v, gives the following equations.

$$s_{max} = \frac{Mh_1}{Aea} \qquad \text{when} \quad v = h_1 \tag{40}$$

$$s_{min} = -\frac{Mh_2}{Aec} \qquad \text{when} \quad v = -h_2 \tag{41}$$

Since these equations are sensitive to small variations in the value of e, considerable care must be exercised in determining this quantity accurately.

Additional useful equations can be obtained by letting $v = v_1 - e$ in Eq. (c).

$$\int \frac{v}{r-v}\,dA = \int \frac{v_1 - e}{r - v_1 + e}\,dA = \int \frac{v_1 - e}{R - v_1}\,dA = 0 \tag{h}$$

The integral on the right may be written

$$\int \frac{v_1\,dA}{R - v_1} = e\int \frac{dA}{R - v_1} \tag{i}$$

$$= \frac{e}{R}\int \frac{R - v_1 + v_1}{R - v_1}\,dA \tag{j}$$

$$= \frac{e}{R}\left[\int dA + \int \frac{v_1\,dA}{R - v_1}\right] \tag{k}$$

Let

$$\int \frac{v_1\,dA}{R - v_1} = m_1 A \tag{42}$$

where A is the area of the cross section, and m_1 is another constant. Substitution in Eq. (k) will give the following equation for e.

$$e = \frac{m_1 R}{1 + m_1} \tag{43}$$

Substitution in Eq. (i) gives

$$\int \frac{dA}{R - v_1} = \frac{A}{R}(1 + m_1) \tag{44}$$

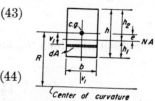

The integral of Eq. (44) can be evaluated for simple types of cross sections and the value of m_1 can then be found. Eccentricity e can then be found by use of Eq. (43), and the stress by use of Eqs. (40) and (41).

Fig. 12-22. Curved beam of rectangular cross section.

13. Curved Beam of Rectangular Cross Section

The foregoing general equations for the stresses in a curved beam are now adapted to the rectangular cross section. Equation (44) can be written

$$A(1 + m_1) = \int_{-h/2}^{+h/2} \frac{dA}{1 - (v_1/R)} \tag{a}$$

When the numerator is divided by the denominator, the following result is obtained.

$$A(1 + m_1) = \int_{-h/2}^{+h/2} \left[1 + \frac{v_1}{R} + \frac{v_1^2}{R^2} + \frac{v_1^3}{R^3} + \frac{v_1^4}{R^4} + \cdots \right] b \, dv_1$$

This expression should now be integrated term by term and the limits substituted.

$$A(1 + m_1) = b \left[h + \frac{h^3}{12R^2} + \frac{h^5}{80R^4} \right] \tag{b}$$

or

$$m_1 = \frac{h^2}{12R^2} + \frac{h^4}{80R^4} \tag{c}$$

Let $c_1 = 2R/h$, where c_1 is called the index of curvature. When this substitution is made, Eq. (c), becomes

$$m_1 = \frac{1}{3c_1^2} + \frac{1}{5c_1^4} = \frac{1}{3c_1^2} \left[1 + \frac{0.6}{c_1^2} \right]$$

$$= \frac{1}{3c_1^2} \left[\frac{c_1^2 + 0.6}{c_1^2} \right] \approx \frac{1}{3c_1^2} \left[\frac{c_1^2}{c_1^2 - 0.6} \right] = \frac{1}{3c_1^2 - 1.8} \tag{d}$$

The eccentricity e is found by substitution into Eq. (43).

$$e = \frac{hc_1}{2(3c_1{}^2 - 0.8)} \tag{45}$$

Substitution for e, h_1, and a in Eq. (40) gives the maximum stress.

$$s_{max} = \frac{6M}{bh_2} \times \frac{3c_1{}^2 - c_1 - 0.8}{3c_1(c_1 - 1)} = K_c \frac{6M}{bh^2} \tag{46}$$

where

$$K_c = \frac{3c_1{}^2 - c_1 - 0.8}{3c_1(c_1 - 1)} \tag{47}$$

Equation (47) gives the value of the stress concentration factor for curvature for a rectangular cross section.

Example 12. Let the width b of the rectangle be 4 in. and the depth of section h be 6 in. The radius of curvature R to the center of gravity is also equal to 6 in. Find the value of the eccentricity e, the stress concentration factor K_c, and the maximum stress.

Solution.

$$c_1 = \frac{2R}{h} = 2$$

In Eq. (45):

$$e = \frac{6 \times 2}{2(3 \times 2^2 - 0.8)} = 0.536 \text{ in.}$$

In Eq. (47):

$$K_c = \frac{3 \times 2^2 - 2 - 0.8}{3 \times 2(2 - 1)} = 1.533$$

In Eq. (46):

$$s_{max} = 1.533 \frac{6M}{4 \times 6^2} = 0.0639M$$

Sometimes the cross section of a curved beam is so shaped that no analytic expression can be derived for the eccentricity e. The integration of Eq. (42) can be performed numerically if the equation is written

$$m_1 A = \sum \frac{v_1 \Delta A}{R - v_1} \tag{48}$$

Accurate results can be obtained by this method if the cross section is divided into a sufficient number of elemental strips ΔA.

Example 13. Find the value of the maximum stress for the beam of Example 12 by use of Eq. (48) and compare with the results obtained by use of Eq. (46).

    Solution. Divide the cross section into 12 strips, as shown by Fig. 12-23. The computations of Eq. (48) have been carried out in Table 12-5. Substitution

TABLE 12-5

No.	v_1	$R - v_1$	$\dfrac{v_1\,\Delta A}{R - v_1}$
1	2.75	3.25	1.6923
2	2.25	3.75	1.2000
3	1.75	4.25	0.8235
4	1.25	4.75	0.5263
5	0.75	5.25	0.2857
6	0.25	5.75	0.0870
7	−0.25	6.25	−0.0800
8	−0.75	6.75	−0.2222
9	−1.25	7.25	−0.3448
10	−1.75	7.75	−0.4516
11	−2.25	8.25	−0.5454
12	−2.75	8.75	−0.6286

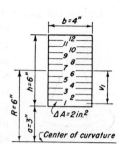

Fig. 12-23. Cross section of Example 13 divided into elementary strips.

$$\sum \frac{v_1 \Delta A}{R - v_1} = 2.3422$$

of the summation of the right-hand column in Eq. (48) gives

$$m_1 A = 2.3422$$

Solving: $$m_1 = \frac{2.3422}{24} = 0.0976$$

In Eq. (43): $$e = \frac{0.0976 \times 6}{1 + 0.0976} = 0.534 \text{ in.}$$

Hence: $$h_1 = 2.466 \text{ in.}$$

$$h_2 = 3.534 \text{ in.}$$

In Eq. (40): $$s_{max} = \frac{2.466M}{24 \times 0.534 \times 3} = 0.0642M$$

Numerical integration thus gives accurate results, and the method can therefore be used for odd-shaped cross sections.

14. Curved Beam of Circular Cross Section

By a similar process, the equation for the maximum stress in a curved beam of round cross section can be shown to be

$$s_{max} = K_c \frac{32M}{\pi d^3} \tag{49}$$

where $$K_c = \frac{4c_1^2 - c_1 - 1}{4c_1(c_1 - 1)} \tag{50}$$

The index of curvature c_1 is equal to $2R/d$.

15. Angular Deflection of Curved Bar

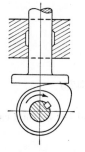

Unless the index of curvature, $2R/d$ or $2R/h$, is very small, the angular change between 2 cross sections of a curved beam caused by the moments M is approximately the same as would take place if the beam were straight. For a straight beam, the relationship between bending moment and radius of curvature is given by the equation $1/r = M/EI$. Since the moment M is the same at all points, the radius r is also constant, and the elastic line is a circle, as shown by Fig. 12-24. Since

Fig. 12-24. Angular deformation caused by moments.

$r\theta = l$, substitution for r gives the value of θ as

$$\theta = \frac{Ml}{EI} \tag{51}$$

16. Cams

A cam provides a convenient means for transforming rotary motion into reciprocating motion. Since the cam faces may be given a wide variety of shapes, many different types of motion can be secured. The plate cam, illustrated in Fig. 12-25, moves the follower in a direction at right angles to the cam axis. For the cylindrical cam of Fig. 12-26, the

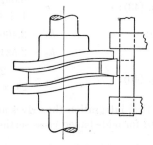

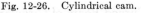

Fig. 12-25. Plate cam with mushroom follower.

Fig. 12-26. Cylindrical cam.

follower moves in a direction parallel to the cam axis. The cam must have the proper shape if the desired type of motion is to be imparted to the follower.

Figure 12-27 illustrates the fundamental relationships for a disk cam with an offset roller follower. The computations are made for the pitch surface. The base circle has a radius r_o. Lift L occurs during a rotation of θ_o. The follower is offset by the amount z_o. Rise x occurs during a rotation θ measured from the radius at the start of the rise to radius r to the roller center. Let rotation θ occur during time t; hence $\theta = \omega t$, where ω is the angular velocity in radians per second. Then $d\theta/dt = \omega$.

From Fig. 12-27,

$$y_o{}^2 = r_o{}^2 - z_o{}^2 \qquad (52)$$

also

$$r^2 = (y_o + x)^2 + z_o{}^2 \qquad (a)$$

$$= r_o{}^2 + 2y_o x + x^2 \qquad (53)$$

Equation (53) is obtained by substituting Eq. (52) into Eq. (a).

Cams can be shaped so that the rise is parabolic, harmonic, or cycloidal. These terms refer to the equations for rise x of the follower, and are given in Table 12-6.[10] The pitch surface can be

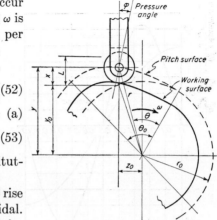

Fig. 12-27. Fundamental relationships for plate cam.

plotted by substituting the appropriate expression for x in Eq. (53). Displacement curves for the 3 types of cams are given in Fig. 12-28.

Table 12-6 also gives the equations for velocity and acceleration of the follower for each of the three types of cams. Velocities are plotted in Fig. 12-29, and accelerations are shown in Fig. 12-30. The inertia forces

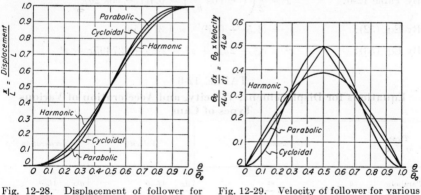

Fig. 12-28. Displacement of follower for various types of cams.

Fig. 12-29. Velocity of follower for various types of cams.

induced in the cam driven masses are proportional to the acceleration of the follower. The parabolic cam has the smallest maximum value for acceleration, but has the undesirable property of having sudden changes

[10] See reference 41, Bibliography.

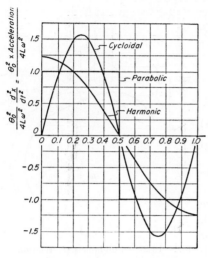

Fig. 12-30. Acceleration of follower for various types of cams.

in value at the start, the mid-height, and end of the rise. The harmonic cam has a gradual change in the value of the acceleration except at the start and end of cam action. The cycloidal cam has a higher peak value for the acceleration than the others, but its value does not change as abruptly.

Example 14. A harmonic cam has a base circle radius of 1.5 in. and a lift of 0.8 in. Rise takes place during 90° of rotation. Offset z_0 is 0.6 in. Compute values of radius r for the pitch surface for angular positions of 0°, 15°, 30°, 45°, 60°, 75°, and 90°. What is the maximum value of the acceleration if the rpm is 600?

Solution.

$$\theta_o = \frac{\pi}{2} \quad \text{or} \quad \frac{\pi}{\theta_o} = 2$$

By Table 12-6: $x = \dfrac{L}{2}\left(1 - \cos\dfrac{\pi\theta}{\theta_o}\right) = 0.4(1 - \cos 2\theta)$

By Eq. (52): $y_o = (1.5^2 - 0.6^2)^{\frac{1}{2}} = 1.3748$ in.

By Eq. (53): $r^2 = r_o{}^2 + 2y_o x + x^2 = 2.25 + 2.7495x + x^2$

TABLE 12-6
Equations for Displacement, Velocity, and Acceleration of Various Types of Cam

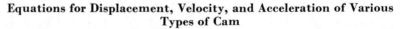

Type of Cam	Displacement		Velocity	Acceleration
Parabolic or constant acceleration	For $\dfrac{\theta}{\theta_o} \lessgtr 0.5$, $\quad x = 2L\dfrac{\theta^2}{\theta_o{}^2}$		$\dfrac{dx}{dt} = \dfrac{4L\omega\theta}{\theta_o{}^2}$	$\dfrac{d^2x}{dt^2} = \dfrac{4L\omega^2}{\theta_o{}^2}$
	For $\dfrac{\theta}{\theta_o} \gtrless 0.5$, $\quad x = L\left[1 - 2\left(1 - \dfrac{\theta}{\theta_o}\right)^2\right]$		$\dfrac{dx}{dt} = \dfrac{4L\omega}{\theta_o}\left(1 - \dfrac{\theta}{\theta_o}\right)$	$\dfrac{d^2x}{dt^2} = -\dfrac{4L\omega^2}{\theta_o{}^2}$
Harmonic	$x = \dfrac{L}{2}\left(1 - \cos\dfrac{\pi\theta}{\theta_o}\right)$		$\dfrac{dx}{dt} = \dfrac{\pi L\omega}{2\theta_o}\sin\dfrac{\pi\theta}{\theta_o}$	$\dfrac{d^2x}{dt^2} = \dfrac{\pi^2 L\omega^2}{2\theta_o{}^2}\cos\dfrac{\pi\theta}{\theta_o}$
Cycloidal	$x = \dfrac{L}{\pi}\left(\dfrac{\pi\theta}{\theta_o} - \dfrac{1}{2}\sin\dfrac{2\pi\theta}{\theta_o}\right)$		$\dfrac{dx}{dt} = \dfrac{L\omega}{\theta_o}\left(1 - \cos\dfrac{2\pi\theta}{\theta_o}\right)$	$\dfrac{d^2x}{dt^2} = \dfrac{2\pi L\omega^2}{\theta_o{}^2}\sin\dfrac{2\pi\theta}{\theta_o}$

The calculations can be conveniently carried out in tabular form.

θ	$\dfrac{\pi\theta}{\theta_o} = 2\theta$	$\cos\dfrac{\pi\theta}{\theta_o}$	$1 - \cos\dfrac{\theta\pi}{\theta_o}$	x	$2.7495x$	x^2	r^2	r
0°	0°	1.00000	0	0	0	0	2.2500	1.5000
15°	30°	0.86603	0.13397	0.0536	0.1474	0.0029	2.4002	1.5493
30°	60°	0.50000	0.50000	0.2000	0.5499	0.0400	2.8399	1.6852
45°	90°	0	1.00000	0.4000	1.0998	0.1600	3.5098	1.8734
60°	120°	−0.50000	1.50000	0.6000	1.6497	0.3600	4.2597	2.0639
75°	150°	−0.86603	1.86603	0.7464	2.0523	0.5571	4.8594	2.2044
90°	180°	−1.00000	2.00000	0.8000	2.1996	0.6400	5.0896	2.2560

$$\omega = \frac{600 \times 2\pi}{60} = 20\pi$$

By Table 12-6, $\left(\dfrac{d^2x}{dt^2}\right)_{max} = \dfrac{\pi^2 L\omega^2}{2\theta_o{}^2} = \dfrac{\pi^2 \times 0.8 \times 400\pi^2}{2\pi^2/4} = 640\pi^2$

$$= 6{,}317 \text{ in./sec}^2 = 16.36g$$

where g is the gravitational constant, 386 in./sec².

The force exerted by the cam is directed normal to the cam surface, which in most cases is not in the direction of the follower motion. The angle between these directions[11] is known as the pressure angle φ as illustrated in Fig. 12-27. The sidewise force exerted by the follower on its guides depends on the magnitude of the pressure angle. It is sometimes specified that the pressure angle should not exceed 30°. The permissible value is influenced by the speed of operation and the weight of the connected parts.

The manufacture of an accurate master cam is difficult. The work is usually done on a milling machine with a cutter of the same diameter as the roller follower. Calculations for r to the pitch surface must usually be made for every degree of cam rotation. The final finishing is then done by hand.

17. Circular Arc Cams with Roller Follower

Plate cams composed of arcs of circles have the advantage of being comparatively easy to manufacture.

Figure 12-31 shows such a cam with a roller follower not offset. Arc CK_o has radius r_o, and center at point O. Arc K_oK_2 has its center at A_1,

[11] See reference 39, Bibliography.

and arc K_2K_4 has radius r_n and center at A_2. The rise L of the cam therefore takes place during angular rotation β.

In making a cam analysis it is usual practice to consider the cam as stationary and have the follower assume various angular positions about center of rotation O.

When the roller makes contact with arc CK_o, no vertical motion of the follower occurs. When the roller makes contact somewhere on arc K_oK_2,

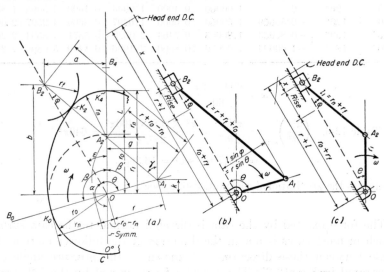

Fig. 12-31. Cam composed of circular arcs with nonoffset follower.

radii A_1K_2 and r_f are constant, so that A_1B_2 or l remains constant. Radius OA_1 is also a constant. As the cam rotates, the motion of follower center B is exactly like that of the slider of the slider crank mechanism shown in Fig. 12-31(b).

Let the origin of coordinates in Fig. 12-31(b) be taken at the head end, dead center. Displacement x of the slider is equal to

$$x = l + r - r \cos \theta - l \cos \varphi \qquad (54)$$

where r is radius OA_1, θ is the angular position of r with respect to OB_2, and φ is the angle between connecting rod l and OB_2. The crank mechanism of Fig. 12-31(b) is valid for all positions of the roller from B_0 to B_2.

The rise of the follower, at any value of θ, is equal to the distance from O to the slider minus $(r_o + r_f)$, the height of the follower at its lowest position. Thus

$$\text{rise} = r + l - x - (r_o + r_f)$$

$$= r \cos \theta + l \cos \varphi - (r_o + r_f) \qquad (55)$$

Differentiation of x with respect to time t gives the velocity $\dot{x}$ or dx/dt of the slider.

$$\dot{x} = r \sin \theta \frac{d\theta}{dt} + l \sin \varphi \frac{d\varphi}{dt} \tag{a}$$

Angular velocity of the crank, $d\theta/dt$ is usually written as ω. From the figure, $l \sin \varphi = r \sin \theta$ or $\sin \varphi = m \sin \theta$ where $m = r/l$; then

$$\varphi = \sin^{-1}(m \sin \theta)$$

$$\frac{d\varphi}{d\theta} = \frac{m \cos \theta}{\sqrt{1 - m^2 \sin^2 \theta}} = \frac{m \cos \theta}{\cos \varphi}$$

$$\frac{d\varphi}{dt} = \frac{d\theta}{dt} \times \frac{d\varphi}{d\theta} = \frac{\omega m \cos \theta}{\cos \varphi} = \frac{r\omega \cos \theta}{l \cos \varphi}$$

Substitution into Eq. (a) gives

$$\dot{x} = r\omega \sin \theta + l \sin \varphi \frac{r\omega \cos \theta}{l \cos \varphi}$$

$$\dot{x} = r\omega(\sin \theta + \cos \theta \tan \varphi) \tag{56}$$

Differentiation of Eq. (56) gives acceleration d^2x/dt^2 of the slider, usually written $\ddot{x}$.

$$\ddot{x} = r\omega \left[\omega \cos \theta + \cos \theta \sec^2 \varphi \frac{d\varphi}{dt} - \omega \sin \theta \tan \varphi \right]$$

$$= r\omega \left[\omega \cos \theta + \frac{\cos \theta}{\cos^2 \varphi} \frac{\omega m \cos \theta}{\cos \varphi} - \omega \sin \theta \tan \varphi \right]$$

$$= r\omega^2 \left[\cos \theta + \frac{m \cos^2 \theta}{\cos^3 \varphi} - \sin \theta \tan \varphi \right] \tag{57}$$

The cosine theorem applied to triangle OA_1A_2 gives the following useful equation.

$$\overline{A_1A_2}^2 = (r + r_o - r_n)^2 = r^2 + r_1^2 - 2rr_1 \cos \beta' \tag{58}$$

where r_1 is the vertical height OA_2 and angle β' is angle A_1OA_2. Note also that

$$r_1 + r_n = L + r_o \tag{59}$$

Lengths k and g are easily computed. Then

$$\tan \gamma = \frac{g}{r_1 - k} \tag{60}$$

$$a = (r_f + r_n) \sin \gamma \tag{61}$$

$$b = r_1 + (r_f + r_n) \cos \gamma \tag{62}$$

$$\tan \epsilon = \frac{a}{b} \tag{63}$$

With roller at B_2: $\qquad\qquad \varphi = \gamma - \epsilon$ $\qquad\qquad\qquad\qquad$ (64)

For Fig. 12-31(b): $\qquad\qquad \theta = \epsilon + \beta'$ $\qquad\qquad\qquad\qquad$ (65)

For Fig. 12-31(c): $\qquad\qquad \theta = \epsilon$ $\qquad\qquad\qquad\qquad\qquad$ (66)

When the roller makes contact with arc $K_2 K_4$, radius r_1 becomes the crank, and l_1 the connecting rod of the equivalent slider crank mechanism shown in Fig. 12-31(c). Equations for this mechanism are similar to Eqs. (54), (56), and (57), but contain r_1, l_1, and $m_1 = r_1/l_1$ instead of r, l, and m.

The resisting force of the follower is directed along OB_2. The actuating force of the driver is directed along $A_1 B_2$. The pressure angle for this cam is thus angle $OB_2 A_1$ or angle φ.

Example 15. A cam composed of circular arcs is to have a lift L of 0.375 in. for a rotation β of the shaft equal to 65°. The speed of the shaft is 900 rpm; $r_f = 0.60$ in.; $r_n = 0.25$ in.; and $r_1 = 0.90$ in. Find the remaining cam dimensions, and compute values for displacement, velocity, and acceleration for different cam positions and plot results.

Solution. $\qquad\qquad \beta' = 180° - 65° = 115°$

By Eq. (59): $\qquad\qquad r_0 = r_1 + r_n - L$

$\qquad\qquad\qquad\qquad = 0.90 + 0.25 - 0.375 = 0.775$ in.

In Eq. (58):

$$(r + 0.775 - 0.25)^2 = r^2 + 0.90^2 - 2r \times 0.90 \cos 115°$$

Solving for r: $\qquad\qquad r = 1.8472$ in.

$$l = r + r_f + r_0$$

$$= 1.8472 + 0.6000 + 0.7750 = 3.2222 \text{ in.}$$

$$l_1 = r_f + r_n = 0.6000 + 0.2500 = 0.8500 \text{ in.}$$

$$k = -r \sin 25° = -1.8472 \times 0.42262 = -0.7807 \text{ in.}$$

$$g = r \cos 25° = 1.8472 \times 0.90631 = 1.6742 \text{ in.}$$

In Eq. (60): $\qquad \tan \gamma = \dfrac{g}{r_1 - k} = \dfrac{1.6742}{0.90 + 0.7807} = 0.99612, \quad \gamma = 44°53.3'$

In Eq. (61): $\qquad a = (r_f + r_n) \sin \gamma = 0.85 \times 0.70573 = 0.5999$ in.

In Eq. (62): $\qquad b = r_1 + (r_f + r_n) \cos \gamma = 0.90 + 0.85 \times 0.70849$

$$= 0.90 + 0.6022 = 1.5022 \text{ in.}$$

In Eq. (63): $\qquad \tan \epsilon = \dfrac{a}{b} = \dfrac{0.5999}{1.5022} = 0.39932, \quad \epsilon = 21°46'$

When roller
is at B_2: $\qquad\qquad \varphi = \gamma - \epsilon = 44°53.2' - 21°46' = 23°7.2'$

In Fig. 12-31(b): $\theta = \epsilon + \beta' = 21°46' + 115° = 136°46'$

In Fig. 12-31(c): $\theta = \epsilon = 21°46'$

The results of the calculations for displacement, velocity, and acceleration are shown in Fig. 12-32. Two sets of computations can be made

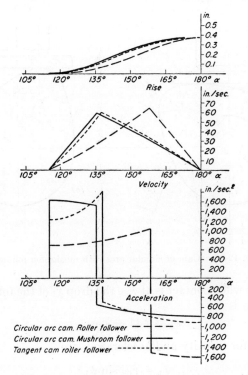

Fig. 12-32.   Displacement, velocity, and acceleration for cam of Example 15.

when the roller is at B_2, one for each of the two slider cranks for this position. The calculations give identical values for rise and velocity, but the values for acceleration are different.

18. Circular Arc Cam with Mushroom Follower

A circular arc cam with mushroom follower is shown in Fig. 12-33. The profile of the cam is composed of arc K_oK_2 with center at A_1, and arc K_2K_4 with center at A_2. In sketch (a) when contact is at K_1 for angular position ψ, the rise x of the follower from the lowest position is

$$x = r(1 - \cos \psi) \qquad (67)$$

Equations for velocity $\dot{x}$ and acceleration $\ddot{x}$ of follower can be easily obtained by differentiation. Thus

$$\dot{x} = r\omega \sin \psi \tag{68}$$

$$\ddot{x} = r\omega^2 \cos \psi \tag{69}$$

where ω is equal to $d\psi/dt$.

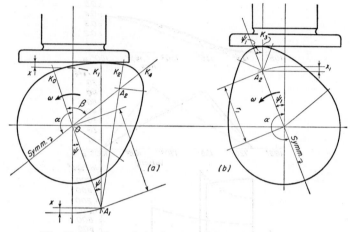

Fig. 12-33.   Cam of circular arcs with mushroom follower.

In sketch (b) when contact is at K_3, the drop x_1 of the follower from the highest position is

$$x_1 = r_1(1 - \cos \psi_1) \tag{70}$$

The equations for velocity and acceleration are

$$\dot{x}_1 = r_1\omega \sin \psi_1 \tag{71}$$

$$\ddot{x}_1 = r_1\omega^2 \cos \psi_1$$

where ω is equal to $d\psi_1/dt$.

Curves for displacement, velocity, and acceleration for the cam of Example 15 but with a mushroom follower are given in Fig. 12-32.

19. Straight Sided Cam with Roller Follower

Figure 12-34 shows a cam with a straight side for K_oK_2. Arc K_2K_4 is a circle with center at A_2; previous results apply for contact in this region.

For the K_oK_2 portion, rise x is given by

$$x = (r_o + r_f)(\sec \alpha_1 - 1) \tag{72}$$

where α_1 is the angle denoting the angular position of the cam.

The velocity $\dot{x}$ and acceleration $\ddot{x}$ of the follower are found by differentiation of Eq. (72).

$$\dot{x} = \frac{\omega(r_o + r_f) \tan \alpha_1}{\cos \alpha_1} \tag{73}$$

$$\ddot{x} = \omega^2(r_o + r_f)(\sec^3 \alpha_1 + \tan^2 \alpha_1 \sec \alpha_1)$$

$$= \frac{\omega^2(r_o + r_f)}{\cos \alpha_1}(1 + 2\tan^2 \alpha_1) \tag{74}$$

where $\omega = d\alpha_1/dt$.

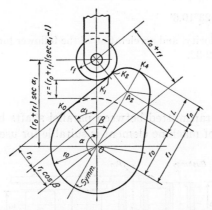

Fig. 12-34.   Tangential cam with roller follower.

From Fig. 12-34, the following relationships are apparent.

$$r_o + L = r_1 + r_n \tag{75}$$

$$r_o = r_n + r_1 \cos \beta \tag{76}$$

The equations above can be combined to give

$$L = r_1(1 - \cos \beta) \tag{77}$$

When the roller makes contact at K_o, angle α_1 is zero. For contact at K_2 the end of the tangent section, angle α_1 can be found from

$$\tan \alpha_1 = \frac{r_1 \sin \beta}{r_f + r_o} \tag{78}$$

Example 16. A plate cam with tangent sides has a lift of 0.375 in. that takes place during a rotation of 65°. The radius of follower roller is 0.6 in. The distance between the cam center and the roller center at the maximum rise is 1.75 in. Find values for r_n and r_o.

Solution.

By Eq. (77): $r_1 = \dfrac{L}{1 - \cos \beta} = \dfrac{0.375}{1 - 0.42262} = 0.6495$ in.

$$r_0 = 1.75 - L - r_f = 1.75 - 0.375 - 0.600 = 0.775 \text{ in.}$$

By Eq. (75): $r_n = r_0 + L - r_1 = 0.775 + 0.375 - 0.6495 = 0.5005$ in.

For contact at K_2:

$$\tan \alpha_1 = \frac{r_1 \sin \beta}{r_f + r_o} = \frac{0.6495 \times 0.90631}{0.60 + 0.775} = 0.42811,$$

$$\alpha_1 = 23°10.6'$$

Values for rise, velocity, and acceleration of the follower for a speed of 900 rpm are plotted in Fig. 12-32.

20. Roller Chains

Power may be transmitted between parallel shafts by means of roller chains. This type of machine element is suitable for use with either small

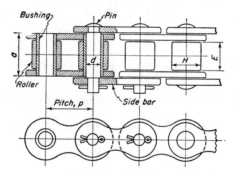

Fig. 12-35. Construction of typical roller chain.

or large amounts of power and with both low and high speeds. No initial tension is required, and no slippage can occur. The mechanical efficiency is very high, 98 per cent or 99 per cent. Typical construction for a roller chain is shown in Fig. 12-35. The rollers turn on the bushings, which are swaged to the inner side bars; the pins are fixed in the outer side bars. Sizes and dimensions for standardized roller chains are given in Table 12-7.

Roller chains must not be operated at excessive speeds. Recommended maximum sprocket speeds[12] for various sizes of chains are given in Table 12-8.

[12] See reference 46, Bibliography.

TABLE 12-7

Dimensions of Standard Roller Transmission Chains

Chain No.	Pitch p in.	Roller		Pin Dia d in.	Bushing Length a in.	Av. Ult. Strength lb.	Weight per ft W_1 lb
		Dia H in.	Width E in.				
35	$\frac{3}{8}$	0.20	$\frac{3}{16}$	0.141	0.288	1,400	0.21
41	$\frac{1}{2}$	0.306	$\frac{1}{4}$	0.141	0.350	2,000	0.30
40	$\frac{1}{2}$	$\frac{5}{16}$	$\frac{5}{16}$	0.156	0.433	3,200	0.40
50	$\frac{5}{8}$	0.400	$\frac{3}{8}$	0.200	0.535	5,200	0.69
60	$\frac{3}{4}$	$\frac{15}{32}$	$\frac{1}{2}$	0.234	0.688	7,300	1.05
80	1	$\frac{5}{8}$	$\frac{5}{8}$	0.312	0.875	12,200	1.75
100	$1\frac{1}{4}$	$\frac{3}{4}$	$\frac{3}{4}$	0.375	1.062	21,000	2.60
120	$1\frac{1}{2}$	$\frac{7}{8}$	1	0.437	1.374	30,500	3.87
140	$1\frac{3}{4}$	1	1	0.500	1.438	42,500	5.14
160	2	$1\frac{1}{8}$	$1\frac{1}{4}$	0.562	1.750	52,500	6.87
200	$2\frac{1}{2}$	$1\frac{9}{16}$	$1\frac{1}{2}$	0.781	2.124	90,000	11.00

TABLE 12-8

Recommended Maximum Rpm of Sprockets for American Roller Chains

Chain No.	35	41	40	50	60	80	100	120	140	160	200
Pitch	$\frac{3}{8}$	$\frac{1}{2}$	$\frac{1}{2}$	$\frac{5}{8}$	$\frac{3}{4}$	1	$1\frac{1}{4}$	$1\frac{1}{2}$	$1\frac{3}{4}$	2	$2\frac{1}{2}$
Teeth											
11	2260	1020	1690	1220	920	580	415	325	235	200	145
12	2590	1170	1940	1400	1050	670	475	375	270	230	165
13	2900	1310	2180	1570	1180	750	535	415	305	260	185
14	3170	1430	2380	1720	1290	820	585	455	335	280	205
16	3630	1630	2720	1960	1480	935	670	520	380	325	235
18	3970	1790	2980	2150	1610	1020	730	570	415	355	255
20	4210	1890	3160	2280	1720	1090	775	605	440	375	270
22	4380	1970	3290	2370	1780	1130	805	630	460	390	280
25	4510	2030	3380	2440	1830	1160	830	650	475	400	290
30	4490	2020	3370	2430	1830	1160	825	645	470	400	290
35	4290	1930	3220	2320	1740	1110	790	615	450	380	275
40	3970	1780	2970	2140	1610	1020	730	570	415	355	255
50	3110	1400	2330	1680	1270	805	575	450	325	275	200

Horsepower capacity for a single strand chain can be determined by the following empirical equation.

$$\text{hp} = p^2 \left\{ \frac{V}{23.7} - \frac{\left[1 + 25 \left(1 - \cos \frac{180}{N_1} \right) \right] V^{1.41}}{1050} \right\} \quad (79)$$

where p is the pitch in inches, V is the chain speed, feet per minute, and N_1 is the number of teeth in the smaller sprocket.

Example 17. Find the permissible horsepower for a No. 80 standard roller chain. The small sprocket has 15 teeth and rotates at 350 rpm.

Solution. Each link on the sprocket subtends an angle equal to $\frac{360}{15}$ or 24°. The sine of 12° is then equal to half the pitch divided by the pitch radius r. Hence

Pitch radius: $\quad r = \dfrac{0.5p}{\sin 12°} = \dfrac{0.5 \times 1}{0.20791} = 2.4049$ in.

Pitch diameter: $\quad d = 2 \times 2.4049 = 4.8098$ in.

$$V = \frac{\pi dn}{12} = \frac{\pi 4.8098 \times 350}{12} = 440.7 \text{ fpm}$$

$$\log V^{1.41} = 1.41 \log V = 1.41 \times 2.64416 = 3.72827$$

$$V^{1.41} = 5,349$$

By Eq. (79): $\quad \text{hp} = 1^2 \left\{ \frac{440.72}{23.7} - \frac{\left[1 + 25 \left(1 - \cos \frac{180}{15} \right) \right] \times 5,349}{1050} \right\}$

$$= 18.62 - 7.86 = 10.76$$

Multiple-strand roller chains have load capacities in proportion to the number of strands.

Proper lubrication is necessary to minimize the effect of metal-to-metal contact. The method of application of the lubricant depends on the speed of the chain: up to 600 fpm, drip, shallow bath, or manual with brush or spout; 600 to 1,500 fpm, rapid drip or continuous with shallow bath, disk or slinger (a circulating pump may be necessary); above 1,500 fpm, continuous with disk slinger or circulating pump.

When the number of teeth in the sprockets is small, the driven shaft of a roller chain drive may be given a pulsating or jerky motion. In Fig. 12-36, the shaft centers are located not an integral number of pitches apart, but some number plus one-half pitches apart. If the driver is assumed to be rotating uniformly, the driven shaft has the angular velocities indicated in the figures. In (a) the driven sprocket is rotating at a higher speed than the driver, whereas in (b) the driven shaft is moving

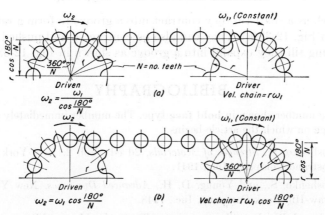

Fig. 12-36.   Variation in velocity of driven sprocket caused by shaft centers not being an integral number of pitches apart.

slower. The equations for ω_2 indicate, for example, that for sprockets having 10 teeth, the velocity of the driven shaft will vary from 5 per cent above to 5 per cent below that of the driver. The chain velocity also varies. Sometimes long-link conveyor chains are operated on sprockets having as few as 5 or 6 teeth. The variation in velocity will then be most undesirable, and there will be an increase in the stresses in the chain and connected parts.

The silent or inverted tooth chain, shown in Fig. 12-37, is in wide use for power transmission up to speeds of 4,500

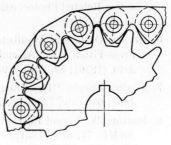

Fig. 12-37.   Silent chain.

fpm. Detailed design data are given in the manufacturers' catalogs.

21. Snap Rings

Snap rings or retaining rings are made of hardened steel wire of round or rectangular cross section. They can be expanded over a cylindrical

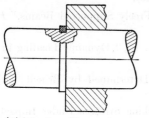

(a) Collar formed by snap ring.

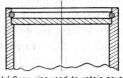

(b) Snap ring used to retain cover on tubular container.

Fig. 12-38.   Two applications of snap-rings.

body such as a shaft till they contract into a groove to form a retainer as shown in Fig. 12-38(a). They can also be contracted and pushed through an opening till they expand into a groove as shown in Fig. 12-38(b).

BIBLIOGRAPHY

Volume number shown in **bold face** type. The number immediately following is the page on which the article begins.

1. Timoshenko, S., *Strength of Materials*, 2d ed., Vol. 2. New York: D. Van Nostrand Company, Inc., 1941.

2. Timoshenko, S., and Young, D. H., *Advanced Dynamics*. New York: McGraw-Hill Book Company, Inc., 1948.

3. Baugher, J. W., Jr., "Transmission of Torque by Means of Press and Shrink Fits," *Trans. ASME*, **53**, MSP-53-10, 85 (1931).

4. Horger, O. J., and Nelson, C. W., "Design of Press- and Shrink-Fitted Assemblies," *Trans. ASME*, **59**, A-183 (1937); **60**, A-32 (1938).

5. Peterson, R. E., and Wahl, A. M., "Fatigue of Shafts at Fitted Members, with a Related Photoelastic Analysis," *Trans. ASME*, **57**, A-1, A-69 (1935); **58**, A-74 (1936).

6. Horger, O. J., and Maulbetsch, J. L., "Increasing the Fatigue Strength of Press-Fitted Axle Assemblies by Surface Rolling," *Trans. ASME*, **58**, A-91 (1936); **59**, A-37 (1937).

7. Marin, Joseph, "Designing Shrink-Fit Assemblies," *Machine Design*, **14**, June, 68; July, 72; Aug., 78 (1942).

8. Buxton, W. J., and Burrows, W. R., "Formula for Pipe Thickness," *Trans. ASME*, **73**, 575, (1951).

9. Faupel, J. H., "Yield and Bursting Characteristics of Heavy-Wall Cylinders," *Trans. ASME*, **78**, 1031 (1956).

10. Hoppmann, W. H., "Impact of a Mass on a Column," *Trans. ASME*, **71** (1949); *Jour. of App. Mech.* 370.

11. Johnson, R. C., "Impact Forces in Mechanisms," *Machine Design*, **30**, June 12, 138 (1958).

12. Donnell, L. H., "Longitudinal Wave Transmission and Impact," *Trans. ASME*, **52**,(1), APM-52-14-153 (1930).

13. Arnold, R. N., "Impact Stresses in Freely Supported Beams," *Proc. Inst. Mech. Engrs.*, **137**, 217 (1937).

14. Dohrenwend, C. O., and Mehaffy, W. R., "Dynamic Loading in Design," *Machine Design*, **15**, 99 (1943).

15. Hagenbook, L. D., "Impact Loads Determined by Brinell Techniques," *Product Eng.*, **14**, 300 (1943).

16. Davidenkoff, N. N., "Allowable Working Stresses Under Impact," *Trans. ASME*, **56**, APM-56-1, 97 (1934).

17. "Symposium on Impact Testing," *Proc. ASTM*, **38**, 105 (1938).

18. Rossheim, D. B., and Markl, A. R. C., "Gasket Loading Constants," *Mech. Eng.*, **65**, 647 (1943); **66**, 72 (1944).

19. Petrie, E. C., "The Ring Joint," *Valve World*, **34**, 83 (1937).

20. Roberts, Irving, "Gaskets and Bolted Joints," *Trans. ASME*, **72**, 169 (1950).

21. Adams, R. E., and Corcoran, J. L., "Sealing of High-Pressure Steam Safety Valves," *Trans. ASME*, **72**, 1137 (1950).

22. Cheyney, L. E., Mueller, W. J., and Duval, R. E., "Frictional Characteristics of O-Rings With a Typical Hydraulic Fluid," *Trans. ASME*, **72**, 291 (1950).

23. Beacham, T. E., "Rotary and Oscillating Seals," *Proc. Inst. Mech. Engrs.*, **160**, 532 (1949).

24. Dresden, D., "On the Theory of the Packing Gland for Reciprocating Machines," *Engineers' Digest*, **11**, 343 (1950).

25. Schmitz, C. E., "The Mechanical Seal—Its Construction, Application and Utility," *Trans. ASME*, **71**, 635 (1949).

26. Linderoth, L. S., Jr., "Selecting Hydraulic Seals," *Machine Design*, **17**, Sept., 119 (1944).

27. Ten Bosch, M., "New Criterion for the Design of Wire Ropes," *Engineers' Digest*, **4**, 67 (1947).

28. Drucker, D. C., and Tachau, H., "A New Design Criterion for Wire Rope," *Trans. ASME*, **66**, A-33 (1945). Disc. **68**, A-75, (1946).

29. Starkey, W. L., and Cress, H. A., "An Analysis of Critical Stresses and Mode of Failure of a Wire Rope," *Trans. ASME*, **81** (1959); *Jour. of Engrg. for Industry*, 307.

30. Vidosic, J. P., Bogardus, F. J., and Durden, J. C., "Curved Beams with Eccentric Boundaries," *Trans. ASME*, **79**, 1317 (1957).

31. Wahl, A. M., "Calculation of Stress in Crane Hooks," *Trans. ASME*, **68**, A-239 (1946).

32. Bartlett, G. M., "New Basis for Rating Roller-Chain Drives," *Trans. ASME*, **57**, 97, 443 (1935).

33. Bremer, N. C., "Heavy-Duty Chain Drives for Marine Propulsion Service," *Trans. ASME*, **69**, 441 (1947).

34. Stamets, W. K., Jr., "Dynamic Loading of Chain Drives," *Trans. ASME*, **73**, 655 (1951).

35. Young, Vincent C., "Considerations in Valve Gear Design," *SAE Quart. Trans.*, **1**, 359 (1947).

36. Olmstead, E. H., and Taylor, E. S., "Poppett Valve Dynamics," *J. Aeronaut. Sci.*, **6**, 370 (1938–1939).

37. Huckert, J., "Accelerations by Vector Methods in Disk Cam Mechanisms," *Product Eng.* **19**, Dec., 128 (1948).

38. Holowenko, A. R., and Hall, A. S., "Cam Curvature," *Machine Design*, **25** (Aug. 170, Sept. 162, Nov. 148, 1953).

39. Lengyel, A., and Church, A. H., "Radial Disk Cam Design Charts for Maximum Pressure Angle," *Product Eng.* **22**, March, 155 (1951).

40. Candee, A. H., "Kinematics of Disk Cam and Flat Follower," *Trans. ASME*, **69**, 709, 718 (1947).

41. Hrones, J. A., "An Analysis of the Dynamic Forces in a Cam-Driven System," *Trans. ASME*, **70**, 473 (1948).

42. Rothbart, H. A., *Cams.* New York: John Wiley & Sons, Inc., 1956.

43. Carver, W. B., and Quinn, B. E., "An Analytical Method of Cam Design," *Mech. Eng.*, **67**, 523 (1945).

44. Dudley, Winston M., "New Methods in Valve Cam Design," *SAE Quart. Trans.*, Vol. **2**, 19 (1948). Also *Machine Design*, **19**, July, 143 (1947).

45. Jehle, F., and Spiller, W. R., "Idiosyncrasies of Valve Mechanisms and Their Causes," *SAE Journal*, **24**, 133 (1929).

46. *Transmission Roller Chains and Sprocket Teeth, ASA B29.1-1950.* New York: American Standards Association.

PROBLEMS

1. (a) A steel disk is shrunk on a steel shaft. The radius of the disk is very large as compared to the radius of the shaft. The diametral interference is equal to 0.001 times the shaft diameter. Find the values of tangential and normal stress. $E = 30,000,000$ psi.

(b) Work part (a) but with $b = 2a$.

(c) Work part (a) but with the disk made of cast iron, $E = 15,000,000$ psi. The shaft is steel. $\mu = \frac{1}{3}$.

(d) Repeat part (c) except that $b = 2a$.

    Ans.   (a) $s_t = s_r = 15,000$ psi; (b) $s_t = 18,750$ psi; $s_r = 11,250$ psi,
        (c) $s_t = s_r = 9,000$ psi; (d) $s_t = 10,710$ psi; $s_r = 6,430$ psi.

2. A steel shaft is pressed on a steel disk twice the shaft diameter, and with a thickness $1\frac{1}{2}$ times the shaft diameter. The shearing stress in the shaft caused by the torque which the pressed fit can carry is equal to 12,000 psi. Find the value of the diametral interference. $E = 30,000,000$ psi. The coefficient of friction is 0.12.
        Ans. $\Delta = 0.00148\ a$.

3. A 2 in. shaft has a torsional shear stress of 12,000 psi. It has a shrink fit in an 8 in. steel disk 3 in. thick. Find the tangential stress and diametral interference if the entire torque of the shaft is to be transmitted through the shrink-fit friction. $E = 30,000,000$ psi. The coefficient of friction is 0.12.   *Ans.* $\Delta = 0.00118$ in.

4. A disk whose diameter is 3 times that of the shaft, and whose thickness is twice the shaft diameter, has a diametral interference of 0.0005 times the shaft diameter. For the shaft, $E = 30,000,000$ psi. For the disk, $E = 15,000,000$ psi. Poisson's ratio = 0.25. If the torsional stress in the shaft is equal to 10,000 psi, find the coefficient of friction required if the entire torque is to be carried by the shrink-fit friction.   *Ans.*   Coefficient of friction = 0.156.

5. A disk of Class 30 cast iron is to be shrunk on a 6 in. steel shaft. The tangential stress in the disk is not to exceed 8,000 psi. Diametral interference of the metal is 0.004 in. $\mu = 0.3$. Find the shrink-fit pressure between disk and shaft. Find the minimum permissible outside diameter of the disk. Find the factor of safety. *Ans.* $p = 2,610$ psi; $b = 4.21$ in., $FS = 3.44$.

6. A 10 in. diameter steel shaft is to be pressed into a steel disk 18 in. in diameter and 8 in. thick. The interference of the metal must be such that the force required to press the parts together must lie between 144 and 200 tons. If the coefficient of friction is 0.15, find the maximum and minimum values for the diametral interference of metal. *Ans.* 0.0074 to 0.0102 in.

7. A bronze bushing 2 in. OD and $1\frac{3}{8}$ in. ID is to be pressed into a hollow cylinder of 4 in. OD. The diametral interference of the metal is 0.002 in. Find the tangential and normal stresses for the steel and bronze at the boundary between the 2 parts.
Ans. $p = 4,320$ psi; bronze, $s_t = -12,050$ psi; steel, $s_t = 7,190$ psi.

8. A 4 in. diameter steel shaft is pressed into a steel disk 12 in. in diameter and 5 in. thick. The shaft has a shearing stress equal to 8,000 psi with the torque resisted by the shrink fit. The coefficient of friction is 0.15. Find the diameter of the hole in the disk before assembly. *Ans.* 3.9984 in.

9. A 3 in. diameter steel shaft is to be press fitted into a Class 30 cast iron hub of 7 in. OD. Find the diametral interference of the metal if the *FS* against breakage of the hub from the press fit is to be 4. *Ans.* $\Delta = 0.0019$ in.

10. A disk flywheel is to be cut from 3 in. rolled steel plate. The bore is 0.2 of the outside diameter. Maximum speed is 3,000 rpm with a maximum stress from rotation equal to 12,000 psi. Find the diameter of the flywheel and the amount of energy delivered for a 10 per cent drop in speed.
Ans. Dia $= 28.24$ in.; $\Delta KE = 107,080$ ft-lb.

11. A disk flywheel is cut from $2\frac{1}{2}$ in. steel plate. Outside diameter is 36 in., bore is 6 in. Rpm $= 3,000$. Find the value of maximum stress in the material. Find *KE* delivered for a 5 per cent drop in speed.
Ans. $s_t = 19,460$ psi; $\Delta KE = 121,100$ ft-lb.

12. A rolled steel disk flywheel is 24 in. in outside diameter and 3 in. thick. It rotates on a 2.5 in. diameter shaft. Normal speed is 2,400 rpm with a 20 per cent drop during the working cycle. Find the maximum stress in the material and the energy delivered per cycle.
Ans. $s_t = 5,510$ psi; $\Delta KE = 67,890$ ft-lb.

13. A 42-in. outside diameter cast iron flywheel has 4 spokes and rotates 800 rpm. The rim is 4 by 4 in. The spoke is 2 by 3 in. Find the stress in rim and spokes. *Ans.* Rim, $s = 2,450$ psi; spoke, $s = 600$ psi.

14. The load cycle for each revolution of a shaft is shown in Fig. 12-39. The shaft is driven by a belt and can be assumed to receive a constant torque from the driving motor. Find the energy delivered per cycle for a flywheel mounted on the shaft for a coefficient of fluctuation of 0.05. The speed is 600 rpm. Find the outside diameter of the flywheel if it is solid and cut from a 1 in. steel plate.
Ans. $\Delta KE = 108$ ft-lb; dia. $= 17.38$ in.

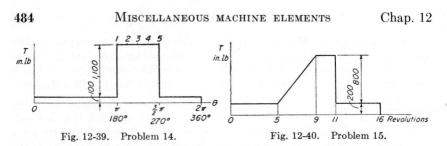

Fig. 12-39.   Problem 14.   Fig. 12-40.   Problem 15.

15. The load cycle for a shaft is shown in Fig. 12-40. The shaft is driven by a belt and can be assumed to receive a constant driving torque. Find the energy delivered per cycle for a flywheel mounted on the shaft for a coefficient of fluctuation of 0.10. Speed is 150 rpm. Find the outside diameter if the flywheel is solid and cut from $2\frac{1}{2}$ in. steel plate.   *Ans.* $\Delta KE = 1,100$ ft-lb; dia. $= 41.5$ in.

16. Let the bolt in Fig. 12-12 be $\frac{3}{4}$ in. in diameter, and let length l be equal to 15 in. The threads at the bottom are 10 per inch, stopping immediately above the nut. Ignore the effect of the weight of the bolt. The bolt is made of steel.

(a) If a weight W of 70 lb drops 0.1 in. to the nut, find the stress in the gross and net sections of the bolt.

(b) Find the stress if the entire body of the bolt above the nut is reduced to the stress area of the threads.

(c) Find the stress if one-half the length of the bolt is reduced to the stress area.

(d) If bolt is made of phosphor bronze, and $\gamma = 0.32$ lb/in.³, find the stress in the net section of the thread.

Ans.   (a) $s = 8,120$ psi; $s = 10,740$ psi; (b) $s = 9,370$ psi; (c) $s = 9,980$ psi; (d) $s = 7,660$ psi.

17. If the bolt in Fig. 12-12 is $\frac{1}{2}$ by 18 in., and weight W is 10 lb, find the height h which will cause an impact stress of 40,000 psi in the gross area of the bolt. $E = 30,000,000$ psi; $\gamma = 0.283$ lb/in.³   *Ans.* $h = 9.7$ in.

18. A 4 by 4-in. by 4 ft wooden post stands on a rigid foundation. From what height a 500 lb weight must be dropped on the upper end of the post to give an impact stress of 4,000 psi. Ignore the effect of the weight of the post. $E = 1,500,000$ psi.   *Ans.* $h = 8.06$ in.

19. In Fig. 12-41, the crane had been lowering the load at the uniform rate of 2 fps when the brakes on the drum were suddenly applied. Assuming that the upper

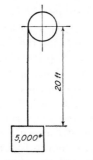

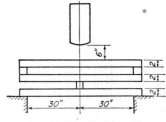

Fig. 12-41.   Problem 19.   Fig. 12-42.   Problem 20.

end of the cable had been stopped instantaneously, find the maximum force induced in the cable. Include the effect of the static load. Let E for the twisted wire cable be 16,000,000 psi. $A = 0.5$ in.² *Ans.* $F = 20,770$ lb.

20. The steel beams in Fig. 12-42 are 3 in. wide. Find the maximum stress due to impact. Weight = 1,000 lb. *Ans.* $s = 62,780$ psi.

21. What must be the rate of the spring, lb per in., if the force caused by the falling weight in Fig. 12-43 is equal to 1,000 lb? Rod and spring are of brass.

Ans. $k_s = 557$ lb/in.

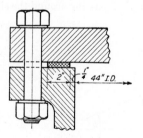

Fig. 12-43.   Problem 21.

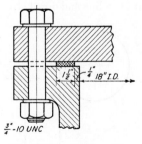

Fig. 12-44.   Problem 22.

22. In Fig. 12-44 all parts are of steel. Find the stress in the bolt and in the beam due to impact.   *Ans.*   Bolt, $s = 51,560$ psi; beam, $s = 32,400$ psi.

23. The gasket in Fig. 12-45 is of cloth inserted hard rubber. If the bolts are only tightened sufficiently to seat the gasket, find the permissible value of the internal pressure.   *Ans.* $p = 16.2$ psi.

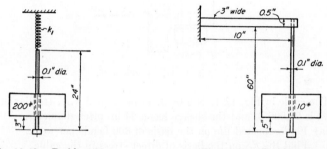

Fig. 12-45.   Problem 23.

Fig. 12-46.   Problem 24.

24. The asbestos composition gasket shown in Fig. 12-46 is $\frac{1}{8}$ in. thick. The cover is held in place by 24 bolts. If the bolts are tightened only sufficiently to seat the gasket, find the permissible value of the internal pressure. By use of Eq. (8), Chapter 5, find the force at the end of a 2 ft wrench handle required to tighten the bolts.   *Ans.* $p = 118.5$ psi; $F = 12$ lb.

25. The gasket shown in Fig. 12-47 is of soft copper $\frac{3}{16}$ in. thick, held in place by 24 bolts. If the bolts are only tightened sufficiently to seat the gasket, find the permissible value of the internal pressure. Find the torque required to tighten the bolts.   *Ans.* $p = 580$ psi; $T = 1,920$ in-lb.

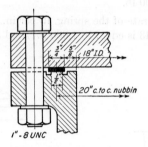

Fig. 12-47.   Problem 25.

26. The cable in Fig. 12-48 is 6 by 37 of plow steel wire. Its diameter is $1\frac{1}{4}$ in. The load is 20,000 lb and the sheave has a 24 in. pitch diameter.

(a) Find expected life on the basis of 300 bends per week.

(b) Find the FS on the basis of direct stress in the cable.

(c) Find the resultant stress when the cable is passing around sheave.

(d) Find the minimum pitch diameter of the sheave and drum if fatigue effects are to be avoided.

               Ans.   (a) 7.7 yr; (b) $FS = 11$; (c) $s = 86,870$ psi, $d_s = 51$ in.

27. The cable in Fig. 12-48 is 6 by 19 and is 1 in. in diameter. The sheave is 24 in. in diameter. Resulting bending and direct stress in the cable when passing around the sheave is equal to 100,000 psi. Find the value of W.

                                    Ans. $W = 17,680$ lb.

28. A 1 in. diameter 6 by 19 wire rope is made of improved plow steel wire. The resultant bending and direct stress is 100,000 psi when passing around the sheaves.

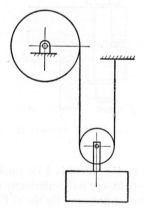

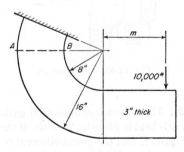

Fig. 12-48.   Problem 27.   Fig. 12-49.   Problem 29.

Expected life is 8 years at 400 bends per week and 50 weeks per year. Find the force in the rope and compute the minimum permissible sheave diameter.

Ans. $T = 7,630$ lb, $d_s = 23.1$ in.

29. Find the value of m in Fig. 12-49 that gives a resultant stress value of 10,000 psi on cross section AB. *Ans.* $m = 11.8$ in.

30. Figure 12-50 shows the shackle at one end of a symmetrically arranged leaf spring. The spring supports a load of 4,000 lb at its center. Find the maximum normal stress on cross section AB. *Ans.* $s = -17,260$ psi.

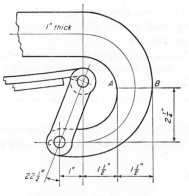

Fig. 12-50. Problem 30.

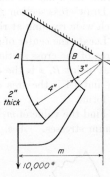

Fig. 12-51. Problem 31.

31. Find the value of length m in Fig. 12-51 that causes the tensile stress at A to be numerically equal to the compressive stress at B. *Ans.* $m = 7.24$ in.

32. Find the value of force H if the resultant stresses normal to the horizontal cross section in Fig. 12-52 are to be numerically equal at points A and B.

Ans. $H = 1,465$ lb.

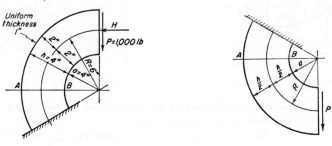

Fig. 12-52. Problem 32.

Fig. 12-53. Problem 33.

33. (a) Starting with Eq. (46) for the maximum bending stress in a curved beam of rectangular cross section, add the effect of the direct stress, and thus arrive at an expression for the resultant normal stress for point B in Fig. 12-53 in terms of load P, area of cross section A, and ratio c_1.

(b) If $s = 7,500$ psi at B, $P = 5,000$ lb, $h = 4$ in., and thickness equals 2 in., find the corresponding value of a.

$$Ans. \quad (a) \quad s = \frac{P}{A}\left[\frac{3c_1{}^2 - 1.8}{c_1 - 1}\right]$$

$$(b) \quad a = 3.55 \text{ in.}$$

34. What value of c_1 will make the bending stress at the inner edge of a curved beam of rectangular cross section loaded in pure bending 5 per cent higher than that in a straight beam of the same cross section? 10 per cent higher?

$$Ans. \quad c_1 = 13.95; c_1 = 7.30.$$

35. A crane hook has the loading and dimensions given in Fig. 12-54.

(a) Draw cross section AB to full-size scale and divide into 18 strips one-quarter inch wide running at right angles to line AB.

(b) Locate the center of gravity by use of the integral $A\bar{x} = \int x \, dA$, where A is the area of the cross section, $\bar{x}$ is the distance from the center of gravity to one end, say point B, x is the distance from point B to the center of gravity of each strip, and dA is the area of the strip. This operation should be carried out in tabular form.

(c) Find the value of m_1 by use of Eq. (48), and the value of the maximum and minimum stresses. *Ans.* $\bar{x} = 2.06$ in.; $s_{max} = 14,600$; $s_{min} = -6,200$ psi.

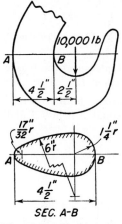

Fig. 12-54.   Problem 35.

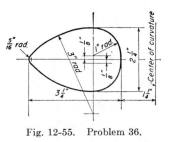

Fig. 12-55.   Problem 36.

36. Perform the operations of Problem 35 for the cross section of Fig. 12-55. Divide into 13 quarter-inch strips. Load is 5,000 lb.

$$Ans. \quad \bar{x} = 1.46 \text{ in.}, s_{max} = 11,000 \text{ psi}, s_{min} = -3,750 \text{ psi.}$$

37. Compute the values of r and the maximum acceleration for a cycloidal cam with the same data as Example 14.   *Ans.*   Max. accel. $= 8,040$ in./sec².

38. In Fig. 12-31 let $r_1 = 1.5$ in., $r = 1.5$ in., $r_n = 0.75$ in., $r_f = 1.0$ in., and angle $\beta' = 105°$. Find the lift of the cam. Compute the rise when contact is at K_2, and find the 2 values of the acceleration for this point for a velocity of 600 rpm.

$$Ans. \quad L = 0.6199 \text{ in., rise } = 0.2583 \text{ in., accel. } = -4,100 \text{ and } 10,050 \text{ in./sec².}$$

39. The acceleration for a circular arc cam with roller follower at the start of the rise is equal to $80g$. The acceleration at the nose is $20g$; $L = 0.375$ in., $r_o = 0.8$ in., $r_f = 0.5$ in., rpm $= 600$. Find radius at the nose and at the start of the rise. Find the angle of rotation through which the rise takes place.

Ans. $r_n = 0.2728$ in., $r = 1.9638$ in. $\beta' = 64°20'$.

40. A circular arc cam with a roller follower has the following dimensions. $r = 1.125$ in., $r_o = 1.250$ in., $r_1 = 1.1918$ in., $r_f = 0.75$ in., $\beta' = 75°$; rpm $= 80$. Compute and plot to suitable scale the curves for rise, velocity, and acceleration.

Ans. $L = 0.906$ in., max. vel. $= 8.20$ in./sec, max. accel. $= 141.8$ in./sec^2.

41. A circular arc cam with a roller follower has the following dimensions· $r = 2$ in., $r_o = 1.75$ in., $r_1 = 2.125$ in., $r_f = 1.25$ in., $\beta' = 82.5°$, rpm $= ?$ Compute and plot to suitable scale the curves for rise, velocity, and acceleration.

Ans. $L = 1.4035$ in., max. vel. $= 1.58$ in./sec, max. accel. $= 3.65$ in/sec^2.

42. In Fig. 12-31 let the value of the acceleration when the roller is in contact with the nose of the cam be called A. Radii r_o and r_f are given, as well as the lift L. Angular velocity ω is also known. Derive an equation for r_1.

$$\text{Ans.} \quad r_1 = \frac{A(r_o + r_f + L)}{A + w^2(r_o + r_f + L)}.$$

43. Find the horsepower that a No. 60 roller chain can carry when operating at the recommended sprocket speed. The sprocket has 25 teeth.

Ans. hp $= 20.0$.

The following problems are presented without answers.

44. A 2 in. diameter steel shaft is to be press-fitted into a 7 in. diameter by 3 in. thick steel disk. Diametral interference of the metal is to be 0.0018 in. Find the force required to assemble them if the coefficient of friction is 0.15.

45. A 2 in. diameter steel shaft is to be press-fitted into a 6 in. diameter by $2\frac{1}{2}$ in. thick steel disk, with a Class 7 fit. Find the maximum required assembly force for a coefficient of friction of 0.15. Assume the tightest permissible fit.

46. A 4 in. diameter steel shaft is to be press-fitted into a 8 in. diameter Class 50 cast iron hub. FS for hub is to be 5. Find the value of the radial and tangential stresses for the hub at the hole.

47. A steel shaft 3.5 in. in diameter is to be press-fitted into a Class 50 cast iron hub 8 in. in diameter. Find the required diametral interference of the metal if the hub has a FS of 4 from the press-fit stresses.

48. A hardened steel beam is 25 in. long with simple supports. An 80 lb weight drops 4 in. and strikes the beam at the center. Find the value of the bending stress for the following conditions. Ignore W_b in the calculations.

(a) The beam is $\frac{1}{2}$ in. × 2 in. set on edge.

(b) The beam is 1 in. × 1 in.

(c) The beam is $\frac{1}{2}$ in. × 2 in. laid on the flat.

13

Dimensioning and Details

THE design of a machine includes many factors other than those of determining the loads and stresses and selecting the proper materials. Before construction or manufacture can begin, it is necessary to have complete assembly and detail drawings to convey all necessary information to the shop men. The designer usually does not make such drawings, but he frequently is called upon to supervise the draftsmen who do this detailing or to check the drawings before they are sent to the shop. Much experience and familiarity with manufacturing processes are needed before one can become conversant with all phases of production drawings. Some of the factors involved are discussed in this chapter.

1. Dimensioning

Tolerances must be placed on the dimensions of a drawing to limit the permissible variations in size because it is impossible to manufacture a part exactly to a given dimension. Although small tolerances give higher quality work and a better-operating mechanism, the cost of manufacture increases rapidly as the tolerances are reduced, as indicated by the typical curve of Fig. 13-1. It is therefore important that the tolerances be specified at the largest values that the operating or functional considerations permit.

The development of production processes for large-volume manufacture at low cost has been largely dependent upon interchangeability of component parts. Thus the designer must determine both the proper tolerances for the individual parts, and the correct amount of clearance or interference to permit assembly with the connecting parts. The manner of placing tolerances on drawings depends somewhat on the kind of product or type of manufacturing process. If the tolerance on a dimension is not specifically stated, the drawing should contain a blanket note which gives the value of the tolerance for such dimensions. However, some concerns do not use blanket notes, on the supposition that if each dimension is considered individually, wider tolerances than those called for in the note could probably be specified. In any event it is very important that a drawing be free from ambiguities and be subject only to a single interpretation.

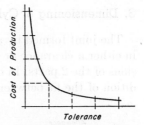

Fig. 13-1. Relationship between size of tolerance and cost of production.

2. Redundant Dimensioning

In a given direction, a point should be located by 1 and only 1 dimension. Much confusion and expense arise from violation of this rule.[1]

For example, consider the horizontal dimension of the part shown in Fig. 13-2(a). For a part made as in sketch (b), lengths AB and AC are

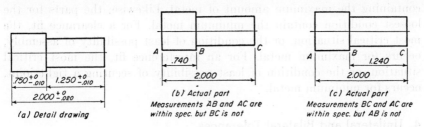

| (a) Detail drawing | (b) Actual part
Measurements AB and AC are
within spec. but BC is not | (c) Actual part
Measurements BC and AC are
within spec. but AB is not |

Fig. 13-2.   Example of incorrect production parts caused by redundant dimension.

in accord with the drawing, but BC is not. Perhaps length BC is the important one for proper functioning, but a production man could argue that technically he had followed the drawing by making AB and AC correctly. Similarly in sketch (c), lengths BC and AC are in accord with the drawing, but AB is not.

The difficulty can be corrected merely by omitting 1 of the dimensions

[1] See p. 48 of reference 1, Bibliography.

in Fig. 13-2(a). The 2 dimensions that should be retained are determined by the functional requirements of the design.

3. Dimensioning of Cylindrical Fits. Maximum Metal. Minimum Metal

The joint formed by a shaft in a hole, as shown in Fig. 13-3, can result in either a clearance or interference fit, depending on the relative dimensions of the 2 parts. In order to secure a better mental picture of the condition of the fit between the 2 parts, a bar diagram[2] has been formed by

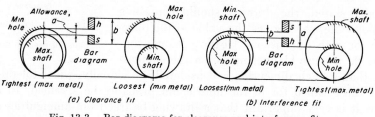

Fig. 13-3.   Bar diagrams for clearance and interference fits.

plotting the diametral tolerance h for the hole, and the diametral tolerance s for the shaft to large scale, as shown in the figure. A clearance fit results when there is a clearance between the smallest hole and largest shaft. The value of the clearance a for the tightest condition is technically called the *allowance*. An interference fit results when the shaft is larger than the hole, as illustrated in Fig. 13-3(b).

All the parts for the tightest condition in Fig. 13-3 are at the limit containing the maximum amount of metal. Likewise, the parts for the loosest condition contain the minimum metal. For a clearance fit, the most critical situation, or the condition of least possibility of assembly, occurs for maximum metal. For an interference fit, the most critical situation, or the condition of least possibility of securing a tight joint, occurs for minimum metal.

4. Unilateral and Bilateral Tolerances

The tolerances for the cylindrical fit may be placed on a drawing in a number of different ways. Figure 13-4(a) shows the unilateral method, in which one tolerance dimension is zero, and the other tolerance takes care of all the permissible variation in size. The basic dimensions (4.000 and 3.997 in.) refer to the tightest permissible fit. It is customary in clearance fits to specify the maximum metal condition by the basic dimensions. By so doing, the clearance for the most difficult assembly condition can

[2] See reference 2, Bibliography.

be obtained directly from the basic dimensions without paying attention to the tolerances. The directions of the tolerances are then such as to recede from the most critical condition.

Figure 13-4(a) represents what would nominally be called a "4 inch shaft." It should be noted, however, that the 4 in. dimension is placed, not on the shaft, but on the dimension for the hole. When this is done, the dimensioning is said to be on the *basic hole system*. This method is advantageous because the manufacturing department can use standard-size reamers for the holes, and then machine the shafts to fit.

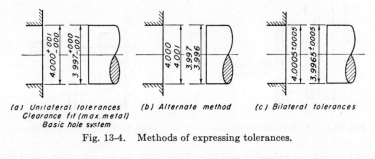

(a) *Unilateral tolerances*   (b) *Alternate method*   (c) *Bilateral tolerances*
    Clearance fit (max. metal)
    Basic hole system

Fig. 13-4.   Methods of expressing tolerances.

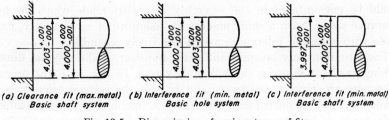

(a) *Clearance fit (max. metal)*   (b) *Interference fit (min. metal)*   (c) *Interference fit (min. metal)*
    Basic shaft system   *Basic hole system*   *Basic shaft system*

Fig. 13-5.   Dimensioning of various types of fits.

However, the manufacturing departments may prefer to use ground shafting of standard sizes. When this material is used, the holes must be made to fit the shafts. The nominal shaft size then appears in the dimensions for the shaft and not for the hole. This method of dimensioning is known as the *basic shaft system*. When applied to the case of Fig. 13-4(a), the dimensions of Fig. 13-5(a) result.

Sometimes the upper and lower limits are given in full, as shown in Fig. 13-4(b). Here there is no need to make arithmetical calculations for finding the limiting sizes, and the possibility of making mistakes is reduced. A definite procedure is used for the order of stating the dimensions. In Fig. 13-4(b), the top figures give the maximum metal condition, and the shop workman would normally aim to machine to these upper dimensions. If he misses, but is within the tolerance zones, the parts still are acceptable.

Bilateral tolerances, in which the variations are given in both directions from basic dimensions, are illustrated by Fig. 13-4(c). Examples of interference fits, when dimensioned on the basic hole and basic shaft systems, for minimum metal, are shown in Figs. 13-5(b) and (c).

The unilateral system of dimensioning possesses distinct advantages in interchangeable manufacture. In Fig. 13-6, the tolerances for hole and shaft are represented to scale by h_1 and s_1, respectively. Later it may be found feasible to increase the tolerances on the parts to h_2 and s_2, and thus effect additional economies of manufacture. Should the new

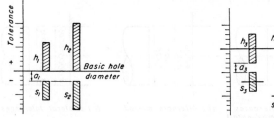

Fig. 13-6.   Unilateral tolerances.   Fig. 13-7.   Bilateral tolerances.

and old parts be mixed together, Fig. 13-6 indicates that no difficulty would be encountered in the assembly of a part made when the hole tolerance was h_1 with a shaft made with tolerance of s_2. Similarly, parts made with s_1 and h_2 tolerances would also freely assemble.

The situation may be quite different, however, if the original dimensioning has been done on the bilateral system. In Fig. 13-7, the original tolerances are represented by h_3 and s_3, and the revised tolerances by h_4 and s_4. Although parts made with h_3 and s_4 tolerances can be assembled, a clearance fit between parts with s_3 and h_4 tolerances may not be possible. Thus, if the unilateral system of tolerances is used, the value of the tolerances may be changed at will without incurring difficulties in the assembly of a mixture of new and old parts. Drawings made with unilateral tolerances are usually easier to check than are those made with bilateral tolerances.

In some situations, the bilateral method of tolerancing is very appropriate. The locations of hole centers, for example, when the variation from the basic dimension is equally critical in both directions, are usually so dimensioned. For practical manufacturing purposes, welded assemblies may be dimensioned with bilateral tolerances. The same applies to loosely toleranced dimensions. If the tolerances are large, it is sometimes more convenient to give the mean dimension, and the variation each way as plus and minus values.

Fits between mating parts are designated by the terms "class" and "grade." The class of the fit refers to the allowance a; the grade refers to the maximum clearance b for an assembly at the loosest condition.

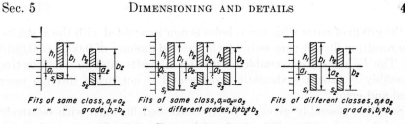

Fig. 13-8. Classes and grades for clearance fits.

Various possibilities of classes and grades are illustrated by the bar diagrams for shafts and holes in Fig. 13-8.

5. Selective Assembly

No difficulty arises in maintaining suitable tolerances if the fit is very loose. The same is true for very tight fits or fits having considerable interference. However, when the difference between allowance and maximum clearance must be small, the tolerances for hole and shaft may become excessively small, with consequent increase in the cost of production.

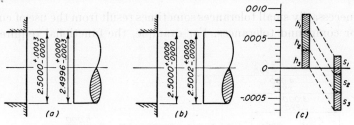

Fig. 13-9. Dimensioning for selective assembly.

These costs may be minimized by selective assembly, which consists of first making each of the mating parts with large tolerances and then sorting them into groups having small tolerances. Suppose, for example, in Fig. 13-9(a), it is necessary that the clearance between a hole and shaft should vary from 0.0004 in. to 0.0010 in. The tolerances for each part, if divided equally, will thus be only 0.0003 in., and the cost of manufacture would be high. If selective assembly is used, the tolerances can be increased to larger values, as shown in Fig. 13-9(b). The bar diagram for this fit, given in Fig. 13-9(c), indicates that the parts are to be sorted into 3 groups, each with a variation in size of 0.0003 in., as follows:

Holes			Shafts		
Group h_1	2.5006	$+0.0003$ -0.0000	Group s_1	2.5002	$+0.0000$ -0.0003
h_2	2.5003	$+0.0003$ -0.0000	s_2	2.4999	$+0.0000$ -0.0003
h_3	2.5000	$+0.0003$ -0.0000	s_3	2.4996	$+0.0000$ -0.0003

If the group of parts with the h_1 holes is now assembled with the s_1 shafts, the resulting fit will vary only by the desired amount of 0.0004 to 0.0010 in. The h_2 holes are assembled with the s_2 shafts, and so on. Selective assembly is thus a systematic process and is not made through mere trial and error.

Selective assembly gives a closely controlled fit, even with relatively large shop tolerances. The method, however, has a number of disadvantages. The sorting operation and the requirements for additional gages increase production costs. Universal interchangeability is no longer maintained; servicing is more complicated; and a whole subassembly may have to be replaced rather than a single part. After sorting, unless the parts are made in large quantities, the corresponding groups of components, which must be assembled together, may not contain equal numbers of parts. However, selective assembly, is advantageous for interference fits where small changes in size may either cause the fit to become too loose to hold, or so tight that the press-fit stresses are excessive.

6. Cumulative and Noncumulative Tolerances

Unnecessarily small tolerances sometimes result from the use of cumulative or compound tolerances. For example, the functional requirements

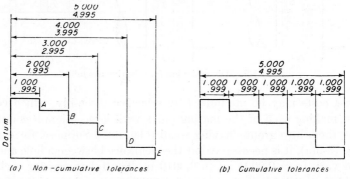

Fig. 13-10.   Increase in tolerance obtained by non-cumulative dimensioning.

of a part may be such as to permit a tolerance of 0.005 in. from the datum plane for each of the vertical surfaces in Fig. 13-10(a). When each surface is dimensioned individually from the datum, full advantage is taken of the permissible variation in size. But, if the dimensioning is done chain fashion from surface to surface, as shown in Fig. 13-10(b), the variation of 0.005 in. in the over-all length must be divided among the 5 dimensions, and the permissible tolerance is reduced to but 0.001 in., with consequent increase in manufacturing difficulties. Thus, in general, cumulative or compound tolerances should be avoided.

However, suppose that the relationship between certain features must be held within small limits between themselves, but that a relatively large variation in their location from the datum plane is permissible. In such cases, the introduction of a compound tolerance may be preferable to noncumulative dimensioning.

7. Datum and Functional Surfaces

The surfaces of a part perform various duties in fulfilling the objective of the design. The surfaces to which the various features of a part are

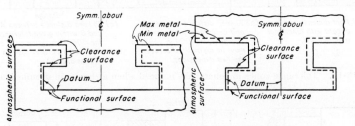

Fig. 13-11. Tolerance zones for *T*-slide.

located by means of dimensions are called the datum planes. The functional surfaces are those operating or positioning surfaces that control the operation or location of the mechanism. Clearance surfaces provide continuity in the part, but have no functioning characteristics. Atmospheric surfaces have no contact relationship to the other surfaces of the part. Examples would be the outside of castings and exposed bolt heads.

The datum surfaces for a part, in general, consist of 3 mutually perpendicular planes. In order to facilitate manufacture and inspection, it is important that the datum surfaces pass through actual physical features on the part and not be merely imaginary planes in space.

For example, it is both natural and convenient in the T slide of Fig. 13-11, to run the horizontal dimensions from the vertical center line. Manufacture and inspection, however, may be difficult if this imaginary plane is devoid of all physical features. If it is possible to place two holes along the central datum plane, dowels can be fitted therein which permit this plane to be located with respect to the tools for machining and the gages for inspection.

One of the vertical functional surfaces could of course be used for the datum instead of the imaginary plane through the center. In general, however, it is found that once a datum is chosen and the tolerance zones established in relationship to it, it is not possible to shift the dimensioning to a new datum and preserve the same tolerance zones as originally planned.

The effect on the size of the tolerances caused by shifting the datum plane is illustrated by Fig. 13-12. Suppose the functional requirements are met by the dimensions from surface B as shown in Fig. 13-12(a). If the datum is shifted to the top surface, as in sketch (b), the tolerances on the dimensions are reduced as shown. Sketch (c) shows the reduction

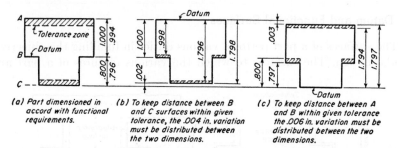

(a) Part dimensioned in accord with functional requirements.

(b) To keep distance between B and C surfaces within given tolerance, the .004 in. variation must be distributed between the two dimensions.

(c) To keep distance between A and B within given tolerance the .006 in. variation must be distributed between the two dimensions.

Fig. 13-12.   Tolerance zones in general are reduced when a change in datums is made.

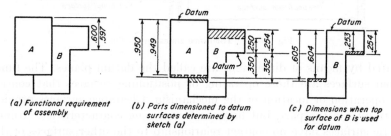

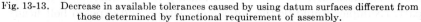

(a) Functional requirement of assembly

(b) Parts dimensioned to datum surfaces determined by sketch (a)

(c) Dimensions when top surface of B is used for datum

Fig. 13-13.   Decrease in available tolerances caused by using datum surfaces different from those determined by functional requirement of assembly.

in the size of the tolerances necessitated by a shift of the datum to the bottom surface.

In Fig. 13-13(a), let the functional requirements after assembly of the 2 parts be given by the dimensions of 0.600–0.597 in. The dimensioned surfaces of sketch (a) are used as the datum planes for the detail dimensions of the parts as shown by Fig. 13-13(b). If the datum plane for part B is shifted to the top surface, a reduction in the tolerance zones occurs, as is shown in Fig. 13-13(c).

8. Dimensioning of Hole Centers

The cylindrical surface of a hole can be located by means of dimensions for the center and for the hole diameter. When these dimensions have tolerances, a cumulative or compound tolerance results.

When the hole center is located by means of right-angle dimensions with tolerances, as shown in Fig. 13-14(a), the tolerance zone for the hole center consists of a small square, which, for this example, is 0.002 in. on the side. Note that the tolerance zones for the centers in Figs. 13-14(b) and (c) are not completely specified, although shop workmen would probably interpret the drawing as implying that the same tolerance is intended in both directions. When holes are to be made on a jig-borer,

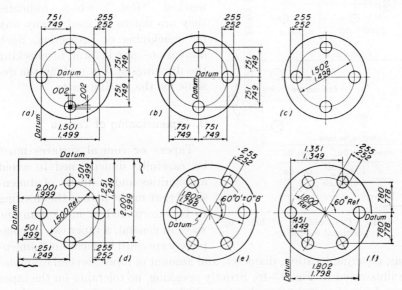

Fig. 13-14.   Various methods of dimensioning hole centers.

it is customary to select data on the left and top sides of the part, as shown in Fig. 13-14(d), and run all dimensions to the right and downward. Tolerance zones may also be completely defined by tolerances on the diameter of the hole circle and on the angular dimensions, as shown in Fig. 13-14(e). For sheet-metal work or once-only job shops, this method is very convenient. In many cases, the horizontal and vertical coordinates are used for locating the hole centers as illustrated by Fig. 13-14(f).

Other methods for dimensioning hole centers are available. One method uses untoleranced dimensions to locate the true geometrical center, and then permits the center to lie anywhere within a circular tolerance zone of specified diameter. The letters PT are added to the untoleranced dimensions to denote their association with positional tolerances which are given as a note on the drawing. This method permits the use of chain dimensioning without involving the accumulation of tolerances. The method is illustrated in Fig. 13-15.

The method above provides suitable tolerance zones for the centers of a series of holes located along a straight line. By the conventional method of dimensioning, a tolerance is specified in the direction of the row but not in the direction normal thereto.

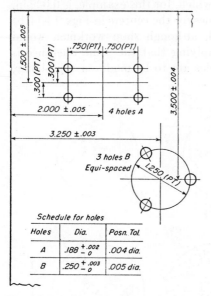

Reference dimensions are dimensions without tolerance placed on drawings for information or calculating purposes. They should be marked "Ref.," which indicates they are not to be used in any way for machining or inspection. Such dimensions are helpful in checking the drawings and in making the designs for the mating parts.

9. Dimensioning of Tapers

Tapers or conical surfaces must be carefully dimensioned to avoid ambiguities and conflicts of dimensions that might permit the drawing to be interpreted in more than one way. In general, a taper can be completely specified by means of 3 dimensions, covering location, diameter, and amount of taper. Several examples are illustrated in Fig. 13-16. Strictly speaking, no tolerance on the taper or angle in sketches (a) and (b) would be required in laying out either the maximum metal condition or the minimum metal condition. A compound tolerance is introduced by use of a tolerance on these taper and angle dimensions.

Fig. 13-15. Dimensioning of holes by positional tolerances.

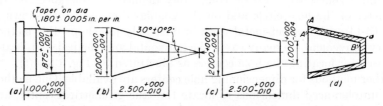

Fig. 13-16. Various methods of dimensioning tapers.

In sketch (c) dimensions for both large and small diameters and the length are given. The tolerance zone specified by these 3 dimensions is represented by Fig. 13-16(d). Since no tolerance for the taper is given in sketch (c), the interpretation can be placed on the drawing that any part falling within the tolerance zone will be acceptable. The angle for the taper could then vary from that represented by line AB' to line $A'B$. Thus the tolerances on the diameters can cause a considerable variation in the angle of the taper. This variation must be checked carefully by the designer to make certain that it will be acceptable.

When dimensions are made to corners, as in Figs. 13-16(b) and (c), it is understood that the theoretically sharp corner is referred to. Actual measurements on a part must be made by means of rolls or by a comparator, since a theoretically sharp corner does not exist. When a fourth dimension is placed on a drawing for a taper, ambiguities immediately arise. For example, suppose an additional dimension for the small diameter were given in Fig. 13-16(b). Examination indicates that a variety of interpretations could then be placed on the drawing and much confusion arise.

10. Positional Tolerances

When a high degree of accuracy is required, tolerances for the positional features, such as parallelism, squareness, concentricity, and flatness, must be placed on the drawing. The control of such features presents the most

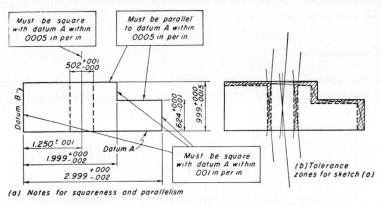

(a) Notes for squareness and parallelism

Fig. 13-17.   Methods of representing positional tolerances.

troublesome phase of proper dimensioning procedure. As a rule, such information cannot be conveyed by dimensions, but must be handled by suitably worded notes. Care and attention must be given to the wording in order that no ambiguities or misinformation appear on the drawing.

A view of a body with notes for squareness and parallelism is given in Fig. 13-17(a). Should these notes be omitted from the drawing, it would still be necessary, in the manufacture and inspection of the part, to have limitations for the permissible variations in squareness and parallelism. The tolerances on the dimensions form the zones of Fig.

13-17(b). The drawing without notes might then be interpreted as meaning that any part falling within the tolerance zones of Fig. 13-17(b) would be acceptable. It is seen that this interpretation may give a set of variations for squareness and parallelism different from the limitations imposed by the notes.

When necessary, the permissible deviation of a surface from a true plane must be marked on the drawing. When the drawing is not so marked, the interpretation is sometimes made that the waviness, or departure from a true plane, must be limited by the tolerance for the location of the surface, as illustrated in Fig. 13-18. An uncertainty, however, immediately arises when a surface of the part is used as the datum, since no tolerance zone can be given for such a surface.

Fig. 13-18.   Limitation of waviness determined by tolerance zone of surface.

When many positional features must be specified, the notes become numerous and bulky. To produce a more clean-cut drawing, various systems of symbols have been proposed as a shorthand method for conveying the needed information.[3] Lack of agreement on the type and usage of the symbols, as well as lack of understanding of their meaning on the part of workmen, has hindered progress in this direction.

11. Concentricity

An example of a note for the variation in the concentricity of coaxial cylinders is given in Fig. 13-19(a). If the permissible value of the full

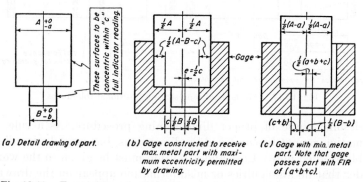

(a) Detail drawing of part.   (b) Gage constructed to receive max. metal part with maximum eccentricity permitted by drawing.   (c) Gage with min. metal part. Note that gage passes part with FIR of (a+b+c).

Fig. 13-19.   Eccentricity of cylindrical surfaces and gage for checking same.

indicator runout FIR between the cylindrical surfaces is equal to c, the maximum displacement of the axes is equal to $0.5c$.

[3] See reference 3, Bibliography.

The diameters of the cylinders in Fig. 13-19(a) can be easily checked by micrometers or snap gages. If a gage for checking eccentricity be constructed as in Fig. 13-19(b) with the large diameter equal to A, and the small diameter equal to $B + c$, it will receive a maximum metal part with the maximum eccentricity specified by the drawing. For all other parts, not at the maximum metal size, the gage passes parts with eccentricities larger than the specified limit. The worst violation occurs with a minimum metal part as shown in Fig. 13-19(c) where the full indicator runout is equal to $a + b + c$. Although the gage shown here passes parts whose eccentricities exceed the limits of the drawing, such parts can be assembled with the remainder of the structure.

12. Manufacturing and Gage Tolerances

The accuracy of the different machining operations varies considerably. In addition, accuracy is usually more difficult to achieve on large parts

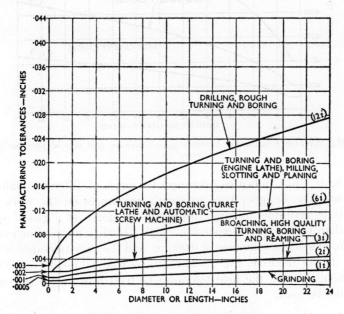

Fig. 13-20. Average relationship between manufacturing tolerance and size of part for various kinds of machining operations.

than on small parts. Figure 13-20 may be taken as a suitable guide of expected accuracies if actual experience on the part in question is lacking.[4]

[4] See reference 3, Bibliography.

These curves are plotted as multiples of i, where

$$i = \sqrt{20d} + 1 \tag{1}$$

and where d is the diameter or length.

Tolerances are also necessary for the manufacture of gages, and may be from 5 per cent to 10 per cent of the tolerances on the work. Thus, if unnecessarily small work tolerances are specified, gage costs will be very

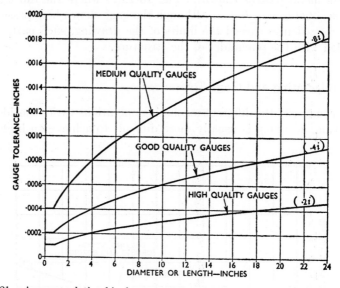

Fig. 13-21. Average relationship between gage tolerance and size of part for gages of different qualities.

high. Figure 13-21 indicates tolerances for gages of different qualities or accuracies. The designer tries to specify tolerances on the work which will permit manufacture and inspection by gages of "good" quality rather than by the more expensive "high" quality gages. For example, if a 2 in. hole has a tolerance of 0.003 in. and the gage tolerance is 10 per cent of that of the hole, Fig. 13-21 indicates that a "good" quality gage is sufficient. Should the hole tolerance be 0.0015 in., a "high" quality gage must be used.

13. Standardized Cylindrical Fits

Fits between cylindrical bodies and holes have been standardized into 8 classes by the American Standards Association. When the class number is specified, the hole tolerance, shaft tolerance, and allowance or average interference can be determined from the diameter by means of the formulas given in Fig. 13-22. Classes 1 to 4 are clearance fits, and Classes 7 and 8 are interference fits. However, Classes 5 and 6 may be either clearance or interference fits, depending on the random assembly of the parts. They are accordingly called transitional fits.

As shown by the bar diagrams, Class 1 is the loosest fit and has the largest tolerances on the parts. It is used for fits where accuracy is not essential. The allowance and tolerances for Class 2 are also liberal. Class 3 is used for sliding fits and for the more accurate machine tool and automotive parts. Considerable precision is required in making parts for

Class of fit	1	2	3	4	5	6	7	8
Bar diagram (Basic hole system) 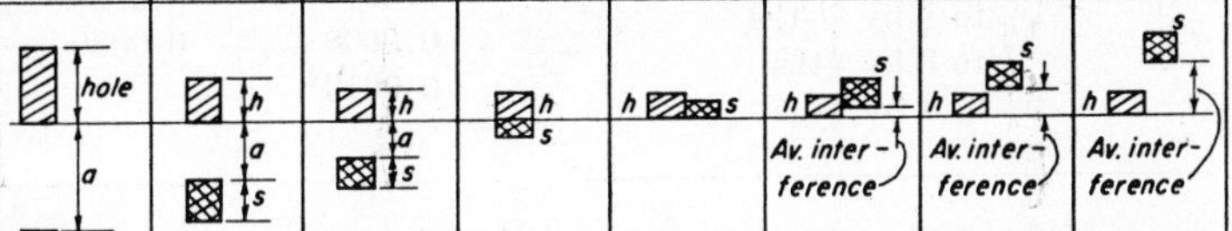	Loose fit	Free fit	Medium fit	Snug fit	Wringing fit	Tight fit	Medium force fit	Heavy force and shrink fit
Hole tolerance	$.0025\sqrt[3]{d}$	$.0013\sqrt[3]{d}$	$.0008\sqrt[3]{d}$	$.0006\sqrt[3]{d}$	$.0006\sqrt[3]{d}$	$.0006\sqrt[3]{d}$	$.0006\sqrt[3]{d}$	$.0006\sqrt[3]{d}$
Shaft tolerance	$.0025\sqrt[3]{d}$	$.0013\sqrt[3]{d}$	$.0008\sqrt[3]{d}$	$.0004\sqrt[3]{d}$	$.0004\sqrt[3]{d}$	$.0006\sqrt[3]{d}$	$.0006\sqrt[3]{d}$	$.0006\sqrt[3]{d}$
Allowance, a	$.0025\sqrt[3]{d^2}$	$.0014\sqrt[3]{d^2}$	$.0009\sqrt[3]{d^2}$	0				
Av. interference					0	.00025 d	.0005 d	.001 d

Fig. 13-22. ASA B4a-1925 classification of cylindrical fits.

Class 4 fits. Selective assembly is usually practiced with Class 5 fits. Class 6 is suitable for drive fits for gears, pulleys, rocker arms, and so forth. It is also used for drive fits in thin sections or for extremely long fits in other sections. It is suitable for automotive, ordnance, and general machine manufacturing. Considerable pressure is required for the assembly of parts for Class 7. This fit is used for fastening the shafts to locomotive and railroad car wheels. It is also used for crank disks and for the armatures of motors and generators. It is the tightest fit that is recommended when the part with the hole is of cast iron. Class 8 is suitable for heavy force or shrink fits when the part with the hole is made of steel.

In order to reduce the expense of tools and gages, cylindrical sizes called for on drawings should be kept as few as possible. Preferred basic sizes are given in Table 13-1. The number of tolerances that may be used with each diameter should also be kept to a minimum to save the expense of an excessive number of gages. Recommended values for tolerances and allowances are given in Table 13-2.

It is possible to arrange standardized fits of combinations of clearance,

TABLE 13-1

Preferred Basic Sizes, Inches

	0.0100		0.0500
	0.0125	$\frac{1}{16}$,	0.0625
$\frac{1}{64}$,	0.015625		0.0800
	0.0200	$\frac{3}{32}$,	0.09375
	0.0250		0.1000
$\frac{1}{32}$,	0.03125	$\frac{1}{8}$,	0.1250
	0.0400	$\frac{5}{32}$,	0.15625

$\frac{3}{16}$ to $\frac{3}{4}$ by $\frac{1}{16}$ths
$\frac{7}{8}$ to 3 by $\frac{1}{8}$ths
$3\frac{1}{4}$ to 4 by $\frac{1}{4}$ths

TABLE 13-2

Recommended Tolerances and Allowances

0.0001	0.0012	0.0100*
0.00015	0.0015	0.0120
0.0002*	0.0020*	0.0150
0.00025	0.0025	0.0200*
0.0003	0.0030	0.0250
0.0004	0.0040	0.0300*
0.0005*	0.0050*	(Preferred
0.0006	0.0060	values are
0.0008	0.0080	indicated
0.0010*		by aster-
		isks.)

or interference, and hole and shaft tolerances, different from those of Fig. 13-22. In fact, designers have felt the need for a system of cylindrical fits of greater flexibility than the Classes 1 to 8 now in use. Standardizing committees are actively at work on this problem.

14. Production Process in Statistical Control

A variation in length or other quality can occur from 2 general types of causes. A variation can occur as a result of a large number of chance causes. These occur at random and are inherent in the entire production process and method of measurement.

The other type of variation does not occur at random, and is due to an assignable cause. When all the variations due to assignable causes are located one by one and corrected, the desired state of control is approached, and the system is then said to be in statistical control, or is called a constant cause system.

When a process is in statistical control, and measurements are made on the product, it is found that the number of parts with small variations are more numerous than are parts with large variations. When a plot is made of the frequency of occurrence vs. variation or error for a large number of parts, a smooth curve, known as the normal frequency curve, is obtained.

Although unilateral tolerances have advantages for production drawings, it is usually more convenient to rewrite the dimensions with bilateral tolerances for consideration from the standpoint of statistics. The mean or average dimension is usually designated by placing a bar on top of the symbol.

Application of the normal frequency curve to the variations in the length of a part is illustrated by Fig. 13-23. The area under the curve represents the total production. The curve is asymptotic to the plus and minus horizontal or error axis. The so-called "natural tolerance of a process" is that spread of the curve that includes 99.73 per cent of the total production.

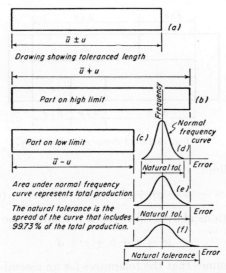

Fig. 13-23.   Distribution of lengths when process is in statistical control.

The drawing for the part specifies a total variation in length of $2u$. If the part can be made by a highly accurate production process, as shown in Fig. 13-23(d), with a natural tolerance equal to about three-quarters of the permissible variation, ideal and trouble-free production results. When the process is not so accurate, with a natural tolerance about equal to the specifications as shown in Fig. 13-23(e), the entire production is still acceptable. However small variations in the value of the average length, such as might be occasioned by tool wear, will give parts longer or shorter than the required value. Sketch (f) shows the frequency curve for a process whose natural tolerance is greater than specification $2u$. Some few parts are longer and some are shorter than the specified values, as shown by the areas in the tails of the curve. One hundred per cent inspection may be necessary to locate such unacceptable parts.

15. Dimensioning of Assemblies

The assembly of a number of parts into a final product is shown schematically in Fig. 13-24. If parts 1, 2, 3, and 4 have the dimensions shown, the mean value $\bar{w}$ of the resultant dimension is $-\bar{a} + \bar{b} + \bar{c} - \bar{d}$. The maximum value of the opening occurs when 1 and 4 are at the low limit, and 2 and 3 are at the high limit. Hence

$$\bar{w} + w = -(\bar{a} - a) + (\bar{b} + b) + (\bar{c} + c) - (\bar{d} - d) \qquad (a)$$

The minimum value occurs when 1 and 4 are at the high limit and 2 and

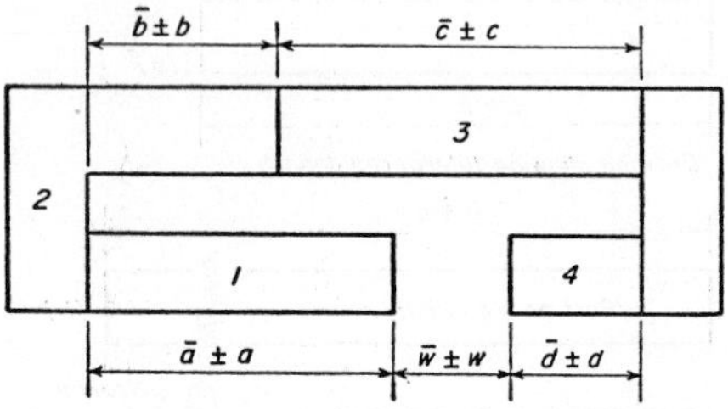

Fig. 13-24.   Tolerances for assembly.

3 are at the low limit. Hence

$$\bar{w} - w = -(\bar{a} + a) + (\bar{b} - b) + (\bar{c} - c) - (\bar{d} + d) \qquad (b)$$

From the 2 equations above, tolerance w is found to be

$$w = a + b + c + d \qquad (2)$$

This equation assumes that the tolerances for an assembly are arithmetic or additive.

The simultaneous occurrence of all parts at the extreme limits assumed by Eqs. (a) and (b) is exceedingly rare. Suppose the dimensions of the different members of an assembly are in no way dependent on each other. In addition, let the lengths of the production parts be distributed normally, and let the assembly be random. Then, if the natural tolerances of the parts are all proportional to the corresponding tolerances of the drawings, the following equation will give a more realistic value for the tolerance w of the assembly.[5]

$$w = \sqrt{a^2 + b^2 + c^2 + d^2 + \cdots} \qquad (3)$$

Example 1. In Fig. 13-24 let $a = b = c = d = 0.002$ in. Find variation w of the assembly by the additive and Pythagorean rules.

Solution.

By additive rule: $w = 4 \times 0.002 = 0.008$ in.

By Pythagorean rule: $w = \sqrt{4 \times 0.002^2} = 0.004$ in.

[5] See references 5 and 6, Bibliography.

16. Assembly of Parts with Loose Bolts

Figure 13-25(a) shows the detail drawing for parts that are to be assembled to each other by loose bolts. Sketch (b) shows that the minimum opening for the insertion of the bolt occurs when the parts have the limiting values for the center distance, together with holes of the minimum diameters. The maximum bolt diameter is therefore $H - 2m$.

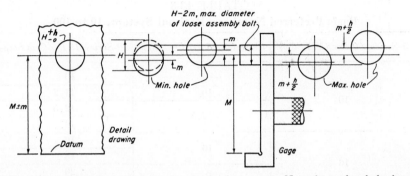

Fig. 13-25.   Inspection of hole location by fixed-type gage. Note that unless holes have their minimum diameters that gage will pass parts with hole centers exceeding tolerances of the drawing.

Hole diameters of the parts can be inspected by a go and no-go plug gage. A gage for checking the position of the holes in Fig. 13-25(b) can be constructed as in sketch (c). It should be noted, however, that such a gage, when the hole diameters are not at the low limit, passes parts whose center distances exceed the limits called for by the drawing. The worst situation occurs when the holes have their maximum diameters. As shown by sketch (d) it is possible for the center distance to vary by as much as $\pm (m + \frac{1}{2}h)$. Although such a gage is incapable of rejecting parts whose center distance exceeds the limits of the drawing, all such parts can be assembled successfully, and in many cases that is the feature of most importance. If for any reason it is necessary to maintain the limits on the center distance, this dimension can be marked "irrespective of hole size" which indicates that inspection cannot be made by the gage of sketch (c).

The remarks above apply also to the case where the dimension runs from center to center of 2 holes. The tolerance on the center distance should now be called $\pm 2m$.

17. Preferred Numbers

The factor of size or capacity must be considered in all manufactured articles or items of commerce. The term "size" may refer to linear dimensions, volume, weight, speed, power, or other features of the product. When an item is produced in a number of sizes, it is logical that the progression of sizes should be geometric rather than arithmetic. Each size is then larger than the preceding by a fixed percentage. Small sizes will then differ from each other by small amounts, and large sizes by larger amounts.

TABLE 13-3
Basic Preferred Numbers, Decimal System, 10 to 100

5-Series, 60 Per Cent Steps	10-Series, 25 Per Cent Steps	20-Series, 12 Per Cent Steps
		10
	10	11.2
	12.5	12.5
10		14
	16	16
		18
16	20	20
		22.4
	25	25
		28
25	31.5	31.5
		35.5
	40	40
		45
40	50	50
		56
	63	63
		71
63	80	80
		90

It is important from an economic standpoint that the number of sizes in a series be standardized at the smallest number that permit the product to take care of its intended range. The value of the step from one size to the next will of course depend upon the product under consideration. The system of *preferred numbers* has been devised in order that the various sizes of a series can be determined in an orderly fashion.[6]

In the range from 10 to 100, the 5-series has 5 numbers, each of which is approximately 60 per cent greater than the preceding. The 10-series

[6] See reference 15, Bibliography.

gives 10 numbers approximately 25 per cent apart, and the 20-series gives 20 numbers approximately 12 per cent apart. These numbers are shown in Table 13-3.

Preferred numbers below 10 are formed by dividing the numbers between 10 and 100 by 10. If still smaller numbers are desired, division is by 100. Preferred numbers above 100 are formed by multiplying the numbers between 10 and 100 by 10 or by 100. Tables for 40-series and 80-series numbers are available when the steps must be closer together. Tables using fractional numbers rather than decimal have also been constructed.

18. Surface Roughness

The properties and performance of machine parts may be affected in many ways by the degree of roughness of the various surfaces. Among these effects, the following may be mentioned.

(1) The friction and wear between unlubricated surfaces are increased with increase of roughness.

(2) Friction and danger of seizure in lubricated surfaces are reduced for smooth surfaces.

(3) Interference fits made on rough surfaces may have a reduced area of contact and a consequent reduction in the holding ability of the joint.

(4) Fatigue strength of parts is increased as the surfaces become more smooth.

(5) Fluid flow in small passageways is reduced as the roughness of the walls is increased.

A demand has gradually grown up for a more exact method of specifying roughness than simply by marking the drawing "finish," "grind," or "lap." The roughness of a surface can be specified by calling for the height of the irregularities above and below the mean plane.

A true profile section, magnified equally in the horizontal and vertical directions, is shown in Fig. 13-26(a). The condition of the surface can be studied in more detail by exaggerating the roughness effect. Figure 13-26(b) shows the same profile when an additional magnification of 25 times has been given to the vertical direction with no change in the horizontal direction. Waviness also occurs in surfaces, as shown in Fig. 13-26(c). No exact differentiating point exists between roughness and waviness, although the pitch of the undulations must be about 0.040 in. or more before they are spoken of as waves. Specimens can be prepared for viewing under the microscope by a process called taper sectioning, in which the surface is ground at a small angle, thus accentuating the heights of the irregularities. An angle of 2°17' gives a magnification of 25.

It is necessary to support the surface with a coating of nickel plating to prevent smearing of the contour during the sectioning process. A surface that has been prepared in this way is illustrated in Fig. 13-27.[7]

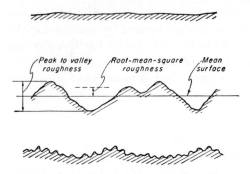

(a) True profile section magnified equally in horizontal and vertical directions.

(b) Exaggerated appearance of surface (a) by further magnification of 25 times in vertical direction only, no change in horizontal magnification.

(c) Roughness consisting of fine irregularities superposed on larger wavelike variations.

Fig. 13-26.   Cross section of surface showing irregularities of roughness and waviness.

Heights above and below the mean surface are expressed in microinches or millionths of an inch, 0.000001 in., in terms of a special kind of average distance called the root mean square height, h_{rms}. This height is found by taking the ordinates at equidistant points on the profile, squaring, adding, dividing by the number of terms, and then taking the square root of this average. This method of calculating gives more weight to the higher peaks of the surface, since it is felt that high, narrow peaks

Fig. 13-27.   Taper section of cylindrical surface finished by grinding.

may have considerable influence on the surface qualities, but would have negligible effect in shifting the position of the mean line. The root mean square height is thus slightly larger than the arithmetic average of the ordinates.

A symbol for surface finish in wide use is the check mark with the bar on the top shown in Fig. 13-28. The sides of the mark are inclined at 60° to the surface, and the roughness height in microinches is represented thereon as shown. The drawing should contain a note stating whether

[7] See reference 11, Bibliography.

root mean square, arithmetic average, or peak-to-valley height is referred to. Sometimes the roughness width and height of wave for a wavy surface are given by means of additional numbers on the symbol. The lay of the surface, or the direction of the predominant surface pattern as formed by the machining or grinding operation, can also be placed on the symbol if desired.

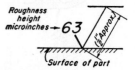

Fig. 13-28. Symbol and marking for surface finish.

Measurements of surface roughness can be made by instruments like the Brush Surface Analyzer or the Profilometer. Both instruments use a diamond tracing point, which is slowly moved over the surface of the specimen. The Brush instrument is direct inking and produces the record of the surface on a paper tape; the Profilometer indicates average roughness heights by a meter. Fortunately, it is not necessary to make an actual measurement of the surface to determine whether or not it meets a specified value for the roughness. In most cases, the roughness can be gaged with sufficient accuracy by comparing the surface with a calibrated

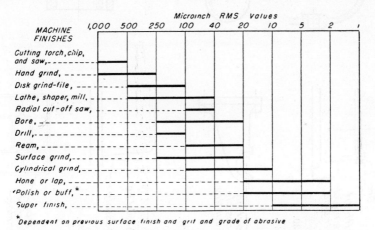

Fig. 13-29.   Range of surface roughness produced by various machining operations.

specimen which has been prepared by the same machining operation. This comparison can be made by rubbing the fingernails across the work piece and then over the sample. Samples can be obtained for this purpose in a variety of roughnesses, such as produced by turning, milling, grinding, lapping, and so forth.

Different types of machining operations give surfaces of various degrees of roughness with a considerable range of variation for any particular operation. The approximate range of such variations[8] is shown in Fig. 13-29. Among the numbers that are recommended for specifying the rms

[8] See reference 9, Bibliography.

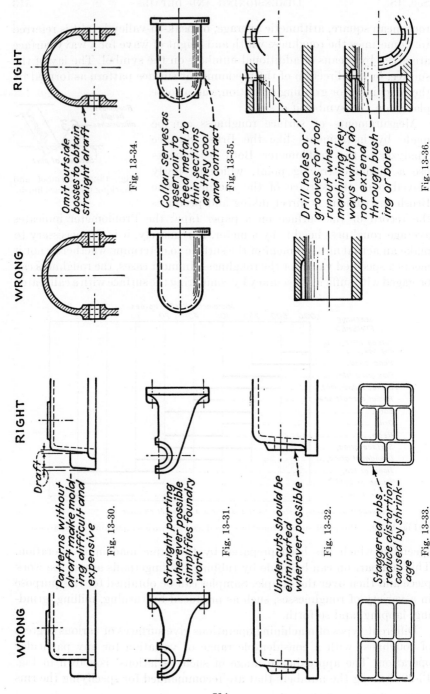

WRONG   RIGHT

Omit outside bosses to obtain straight draft

Fig. 13-34.

Collar serves as reservoir to feed metal to thin sections as they cool and contract

Fig. 13-35.

Drill holes or grooves for tool runout when machining keyways which do not extend through bushing or bore

Fig. 13-36.

WRONG   RIGHT

Patterns without draft make molding difficult and expensive

Draft

Fig. 13-30.

Straight parting wherever possible simplifies foundry work

Fig. 13-31.

Undercuts should be eliminated wherever possible

Fig. 13-32.

Staggered ribs reduce distortion caused by shrinkage

Fig. 13-33.

WRONG RIGHT

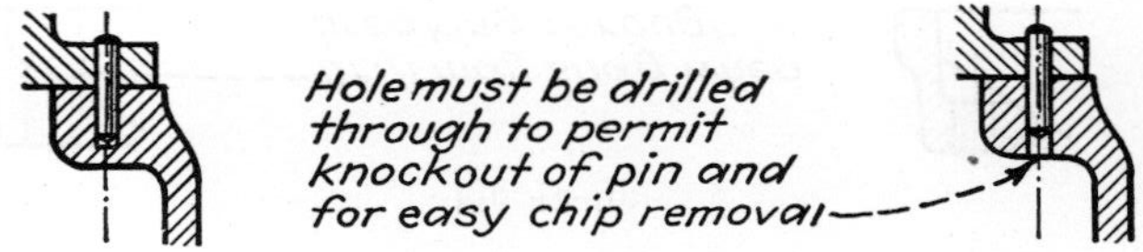
Hole must be drilled through to permit knockout of pin and for easy chip removal

Fig. 13-37.

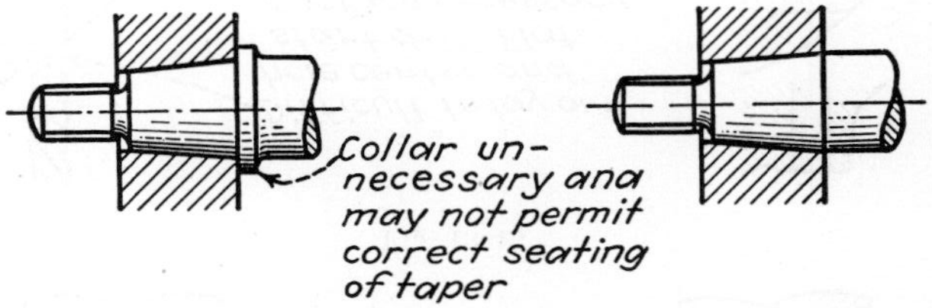
Collar unnecessary and may not permit correct seating of taper

Fig. 13-38.

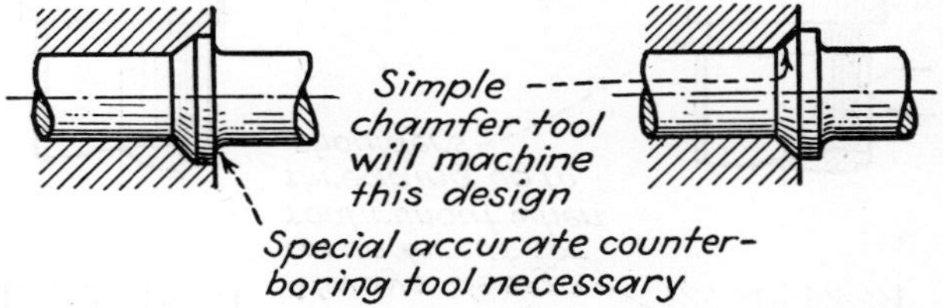
Simple chamfer tool will machine this design
Special accurate counterboring tool necessary

Fig. 13-39.

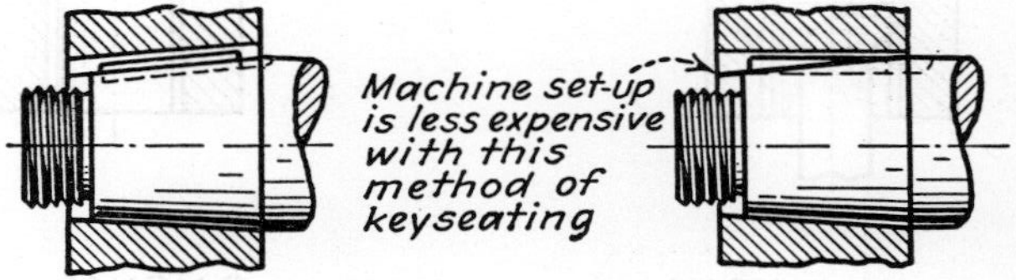
Machine set-up is less expensive with this method of keyseating

Fig. 13-40.

WRONG RIGHT

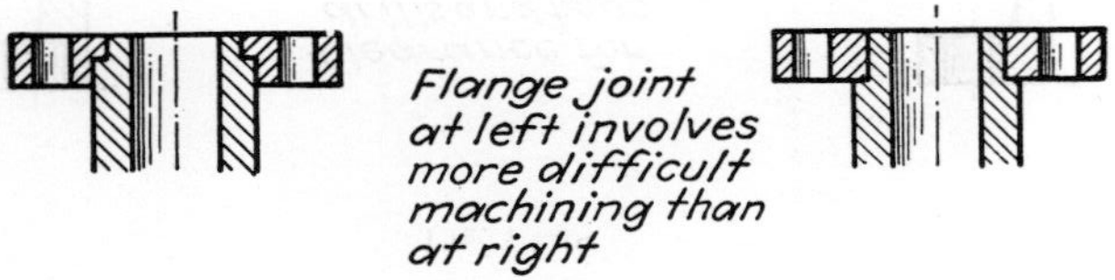
Flange joint at left involves more difficult machining than at right

Fig. 13-41.

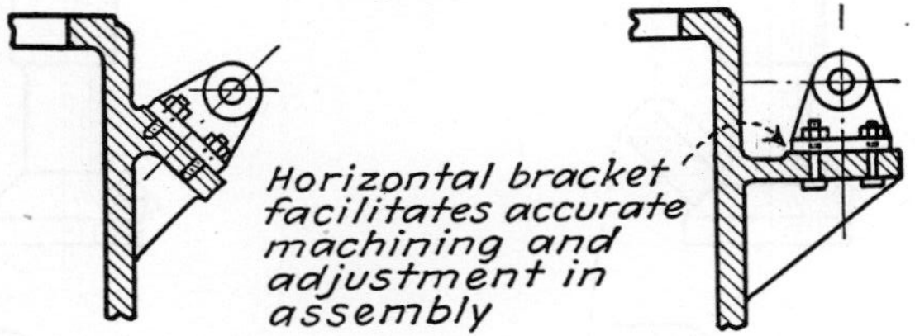
Horizontal bracket facilitates accurate machining and adjustment in assembly

Fig. 13-42.

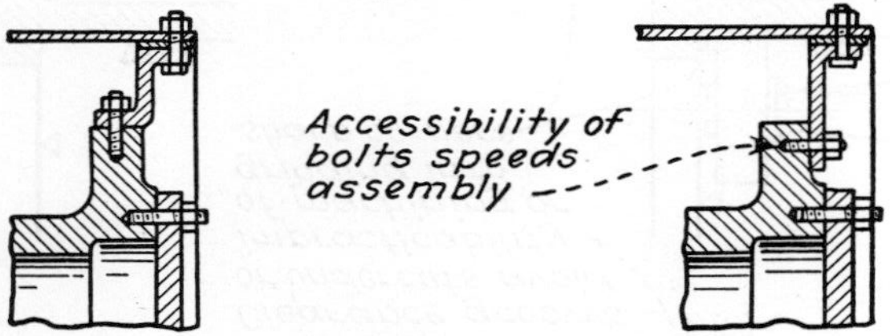
Accessibility of bolts speeds assembly

Fig. 13-43.

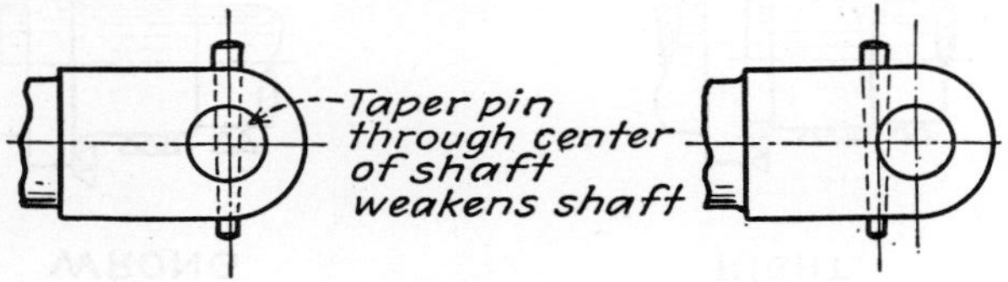
Taper pin through center of shaft weakens shaft

Fig. 13-44.

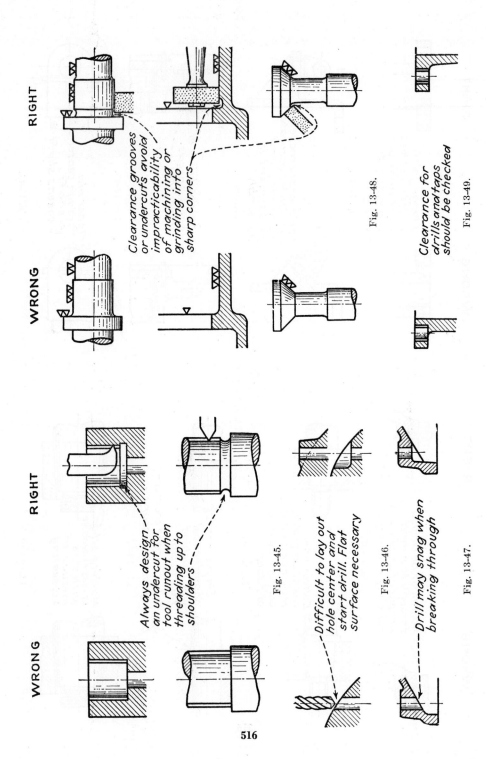

RIGHT

WRONG

Clearance grooves or undercuts avoid impracticability of machining or grinding into sharp corners

Fig. 13-48.

Clearance for drills and taps should be checked

Fig. 13-49.

RIGHT

WRONG

Always design an undercut for tool runout when threading up to shoulders

Fig. 13-45.

Difficult to lay out hole center and start drill. Flat surface necessary

Fig. 13-46.

Drill may snag when breaking through

Fig. 13-47.

height of irregularities, the following may be mentioned: 1, 2, 4, 8, 16, 32, 63, 250, 1,000, 4,000, etc., microinches.[9]

The inverse problem is also of interest to designers. In other words, when the rms height of a surface has been specified, how far below the peaks are the deepest valleys? It is easy to visualize a surface in terms of peak-to-valley distance, but it is difficult to determine what this range would probably be when only the rms height is known. Experiments[10] have shown that the average peak-to-valley roughness can be obtained from the rms value by multiplying by $4\frac{1}{2}$ for cylindrical ground surfaces, by 6 or 7 for other types of fixed-abrasive finishes, and by 10 for loose-abrasive lapped surfaces. The factors quoted give average values for "predominant peak" roughness that occurs more or less uniformly over the entire surface. Another type of irregularity that occurs at intervals that are large as compared to the width of the irregularities themselves is termed "deepest maximum" roughness. The foregoing factors should be doubled to obtain deepest maximum values.

19. Detailing

When the design has been completed, detail or shop drawings must be made before actual manufacture or construction can begin. The detail draftsmen perform a very important function in industry, since the success of a project depends on correct details and shopwork as well as on design calculations. Skill and cleverness in arranging the mechanical details can be acquired only after considerable time has been spent in actual practice in this line of work. A few of the more obvious examples of good and bad detailing are illustrated in Figs. 13-30 to 13-49, inclusive.[11]

BIBLIOGRAPHY

Volume number shown in **bold face** type. The number immediately following is the page on which the article begins.

1. Buckingham, Earle, *Principles of Interchangeable Manufacture*. New York: The Industrial Press, 1941.

2. Gaillard, John, *Tolerances for Cylindrical Fits*. New York: American Standards Association.

3. Gladman, C. A., "Drawing Office Practice in Relation to Interchangeable Components," *Proc. Inst. Mech. Engrs.*, **152**, 388 (1945).

4. Rice, Wm. B., "Setting Tolerances Scientifically," *Mech. Eng.*, **66**, 801 (1944).

[9] See reference 10, Bibliography.
[10] See reference 11, Bibliography.
[11] See reference 16, Bibliography.

5. Acton, F. S., and Olds, E. G., "Tolerances—Additive or Pythagorean," *Ind. Quality Control,* **5,** Nov., 6 (1948).

6. Barrows, M. D., "Probability Methods for Establishing Tolerances," *Product Eng.* **20,** Nov., 106 (1949).

7. Hailes, G. M., "Some Statistical Principles of Tolerances," *Ind. Quality Control,* **7,** May, 77 (1951).

8. Hinman, C. W., and Lord, C. B., "Redimensioning for the Jig Borer," *Am. Machinist,* **74,** 231, 273, (1931).

9. Broadston, J. A., "Standards for Surface Quality," *Product Eng.,* **15,** 622, 704, 756, 806 (1944).

10. Norton, M. R., "Development of Standards for Army Ordnance Finishes," *Mech. Eng.,* **64,** 703 (1942).

11. Tarasov, L. P., "Relation of Surface Roughness Readings to Actual Surface Profile," *Trans. ASME,* **67,** 189 (1945).

12. Belitsos, P. G., "Drafting Practice and More Realistic Tolerancing," *Magazine of Standards,* **25,** 321 (1954).

13. Way, Stewart, "Surface Finish-Straight Edge Shadow Method of Observation and Measurement," *Mech. Eng.,* **59,** 826 (1937).

14. Abbott, E. J., and Goldschmidt, Edgar, "Surface Quality," *Mech. Eng.,* **59,** 813 (1937).

15. *Preferred Numbers, ASA Z17.1-1936.* New York: American Standards Association.

16. Geiger, Ernest, "The Rights and Wrongs of Details," *Product Eng.,* **12,** 72, 122, 248 (1941).

PROBLEMS

1. Draw and dimension the bar diagram for a $3\frac{3}{8}$ in. shaft, Class 3 fit. Draw and dimension a typical hole and shaft for this fit. Use unilateral tolerances and basic hole system for maximum metal. Use dimensions to nearest 0.0001 in.

2. Draw and dimension the bar diagram for a $3\frac{3}{4}$ in. shaft, Class 2 fit. Draw and dimension a typical hole and shaft for this fit. Use unilateral tolerances and the basic shaft system for minimum metal. Use dimensions to nearest 0.0001 in.

3. Draw a typical detail for a $3\frac{7}{16}$ in. shaft and bearing with an allowance of 0.0025 in. Shaft tolerance is 0.0015 in., bearing tolerance is 0.0020 in. Use unilateral tolerances.

    (a) Dimension for basic shaft system and maximum metal.
    (b) Dimension for basic shaft system and minimum metal.
    (c) Dimension for basic hole system and maximum metal.
    (d) Dimension for basic hole system and minimum metal.

4. Draw and dimension the bar diagram for an 8 in. shaft, Class 8 fit. Draw and dimension a typical hole and shaft for this fit. Use unilateral tolerances and basic hole system for maximum metal. Use dimensions to nearest 0.0001 in.

5. Draw and dimension the bar diagram for a 4 in. shaft, Class 3 fit. Compute the value of the ratio of the diametral clearance to the shaft diameter for the fit at the tightest condition. Do the same for the loosest permissible fit.

Draw and dimension the bar diagram for a 4 in. bearing for a minimum value for the c/r ratio of 0.0015 and for a maximum value of c/r of 0.0020. Compare the tolerance conditions of the bearing with those of a Class 3 fit.

6. A part having a hole of 1.000 in. diameter is mated with a shaft of diameter 0.995 in. What class or classes of standardized cylindrical fits can the resulting assembly be designated? Answer the question for shaft diameters of 0.997, 0.9975, 0.9988, and 0.9992 in.

7. (a) Draw and dimension the bar diagram for a 6 in. shaft, Class 7 fit. Draw and dimension a typical hole and shaft for this fit. Use unilateral tolerances and basic shaft system for minimum metal. Use dimensions to nearest 0.0001 in.

(b) Suppose the shaft is of steel, and disk is of cast iron 12 in. in diameter. What is the value of the maximum tangential stress in case the maximum size shaft is assembled with a minimum diameter hole? What is the value of the stress if the minimum diameter shaft is assembled with the maximum size hole? $\mu = 0.3$. For cast iron, $E = 15,000,000$ psi.   *Ans.* (b) Tightest fit, $s_t = 7,370$ psi.

Loosest fit, $s_t = 3,420$ psi.

8. A part is dimensioned as in Fig. 13-50.

(a) Determine suitable dimensions when the top surface is used as the datum.

(b) Determine suitable dimensions when datum is taken at the intermediate surface.

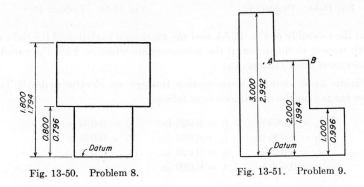

Fig. 13-50.   Problem 8.   Fig. 13-51.   Problem 9.

9. A part is dimensioned as in Fig. 13-51. Determine suitable dimensions when the AB surface is used as the datum.

10. A part is dimensioned as in Fig. 13-52. (a) Find suitable dimensions when the bottom surface is used as the datum. (b) Find suitable dimensions when the AB surface is used as the datum.

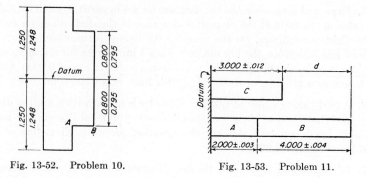

Fig. 13-52.   Problem 10.   Fig. 13-53.   Problem 11.

11. In the assembly of Fig. 13-53, find the maximum and minimum values of dimension d if the tolerances are additive. Find the values by the Pythagorean rule.

12. In the assembly of Fig. 13-54, find the maximum displacement of the right ends with respect to each other if the tolerances are additive. Find the displacement if the tolerances are Pythagorean.

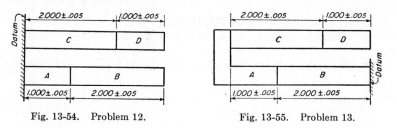

Fig. 13-54.   Problem 12.   Fig. 13-55.   Problem 13.

13. In the assembly of Fig. 13-55, find the maximum variation of the right end of D with respect to the datum if the tolerances are additive. Find the variation if the tolerances are Pythagorean.

14. Figure 13-56 shows a cross section through an electric motor.[12] Total tolerance range t on the dimensions is as follows.

$$t_a = 0.060 \text{ in.} \qquad t_f = 0.020 \text{ in.} \qquad t_m = 0.020 \text{ in.}$$
$$t_b = 0.020 \text{ in.} \qquad t_j = 0.020 \text{ in.} \qquad t_n = 0.020 \text{ in.}$$
$$t_c = 0.010 \text{ in.} \qquad t_k = 0.020 \text{ in.} \qquad t_p = 0.010 \text{ in.}$$
$$t_d = 0.020 \text{ in.} \qquad t_l = 0.060 \text{ in.}$$

Total tolerance in brush location due to eccentricity and fit of tubes:

Fiber, $e_1 = 0.004$ in.,   brass, $e_2 = 0.004$ in.

(a) Find the total tolerance range t_g for the shaft extension g.

(b) Find the total tolerance range t_r for armature end play r. This variation must be taken up by shims.

[12] See reference 6, Bibliography.

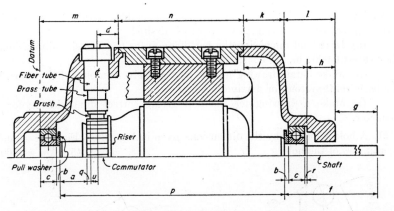

Fig. 13-56. Problem 14.

(c) Let the length of the commutator be made equal to the width of the brush plus the total variation in dimension q. In this way the brush will not extend beyond the end of the commutator or interfere with the riser as long as dimension q satisfies its tolerance. Find t_q, the total tolerance range for dimension q according to the Pythagorean rule. What is the length of the commutator if the width of the brush is 0.25 in.?

Find t_q and the length of the commutator by addition of tolerances. What per cent increase in commutator length is required by this method for determining t_q?

Ans. (c) 0.320, Pythagorean; 0.388, additive; 21 per cent, saving.

15. Bolts of maximum diameter 0.500 in. are to be used for the assembly of parts with 2 holes of minimum diameter 0.505 in. What should be the tolerance for the center distance for the holes?

16. Bolts of maximum diameter 0.625 in. are to be used for the assembly of parts with 2 holes of minimum diameter 0.629 in. What is the tolerance on the center distance for the holes?

17. Parts have 2 holes with center distance dimensioned 2.875 ± 0.003 in. Holes are dimensioned 0.937 in. plus 0.002 in. minus zero. What is the maximum permissible diameter of the assembly bolt?

18. Two bolts of diameter 0.999 ± 0.001 are used for the assembly of 2 parts. Tolerance for the holes in the parts is ±0.0015 in. The mean center distance for the holes is 2.5 in. Make a detail drawing for the bolt and part on the basic shaft system for maximum metal. Allowance between bolt and hole is 0.002 in.

19. Two bolts of nominal diameter $1\frac{1}{4}$ in. are used to assemble 2 loose parts. The total hole tolerance is 0.002 in. Total tolerance on the bolt diameter is 0.004 in. Mean center distance for the holes is 4 in. Determine the tolerance on the center distance to be placed on the drawing if the maximum variation on center distance passed by the gage is to be ±0.005 in.

Make detail drawings and show all necessary dimensions. Use the basic shaft system for maximum metal. Use unilateral tolerances on diameters and bilateral tolerance on center distance.

20. Two parts with 2 holes each are to be assembled with $1\frac{9}{16}$ in. bolts. The mean center distance is 5 in. A Class 2 fit is desired

(a) Draw and dimension the bar diagram for this fit using dimensions to the nearest 0.0001 in.

(b) Make detail drawing for the part and give complete dimensions. Use the basic shaft system for maximum metal.

(c) Make a drawing for the bolt giving correct dimensioning for the diameter.

21. A hole is located by the dimensions given in Fig. 13-57. Find the x- and y-coordinates of the hole.   *Ans.* $x = 0.45$ in., $y = 0.60$ in.

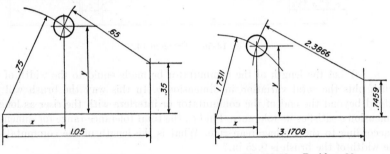

Fig. 13-57.   Problem 21.   Fig. 13-58.   Problem 22.

22. A hole is located by the dimensions given in Fig. 13-58. Find the x- and y-coordinates correct to the nearest 0.0001 in.

Ans. $x = 0.8996$ in., $y = 1.4790$ in.

14

Engineering Materials

THE composition and physical properties of the principal materials used in machine construction will be discussed in this chapter. It is fully as important that a machine element be made of a material that has properties suitable for the conditions of service as it is for the loads and stresses to be accurately determined. Frequently, the limitations imposed by the material are the controlling factors in a design. The designer must be acquainted with the effects that the methods of manufacture and heat treatment have on the properties of engineering materials. The manufacturing process used for fabrication of the part will also influence the type of material that can be used. Sometimes the help of a professional metallurgist is needed to insure the best possible choice of material and heat treatment.

1. The Tension Test

The tension test is widely used for determining yield point stress, ultimate or tensile stress, breaking or rupture stress, elongation, and reduction of area for various materials. Mild- or low-carbon steel is unique among the metals in having a pronounced elongation at the yield point. The phenomenon of the upper and lower yield points, shown in Fig. 14-1(b), is sometimes explained[1] by defining the upper yield point as the stress which will start the flow process, and the lower yield point

[1] See reference 34, Bibliography.

as the lowest stress at which the extension proceeds still further. The shape of the stress-strain curve is influenced to a large extent by the type of machine on which the tests are made. The constant-strain-rate type of machine, shown in Fig. 14-1(a), stretches the specimen at a uniform

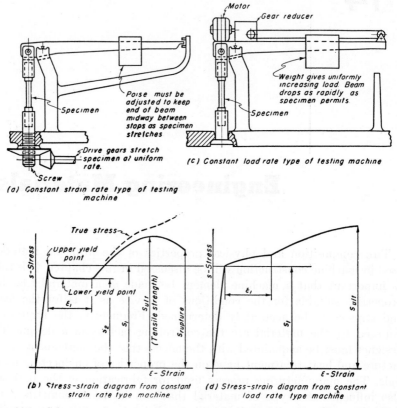

Fig. 14-1.   Schematic drawings of testing machines and corresponding stress-strain diagrams for low-carbon steel.

rate by means of power-driven screws. As soon as yielding starts, the poise must be reverted to the left to keep the beam in balance between the stops at the right end. The material continues to yield until it is strengthened by strain or work hardening. A higher stress then is necessary for additional stretching.

In the second type of machine, illustrated in Fig. 14-1(c), the beam is allowed to drop as rapidly as the specimen stretches from the effect of a constantly increasing load.[2] No reduction in stress can occur with this kind of loading. The stress-strain diagram which appears looks like that

[2] See reference 5, Bibliography.

shown in (d). The diagram from the constant-load-rate type of machine depends on the rapidity with which the load is applied. Experiments have shown that the yield point stress s_1 and yield point elongation ϵ_1 are increased as the speed of loading increases. Some diagrams obtained on $\frac{1}{2}$ by $\frac{3}{16}$ in. mild-steel strips are shown in Fig. 14-2.

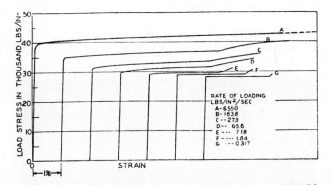

Fig. 14-2.   Stress-strain diagrams for constant load rate tests for mild steel.

The conditions under which constant-strain-rate tests are made are somewhat analogous to drawing or rolling operations in metal forming. However, machine parts are employed in such a manner that if an overload causes the yield point of the material to be exceeded, the deformations can take place as rapidly as the stretch of the material permits.

Alloy and heat-treated steels, steels which have been cold worked, cast iron, and nonferrous metals do not exhibit the well-defined yield point of mild steel. The yield strength for such materials is generally taken as the stress corresponding to some arbitrarily selected value of permanent deformation which the material can have without undergoing appreciable structural damage. This elongation is often taken as 0.2 per cent as shown in Fig. 14-3, although smaller values are sometimes used.

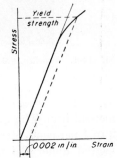

Fig. 14-3.   Yield strength for material not having a well-defined yield point.

Stretching of a soft steel specimen is accompanied by a decrease in diameter. After the ultimate stress is reached, a pronounced reduction of area, called necking down, occurs at some point in the stressed region. For the constant-strain-rate type of machine, the total load which the specimen can then support with the beam in balance is reduced. It is standard practice to compute the stresses for the stress-strain diagram using the original cross-sectional area. There is thus an apparent decrease of stress in the right-hand portion of the diagram. This supposed reduction does not occur if the actual values of the cross sections are determined and used for computing the stress as shown by the dashed curve in Fig. 14-1(b).

2. Physical Constitution of Steel

Steel is an alloy of iron and carbon, or of iron, carbon, and other alloying elements. Carbon must be present to the extent of about 0.05 per cent

Fig. 14-4.   Pearlite, 0.9% carbon steel, magnification 1,000 diameters (*Courtesy United States Steel Corp. Research Laboratory*).

by weight in order for the material to be known as steel rather than commercial iron. The quantity of carbon is much higher in cast iron, about 2 to 4 per cent. Steel, like other metals, has a crystalline structure when viewed under the microscope, with grains varying in size from about 0.001 in. to 0.010 in. in diameter.

A number of different metallurgical terms are used in describing the structure of steel. Pure iron, for example, is known as ferrite. Ferrite is soft and ductile and has a tensile strength of about 40,000 psi. Cementite is the chemical compound of iron and carbon, Fe_3C. It is nonductile and very hard. Another constituent of steel is pearlite. As shown in Fig. 14-4, pearlite grains have a laminar structure of alternate layers of ferrite and cementite. The carbon content of pearlite is 0.83 per cent by weight. When slowly cooled from above the upper critical temperature, a steel of less than 0.83 per cent carbon is composed of a mixture of grains of ferrite and pearlite. For carbon percentages higher than 0.83, the steel is a mixture of grains of pearlite and cementite upon slow cooling. When the percentage of carbon is exactly 0.83, the so-called "eutectoid structure" results, which is wholly composed of grains of pearlite.

When steels are heated, transformations in the crystal structure take place at certain temperatures. The magnified grains of a 0.30 per cent carbon steel are shown schematically in Fig. 14-5. When the steel is heated to the lower critical temperature of 1330 F, a new constituent, called austenite, appears. Austenite is formed from pearlite by the carbon of the cementite going into solid solution in the ferrite. The situation is analogous to the solution of a salt in water, except that the solvent, in the case of metals, is in the solid condition. As the temperature continues to rise, the austenite dissolves the free ferrite until at the upper critical temperature the steel consists wholly of austenite.

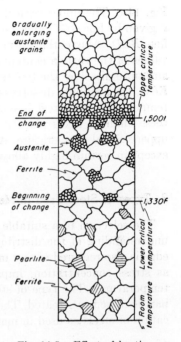

Fig. 14-5. Effect of heating on the microstructure of 0.30% C steel.

The upper critical temperature depends on the carbon content, as indicated by a portion of the iron-carbon equilibrium diagram shown in

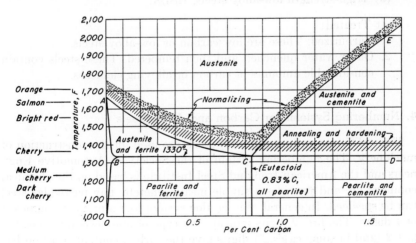

Fig. 14-6. Portion of iron-carbon equilibrium diagram showing critical temperatures and temperature ranges for normalizing, annealing and hardening.

Fig. 14-6. The upper critical temperature, for any percentage of carbon, is given by line ACE, and the lower critical temperature is represented by line BCD. Above the lower critical temperature, the pearlite, for all values of the carbon content, has become austenite. In region ACB, the austenite dissolves the free ferrite as the temperature rises, and in region ECD, the austenite dissolves the free cementite. Above the upper critical temperature, the steel is composed wholly of austenite. A reversal of these changes takes place if the steel is slowly cooled from above the upper critical temperature. Austenite rarely exists at room temperature except in certain highly alloyed steels.

3. Types of Steel Used in Machine Construction

The selection of a suitable steel for a machine part depends on a full understanding of the distribution and fluctuation of the stress. Knowledge is also required of any unusual conditions that may be present such as stress concentration, impact, corrosion, abrasion, and high or low temperatures. The type of steel selected depends on whether or not the part is to be heat treated. The following summary gives a general classification of steels as used in machine construction:

Not Heat Treated:
  (a) Plain, low-carbon steel, hot rolled or cold drawn.
  (b) Free cutting steels or steels resulphurized for ease of machining.
  (c) Low-carbon sheets for forming, drawing, or spinning.
  (d) High-strength low-alloy steels, HSLA.

Heat Treated:
  1. Carburized. These are low-carbon or low-alloy steels.
  2. Oil or water quenched and then tempered. These steels contain considerable amounts of carbon or alloying elements.

4. Numbering Systems for Carbon and Alloy Steels

Many different carbon and alloy steels are used for the construction of machinery. The numbering system of the Society of Automotive Engineers and the American Iron and Steel Institute is based on the chemical composition, and provides a simple means whereby any particular steel can be specified. In general, this catalog system uses a number composed of 4 digits. The first 2 digits indicate the type or alloy classification; the last 2 (and in some cases, 3) digits give the carbon content. Carbon has such a pronounced effect on the strength and hardness of steel that the content is thus incorporated in the catalog number. Plain carbon steel, for example, is denoted by the basic numerals 10. Thus, steel 1045 indicates a plain carbon steel containing 0.45 per cent carbon. The basic numerals for the various types of steels are given in Table 14-1. The

TABLE 14-1
Basic Numerals for SAE and AISI Steels

Carbon Steels	1xxx	Molybdenum Steels	4xxx
Plain Carbon	10xx	Carbon-Molybdenum	40xx
Free Cutting Screw Stock	11xx	Chromium-Molybdenum	41xx
		Chromium-Nickel-Molybdenum	43xx
Manganese Steels	13xx	Nickel-Molybdenum; 1.75% Ni	46xx
		Nickel-Molybdenum; 3.50% Ni	48xx
Nickel Steels	2xxx		
3.50% Ni	23xx	Chromium Steels	5xxx
5.00% Ni	25xx	Low Chromium	51xx
		Medium Chromium	52xxx
Nickel-Chromium Steels	3xxx	Corrosion and Heat Resisting	51xxx
1.25% Ni, 0.60% Cr	31xx		
1.75% Ni, 1.00% Cr	32xx	Chromium-Vanadium Steels	6xxx
3.50% Ni, 1.50% Cr	33xx	1.00% Cr	61xx
Corrosion and Heat Resisting	30xxx	Silicon-Manganese Steels	9xxx
		2.00% Si	92xx
			AISI
		Chromium-Nickel-Molybdenum Steels	86xx
		Chromium-Nickel-Molybdenum Steels	87xx

arrangement of Table 14-2 may serve as an aid in committing some of the series numbers to memory.

TABLE 14-2
Basic Numerals for Several Widely Used Steels

Nickel	23xx, 25xx
Nickel-Chromium	31xx, 32xx, 33xx
Chromium-Molybdenum	41xx
Chromium-Nickel-Molybdenum	43xx
Nickel-Molybdenum	46xx, 48xx

The AISI number for a steel is similar to the SAE number, but capital-letter prefixes are included to indicate the process of manufacture

TABLE 14-3

Chemical Composition of Selected Carbon and Alloy AISI and SAE Steels
(Prefixes A, B, or C Are Omitted in the SAE System)

Plain Carbon Steels

AISI	Carbon	Manganese	Sulphur
C1010	0.08-0.13	0.30-0 60	0.05 max.
C1020	0.18-0.23	0.30-0.60	0.05 max.
C1035	0.32-0.38	0.60-0.90	0.05 max.
C1045	0.43-0.50	0.60-0.90	0 05 max.
C1060	0.55-0.65	0.60-0.90	0.05 max.
C1095	0.90-1.05	0.30-0.50	0.05 max.

Free Cutting Steels

AISI	Carbon	Manganese	Sulphur
B1112	0.08-0.13	0.70-1.00	0.16-0.23
B1113	0.08-0.13	0.70-1.00	0.24-0.33
C1117	0.14-0.20	1.00-1.30	0.08-0.13
C1137	0.32-0.39	1.35-1.65	0.08-0.13
C1141	0.37-0.45	1.35-1.65	0.08-0.13

Nickel Steel

AISI	Carbon	Manganese	Nickel
A2317	0.15-0.20	0.40-0.60	3.25-3.75

High-Strength Low-Alloy Steels

AISI	
950 (HSLA)	C 0.12 max., Mn 0.50-1.00 Si 0.15 max., Cu 0.55-1.30 Ni 0.30-0.75, Mo 0.18 max. These are proprietary steels. Composition can vary with producer.

Nickel-Chromium Steels

AISI	Carbon	Manganese	Nickel	Chromium	Molybdenum
A3140	0.38-0.43	0.70-0.90	1.10-1.40	0 55-0.75	

Chromium-Moly'denum Steels

AISI	Carbon	Manganese	Nickel	Chromium	Molybdenum
A4140	0.38-0.43	0.75-1.00		0.80-1.10	0.15-0.25

Nickel-Chromium-Molybdenum Steels

AISI	Carbon	Manganese	Nickel	Chromium	Molybdenum
A4320	0.17-0.22	0.45-0.65	1.65-2.00	0.40-0.60	0.20-0.30
A4340	0.38-0.43	0.60-0.80	1.65-2.00	0.70-0.90	0.20-0.30

Nickel-Moly'denum Steels

AISI	Carbon	Manganese	Nickel	Chromium	Molybdenum
A4620	0.17-0.20	0.45-0.65	1.65-2.00		0.20-0.30
A4640	0.38-0.43	0.60-0.80	1.65-2.00		0.20-0.30
A4815	0.13-0.18	0.40-0 60	3.25-3.75		0.20-0.30

Plain Chromium Steels

AISI	Carbon	Manganese	Nickel	Chromium	Molybdenum
E52100	0.95-1.10	0.25-0.45		1.30-1.60	

Chromium Vanadium Steels

AISI	Carbon	Manganese	Nickel	Chromium	Molybdenum
A6150	0.48-0.53	0.70-0.90		0.80-1.10	0.15 min. V.

Nickel-Chromium-Molybdenum Steels

AISI	Carbon	Manganese	Nickel	Chromium	Molybdenum
A8620	0.18-0.23	0.70-0.90	0.40-0.70	0.40-0.60	0.15-0.25
A8640	0.38-0.43	0.75-1.00	0.40-0.70	0.40-0.60	0.15-0.25

Silicon Manganese Steels

AISI	Carbon	Manganese	Nickel	Chromium	Molybdenum
A9260	0.55-0.60	0.70-1.00			1.8-2.2 Si

Silicon content for basic open-hearth alloy steels is 0.20-0.35 per cent.
The steels listed above contain nominal amounts of phosphorous and sulphur as impurities.

as follows:

> A—Basic open-hearth alloy steel
> B—Acid bessemer carbon steel
> C—Basic open hearth carbon steel
> D—Acid open hearth carbon steel
> E—Electric furnace alloy steel

The chemical compositions for a selected number of steels used for machinery are given in Table 14-3. The mechanical properties for these

TABLE 14-4

Mechanical Properties of Typical Low-Carbon and Case Hardening Steels*

Steel	Condition	Tensile Strength	Yield Strength	% El. in 2 in.	% Red. Area	BHN	Rock-well C	Machin-ability %
1010	Hot-rolled	51,000	29,000	38	70	101		40
	Cold-drawn	56,000	33,000	35	65	113		45
1020	Hot-rolled	67,000	45,000	32	65	137		52
	Cold-drawn	69,000	48,000	30	63	143		60
1112	Hot-rolled	67,000	40,000	27	47	140		
	Cold-drawn	80,000	62,500	16	43	170	6	100
1113	Cold-drawn	83,000	73,000	15	45	180	8	120–140
1117	Hot-rolled	71,000	45,000	28	52	135		
	Cold-drawn	82,000	63,000	18	44	162		94
2317	Hot-rolled	85,000	56,000	29	60	163		50
	Cold-drawn	95,000	75,000	25	58	197	12	
4320	Hot-rolled	87,000	59,000	30	60	179	10	55
	Cold-drawn	99,000	65,000	23	54	207	16	
4620	Hot-rolled	82,000	55,000	30	61	167	4	58
	Cold-drawn	98,000	70,000	18	55	203	14	
4815	Hot-rolled	105,000	73,000	24	58	212	15	55
	Cold-drawn	110,000	78,000	23	55	217	17	
8620	Hot-rolled	91,000	64,000	29	56	185		
	Annealed	76,000	51,000	32	63	155		
950	Hot-rolled†	70,000	50,000	22		156		

* Taken mainly from Table 35, Hoyt, S. L., "Metals and Alloys Data Books," 1943, Reinhold Publishing Corp.
† For ¾ in. and under. Slightly less for larger sections.

materials are given in Tables 14-4 and 14-5. The SAE and AISI lists of steels are constantly being revised, and it is necessary to consult an up-to-date list if one is in doubt whether or not a particular steel is in regular production.

Tests have shown that the tensile strength and Brinell Hardness Number have a direct relationship. For most steels, the tensile strength is

TABLE 14-5

Mechanical Properties of Typical Medium-Carbon or Direct-Hardening Steels*

Steel	Condition	Tensile Strength	Yield Strength	% El. in 2 in.	% Red. Area	BHN	Rockwell C	Machinability %
1035	Hot-rolled	88,000	55,000	30	56	179	10	60
	Cold-drawn	92,000	59,000	25	50	200	12	62
	1″ Rd. WQ 1525 F							
	Drawn 1000 F	103,000	78,000	24	62	230	20	55
1045	Hot-rolled	99,000	60,000	24	47	200	12	55
	Cold-drawn	110,000	69,000	19	41	235	21	58
1060	Hot-rolled, annealed	95,000	59,000	25	52	197	14	53
	1″ Rd. Oil Q 1550 F							
	Drawn 1000 F	122,000	90,000	19	53	255	25	
1095	Hot-rolled, annealed	106,000	60,000	23	47	201	12	45
1137 ⎱	Hot-rolled,	92,000	60,000	20	35	185	9	70
1141 ⎰	Cold-drawn	105,000	80,000	15	30	212	15	
	1″ Rd. Oil Q 1500 F							
	Drawn 1000 F	123,000	96,000	20	53	245	24	55
3140	Hot-rolled, annealed	96,000	64,000	26	56	195	12	57
	Annealed, cold-drawn	115,000	98,000	17	45	248	24	
4140	Hot-rolled, annealed	90,000	63,000	27	58	187	12	56
	Annealed, cold-drawn	114,000	90,000	18	50	241	23	
4340	Hot-rolled, annealed	115,000	95,000	18	45	235	21	58
4640	Hot-rolled, annealed	100,000	87,000	21	50	201	12	60
	Annealed, cold-drawn	126,000	97,000	14	39	269	27	
52100	Hot-rolled, annealed	109,000	80,000	25	57	235	22	45
	1″ Rd Oil Q 1550 F							
	Drawn 1000 F	185,000	170,000	9	34	415	43	
6150	Hot-rolled, annealed	103,000	70,000	27	51	217	18	
	Annealed, cold-drawn	118,000	94,000	20	43	255	25	
8640	Hot-rolled	126,000	89,000	20	40	254		
	Annealed	95,000	63,000	26	55	193		55
9260	Hot-rolled, annealed	142,000	92,000	18	38	302	31	

found to be approximately 500 times the BHN. Tests show that the ductility becomes less as the hardness increases.

5. Plain Carbon Steel

When the only alloying element in steel is carbon, it is known as plain carbon steel. Carbon is a powerful alloying agent, and wide changes in strength and hardness can be secured by varying the amount of this element. The range of desired properties can be further enhanced by heat treatment. Some of the many uses for plain carbon steels are given in Table 14-6. This type of steel is usually easier to anneal and machine than is alloy steel. Plain carbon steel is the cheapest, and the designer will normally use it except where severity of service conditions or difficulty of heat treatment necessitates the use of a more expensive alloy steel. Carbon steels are manufactured in larger quantities than any of the others.

Carbon steels can be hardened and therefore strengthened by heat treatment when the carbon content is about 0.30 per cent or more. Heat treatment generally consists of heating the part above the upper critical temperature, as shown by the zones in Fig. 14-6, and then quenching by submerging in a cooling medium such as water. After quenching, the

TABLE 14-6
Different Uses of Plain Carbon Steels

Carbon Range, %	Uses of Carbon Steel
0.05–0.10	Stampings, sheets, wire, rivets, welding stock, cold drawn parts.
0.10–0.20	Structural shapes, machine parts, carburized parts, screws.
0.20–0.30	Gears, shafting, levers, welded tubing, carburized parts.
0.30–0.40	Can be heat treated. Seamless tubing, shafts, connecting rods, crane hooks, axles.
0.40–0.50	Forgings, shafts, gears, studs.
0.60–0.70	Drop hammer dies, set screws, locomotive tires, lock washers, hard drawn spring wire.
0.70–0.80	Plow beams, cultivator disks, anvil faces, band saws, hammers, wrenches.
0.80–0.90	Plow shares, shovels, harrow blades, punches, rock drills, cold chisels, hand tools, music wire, leaf springs.
0.90–1.00	Springs, knives, axes, dies, hay rake teeth, harrow blades.
1.00–1.10	Drills, taps, milling cutters, knives.
1.10–1.20	Drills, lathe tools.
1.20–1.30	Files, reamers, knives, metal cutting tools.
1.25–1.40	Razors, saws, wire-drawing dies, metal-cutting saws.

steel will be very strong, but it will not be suitable for use because of lack of ductility and the presence of residual stresses. Quenching stresses are removed and ductility is restored, but tensile strength is reduced, by a subsequent operation called tempering or drawing. This operation consists of reheating the part and then quenching or cooling it in air. The reduction in the tensile strength and the increase in the ductility depend on the temperature used for tempering.

During quenching, the heat can be dissipated only through the surface where the part is in contact with the cooling medium. For parts of large cross section and large amounts of heat, the cooling rate for the interior may be so low that the metallurgical changes required for hardening cannot be secured. Under such conditions, only the material near the surface will be hardened and therefore strengthened; the interior of the

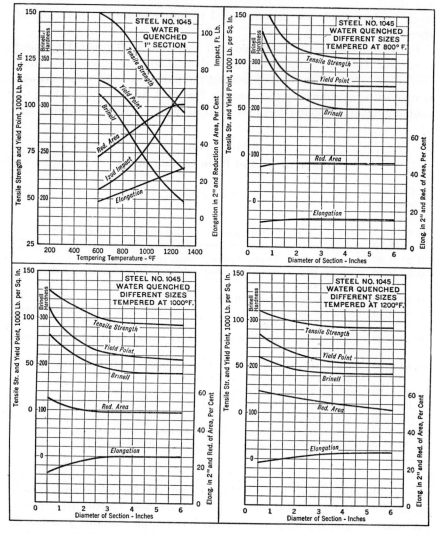

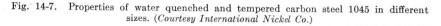

In section ½" to 2" incl., quenched from 1475/1525° F.; over 2" to 4" incl., from 1500/1550° F.; over 4", from 1525/1575° F

Fig. 14-7. Properties of water quenched and tempered carbon steel 1045 in different sizes. (*Courtesy International Nickel Co.*)

body will largely be unaffected. The situation is generally referred to as mass effect or the effect of section size.

Curves for the mechanical properties of plain carbon steel 1045 for various tempering temperatures and various section sizes are given in Fig. 14-7. The curves show average values only. Fluctuations are to be expected; they are due principally to the permissible variations in composition, as indicated by Table 14-3.

The principal shortcoming of plain carbon steel lies in the shallow penetration of the hardening. The cooling rate must be very rapid, and high residual stresses, distortion, lack of ductility, and even quenching cracks will occur. The use of plain carbon steel in applications requiring only a hardened surface is sometimes prevented by the foregoing disadvantages.

Wrought iron, although its method of manufacture is different, is essentially a very low carbon steel with slag inclusions. Due to rolling, the slag inclusions are elongated into long stringers and do not greatly reduce the strength. Wrought iron is tough and welds easily. It is widely used for making iron pipe.

6. Alloy Steels

When a suitable alloy is present in addition to the carbon, the metallurgical changes which take place during quenching occur at a faster

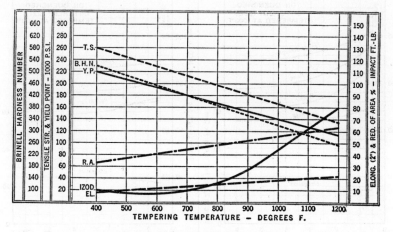

Fig. 14-8. Properties of normalized and tempered chromium-molybdenum steel 4140.
(*Courtesy Climax Molybdenum Co.*)

rate, the cooling effects penetrate deeper, and a larger portion of the part is strengthened. The quenching can usually be done in oil. The heat is removed less drastically, and the residual stresses are smaller than for carbon steel. Hence there is less danger of distortion or formation of hardening cracks. A carbon steel part that might distort or crack from water quenching can sometimes be made of an alloy steel and quenched in oil. This ability to confer depth of hardening, or hardenability, is one of the principal reasons for the use of alloys. Of the various alloying

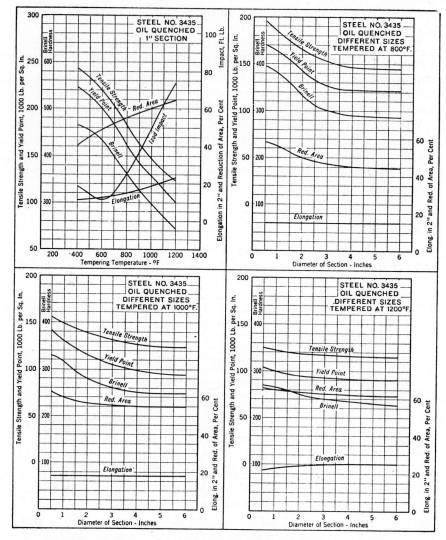

In sections ½" to 2" incl., quenched from 1425/1475° F.; over 2" to 4" incl., from 1450/1500° F.; over 4", from 1475/1525° F.

Fig. 14-9.   Properties of oil quenched and tempered nickel-chromium-molybdenum steel 4340 in different sizes. (*Courtesy International Nickel Co.*)

elements, manganese is used in almost all alloy steels to confer depth of hardening. Nickel, chromium, and molybdenum, singly or in various combinations, are widely used. The maximum hardness obtainable in a thin section of heat-treated steel depends upon the carbon content and is unaffected by the lack or presence of any alloys.

TABLE 14-7

Effect of Mass on the Physical Properties of Chromium-Molybdenum Steel 4140*

(Normalized and tempered at 1000 F)

Size in in.	Outside Edge of Section						Center of Section					
	Tensile Strength	Yield Point	% El. in 2 in.	% Red. Area	BHN	Izod ft lb	Tensile Strength	Yield Point	% El. in 2 in.	% Red. Area	BHN	Izod ft lb
2	122,650	93,775	18.8	49.1	252	25.4	117,425	87,450	18.7	48.9	241	31 8
3	124,200	90,850	18.5	50.0	255	24.9	118,525	75,625	19.9	51.1	238	30.8
6	108,950	62,150	24.0	56.8	217	44.3	96,265	53,020	25.0	50.6	192	38.3
9	107,290	58,310	21.0	47.8	210	32.2	90,145	48,730	16.9	52.6	175	36.4
12	104,050	58,205	21.8	50.8	207	25.8	93,060	50,215	20.3	37.3	185	27.4

* Data from Climax Molybdenum Co.

The mechanical properties for 1 in. round test pieces of chromium-molybdenum steel 4140 at various tempering temperatures are shown in Fig. 14-8. The properties for this material in different-sized sections are given in Table 14-7.

Curves showing average mechanical properties for steels 4340, 4640. and 9840 are given in Figs. 14-9, 14-10, and 14-12 respectively.

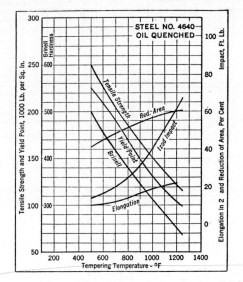

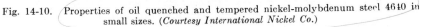

Fig. 14-10. Properties of oil quenched and tempered nickel-molybdenum steel 4640 in small sizes. (*Courtesy International Nickel Co.*)

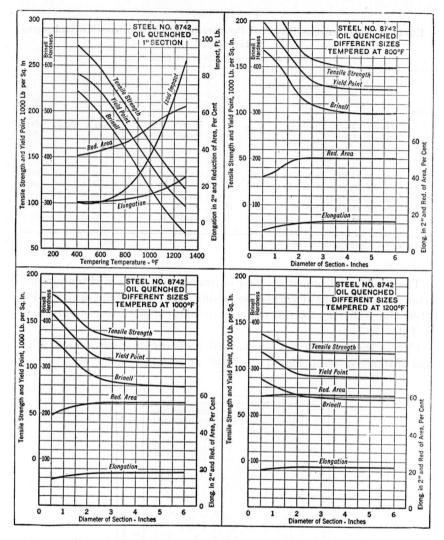

In sections ½″ to 2″ incl., quenched from 1500/1550° F . over 2″ to 4″ incl., from 1525/1575° F . over 4″, from 1550/1600° F.

Fig. 14-11.   Properties of oil quenched and tempered nickel-chromium-molybdenum steel 8742 in different sizes. (*Courtesy International Nickel Co.*)

Curves showing the average properties for nickel-chromium-molybdenum steel A8742 for various-sized sections and various tempering temperatures are given in Fig. 14-11. These curves also indicate the properties of steel A8640 for small sections. For larger sizes, however, steel A8742 is somewhat deeper hardening.

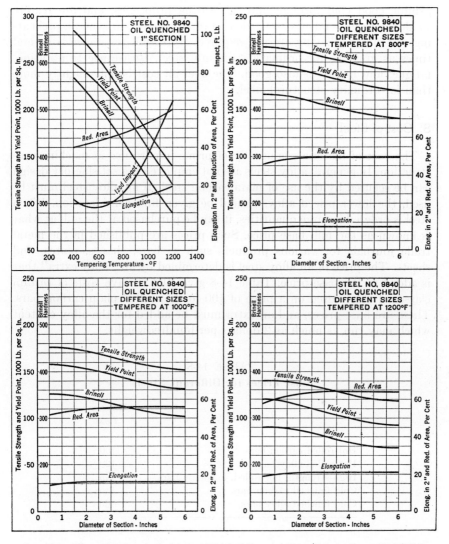

In sections ½″ to 2″ incl., quenched from 1525/1575° F.; over 2″ to 4″ incl., from 1550/1575° F.; over 4″, from 1575/1625° F.

Fig. 14-12.   Properties of oil quenched and tempered nickel-chromium-molybdenum steel 9840 in different sizes. (*Courtesy International Nickel Co.*)

The larger steel warehouses and the various alloy producers will supply expert metallurgical advice upon request.

7. High-strength Low-alloy Steels, HSLA

These steels have superior strength qualities, and, because of the reduced dead weight, are extensively used for mobile equipment. They exhibit good cold forming and fabricating properties, and are readily welded with no tendency to harden on rapid cooling. In general, preheating and stress relieving are not required. Corrosion resistance is several times as great as for ordinary structural steel. Resistance to abrasion, fatigue, and impact is also good. The over-all cost is only slightly more than for ordinary structural steel.

8. Cost of Steel

The cost of materials is usually of prime importance in machine construction. In general, alloy steels are not employed if a satisfactory design can be secured by the use of plain carbon steel. If an alloy steel must be used, the lower priced alloys should be given first consideration. When steel is ordered in large quantities, it can be purchased at the mill at what is known as the mill base price. Such prices are published in the metal trade journals for various products such as bars, shapes, plates, and sheets. The price of an alloy steel is determined by an "alloy extra" that is added to the base price. Table 14-8 gives the relative costs of certain classes of steel based on a price of 100 for hot-rolled plain carbon bars. These are base prices, and an extra must be added for the alloy content which may run as much as 2 dollars per hundredweight.

TABLE 14-8
Base Prices for Different Steels

Type of Steel	Relative Cost
Hot-rolled carbon bars,	100
Hot-rolled alloy bars,	120
High-strength, hot-rolled, low-alloy bars	145
Cold finished carbon bars,	135
Cold finished alloy bars,	160

When steel is not purchased at the mill, but from a steel warehouse, the warehouse base price for such materials applies. This price is higher than the mill base because of extra handling charges, transportation, and warehouseman's profit.

Various other factors add to the price of steel. One of these is the "size extra." The base price applies only to sections of nominal size, and very small or very large sections cost an additional amount. A "quantity extra" is added to the price when the amount ordered is less than a specified minimum amount. A "cutting extra" is also added when stock lengths are not ordered. Other extras, such as annealing, machine straightening, or truck delivery, may further increase the pound price.

For many products where the cost of labor is relatively small, and where the cost of the materials is important, a small increase in the mill price of one steel is all that is needed to cause a widespread change to another type of steel which also gives satisfactory results. When labor costs are relatively very large, as, for example, in aircraft parts, a change in the price of steel may have practically no effect on the composition used.

9. Heat Treatment of Steel

The microstructure that is formed when steel is quenched at a sufficiently rapid cooling rate from above the upper critical temperature is called *martensite*. Steel in the martensitic condition is nonductile and is very hard and strong. Needle-like crystals in angular arrangement appear when prepared specimens are viewed under a microscope. Martensite is unstable and is generally regarded as being a supersaturated solid solution of carbon in iron. Fully hardened steel having the martensitic structure is not only too brittle to use, but contains quenching stresses. As was previously mentioned, a second operation of heating, called *tempering*, is required to relieve the internal stress and restore a suitable amount of ductility. The products formed when martensite is tempered have the structure of very finely divided pearlite. Tempering is usually carried out at temperatures between 800 F and 1200 F. Ductility is increased and tensile strength reduced for an increase of tempering temperature. The tempering temperature must therefore be properly chosen so that the physical properties of the steel after heat treatment will be suitable for the working stress and design of the part. Steel must be heated to a temperature high enough to change the structure into austenite if hardening is to take place upon quenching. Quenching has no effect upon ferrite and pearlite.

When the cooling rate is not sufficiently rapid to form martensite, a finely divided pearlitic structure results from quenching. The ductility is greater and the strength less than for martensite. A further decrease of the cooling rate causes the thickness of the lamellae to increase until the coarse pearlitic structure of annealed or furnace cooled steel is secured.

Prolonged heating of steel within the range 1250–1350 F causes the cementite to coalesce into spherical particles. The resulting structure is called *spheroidized cementite*. Steel in this condition is soft and ductile and is readily machined. Heat treatment after machining may be required to secure the requisite degree of strength and hardness.

Steel, as received from the mill, is frequently given a treatment called *normalizing* to secure a uniform grain structure before it is machined

Normalizing consists of heating the steel above the upper critical temperature, removing it from the furnace, and cooling it in air. Sometimes the mechanical properties developed from normalizing are very satisfactory, and no other heat treatment need be given. The results obtained from annealing and hardening are usually improved if the steel is first normalized. Normalizing is frequently applied to forgings and castings to insure a uniform grain structure.

When the greatest softness and ductility are desired, the steel should be annealed. The heating is done slowly in the furnace and the maximum temperature, as shown by Fig. 14-6, must be maintained long enough to refine the grain structure. Cooling is done very slowly in the furnace or in an insulated container.

By a recent discovery in heat treating, it has been found possible to produce steels of the desired structure and mechanical properties by direct transformation of austenite. The method is patented and is called *austempering*. It consists of giving the heated steel a hot quench in a bath of molten lead or salt maintained at suitable temperatures. The tempering or drawing operations are eliminated when this treatment is used.

The heated parts must be protected from the oxygen of the atmosphere during the heat-treating process to prevent decarburization or loss of carbon by the surface material. If the part in service is subjected to fluctuating tension stress which exceeds the endurance limit, the weak surface layer of low-carbon material will be vulnerable to the formation of a fatigue crack. This crack will propagate inward and cause ultimate failure, even though the interior of the body has been strengthened by the heat treatment. Heat-treating furnaces can be constructed which surround the parts at the quenching temperature with an atmosphere of inert gases. Resistance to decarburization is a valuable property for a heat-treating steel. For good success in heat treatment, a part should be free from reëntrant angles, sudden transitions from thin to thick sections, and thin projections attached to heavy masses.

Permanent deformation of metals is nearly always a shearing phenomenon. The atoms in the crystals are arranged in definite and repeating patterns. This uniformity of arrangement produces planes of weakness to shearing stress. The portions of the crystal, although adhering tightly together, will glide or slip on each other along these planes whenever the loading becomes sufficiently great.

The reasons for the increased strength and hardness resulting from quenching have been of great interest to investigators.[3] The slip-interference theory is perhaps the best known. It is believed that during quenching exceedingly small cementite particles are thrown out of solu-

[3] See p. 410 of reference 26, Bibliography.

tion and dispersed throughout the crystal structure. These particles serve as mechanical keys which resist any motion along the slip planes and thereby give a large increase to the elastic strength of the material.

Hardenability, or depth of hardening, in steels is a question of great importance to the designer. Curves such as those shown in Figs. 14-7 to 14-12 show the average heat treating properties for these steels. It is frequently necessary to have precise information on the hardening ability

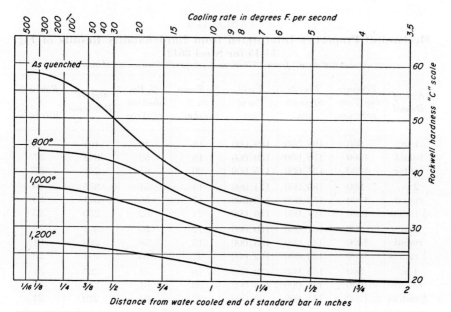

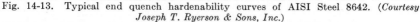

Fig. 14-13. Typical end quench hardenability curves of AISI Steel 8642. (*Courtesy Joseph T. Ryerson & Sons, Inc.*)

for each particular lot of incoming steel. The Jominy test has been devised for this purpose.

A 1 in. diameter specimen is made from the steel whose hardness after quenching is to be determined. The specimen is heated and then quenched by hanging it vertically over a jet of water that impinges gently on the bottom surface. Flats are ground on the sides of the specimen, Rockwell C hardness readings are taken at $\frac{1}{16}$-in. intervals from the quenched end, and the results are plotted. The resulting curve shows the manner in which the hardness decreases with distance from the quenched end. When a round bar of any size, or a machine part, is quenched in the conventional manner, the surface and interior points have cooling rates equal to those of different points of the Jominy specimen. Cooling rate curves and tables are available[4] which show the correlation that exists be-

[4] See references 30 and 33, Bibliography.

tween distances from the quenched end of the Jominy specimen and the diameters of bars of various sizes for cooling of the surface, the center, and intermediate points. The hardness, as given by the Jominy curve of the specimen at the proper distance from the quenched end, will be the hardness of the chosen point of the quenched object. The strength of the particular lot of steel from which the specimen was taken can thus be estimated.

TABLE 14-9

Mechanical Properties Interpreted from Hardenability Results of Fig. 14-13 for Steel 8642

Quenched in oil from 1550 F and tempered (drawn as shown).

Size of Round	Tempering Temperature	Tensile Strength psi	Yield Point psi	% Elong. in 2 inches	% Reduction of Area	Brinell Hardness	Rockwell C Hardness
1 in. round center	800	198,000	189,000	13	46	401	43
	1000	170,000	159,000	16	52	341	37
	1200	131,000	115,000	20	61	262	27
2 in. round $\frac{1}{2}$ radius	800	185,000	174,000	14	51	375	40
	1000	158,000	146,000	17	56	321	34
	1200	127,000	110,000	21	62	255	25
3 in. round $\frac{1}{2}$ radius	800	161,000	150,000	17	55	331	35
	1000	145,000	133,000	19	58	293	31
	1200	120,000	102,000	22	63	241	23
4 in. round $\frac{1}{2}$ radius	800	145,000	133,000	19	58	293	31
	1000	131,000	115,000	20	61	262	27
	1200	114,000	96,000	22	64	229	21

As a typical example, Jominy curves for steel 8642 are shown in Fig. 14-13. The effect of tempering temperatures on the hardness is illustrated by the various curves. The mechanical properties for this steel as interpretated from the hardness results are given in Table 14-9.

10. Residual Stresses from Heat Treatment

The increased strength and hardness resulting from the heat treatment of machine parts is usually accompanied by residual stresses. Since these may be either favorable or unfavorable to the engineering functioning of the part, the subject should be given careful consideration by the designer. Such stresses arise from plastic deformation which takes place while the material is at elevated temperature.

Consider first the purely thermal effects caused by quenching a through-heated steel from a temperature somewhat below the lower critical temperature of 1330 F. Upon immersion in the cooling medium, the surface cools at a very rapid rate. Contraction of the outer layers is largely prevented by the rigid core at the higher temperature. Tensile stresses are thus set up on the surface which are balanced by compressive stresses in the interior. With the decrease in temperature of the core, and the accompanying thermal contraction, the tension on the surface may be reduced to zero and then turned into compression. There will then be a balancing tensile stress in the interior. The situation is as shown in Fig. 14-14, which represents the final stress distribution across the diameter of a long cylindrical body.

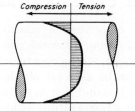

Now suppose the material is through-heated above the critical temperature into the austenitic range. Let it also be assumed that the material contains a sufficient proportion of carbon or alloying elements so that martensite will be formed upon sudden cooling. The thermal tension on the surface forms as before. However the phase change to martensite throughout the body involves an increase in volume which tends to increase the tension on

Fig. 14-14.   Distribution of residual stress along diameter of a long cylindrical body.

the surface and the compression in the interior. The continued thermal shrinkage however reduces the tension on the surface or even turns it into compression.

These thermal and transformation effects occur simultaneously, but the exact manner in which they combine is highly complex and has never been explained to the extent that easily followed rules have been made available. The final quenching stresses on the surface may therefore be either tension or compression depending on the quenching temperature, cooling rate, size and shape of the part, carbon and alloy content, and the temperature at which the transformation to martensite occurs. The stress distribution may also be more complex than that shown in Fig. 14-14. Quenching must be very carefully carried out. A large surface tensile stress may cause warping and distortion or even cracking of the part. The tendency to crack is augmented by the presence of stress raisers such as notches, grooves, holes, reentrant corners, and so on. Oil quenching is less severe than water quenching. The heat is removed less quickly, and the difference in temperature between the surface and the center is less than for water quenching. The tendency for distortion and cracking is therefore less with oil quenching.

A residual surface compressive stress is beneficial for parts with repeated or fatigue loading, and such a stress can effect a worthwhile increase in the factor of safety. It is known, however, that surface residual stresses tend to lessen or fade gradually with repeated stressing. Tempering to restore a portion of the ductility causes a loss of the surface compression. In fact, a tempering temperature of 1,000 F may reduce the compression to zero or turn it into tension.

A surface with residual tension is vulnerable to the formation of fatigue cracks. Such conditions have undoubtedly been the cause of many failures. Residual tension can be removed and the surface left in compression by mechanical operations such as rolling between rollers at high pressure, shot peening, tumbling, or peen hammering.[5]

11. Carburizing and Nitriding

Sometimes a machine part requires a hard surface to resist wear, abrasion, or local deformation from impact loads, combined with a tough, strong core for strength. The case hardening or carburizing process can be used for obtaining such a structure. The parts are packed in a compound rich in carbon and held for a number of hours in the furnace at a temperature within the austenitic range. Carbon is absorbed by the surface layer. The same effect is secured by heating the steel in the presence of gases rich in carbon. The high-carbon surface material is transformed to martensite by quenching, followed by tempering at 300–350 F for relief of quenching stresses. The period of heating may extend from 3 to 24 hours. A depth of case of about $\frac{1}{16}$ in. can be secured after about 8 hours in the furnace. Freedom from warping during the extended heating period is a very desirable property for a carburizing steel. Carburizing steels in general are low in carbon and have good machinability ratings, but all machine work must be completed before the part is carburized. The core properties for a number of steels used for carburizing are given in Table 14-10.

Nitriding produces a very hard surface layer by the absorption of nitrogen during heating that lasts for an extended period at 900–1000 F in the presence of ammonia gas. Special nitriding steels must be used, but no heat treatment subsequent to the hardening is required. Both the carburizing and nitriding processes leave the part with a residual stress of compression throughout the hardened zone. If the working load produces a fluctuating tensile stress, the presence of the residual surface compression gives a favorable stress condition for preventing the formation of a fatigue crack.

The cyaniding process forms a very hard surface layer 0.002 in. to 0.010 in. thick through immersion for a short period, 15 minutes to 1 hour, in a bath of molten sodium cyanide, and then by quenching in water

[5] For additional information on residual stress, see p. 495 of reference 35, Bibliography.

TABLE 14-10

Core Properties of Various Carburizing Steels

Steel	Tensile Strength	Yield Strength	% El. in 2 in.	% Red. Area	Izod ft lb	Steel	Tensile Strength	Yield Strength	% El. in 2 in.	% Red. Area	Izod ft lb
1020	96,000	60,000	19	41	48	4119	137,000	112,000	16	42	
1117	96,000	59,000	23	53	33	4615	110,000	75,000	23	66	67
2315	138,000	108,000	22	61	42	6115	104,000	62,000	28	58	
3115	125,000	85,000	22	54	36	A8620	135,000	108,000	17	48	

1-in. rounds carburized 8 hrs 1650–1700 F, cooled in box, reheated to 1475 F.
Steels 1020 and 1117 are water quenched and tempered at 350 F.
Others are oil quenched and tempered at 300 F.

or oil. The hardness is derived from compounds of nitrogen and carbon absorbed by the surface layer.

12. Flame Hardening

Localized surface heating with a flame or induction coil, followed by rapid cooling, usually leaves the surface in tension. The cool interior of the body does not expand, and the attached heated layer must expand plastically outward. This enlarged material is unable to return to its original size when cooled, and residual tension results.

Grinding cracks can be accounted for by the process above. Brake drums, clutch plates, railroad wheels and rails, and other friction surfaces are affected in the same way. Flame-cut parts are usually left with a surface layer of tension. Contraction of weld metal deposited on relatively cold base metal produces a residual stress of tension. Bent shafts can be straightened by heating them on the outside of the bend. If properly carried out, the residual tensile stress in the region that has been heated will cause the shaft to straighten.

Flame or induction hardening leaves the surface in a state of residual compression only when the steel has a sufficient carbon or alloy content to undergo the phase change to martensite upon quenching from the austenitic condition. The increase in volume from the martensite formation must be sufficient to overcome the thermal contraction of the heated layer.

At the edges of the heated region, the martensite gradually merges into the weaker surrounding material. When the part must be heated in sections, the junctions between the heated regions should be located at points where the loading stresses are low. For example, in hardening the teeth of a gear, the junctions should be placed at the tips of the teeth and not at the base where the maximum bending stress occurs.

13. Strain Hardening

Plastic deformation, resulting from drawing metals through a die, or rolling them between rollers, raises the values of the yield point and tensile strength of ductile materials such as mild steel, stainless steel, copper, brass, and aluminum.[6] This increase in strength is accompanied

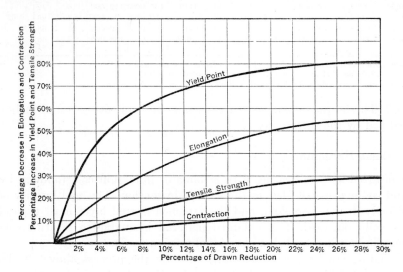

FIG. 14-15.   Effect of cold drawing on the tensile properties of steel. (*Courtesy Bethlehem Steel Co.*)

by a loss of ductility and an increase of hardness. The effect of cold drawing on the properties of steel can be estimated by the curves in Fig. 14-15. The strengthening becomes less at distances removed from the surface, and the properties of bars of large cross section undergo less change because of the cold work. The stress-strain diagram for low-carbon steel loses its characteristic shape if the material is cold worked. The large elongation at the yield point does not take place, but a gradual bending of the curve occurs after the proportional limit has been passed.

Materials that are too weak and soft for use in the annealed condition are sometimes strengthened by cold working. After such treatment, the mechanical properties may no longer be the same in all directions, and usually a definite loss of ductility results in the direction normal to the deformation. In addition, any increase of the yield point in tension produced by stretching is usually accompanied by a decrease of the yield point in compression. This fact must be kept in mind if the material in normal operation is subjected to reversing stresses.

[6] See p. 406 of reference 1, Bibliography.

In general, cold working leaves the part with residual stress on the surface. This is an undesirable situation, since parts made from such materials will warp if a portion of the surface is removed by machining. A tensile residual stress on the surface causes the part to be vulnerable to the formation of a fatigue crack should the stress be fluctuating.

The hardening and loss of ductility produced by plastic deformation disappears if the material is subjected to annealing temperatures. When the fabrication process involves successive steps of cold working, the material may become so brittle that rupture may occur. This danger can be avoided by restoring the ductility periodically by annealing the metal between the cold working operations. Cold rolling and cold drawing are sometimes used for producing a smooth, bright surface and dimensional accuracy on bars and sheets.

An improvement in the strength, ductility, and impact resistance of steel can be secured by hot working at the forging temperature. Hot working gives a finer and more uniform grain structure, and improves the soundness of the material.

14. Hardness

The term hardness is used to designate certain mechanical properties of a material such as resistance to penetration, scratching, abrasion, or cutting. Since a rigorous definition of hardness has not as yet been written, this quality must be specified by numbers which are dependent upon the method of making the test. Manufacturing operations such as cold work, quenching and tempering, and precipitation heat treating change the hardness of many engineering materials. Hardness testing is therefore one of the principal methods for determining the suitability of a material for its intended purpose. Hardness testing is a valuable inspection tool for maintaining uniformity of quality in heat-treated parts. A useful correlation exists between the hardness of a material and the tensile strength, endurance limit, and wear resistance.

The Brinell is one of the best known of the penetration methods for determining hardness. In the standard test, a hardened 10 mm diameter steel ball is pressed into the specimen by a force of 3,000 kg. The diameter of the impression is determined by a hand microscope, and the area of the contact surface between ball and material is computed. The Brinell Hardness Number BHN is found by dividing the load in kilograms by the area in square millimeters. The harder the material, the smaller the indentation, and the higher will be the Brinell number. The tensile strength of steel in pounds per square inch is usually about 500 times the BHN.

The Rockwell machine for measuring hardness is also in wide use. It is a rapid method, since the hardness is read directly by a dial on the machine which eliminates the necessity of making a separate measurement of the impression. Two types of Rockwell readings are in general use: the B and the C. The B reading is made by use of a steel ball penetrator $\frac{1}{16}$ in. in diameter. The dial gives a reading which is dependent upon the penetration caused by a load of 90 kg, after an initial load of 10 kg has first been applied to seat the ball on the specimen. Rockwell B hardness tests are used for unhardened steel and nonferrous metals which are not extremely hard. Both letter and number must be used in specifying Rockwell hardnesses.

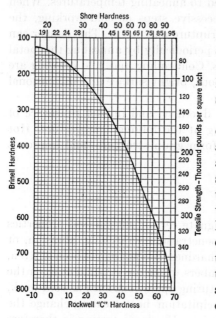

Fig. 14-16. Relationship between tensile strength of steel and hardness by various designations. (*Courtesy International Nickel Co.*)

For the Rockwell C reading, a 120° diamond cone called a brale is used as the penetrator. The initial load is again 10 kg, but the main load consists of 140 additional kg. For very thin specimens, or for parts covered with a shallow, hardened skin, the B or C Rockwell tests penetrate too deeply, and the superficial Rockwell test must be used. In the superficial test, both the initial and major loads are considerably reduced, depending on the thickness of the specimen or of the hardened zone.

Another instrument for hardness testing is the Shore Scleroscope, in which a small diamond-tipped weight is allowed to fall on the specimen. The height of the rebound is used as the measure of the hardness of the material. This instrument has the desirable feature of portability, and can be used on specimens too large to be placed in a regular hardness-testing machine. The relationships between the tensile strength of steel and the Brinell, Rockwell C, and Shore Scleroscope numbers are illustrated in Fig. 14-16.

The Vickers pyramid test uses a small diamond pyramid to indent the specimen. The hardness number, as for the Brinell test, is found by dividing the load by the area of the indentation. Since the loads are light, a high magnification is required to determine the width of the impression.

Scratch hardness tests are also in use. A diamond or sapphire point is drawn over a polished surface under a definite load and the width of the scratch is measured with a microscope. The hardness number is usually considered as varying inversely with the square of the width of the scratch.[7]

15. Machinability

The relative ease with which a given material may be machined, or cut with sharp edged tools, is called its machinability.[8] The ratings given in Tables 14-4 and 14-5 are based on Bessemer screw stock B 1112 as 100 per cent. These refer to a turning operation with a cutting speed of 165 fpm for a depth of cut of 0.500 in. and a feed of 0.0025 in. and for an approximate tool life of 8 hours with high speed tools.

When a part requires a large amount of machining, the designer tries to specify a composition and grain structure best adapted to the cutting operations. Sometimes certain elements, principally sulfur and manganese, are added to steel to improve the cutting properties. Steels with very low carbon content usually have poor machinability. For greatest cutting ease, the carbon content should be about 0.10 per cent for Bessemer steels and 0.20 per cent for open-hearth steels. Alloy steels, because of their higher strength and toughness, are usually harder to machine than plain carbon steels. In general, the machining properties of a steel can be materially improved by cold drawing. Annealing and normalizing heat treatments are beneficial for medium- and high-carbon and alloy steels. For best machining, a steel should be soft and brittle. This is not possible since steel is either soft and tough or hard and brittle. For high surface speeds, medium size pearlite grains, with each grain surrounded by an envelope of ferrite, are desirable. For low speeds and heavy feeds and depths of cut a spheroidal microstructure is best. In general, the machinability rating cannot be correlated with the Brinell Hardness Number. Steels of best machinability have BHN of 187 to 217.

16. Grain Size

A relationship exists between the mechanical properties of steel and the size of the grains or crystals. Coarse-grained steels, in general, harden deeper and are best for rough machining operations. They have good hot-forming characteristics and offer better resistance to high-temperature creep. Fine-grained steels, in contrast, are tougher and are superior for impact resistance, especially at low temperatures. They exhibit less distortion, internal stress, and cracking from heat treatment.

Grain sizes in steel are designated by ASTM grain size numbers 1 to 8. Number 1 is the largest, and has a calculated diameter of equivalent

---

[7] See reference 22, Bibliography.
[8] See also reference 8, Bibliography.

spherical grain of 0.0113 in. Number 8 is the smallest, with a spherical grain diameter of 0.0010 in. Steels of grain sizes 1 to 5, inclusive, are generally called coarse-grained, and fine-grained steels have grain sizes 6 to 8, inclusive.

The grains of austenite that are formed when steel is heated have the smallest size at the upper critical temperature, as indicated by Fig. 14-5. A fine-grained steel therefore results if the material is cooled from the fine-grained austenitic condition. If the steel is heated above the upper critical temperature, the grains of austenite increase in size and a coarse-grained steel results upon cooling. The grain size is therefore to a large extent under the control of the heat treater. Hence, if a fine-grained steel is desired in a hot-rolled or forged product, the hot working must be continued until the temperature drops almost to the upper critical point, or the grains will coarsen in cooling from the high temperature at which hot working was stopped.

Grain size in steel refers to the size of the previously existing austenite grains at the quenching temperature. Therefore, the sample must be quenched from the desired temperature and tempered lightly, and a specimen must then be prepared for examination. The martensite grains reflect the austenitic grain size. The behavior of carburizing steel is usually evaluated by means of a standardized method called the McQuaid-Ehn test.

An uncertainty sometimes exists in the purchase of steel as to whether lots from different sources, but of the same chemical composition, will have identical physical properties when given the same heat treatment. The physical properties, as mentioned in the foregoing, depend on the grain size, which in turn depends upon the grain-coarsening characteristics of the material. It is possible for one piece of steel to remain fine-grained for a considerable temperature range above the upper critical temperature, whereas another piece of steel of the same chemical composition, but from another lot, may coarsen when raised to this temperature. A knowledge of the inherent grain growth tendency is thus very important if consistent physical properties are to be expected after heat treatment. In fact, the term fine-grained is sometimes applied to a steel which does not begin to coarsen until the temperature rises a considerable amount above the upper critical. A coarse-grained steel, then, is one which coarsens rapidly as the temperature rises beyond the upper critical. Closer temperature control is required for the heat treatment of coarse-grained steel. Fine-grained steels have a wider range of safe hardening temperatures, and more predictable results can be obtained in the heat treatment process. The tendency for grain growth at elevated temperatures can be closely controlled by the addition during steel making of such inhibiting agents as minute quantities of finely divided aluminum.

17. Corrosion. Stainless Steel

The loss of metal products due to atmospheric corrosion or by corrosion from food and industrial acids is very great. The effects of corrosion can be minimized by the use of suitable corrosion resistant materials and by careful attention to the details of construction. Sharp corners where moisture, liquids, and solid matter can accumulate should be avoided or drain holes should be provided. Baffles and stiffners in tanks should provide free drainage. Bottoms should be rounded, or sloped with round corners. Drain-out valves and plugs should be flush with the bottom. The use of dissimilar metals in adjacent locations should be avoided.

It has been found that certain high-alloy steels have good corrosion resistance properties. Stainless steels of 2 general types are in wide use: the plain chromium, and the chromium-nickel. Some of the general properties[9] of these materials are given in Table 14-11.

Plain chromium steels of 4 per cent to 6 per cent Cr with low percentages of carbon, as well as steels with more than 16 per cent Cr, may be heated to any temperature without transforming them to austenite. Since quenching has no effect, these steels are said to be ferritic. Plain chromium steels of 12 per cent to 14 per cent Cr become austenitic when heated. Martensite forms upon quenching, and the steel is hardened in the usual manner. These steels are therefore said to be martensitic. Generally 12 per cent or more of Cr is needed to obtain complete protection from the atmosphere. A smooth, polished surface helps to resist staining and corrosion. Plain chromium steels are used in both the cast and wrought forms, and are suitable for various hot and cold forming operations. In general, machining must be done at reduced feeds and cutting speeds. The martensitic type air hardens upon welding and may require annealing to restore ductility. Steels of 12 per cent to 14 per cent Cr resist oxidation up to 1500 F; and steels of 15 per cent to 18 per cent Cr resist oxidation up to 1,600 F.

The chromium-nickel steels such as 18:8 (18 per cent Cr and 8 per cent Ni) remain austenitic at all temperatures and therefore do not respond to heat treatment. They can be used in either the cast or wrought forms and can be both hot and cold worked. Cold rolling or drawing gives a large increase in strength, but a loss in ductility. Fabrication can be readily carried out, but machining is difficult unless special elements such as sulfur or selenium are present to provide a free cutting structure. All types of electric and gas welding can be used. The chromium-nickel steels are more resistant to corrosion than the plain chromium steels. Oxidation is very slow up to about 1650 F. The properties of these steels

[9] See references 9 and 29, Bibliography.

TABLE 14-11

Composition and Mechanical Properties of Selected Stainless Steels

Type No.	Austenitic (Cr 18%, Ni 8%) Hardenable by Cold Working. Nonmagnetic When Fully Annealed				Ferritic (Cr 17%) Non-hardenable. Can be Hot Worked. Magnetic		Martensitic (Cr 12%) Hardenable by Heat Treatment	
	302	*304*	*316*	*347*	*430*	*446*	*410*	*440A*
Cr	17.0–19.0	18.0–20.0	16.0–18.0	17.0–19.0	14.0–18.0	23.0–27.0	11.5–13.5	16.0–18 0
Ni	8.0–10.0	8.0–12.0	10.0–14.0	9.0–12.0	0.5 max	0.5 max	0.5 max	0.5 max
C, max.	0.15	0.08	0.10	0.08	0.12	0.2	0.15	0.60–0.75
Mn, max.	2.0	2.0	2.0	2.0	1.0	1.5	1.0	1.0
Si, max	1.0	1.0	1.0	1.0	1.0	1.0	1.0	1.0
Others			Mo 2.0–3.0	Cb stab.		N .25 max		Mo .75 max
Tensile str.*	80,000	80,000	75,000	80,000	60,000	75,000	60,000†	95,000‡
Yield str.	30,000	30,000	30,000	30,000	35,000	45,000	32,000	55,000
El. in 2 in. %	50	50	40	40	20	20	20	20
Red. Area	60	60	50	50	40	40	50	40
Brinell max.	180	180	200	200	200	200	200	240
Alternate grades available	303 +P & S for FC	305 Higher in Ni	316L Lower C for weld.	321 Ti stab.	430 F +P & S for FC		416 420 F +P & S for FC	440 F FC (free cutting)

* Strength values of table are for annealed or furnace cooled material.

† Heat treated 410:
   $TS = 60$–$200,000$ psi, $YS = 35$–$180,000$ psi, Elong. $= 25$–2%. Brinell $= 120$–400.

‡ Heat treated 440A:
   $TS = 95$–$275,000$ psi, $YS = 55$–$240,000$ psi, Elong. $= 20$–2%, Brinell $= 200$–555.

Austenitic: Basic type 302.
   303   Good machinability. Not suitable for bending or welding.
   305   Minimum work hardening. Good for various cold-forming operations.
   316   High resistance to corrosion and pitting.
   321 347   For service at 800–1,500 F (321 not suitable for deep drawing or spinning.)
Ferritic: Basic type 430.
   430 F   Best machinability of all stainless steels. Not suitable for welding or cold forming.
   446   Highest resistance to corrosion and scaling. Not suitable for resistance welding or deep drawing.
Martensitic: Basic type 410.
   416, 420 F, 440 F   Good machinability. Not suitable for welding or cold forming.

can be modified through a wide range to fit special conditions by making small changes in the composition.

Many processes are in use for applying a corrosion-resistant coating to the surface of steel and iron products. Coatings of zinc, tin, lead, copper, nickel, chromium, and cadmium are in wide use. Application is made by hot dipping, electroplating, or by a molten metal spray, depending on the metals involved. The Parkerizing and Bonderizing processes utilize a coating of iron phosphate as the protective agent or as a base for the application of paint or enamel.

Resistance of steel to atmospheric corrosion can be increased by the addition of about 0.20 per cent of copper. The HSLA steels described in Section 7 are still more resistant to this destructive action.

18. Wear

With the exception of corrosion, wear is usually the most important agent in reducing the service life of a machine. Wear causes loss of dimension by abrasion or grinding away of a metal surface. It has been said that the loss of 5 lb of metal constitutes the difference between a brand new 5-ton truck and one that is worn out. In a general way, metals of high hardness show the smallest loss by wear. There are exceptions, however, for wear is a complicated phenomenon. In general, service

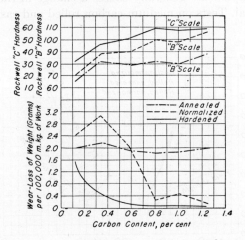

Fig. 14-17.   Effect of carbon content and heat treatment on metal-to-metal wear of steels.

conditions cannot be duplicated by any form of standardized laboratory test.

Wear tests are generally of two types. In the abrasive test, a metal plate under light pressure is used to drag a standard sand or other abrasive across the specimen. In the metal-to-metal wear test, the edges of 2 metal disks are rotated together at regulated pressures. In both types of tests the loss of metal by the specimen is noted. This loss constitutes the measure of the wear resistance. The relationship between carbon content, hardness, and metal-to-metal wear resistance[10] is illustrated by the curves of Fig. 14-17.

The designer should specify the most suitable type of material for reducing the amount of wear. Coarse-grained lamellar pearlite has been found to be more wear resistant than other microstructures. Toughness, or the ability to withstand large deformations without failure, is a desirable property for reducing wear, especially when abrasives are present.

[10] See reference 23, Bibliography; see also p. 133 of reference 24.

In metal-to-metal contact, smooth surfaces will wear less than rough surfaces. The presence of foreign matter and worn-off particles of the metal in the lubricant will hasten the wear process. Hadfield steel, containing 10 per cent to 14 per cent Mn and 1.0 per cent to 1.4 per cent C, possesses exceptional ability to resist abrasion. The impact strength of this material is also very high.

19. Short-term Effects of High Temperatures

A rise in temperature generally causes a change in the physical properties of a metal. Tests on medium-carbon rolled and cast steels indicate

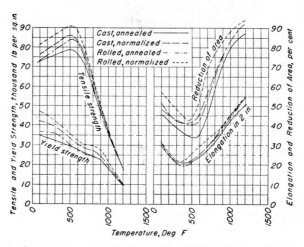

Fig. 14-18. Properties of annealed and normalized 0.28C cast steel and annealed and normalized 0.28C rolled steel at elevated temperatures.

that the tensile stress increases until the temperature rises to the blue-heat point at about 500–550 F. As shown by Fig. 14-18, this increase of strength is accompanied by loss of ductility; it is termed "blue brittleness." A further increase in temperature causes a rapid decrease of strength.[11] Other tests have shown that the impact strength at about 800–900 F is considerably less, but at 1300 F is somewhat greater, than at room temperature. A further rise in temperature, however, is accompanied by a rapid decrease in impact strength.[12] The endurance limit, for a change of temperature, generally follows the same trend as the tensile strength. The modulus of elasticity drops for a rise in temperature, as is shown by Fig. 14-19.

[11] See reference 13, Bibliography.
[12] See p. 474 of reference 14, Bibliography.

Cast iron is but slightly affected by temperatures up to 800 F, but above 900 F a sharp decrease in strength occurs. Malleable iron, above 800 F, shows a decrease in strength and an increase in ductility with increasing temperature.

At subnormal temperatures, there will be an increase in the values for the tensile strength, yield strength, endurance limit, and hardness, and a decrease in the ductility of both ferrous and nonferrous metals.[13] At low temperatures, however, many steels have a marked reduction in impact strength. Consequently, the designer must use special care in avoiding or reducing stress concentrations. A fine-grained

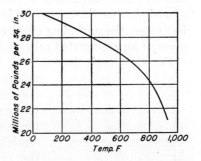

Fig. 14-19.   Reduction in modulus of elasticity for steel at elevated temperatures.

steel is superior to a coarse-grained steel for such service. Three and one half per cent nickel steel, stainless steel of the 18:8 type, or nonferrous alloys are in widest use for impact loads at subnormal temperatures.

20. Creep of Steel at High Temperature

If a part is subjected to stress at high temperature for a long period of time, it will undergo a slow and permanent deformation called creep. When the part operates with close clearances, the designer must make a careful attempt to predict the amount of creep that will probably take place during the useful life of the machine. For applications where close clearances are not involved, the permissible deformations are limited only by the deformations that may cause embrittlement and failure.

The amount that a member deforms or creeps depends upon the stress, the temperature, and the kind of material. Materials which have the same properties at room temperature may differ greatly in creep characteristics at elevated temperature. Hence suitable values for working stresses at high temperatures can be determined only by experiments on each material. Reliable data can be secured only by conducting longtime creep tests which duplicate as nearly as possible the conditions under which the steel will be used. The testing equipment is expensive, and must embody great precision of temperature control and measurement of elongation.

The tensile test, in which the total elongation is plotted as a function of the time, is the most significant. A creep curve, as that shown by the typical examples of Fig. 14-20, consists of 3 parts. In the first stage, the

[13] See references 15 and 16, Bibliography.

material is becoming stronger because of the strain hardening, and the creep rate is therefore decreasing. In the second stage, the strengthening due to strain hardening is counterbalanced by the weakening due to annealing, and the creep rate is approximately constant. In the third or last stage, the annealing effect predominates, and the deformations take place at an accelerated rate until failure results.

For sufficiently low stresses and temperatures, the third stage may not appear within the duration of the test. In fact, since it is usually impossible to conduct the test for as long a time as the service life of the part, designers usually extrapolate the straight portion of the curve beyond the duration of the test in order to predict the expected amount of creep at a future time. However, an element of danger lies in this practice, since the only way to be certain that the curve will remain straight for a service life of 10 or 20 years is to conduct the test for that length of time. Although experiments of such duration are manifestly impractical, it has been recommended that tests extending to 10 per cent of the expected service life be performed whenever feasible. The reliability of short-term creep tests for predicting long-term deformations is decidedly doubtful at the present time.

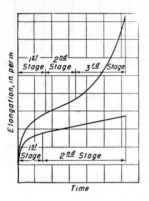

Fig. 14-20.   Creep of mild steel.

The selection of a suitable steel for continuous service at high temperatures is a very difficult task. The following steels have been recommended[14] for use in oil refinery equipment: up to 900 F, 0.08–0.18 C killed (or degasified) steel; 1,000 F, 0.08–0.18 C plus 0.50 Mo; 1,100 F, C-Mo plus 1.25 Cr or 1.50 Si; 1,200 F, 2.0 to 5.0 Cr plus 0.50 Mo; 1,300 F, 18 Cr, 8 Ni; above 1,300 F, 16 Cr, 13 Ni, 3 Mo.

21. Cast Iron

Cast iron or gray iron is characterized by high percentages of carbon and silicon. The average composition of cast iron is shown by Table 14-12. Gray iron is the most extensively used cast construction material. It is cheap, easily cast, and readily machined. Although strong in compression, cast iron has the disadvantage of being weak in tension. When a casting must sustain high tensile loads, some other material, such as alloy cast iron, malleable iron, or cast steel, must be used. Such materials, however, are more expensive than gray iron. Cast iron is notable for its lack of ductility; the elongation for a standard tensile specimen is usually less

[14] See reference 28, Bibliography.

than 1 per cent. Cooling stresses can be relieved and machinability improved by annealing. For bodies of intricate shape, castings have inherent advantages over built-up or fabricated products.

It is general practice to classify cast irons with respect to tensile strength. Some properties[15] of cast irons are shown in Table 14-13. Suitable compositions to meet the strength requirements are chosen by the producing foundry unless the customer specifies otherwise. The cost of the iron increases with increase of strength.

Cast iron contains about 0.70 per cent carbon combined with iron in a pearlitic structure. The remaining carbon appears as more or less finely divided graphite flakes. The flake graphite is responsible for the relatively low hardness and strength of cast iron: the larger and coarser the flakes, the lower the strength. Dispersal of the carbon is aided by the presence of silicon, but is retarded by sulfur. However, sufficient manganese is usually present to form MnS, which alleviates

TABLE 14-12
Composition of Cast Iron

Carbon	2.00 to 4.00%
Silicon	0.50 to 3.00%
Manganese	0.20 to 1.00%
Phosphorus	0.05 to 0.80%
Sulfur	0.04 to 0.15%
Iron	Remainder

TABLE 14-13
Strength of Gray Cast Irons

Class No.	Tensile Strength min. psi	Average Transverse Load* lb	Compressive Strength† psi	Average Shear Strength psi	Modulus of Elasticity psi	BHN	Usual Min. Wall Thickness in.
20	20,000	1,800	80,000	32,500	11,600,000	110	$\frac{1}{8}$
25	25,000	2,000	100,000	34,000	14,200,000	140	$\frac{1}{8}$
30	30,000	2,200	110,000	41,000	14,500,000	170	$\frac{1}{4}$
35	35,000	2,400	125,000	49,000	16,000,000	200	$\frac{3}{8}$
40	40,000	2,600	135,000	52,000	18,100,000	230	$\frac{1}{2}$
50	50,000	3,000	160,000	64,000	22,600,000	250	$\frac{1}{2}$
60	60,000	3,400	150,000	60,000	19,900,000	275	$\frac{3}{4}$

* Specimen 1.2 in. diameter, 18 in. supports, load at center.
† Subject to variations up to ±10 per cent.

the effect of the sulfur. Phosphorus forms the hard constituent, steatite, which has no effect on the graphite dispersal. A finer dispersal and a higher tensile strength are secured by an increase in the cooling rate. Since the cooling rate is affected by the section size, the interior of thick sections is

[15] See reference 27, Bibliography.

weaker than the material near the surface or thin sections of the same composition.

When higher strength and hardness are desired, alloying elements such as nickel, chromium, molybdenum, and copper are added to cast iron.[16] In general, the alloying elements serve to improve the characteristics of the graphite. Compositions are available which will produce castings suitable for resisting impact, abrasion, corrosion, and high and low temperatures. Modern research has developed alloys of cast iron which are suitable for service as gears, crankshafts, and forging and drawing dies. Heat treatments of quenching and tempering are usually practiced with alloy cast iron to obtain full benefit of the expensive alloy additions. The designer should consult with an experienced foundryman on the composition and heat treatment for specialized applications. The engineering staffs of firms which market the various alloys also render expert metallurgical advice.

Cast iron is difficult to weld. Its tendency to crack can be reduced by careful preheating before welding, followed by slow cooling. Bronze welding rods are extensively used on cast iron. Cast iron has excellent vibration-damping characteristics as well as good resistance to wear. The resistance to corrosion is only fair. It is difficult to secure satisfactory results with metal inserts cast in place.

White cast iron results if the cooling rate after pouring is very rapid. The carbon is retained in solution, and the metal is very hard and resistant to wear. White cast iron cannot be machined; if cast iron must be machined, care must be taken that thin sections of a casting are not chilled so rapidly that white iron forms. White cast iron has important applications. For example, the tread or outer surface of the rim of a freight-car wheel can be cooled so rapidly that white iron results while the rest of the casting remains soft and machinable. To do this, a portion of the mold, called a chill, is made of iron. The chill removes heat very rapidly from the molten metal. Other applications of white cast iron include rolling-mill rolls, railroad brake shoes, and plow shares.

White iron is also used in the formation of malleable iron. Malleable iron has the desirable engineering qualities of high strength and ductility. It is soft, tough, and easily machined, and is widely used in places where ordinary cast iron would be too brittle. Malleable iron is formed by giving a long annealing treatment to white iron. Such a treatment turns carbon into fine nodules of graphite called temper carbon. Some of the physical properties of malleable iron are given in Table 14-14. Meehanite iron is made by a patented process in which a fine dispersal of the graphite is secured by the addition of a calcium-silicon alloy.

[16] See p. 210 of reference 6, and also reference 10, Bibliography.

TABLE 14-14

Properties of Malleable Iron, Ductile Iron, and Meehanite

Material	ASTM Spec.	Grade or Type	Tensile Strength	Yield Strength	Comp. Strength	Elong. in 2 in. %	Modulus of Elasticity
Malleable	A47-52	32510	50,000	32,500		10	
		35018	53,000	35,000		18	
Ductile iron	A339-55	60-45-10	60,000	45,000		10	
	A339-55	80-60-03	80,000	60,000		3	
	A396-55T	100-70-03	100,000	70,000		3	
	A396-55T	120-90-02	120,000	90,000		2	
Meehanite		GD	35,000		130,000		15,000,000
		GA	50,000		175,000		21,000,000

22. Cast Steel

Cast steels have approximately the same chemical composition as the wrought steels, except that the percentages of silicon and manganese are larger. Steel is difficult to cast. It shrinks about $\frac{1}{4}$ in. per foot and makes a rough looking casting. The casting first undergoes a reduction in size, known as solidification shrinkage, which is followed by a considerable thermal contraction as the casting cools to room temperature. The casting should be designed in such a manner that the solidification will occur progressively, starting in the portions farthest removed from the molten metal. Uniformity of sections or a gradual transition from thin to thick sections is desirable, and stress concentrations should be reduced as much as possible. Projections should be avoided in long castings, or collapsible molds and cores should be used, to prevent hot tears caused by the large amount of cooling contraction.

Steel castings are in wide use in railway equipment, heavy machinery, oil refineries, and rolling mills. The design of the part must be suitable to the casting characteristics and physical properties of the material. A satisfactory microstructure depends on the conditions present during solidification, and thus on correct foundry practice. Heat treatment, such as annealing, normalizing, or quenching and drawing, gives a more uniform internal structure and improves the physical properties. Castings are usually inferior to corresponding wrought metals in impact resistance. The shock or impact qualities are improved by heat treatment, and also by the use of alloys.

The physical properties of cast steel vary with the carbon content,[17]

[17] See pages 157 and 160 of reference 11, Bibliography.

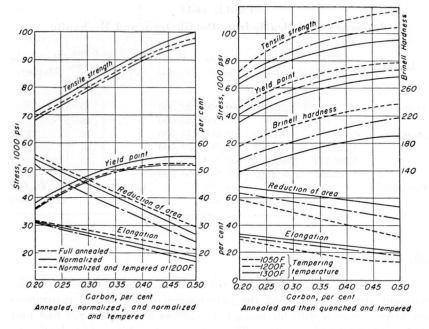

Fig. 14-21. Mechanical properties of medium-carbon cast steel. (*Courtesy Steel Founders' Society of America.*)

as shown in Fig. 14-21. Smaller values for the strength and ductility will be found in the interior[18] of castings of large section size, as is shown in Fig. 14-22.

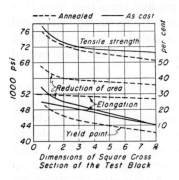

Fig. 14-22. Effect of mass on the mechanical properties of cast carbon steel specimens taken at center of test block.

Low-carbon steel castings, containing 0.15 per cent to 0.30 per cent carbon, have desirable elevated temperature and carburizing properties. Parts made of this material frequently compete with castings made of gray or malleable iron. Cast steel can be readily welded. The microstructure of deposited weld metal is essentially the same as that of cast steel. If the carbon content is high enough to cause hardening and loss of ductility from cooling in air, it may be necessary to preheat the casting before welding, and then follow this by an annealing treatment afterwards.

Medium-carbon steel castings, in the range of 0.30 per cent to 0.40 per cent C, have greater strength but somewhat less ductility than low-carbon

[18] See reference 12, Bibliography.

castings. The increase in the amount of carbon effects an improvement in the casting qualities of the metal. Heat treatment gives improved physical properties over the as-cast condition. High-carbon steel castings contain 0.40 per cent C and over. The greater hardness makes this material suitable for applications involving abrasion and impact. Machining must usually be preceded by an annealing heat treatment.

A wide variety of alloy steel castings is available for specific applications.[19] Both low- and high-alloy castings are made. Heat treatment is usually practiced to secure the full benefit of the alloy additions. All the principal alloying elements used in wrought steel are employed in making steel castings. Certain alloys of high-chromium and nickel content are suitable for high-temperature service or where corrosion conditions are present.

23. Tool Steel

Materials that are used for tools must be very hard and resistant to deformation and wear. High-carbon and alloy steels of high purity meet this requirement. Plain carbon steel of about 0.65 per cent C is used for tools which must withstand considerable battering, such as hammers, heading dies, and hot forging dies. A carbon content of 1.10 per cent is used for general purpose cutting and hand tools. Razors, drawing dies, files, and other tools requiring extreme hardness have percentages of carbon up to 1.40 per cent.

The machining of such high-carbon steels must be preceded by normalizing, annealing, or spheroidizing heat treatments. The quenching and tempering of tool steels require expert handling. The tempering temperatures are low as compared to those of machine steels and are used only for relieving some of the quenching stresses.

The abrasion resistance and toughness of tool steel can be increased by the use of suitable alloys. Also, tool steel can be given a less rapid quenching, in oil for example, and residual stress and distortion will thereby be less. Low residual stress and low distortion are especially valuable if the body contains cross sections of both large and small diameters. Chromium, tungsten, and vanadium, either singly or in various combinations, are the principal alloys used. Compositions are available which hold their hardness and cutting edges even when raised to a red heat from the friction of the cutting.

High-speed steel of the 18-4-1 type contains 18 per cent tungsten, 4 per cent chromium, 1 per cent vanadium, and 0.70 per cent C, and has superior cutting qualities. Its manufacturing and heat-treating processes must be closely controlled. Stellite is a cobalt-chromium-tungsten-

[19] See reference 11, or Chapter 4 of reference 6, Bibliography.

carbon alloy also used for cutting tools. Cemented carbide cutting tools are made by powdered metallurgy, and in general will outlast even high-speed steel.

24. Aluminum Alloys

Lightweight aluminum alloys have found wide applications in manufactured products. The high-strength alloys of this material have practically the same strength as mild steel. As is shown in Table 2-1, the weight per cubic inch and the stiffness are only about one-third as great as for steel. The stiffness of a part made of aluminum is less and the deflection greater than that of a corresponding design in steel. Aluminum is a very versatile metal. It can be extruded, forged, or rolled into sheets. It is suitable for making sand, permanent mold, or die castings, and is also used for automatic screw machine products. The strength can be increased by cold working or heat treatment.

Aluminum objects secure considerable protection from atmospheric corrosion by a coating of aluminum oxide which forms naturally in air. Sometimes this oxide layer is built up artificially by anodic oxidation to give better protection. High-strength aluminum alloys are not so resistant to corrosion as the pure metal. In Alclad sheets, protection from corrosion is secured by rolling a coating of pure aluminum on both sides of a high-strength alloy core.

Soft aluminum is somewhat difficult to machine. The machinability of the alloys and the full heat-treated grades is superior to the machinability of the pure metal. Considerable experience and skill are required for the satisfactory welding of aluminum. Torch, metallic and carbon arc, and electric resistance methods are in use. Unlike steel, aluminum exhibits no change in color to warn the operator that the welding temperature is being approached. The presence of the oxide film adds to the difficulties of securing sound welds. The high strength secured by cold working or heat treatment is usually lost in the heated region. Cold working of welds to restore the strength is sometimes possible. Brazing techniques suitable for certain compositions have also been developed.

The composition and physical properties of several typical wrought-aluminum alloys are given in Table 14-15. Alloys 2S-O and 3S-O are easily drawn, spun, or stamped. Alloys in the work hardened or fully heat-treated condition are not so workable. Suitable radii must be provided on the forming tools, depending on the composition, the thickness of the stock, and the temper. Temper designations are shown in Table 14-16.

Several of the more widely used sand-casting alloys, and their fields of application, are listed in Table 14-17.

TABLE 14-15
Composition and Mechanical Properties of Wrought Aluminum Alloys*

Designa-tion		Nominal Composition Balance Aluminum Plus Impurities					Type
New	Old	Si	Cu	Mn	Mg	Cr	
Sheets and Plates							
1100	2S	1.0	0.20	0.05		Zn 0.1	Commercially pure aluminum.
3003	3S	0.6	0.20	1.0–1.5	Zn 0.1	Fe 0.7	Aluminum-manganese alloy.
5052	52S	0.45	0.10	0.10	2.2–2.8	0.15–0.35	General purpose high strength alloy.
Bars and Rods							
2011	11S	0.4	5.0–6.0		Zn 0.3	Fe 0.7	Heat treatable screw machine alloy.
6061	61S	0.4–0.8	0.15–0.4	0.15	0.8–1.2	0.15–0.35	Fe 0.7. Least expensive heat treatable alloy. Weldable.
6063	63S	0.2–0.6	0.10	0.10	0.45–0.9	0.10	Fe 0.35. Heat treatable alloy.

Alloy and Temper	Tensile Strength	Yield Strength	Elongation 2 in. %		Brinell	Shearing Strength	Endurance Limit
			$\frac{1}{16}$ in. Sheet	$\frac{1}{2}$ in. Round			
1100-O	13,000	5,000	35	45	23	9,000	5,000
1100-H14	18,000	17,000	9	20	32	11,000	7,000
1100-H18	24,000	22,000	5	15	44	13,000	9,000
3003-O	16,000	6,000	30	40	28	11,000	7,000
3003-H14	22,000	21,000	8	16	40	14,000	9,000
3003-H18	29,000	27,000	4	10	55	16,000	10,000
5052-O	28,000	13,000	25	30	47	18,000	16,000
5052-H34	38,000	31,000	10	14	68	21,000	18,000
5052-H38	42,000	37,000	7	8	77	24,000	20,000
2011-T3	55,000	43,000		15	95	32,000	18,000
2011-T8	59,000	45,000		12	100	35,000	18,000
6061-O	18,000	8,000	25	30	30	12,000	9,000
6061-T4	35,000	21,000	22	25	65	24,000	14,000
6061-T6	45,000	40,000	12	17	95	30,000	14,000
6063-O	13,000	7,000			25	10,000	8,000
6063-T4	25,000	13,000	22			16,000	
6063-T6	35,000	31,000	12		75	22,000	10,000
6063-T835	48,000	43,000	8		105	30,000	

Properties are typical; variations must be expected in practice.
* Taken mainly from Alcoa Aluminum *Handbook*.

TABLE 14-16

Temper Designations for Aluminum

Temper	Process
-F	As cast condition.
-O	Annealed temper of wrought materials.
-H14	Cold worked to tensile strength midway between tempers O and H18.
-H18	Cold worked to full hard temper.
-H34	Cold worked beyond temper range and stabilized.
-H38	Same as H34 but with higher strength properties.
-T3	Solution heat treated followed by strain hardening.
-T4	Solution heat treated followed by natural aging.
-T6	Solution heat treated followed by artificial aging.
-T8	Solution heat treated, strain hardening and artificial aging.

TABLE 14-17

**Composition and Mechanical Properties of Aluminum Sand
Casting Alloys***

Alloy No.	Composition†			Applications
	Cu	Si	Mg	
43		12.0		General purpose casting alloy, cooking utensils, architectural and marine applications and pipe fittings.
214			3.8	Food, chemical, marine, and architectural applications.
195	4.5	0.8		Machinery and aircraft structural members.
220			10.0	For high strength and impact castings.
356		7.0	0.3	Automotive and railroad fittings, hardware, valves.

Alloy and Temper	Tensile Strength	Yield Strength	Elong. 2 in. %	Compressive Yield Str.	Brinell	Shearing Strength	End. Limit
43-F	19,000	8,000	8.0	9,000	40	14,000	8,000
214-F	25,000	12,000	9.0	12,000	50	20,000	7,000
195-T6	36,000	24,000	5.0	25,000	75	30,000	7,500
220-T4	48,000	26,000	16.0	27,000	75	34,000	8,000
356-T6	33,000	24,000	3.5	25,000	70	26,000	8,500

* Taken from Alcoa Aluminum *Handbook.* Values shown are typical; variations must be expected in practice.
† Per cent of alloying elements. Aluminum and normal impurities constitute a remainder.

The theory for the increased strength and hardness of heat-treated aluminum alloys differs in several respects from that for steel. After aluminum is quenched, the material is a supersaturated solid solution of the alloying elements. At this time it is soft and ductile. If allowed to stand at room temperature, the alloying elements are precipitated as hard particles which are effective in preventing movement within the crystal structure. Since considerable time may be required for the greatest strength to be reached, the process is called aging. For some alloys the process can be hastened by heating to a temperature that is known to give the optimum particle size for the maximum strength and hardness. After precipitation of the hardening constituents, the material is said to be in the T condition.

25. Magnesium Alloys

Magnesium, in its various cast and wrought forms, provides another medium for achieving lightweight designs. As shown by Table 2-1 the weight per cubic inch and the modulus are lower than for aluminum. Magnesium is less resistant to corrosion than aluminum alloys, and should be protected against a salt atmosphere and against constant contact with water. Proper provision for drainage or ventilation is necessary when moisture is present.

Magnesium has relatively low hardness, and is very easy to machine. No special composition is required for use in automatic screw machines. Magnesium can be hot forged with hammers or mechanical and hydraulic presses. It can be cold formed or drawn, but only with difficulty. The rapid work hardening can be relieved by annealing. Care should be exercised to avoid stress concentration such as caused by notches or sharp fillets. A sharp 60° V-groove will reduce the endurance limit to one-fourth or one-third the value for a standard specimen. When abrasion conditions are present, the soft magnesium must be protected by inserts such as plates, liners, sleeves, shoes, or bushings. Magnesium exhibits a high damping capacity which is effective in preventing vibrations from building up into large amplitudes.

When magnesium is welded with a torch, butt welds are preferable because the removal of the flux is usually easier than for lap welds, and the possibility of corrosion is reduced. All types of joints may be made with the helium arc process, which requires no flux. Resistance welding is satisfactory for magnesium, and may be applied to wrought products or thin-walled castings. Magnesium cannot be used in the form of rivets. Rivets of aluminum alloys 6053 and 6061 have been found to give satisfactory service. Brass and iron rivets should be avoided because of the possibility of galvanic action.

The composition and physical properties for a number of typical magnesium alloys are given in Table 14-18.

26. Copper Alloys

Copper is a very ductile metal, and may be spun, stamped, rolled into sheets, and drawn into wire and tubing. Mechanical working increases

TABLE 14-18
Composition and Mechanical Properties of Magnesium Alloys*

Alloy	Per Cent Composition (Balance magnesium plus minor impurities)					
	Al	Mn min.	Zn	Si max.	Cu max.	Ni max.
AZ31B	2.5–3.5	0.20	0.7–1.3	0.30	0.05	0.005
AZ31C	2.5–3.5	0.20	0.6–1.4	0.30	0.10	0.03
AZ63A	5.3–6.7	0.15	2.5–3.5	0.30	0.10	0.01
AZ81A	7.0–8.1	0.13	0.4–1.0	0.30	0.10	0.01
AZ92A	8.3–9.7	0.10	1.6–2.4	0.30	0.10	0.01
HK31A			Thorium 2.5–4.0, Zirconium 0.50–1.0			

Alloy and Temper	ASTM	Tensile Strength	Yield Strength	Comp. Yield Strength	Shear Strength	Elong. in 2 in. %	Brinell
Sand Castings†							
AZ63A-F	B80-58	29,000	14,000	14,000	18,000	6	50
AZ63A-T4		40,000	14,000	14,000	18,000	12	55
AZ63A-T6		40,000	19,000	19,000	21,000	5	73
AZ81A-T4		40,000	14,000	14,000	18,000	12	55
AZ92A-F	B80-58	24,000	14,000	14,000	19,000	2	65
AZ92A-T4		40,000	14,000	14,000	19,000	10	63
AZ92A-T6		40,000	21,000	21,000	22,000	2	84
Sheets and Plates†,‡							
AZ31B-H24	B90-58	42,000	32,000	26,000	23,000	15	73
AZ31B-O		37,000	22,000	16,000	21,000	21	56
HK31A-H24		37,000	29,000	25,000	21,000	8	57
Rods, Bars, Shapes†							
AZ31B-F ⎱ AZ31C-F ⎰	B107-58	38,000	29,000	14,000	19,000	15	49

* Data courtesy of Dow Chemical Co.
† These values are typical.
‡ Strength values are for minimum sections. Values are somewhat less for larger sizes.

the hardness and strength, but decreases the ductility. The effects of cold work can be removed by annealing. Copper can be fabricated by soldering, welding, or brazing. Copper has excellent heat-conducting qualities, and is used in refrigerators, radiators, water heaters, and air-conditioning equipment. Copper does not make satisfactory castings. It cannot be hardened by quenching unless alloyed with beryllium. Copper resists certain types of corrosion.

The most important copper-base alloys are brass and bronze. Brass is a copper-zinc alloy, and bronze is composed principally of copper and tin.

TABLE 14-19

Brass, Bronze, and Miscellaneous Wrought Copper Alloys

No.	Alloy	Condition	Tensile Strength, psi		Rockwell	Elong. %
1	Copper	Bars, all sizes	A 37,000			25
		" 0.250–0.375 in.	H 45,000			10
		" 0.375–1.0 in.	H 40,000			12
2	Brass, Alloy 3	Plates, sheets, strips	½H 51–61,000,	H 63– 72,000	56B, 72B, 82B	
				Sp 78– 86,000		
3	" , Alloy 6	" " "	½H 57–67,000,	H 71– 81,000	60B, 79B, 89B	
				Sp 91–100,000		
4	" , Alloy 8	" " "	½H 55–65,000,	H 68– 78,000	57B, 76B, 87B	
				Sp 86– 95,000		
5	Brass wire, Alloy 2		½H 56–67,000,	H 64– 74,000		
				Sp 84,000		
6	Brass wire, Alloy 7		½H 79–94,000,	H 92–107,000		
				Sp 120,000		
7	Free cutting brass	Bars, 1 in. & under	A 48,000	YS 20,000		15
		" 1 in.–2 in.	A 44,000	YS 18,000		20
		" 0.50 in. & under	½H 57,000	YS 25,000		7
		" 0.50 in. & 1 in.	½H 55,000	YS 25,000		10
8	Naval brass	Bars, 1 in. & under	A 54,000	YS 20,000		30, 25
		" 1 in.–2.5 in.	A 52,000	YS 20,000		30, 25
		" 0.50 in. & under	½H 60,000	YS 27,000		22, 18
		" 0.50 in.–1.0 in.	½H 60,000	YS 27,000		25, 20
9	Phosphor bronze	Wire, 0.025 & under	Sp 145,000			
		" 0.025–0.0625 in.	Sp 135,000			
		" 0.125–0.250 in.	Sp 125,000			
10	Phosphor bronze, FC	Rounds, 0.25–0.5 in.	H 60,000			10
		" 0.50–1.0 in.	H 55,000			12
11	Manganese bronze	Bars 1.5–2.5 in.	½H 70,000	YS 35,000		15
		" " "	H 73,000	YS 48,000		12
12	Muntz metal	Tube plates under 2 in.	50,000	YS 20,000		35
13	Aluminum bronze	Bars 0.50 in. & under	80,000	YS 40,000		9
		" over 1 in.	72,000	YS 35,000		12
14	Beryllium copper	Rods, bars	A 60– 85,000		92B–103B	
		" up to 0.375 in.	H 95–130,000			
15	18% Ni Silver, Alloy B	Rods 0.02–0.25 in.	H 90–110,000			
		" 0.50–1.0 in.	H 75– 95,000			
16	Monel metal	Cold drawn bars	A 70– 85,000	YS 30–40,000	BHN110–140	35–50

No.	ASTM Spec.	Alloy	Cu %	Sn %	Zn %	Others
1	B133-58T	Copper				
2	B36–56 Alloy 3	Plates, sheets	85.0		15.0	
3	" " Alloy 6	" "	70.0		30.0	
4	" " Alloy 8	" "	65.0		35.0	
5	B134–52 Alloy 2	Brass wire	90.0		10.0	
6	B134–52 Alloy 7	" "	65.0		35.0	
7	B16-58	FC brass	60.0–63.0		remainder	Pb 2.5–3.7
8	B21-58 Alloy A & B	Naval Brass	59.0–62.0	0.5–1.0	remainder*	
9	B159-58 Alloy A	Phos. bronze wire	remainder	4.2–5.8	0.30	P 0.03–0.35
10	B139-58 Alloy B2	FC Phosphor bronze	remainder	3.5–4.5	1.5–4.5	P 0.01–0.50†
11	B138-58 Alloy A	Manganese bronze	58.5		39.0	Fe 1.4, Mn 0.1
12	B171–58	Muntz metal	58.0–61.0	0.25 max.	remainder	Pb 0.4–0.9
13	B150-58 Alloy 1	Aluminum bronze	80.0–93.0	0.60 max.	1.0	Al 6.5–11.0‡
14	B196-52	Beryllium copper	remainder			Be 1.80–2.05
15	B151-58 Alloy B	18% Ni Silver	53.5–56.5	Ni 16.5–19.5	remainder	Mn 0.50 max.
16		Monel metal	30.0	Ni 67.0	Fe 1.4	Mn 1.0

Some alloys have minor amounts of impurities. See specifications for exact compositions.
FC, free cutting; A, annealed or soft; ½H, half hard; H, hard; Sp, spring; YS, yield strength.
* Pb, Alloy A, 0.20 max; Alloy B 0.4–1.0.
† Pb 3.5–4.5.
‡ Fe 4.0 max, Ni 1.0 max, Si 2.2, Mn 1.5.

Zinc is cheaper than tin, so that the cost of brass is less than the cost of bronze. Bronze, however, is usually considered the superior metal. It is commercial practice, to designate certain reddish-colored copper-zinc combinations as "bronze" even though no tin is present.

Brass and bronze are used in both the cast and wrought forms. The strength of brass increases with the zinc content. Most of the copper alloys can be work hardened to higher strengths than pure copper. In general, the machinability of the alloys is satisfactory. The free cutting qualities are improved by the addition of small amounts of lead. Brass is about equal to copper in corrosion resistance, but bronze is superior to both. There are a great many copper alloys with a wide variety of commercial designations. A selected list of the wrought alloys, giving composition and physical properties, is shown in Table 14-19. Several of the most commonly used casting alloys are listed in Table 14-20.

TABLE 14-20

Typical Brass and Bronze Casting Alloys

SAE	ASTM	Nominal Composition				Commercial Designation
		Cu	Sn	Pb	Zn	
40	B62-52, 4A	85	5	5	5	Leaded red brass, composition brass, or ounce metal.
41	B146-52, 6B	67	1	3	29	Leaded yellow brass.
43	B147-52, 8A	58	..	..	39	(Mn 0.25), No. 1 Manganese "bronze."
62	B143-52, 1A	88	10	..	2	Tin bronze or gun metal.
64	B144-52, 3A	80	10	10	..	Phosphor bronze. High leaded tin bronze.
68	B148-52, 9B	89	..	..	..	(Al 10, Fe 1), Grade B Aluminum bronze.

ASTM	Tensile Strength	Yield Strength	Elong. % 2 in.	General Properties and Applications
B62-52, 4A	30,000	14,000	20	Good casting and finishing properties. Free cutting.
B146-52, 6B	30,000	11,000	20	Used where cheapness is main consideration.
B147-52, 8A	65,000	25,000	20	Makes tough, strong castings.
B143-52, 1A	40,000	18,000	20	Withstands heavy gear and bearing pressures.
B144-52, 3A	25,000	12,000	8	Has low friction. Withstands heavy loads.
B148-52, 9B	65,000	25,000	20	BHN 110 ⎱ For heavy service such as
B148-52, H.T.	80,000	40,000	12	BHN 160 ⎰ worms, gears, and similar applications.

27. Alloys for Die Castings

Die castings are formed by forcing a molten alloy into metal molds or dies under high pressure. Only alloys of relatively low melting points are suitable for this process. Die castings are made principally from zinc, aluminum, and magnesium, and to a lesser extent from brass.

Die casting is strictly a machine operation and lends itself to very rapid production of parts. The chief disadvantage is the high cost of dies, which usually limits the use of the method to parts that are to be made in large quantities. Close tolerances on the finished product can be maintained. Consequently, very little or no machining is required. The die casting process is suitable for parts containing very thin sections or intricate shapes. Inserts such as studs or bushings can be included as a part of the casting. Die castings usually have a very smooth surface suitable for direct application of platings or organic finishes. The composition and physical properties of some of the better known die casting alloys are listed in Table 14-21.

Zinc die castings have gained extensive use because of their high strength, long die life, and moderate casting temperatures. The light weight of aluminum die castings is an important advantage in many applications. The casting temperature is higher than zinc, and die life is shorter. Magnesium castings also possess the advantage of low weight. Casting temperature is the same as for aluminum. The surface of magnesium castings is usually treated to inhibit corrosion and to serve as a base for the finish. Brass is cast at the highest temperature used for die casting, and die life is accordingly the shortest. High strength and hardness are advantages possessed by brass die castings.

The designer must give care and attention to all the details of a part to be made by the die casting process. The thickness of the sections should be as uniform as possible throughout the casting. Solidification and cooling will thus take place uniformly, and the casting will be free from "hot spots" resulting from the slow cooling of large volumes of metal. Residual stresses are frequently found in castings of unequal sections. The parting line for the dies should be located at a point that permits easy removal of the flash resulting from the imperfect matching of the dies. If a bead can be located on the parting line, the flash can be very easily sheared off. Undercuts that require the use of slides in the die should be avoided whenever possible. The additional die expense for complex castings with undercuts, if made in sufficiently large quantities, is sometimes justified. Fillets should be used at re-entrant angles to increase the strength and prevent localization of cooling stresses. Threaded holes can sometimes be cored, and a saving in machining costs thereby effected. The designer should consult with a die casting firm on the design

TABLE 14-21

Nominal Composition and Mechanical Properties of Die Casting Alloys

Material	Alloy	Al	Cu	Mg	Mn	Si	Zn	Pb	Sn
Zinc*	Zamak 3	3.9–4.3	0.10 max.	0.03–0.04			remainder	0.003	0.002
	Zamak 5	3.9–4.3	0.75–1.25	0.03–0.04			remainder	0.003	0.002
Aluminum†	Alcoa 13	remainder				5.0			
	360	remainder		0.5		9.5			
	380	remainder	3.5			9.0			
Magnesium‡	AZ91A-F	9.0					0.6		
	AZ91B-F								
Brass§	Z30A	0.25	57.0 min		0.25	0.25 max.	30.0 min.	1.5	1.50
	ZS331A	0.15	63.0–67.0		0.15	0.75–1.25	remainder	0.25	0.25

Material	Alloy	Tensile Strength	Yield Strength	Elong. in 2 in. %	Comp. Strength	Shear Strength	Endurance Limit	Brinell Hardness	Melting Point, F
Zinc	Zamak 3‖	41,000		10	60,000	31,000		82	728
	Zamak 5	47,600		7	87,000	38,000		91	727
Aluminum	Alcoa 13	43,000	21,000	2.5		28,000	19,000		1065–1080
	360	47,000	25,000	3.0		30,000	19,000		1035–1105
	380	48,000	24,000	3.0		31,000	21,000		1000–1100
Magnesium	AZ91A-F	33,000	22,000	3	22,000#	20,000		60	1,105
	AZ91B-F								
Brass	Z30A	45,000	25,000	10				120–130	1,650
	ZS331A	58,000	30,000	15				120–130	1,550

* New Jersey Zinc Co.
† Aluminum Company of America.
‡ Dow Chemical Co.
§ ASTM, B176–57.
‖ As cast.
Compressive yield strength.
Values of normal impurities not shown.
Mechanical properties are typical; variations must be expected in practice.

of the part in order to receive the guidance of specialists in this branch of engineering. Sometimes minor revisions can be made in the design which will result in a lowering of the cost of the dies and the production parts.

Permanent mold castings are made by filling metal molds under gravity head. Both iron and aluminum castings are made by this process. Iron castings are usually annealed to improve the machining properties. Sand cores are used in the so-called "semipermanent mold method."

BIBLIOGRAPHY

Volume number shown in **bold face** type. The number immediately following is the page on which the article begins.

1. Timoshenko, S., *Strength of Materials*, 2d ed., Vol. 2. New York: D. Van Nostrand Company, Inc., 1941.

2. Bullens, D. K., *Steel and Its Heat Treatment*, 5th ed., Vols. 1, 2, and 3. New York: John Wiley & Sons, Inc., 1948.

3. Heyer, Robert H., *Engineering Physical Metallurgy*. New York: D. Van Nostrand Company, Inc., 1939.

4. Sachs, G., and Van Horn, K. R., *Practical Metallurgy*. Cleveland: American Society for Metals, 1940.

5. Davis, E. A., "The Effect of Speed of Stretching and the Rate of Loading on the Yielding of Mild Steel," *Trans. ASME*, **60**, A-137 (1938); **61**, A-89 (1939).

6. Hoyt, Samuel L., *Metals and Alloys Data Book*, rev. ed. New York: Reinhold Publishing Corp., 1952.

7. *SAE Handbook*, New York: Society of Automotive Engineers, Inc., 1960.

8. *Metals Handbook*. Cleveland: American Society for Metals, 1948. *Supplement*, 1954.

9. Thum, Ernest E., *The Book of Stainless Steels*. Cleveland: American Society for Metals, 1935.

10. *Alloy Cast Irons Handbook*, 2d ed. American Foundrymen's Association, 1944.

11. *Steel Castings Handbook*. Cleveland: Steel Founders' Society of America, 1941.

12. Briggs, Charles W., and Gezelius, Roy A., "The Effect of Mass Upon the Mechanical Properties of Cast Steel," *Trans. ASM*, **26**, 367 (1938).

13. "Cooperative Short-Time High Temperature Tension Tests of Carbon Steel K6," *Proc. ASTM*, **33** (1), 213 (1933).

14. Sisco, Frank T., *Alloys of Iron and Carbon*, Vol. 2. New York: McGraw-Hill Book Company, Inc., 1937.

15. "Impact Resistance and Tensile Properties of Metals at Subatmospheric Temperatures," *ASME-ASTM Committee Report*, Aug. (1941).

16. "Behavior of Ferritic Steels at Low Temperatures," *ASME-ASTM Committee Report*, Dec. (1945).

17. Marin, Joseph, "Applying Creep Data in Design," *Machine Design*, **16**, July, 123; August, 113 (1944).

18. McVetty, P. G., "Working Stress for High Temperature Service," *Mech. Eng.*, **56**, 149 (1934).

19. "Symposium on Effect of Temperature on Metals," *ASTM-ASME*, 1931.

20. "Compilation of Available High-Temperature Creep Characteristics of Metals and Alloys," *ASTM-ASME*, 1938.

21. "Symposium on High-Strength Constructional Metals," *ASTM*, 1936.

22. Williams, Samuel R., *Hardness and Hardness Measurements*. Cleveland: American Society of Metals, 1942.

23. Rosenberg, Samuel J., "The Resistance to Wear of Carbon Steels," *J. Research*, **7**, 419 (1931).

24. French, Herbert J., *Alloy Constructional Steels*. Cleveland: American Society for Metals, 1942.

25. Marin, Joseph, *Engineering Materials*. Englewood Cliffs, N. J.: Prentice-Hall, Inc., 1952.

26. Jeffries, Zay, and Archer, Robert S., *Science of Metals*. New York: McGraw-Hill Book Company, Inc., 1924.

27. "Symposium on Cast Iron," *Proc. ASTM*, **33** (2), 115 (1933).

28. Fleishman, M., "Selection of Steel for High Temperatures," *Steel*, **102**, Jan. 17, 34 (1938).

29. Kinzel, A. B., and Franks, Russel, *The Alloys of Iron and Chromium*, Vol. 2, "High-Chromium Alloys," New York: McGraw-Hill Book Company, Inc., 1940.

30. Boegehold, A. L., "Selection of Automotive Steel on the Basis of Hardenability," *SAE Journal*, **52**, 477 (1944).

31. "Standard Classification of Austenite Grain Size in Steels," *ASTM, E 19-46*. Philadelphia: American Society for Testing Materials.

32. Andrews, C. W., "Effect of Temperature of the Modulus of Elasticity," *Metal Progress*, **58**, July, 85 (1950).

33. "Selection of Steel for Automobile Parts," *SAE Journal*, **57**, Aug., 17; Sept., 25, Oct., 33; Nov., 39; Dec., 29 (1949); **58**, Jan., 47 (1950).

34. MacGregor, C. W., "The Yield Point of Mild Steel," *Trans. ASME*, **53**, APM-53-15, 187 (1931).

35. Hetenyi, M., *Handbook of Experimental Stress Analysis*. New York: John Wiley & Sons, Inc., 1950.

36. Van Vlack, L. H., *Elements of Materials Science*. Reading, Mass.: Addison-Wesley Publishing Co., 1959.

37. Holloman, J. H., and Jaffe, L. D., *Ferrous Metallurgical Design*. New York: John Wiley & Sons, Inc., 1947.

38. ASME Handbooks, *Metals Engineering-Design* (1953), *Metals Properties* (1954), *Engineering Tables* (1956), *Metals Engineering-Processes* (1958). New York: McGraw-Hill Book Company, Inc.

INDEX

AND WROTE
MY STORY
ANYWAY